GENERAL BIOLOGY

GENERAL BIOLOGY

THIRD EDITION

LESLIE A. KENOYER, Ph.D.

Head, Department of Biology, Western Michigan College

HENRY N. GODDARD, Ph.D.

Late Professor of Biology, Western Michigan College

DWIGHT D. MILLER, Ph.D.

Associate Professor of Zoology, University of Nebraska

HARPER & BROTHERS PUBLISHERS NEW YORK

Contents

Preface   vii

    I.   Biology   1

   II.   The Cellular Structure of Organisms   14

  III.   The Formation of New Cells from Old Cells   26

  IV.   Chemical and Physical Aspects of Living Things   34

   V.   Metabolism   48

  VI.   The Animal Kingdom   69

 VII.   Protozoa: One-Celled Animals   80

VIII.   Introduction to the Multicellular Animals   98

  IX.   Sponges and Coelenterates   110

   X.   The Simpler Worm Phyla   123

  XI.   The Earthworm and Other Annelids   136

 XII.   Mollusks   153

XIII.   The Crayfish and Other Crustaceans   165

XIV.   Air-Breathing Arthropods   181

 XV.   Echinoderms   213

XVI. Chordates 219

XVII. Vertebrate Morphology and Physiology 269

XVIII. Animal Ontogeny 313

XIX. The Plant Kingdom 331

XX. Thallophytes—Fission Plants 339

XXI. Thallophytes—Algae 365

XXII. Thallophytes—Fungi 378

XXIII. Bryophytes—Mosses and Liverworts 396

XXIV. Vascular Plants—Club Mosses and Horsetails 404

XXV. Vascular Plants—Ferns 411

XXVI. Vascular Plants—Gymnosperms 422

XXVII. Vascular Plants—Angiosperms 434

XXVIII. Genetics 477

XXIX. Evolution 510

XXX. The Organism and the Environment 542

XXXI. Conservation 568

Appendix

Classification of Organisms 589

Glossary 598

References 637

Index 641

Preface

Eight years elapsed between the publication of the first and second editions of *General Biology*, and eight more have passed since the second edition was published. To take into account new developments in biological science and new viewpoints in presentation a third edition is hereby presented.

Much of the text has been rewritten, particularly the chapters on cells and cell propagation, physical and chemical aspects of living things, metabolism, the introductions to the animal and plant kingdoms, genetics, evolution, ecology, and conservation. A number of new examples and illustrations have been introduced. Moreover, there has been considerable rearrangement of material; outstandingly, the chapters on the phyla of the animal kingdom have been arranged in a consecutive series following their evolutionary sequence, and likewise those on the major divisions of the plant kingdom.

In this, as in the earlier editions, the effort has been to stress biological principles, to review them constantly in connection with selected readily available types, and to strike a fair balance in the treatment of the plant and animal kingdoms. The chapters on plants have been placed after those on animals, largely on the practical consideration that since the course is designed to cover the entire school year, the spring months in most sections afford the advantage of greater availability of growing and flowering plant material. But the chapters are so written that the sequence may be altered according to local conditions and the wishes of the instructor.

We appreciate the many helpful suggestions which we have received from our colleagues on the faculties of Western Michigan College and the University of Nebraska. Particularly helpful have been suggestions from Professors E. B. Steen, F. J. Hinds, M. R. Wiseman, and Lillian H. Meyer of Western Michigan College; also very much appreciated have been suggestions from Professors I. H. Blake, C. T. Blunn, J. F. Davidson, R. M. Leverton, R. C. Lommasson, H. W. Manter, W. E. Militzer, W. W. Ray,

C. B. Schultz, and Otis Wade of the University of Nebraska. Numerous suggestions and corrections have been offered by users of the former editions of the book. Especially helpful have been the communications of Professor T. C. Nelson of Rutgers University, Mrs. Jane C. Frost of Woman's College, University of North Carolina, and Professor L. K. Beyer of State Teachers College, Mansfield, Pennsylvania. We wish to express our thanks to the various individuals and institutions who loaned or permitted the borrowing of material for a number of the new illustrations included in this book; the separate acknowledgments of these appear in the captions of the illustrations. We appreciate the cooperation of the artists who prepared drawings for many of the new illustrations—Mr. John Anilane of Kalamazoo, Michigan, Miss Helene Greene of Lincoln, Nebraska, and several others. Most of the excellent drawings made by Jane Roller for the second edition have been retained. The junior author appreciates the assistance of his wife, Mrs. Dorothy S. Miller, and his mother, Mrs. Gertrude R. Miller, in the reading of proofs and in the preparation of the index.

It is hoped that future users of this text will feel free to communicate any corrections, criticisms, and suggestions which they believe will improve later printings and editions.

LESLIE A. KENOYER
DWIGHT D. MILLER

January, 1953

GENERAL BIOLOGY

Chapter I

BIOLOGY

Definition and Aim of Science. Science (Lat. "knowledge") is organized or classified knowledge. In common usage the term is restricted to natural science, which deals with material things. Science depends on facts, and facts are revealed by the senses. To become a part of the body of science, such facts must be organized and interpreted. There are two modes of gathering facts: *observation*, which means the use of any of the senses in investigating objects or occurrences, and *experiment*, which involves the use of the senses in determining the results obtained when the conditions governing occurrences are under control.

To show the nature of an experiment we may use one demonstrating the effect upon an animal of the lack of an important food component. For such experiments, rats are often used. It has been found that these animals develop normally and remain in good health when fed a diet consisting of whole milk and enriched bread (i.e., bread to which have been added certain substances sometimes lost in milling). An experiment was performed to show the effect of feeding enriched bread without the whole milk. Two young rats of the same litter and of approximately the same size were separated, and one of them was fed only enriched bread, while the other received the optimum diet consisting of both enriched bread and whole milk. After seven weeks of this treatment, the two rats differed greatly in size and general appearance (Fig. 1). The rat which had subsisted on bread alone was much smaller than its litter mate, weighed about one-fifth as much as the latter, and showed other, less obvious abnormalities (e.g., an irritable nature). From the results of this experiment it may be concluded that bread alone (even when enriched) is not an adequate food for growth and maintenance of health in rats. (A similar experiment has shown that neither is milk alone a sufficient food.) This conclusion rests on the fact that the two rats were practically identical animals at the beginning and were treated in the same way except for milk's being withheld from one of them; i.e., conditions were controlled so that only the factor under investigation (presence of milk in the diet) was permitted to vary. The rat which was given a deficient diet may be called the *experimental* individual, the one fed the normal diet the *control*.

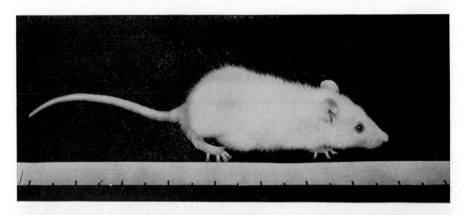

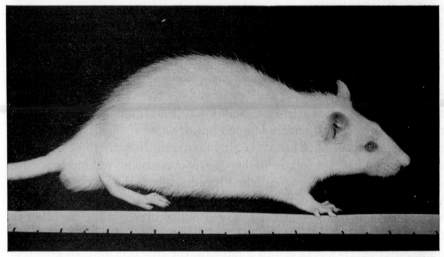

Fig. 1. Results of a controlled experiment. These rats are litter mates which were separated at an early age and given different food. The one above was fed enriched bread alone, while the one below was given both enriched bread and whole milk. These pictures were taken after seven weeks of this treatment. Since these rats were alike before the experiment began and were treated alike except for their food, the difference between them may be attributed to the dietary difference. (Photos, courtesy of Wheat Flour Institute.)

The tremendous advances of science in our present era and their vast alteration of man's mode of life and general welfare make it imperative that the well-informed citizen have at least a fundamental training in science.

Methods of Science. After accumulating a number of facts, the scientist endeavors to fit them into a tentative explanation called a *hypothesis*. As the hypothesis comes to be confirmed by many facts later acquired, it assumes the status of a *theory*, and when established, it may be termed a *scientific law*. In the long history of science it has often been necessary to discard or replace hypotheses, to reconstruct theories or even to revise laws to make them fit newly discovered evidence.

Classification of the Sciences. Although all science is a unity that cannot be sharply divided into compartments, nevertheless for convenience in study and research we separate it into fields called the *sciences*. A partial classification of the sciences follows.

I. *Physical sciences.* Those not restricted to living things. Most of them, however, contribute to an understanding of organisms.
   A. *Physics* (from Gr. "nature"). The science of changes involving primarily the motion of matter or its minute particles, but not involving its substance. A stick of wood may be moved through space, dropped to the ground, bent, or broken, but it remains wood. Such changes are called *physical changes*.
   B. *Chemistry* (Gr. "juice," since it was originally the art of extracting medicinal juices from plants). The science of changes involving the substance of matter. A stick may be burned, undergoing a *chemical change*, for the wood becomes carbon dioxide, water, and ash.
   C. *Geology* (Gr. "earth science"). Science of the earth and of the progressive changes that have occurred on its surface. A subdivision is *paleontology* (Gr. "ancient life science"), the history of life on the earth as revealed by fossils.
   D. *Astronomy* (Gr. "star science"). Science of the celestial bodies.
II. *Biological sciences* or *biology* (Gr. "life science"). The sciences dealing with living things.
   A. *Zoology* (Gr. "animal science"). The study of animals. It may be subdivided into *protozoology*, dealing with one-celled animals; *entomology*, dealing with insects; *ornithology*, dealing with birds; *mammalogy*, dealing with mammals; *anthropology*, dealing with man; and various other subsciences.
   B. *Botany* (Gr. "grass, vegetation"). The science of plants. It may be subdivided into *bacteriology*, the study of bacteria; *algology*, the study of algae; *mycology*, the study of fungi; *bryology*, the study of mosses; and other subsciences concerned with the numerous groups of the plant kingdom.

What Is Life? Life is an abstract term used to designate the sum of the properties pertaining to and the processes carried on by *living things;* these bodies are of great physical and chemical complexity. It would be difficult to formulate any one difference between the living and the nonliving, in fact, there seems to be no sharp line of cleavage between the two. The viruses, exceedingly minute particles which cause such diseases as rabies and influenza, seem to lie somewhere near the border line. In a general way we may be able to recognize living things by the fact that they possess the following characteristics:

1. They are fairly definite in *size* and *form* for any given species. Nonliving bodies of any particular kind may vary widely in size and form.
2. They are composed of from one to very many microscopically small structural units called *cells* (to which are often added certain nonliving cell secretions), and are *organized*, i.e., made up of distinct parts, each of which functions for the good of the whole. For this reason they are called *organisms*.
3. They take in, or construct within themselves, *food*, from which they build up their body substance. The process of constructing their bodies from the ingredients of food is *assimilation* (Lat. "making like to").
4. They automatically tear down their substance through a process of *oxidation*, which liberates energy and produces wastes. Food, therefore, is the fundamental energy-yielding material, necessary to all organisms as the source of their substance and activities.
5. At certain periods in their existence the building-up process exceeds the tearing-down process, and organisms *grow*. Many animals, especially the higher forms, reach a limit to their increase in size; plants more often continue their growth indefinitely.
6. They show *spontaneous movement*, i.e., movement resulting from forces that originate within.
7. They *respond* to external stimuli, or changes in environment, such as increase or decrease in temperature, pressure, light, and concentration of chemicals.
8. They *reproduce* other living bodies similar to themselves.

Several of these characteristics are exhibited by nonliving bodies. A burning candle wastes away, with liberation of energy; a doorbell responds to a stimulus; crystals grow (but not by assimilation). But for all practical purposes there is little difficulty in separating the living from the nonliving on the basis of the characteristics mentioned.

Plants and Animals Compared. A *plant* may be defined as an organism which contains *chlorophyll* (Gr. "leaf green") and manufactures carbohydrates (such food as sugar and starch) from carbon dioxide and water, or which, if lacking these characteristics, is similar in structure and life history to those organisms that do contain chlorophyll and manufacture carbohydrates. All other organisms are *animals*. Since a stationary organism has fairly constant access to the raw materials required for food making, whereas the search for ready-made food usually requires moving about, plants are commonly attached, and animals usually have the power of locomotion. Locomotion as a rule necessitates greater compactness, greater definiteness of structure, and a better development of sense organs and nervous system; these traits are usually found in animals. Plants and animals may be contrasted as in the following summary, but it must be understood that the contrast indicated does not hold for all. Sometimes, indeed, it is hard to draw the line between the two kingdoms, since some organisms possess the characteristics of both.

PLANTS	ANIMALS
Make carbohydrates from the inorganic substances, carbon dioxide, and water (dependent plants are exceptions); also build proteins (nitrogen-containing foods).	Use carbohydrates and proteins which have been made by plants, or have come indirectly from plants by way of other animals.
Attached (in most cases).	Unattached and with power of locomotion (in most cases).
Rather extended (often branching).	Rather compact.
Cell walls usually prominent, giving organism a rigid structure.	Cell walls less prominent, rendering organism somewhat more flexible.
Organs (such as roots, branches, leaves) usually indefinite in number and loosely coordinated.	Organs usually definite in number and closely coordinated.
Sense organs and nervous system poorly developed.	Sense organs and nervous system well developed.

Distribution of Living Things. Living things in infinite variety are found on almost the entire surface of the earth as well as beneath and far above the surface. On the expedition of Byrd's party to the Antarctic Continent, about two dozen species of mosses and lichens were collected from mountains where temperatures permitting growth prevail for a total of only about one week during the entire year. Pond ice obtained at a temperature of 70° below zero F. was found when melted to be teeming with active microscopic organisms. Along the shores of the continent were found representatives of almost every branch of the animal kingdom. Beebe and Barton in diving spheres have explored the ocean depths as far down as 4500 feet and have found weird luminous organisms all the way. Cameras have been lowered to the bottom of the sea to take pictures

(Fig. 2) which reveal organisms at depths greater than a mile. Samplings of the ocean bottom indicate that living things (bacteria) occur at least as deep as 34,000 feet. In the Rocky Mountain area, forest extends to an

FIG. 2. Photograph taken with the Ewing underwater camera on the slope of the continental shelf west of Florida at a depth of 1100 fathoms (1¼ miles) showing the presence of attached animals at this great depth. A sea lily, a colonial horny coral, and other forms appear; the identity of some of them is uncertain. In the foreground are the light source and the trip cord. (Photo, courtesy of D. M. Owen, Woods Hole Oceanographic Institution.)

altitude of 9000 to 12,000 feet (Fig. 3), above which there may be brilliant-flowered mountain meadows. One species of flowering plant, the edelweiss, was collected as high as 20,000 feet on Mount Everest. Above this height lichens grow on the rocks and rugged cliffs. Lindbergh on a transoceanic flight collected about fifty kinds of windblown organisms and spores of organisms 3000 feet above the ocean and far north of the Arctic Circle. There is no desert too dry or any lake too salty to be the home of life, even though it may be relatively sparse (Fig. 4). At the other extreme, life is exceedingly abundant in warm, moist climates. Barro Colorado Island in the Panama Canal Zone, a six-square-mile area of moist tropical forest, contains about twelve hundred species of higher plants, half of which are trees and shrubs (Fig. 5). On the same island are no less than three hundred kinds of birds and a thousand kinds of spiders, to mention only two of the animal groups.

Fig. 3. Timber line at about 10,000 feet altitude, Arapahoe National Forest, Colorado. Distorted pines (*Pinus aristata*) with mountain meadow in the foreground. (Photo by H. L. Shantz, courtesy of U.S. Forest Service.)

Variety of Living Things. Living things vary in size from plants barely visible with the highest magnifications of the microscope (bacteria), to trees three to four hundred feet in height (Fig. 6); from exceedingly minute microscopic animals (protozoans), to the sulfur-bottom whale, which has attained a length of 109 feet and a weight of 150 tons (Fig. 210). About 335,000 different kinds or species of existing plants have been named and described; likewise names have been given to approximately 1,000,000 kinds of animals, more than three-fourths of which are insects.

There are undoubtedly many thousands of species that have not been named, and it is estimated that the number of species which have become extinct is at least ten times as great as the number of living species.

Fig. 4. Scene on an Arizona desert, showing giant cacti (the large columns), prickly pear cacti (in foreground), and various spiny trees and shrubs. The ground is not thickly covered, and the plants are specially modified in such a way that they endure extremely dry situations. (Photo, courtesy of Edwin A. Arnold.)

Biology and the Control of Man's Material Environment. From plants and animals come directly or indirectly all of our food, most of our clothing and fuel, many of our drugs and building materials, much of our power and heat, and various other commodities of great importance to us. Biology, therefore, has extensive applications to everyday life, and its study furnishes a useful foundation for training in the various occupations connected with the obtaining and handling of our daily needs. *Agriculture, horticulture, forestry*, and to a large extent *pharmacology* may be regarded as branches of economic biology.

Biology and Culture. Since plants and animals are our everyday companions, it is worth our while to know something about them. What to the untrained is a mere weed takes on new interest and beauty as we classify it, noting its similarities to and its differences from its nearest of kin; as we work out the details of its complicated structure; as we learn how it carries on its activities and note its adjustment to the soil, the climate, the sunlight, the surrounding plants and animals, and the many other factors in its environment. From variations observed in a weed, the evening primrose, de Vries developed the mutation theory, which has been of importance in leading us to understand how changes in organisms come about. One who does not know the earthworm intimately is likely to view it with contempt; but when he begins to understand its intricate structure, its complicated body processes so like our own yet so different in detail, its interesting behavior, and its great utility to man in loosening, aerating, and mixing the soil, he begins to respect and admire it. One of the most enticing cultural aspects of biology arises from the evidence that organisms were not always as they are now, but that for millions of years they have advanced steadily in complexity and in fitness to meet the conditions of their environments. Moreover, life is never at a standstill but is undergoing changes, usually in the direction of greater complexity and greater diversity. Biological training adds interest and meaning to the commonplace things of the world.

Fig. 5. Interior of a forest in the moist tropics, showing a dense and varied vegetation. Climbing plants are abundant, such as the vanilla vine on the tree at the right. Tropical Biological Laboratory, Barro Colorado Island, Canal Zone, Panama. (Photo by L. A. Kenoyer.)

Biology and Health. Health is one of man's greatest assets. In 1850 the average length of life in the more cultured parts of the earth was about forty years. As the result of the invaluable contributions of biology, one hundred years later (1950) it had been increased by about twenty-eight years. We have learned much concerning the nutrient values of various foods and the relation of vitamins to health and growth. Remarkable results have been accomplished in surgery and tissue grafting largely because, by carefully excluding microorganisms and using germ-destroying chemicals, operations may be performed without danger of disease or death from infection. Microorganisms responsible for various diseases have been discovered and means for their control established, making it possible for us to avoid or overcome disease. We have learned that the

Fig. 6. Grove of giant sequoia (*Sequoia gigantea*), California. At the right are pines. (Photo by A. E. Wieslander, courtesy of U.S. Forest Service.)

inoculation of a person with a mild strain of the disease germ or with toxin produced by the germ renders him free from certain diseases. We are now making extensive use of thyroid extract for cretinism, of insulin for diabetes, and of other endocrines for diseases caused by their deficiency. We have learned the use of liver as a cure for pernicious anemia. The discovery of the sulfa drugs, penicillin, streptomycin, and other chemicals that check bacterial activity has initiated a new era in the control of the organisms that infect wounds and those that cause various diseases. The recognition of insects as factors in the spread of certain diseases has contributed greatly to the control of these ailments. Bubonic plague was once the worst scourge of Europe, 25,000,000 deaths having occurred from it during the fourteenth century. The discovery that it is transmitted to man by the rat flea has resulted in measures for the control of rats and fleas and has almost brought an end to the disease. The association of mosquitoes with malaria and yellow fever is leading to the conquest of these diseases; one result of this progressing conquest was to facilitate the construction of the Panama Canal after earlier attempts had proved futile because of disease. Appreciation of the fact that the common housefly is a menace to health has aided in almost eliminating such diseases as typhoid fever and infantile diarrhea.

Biology and Mental Discipline. For success in any pursuit, it is highly important that we be accurate in observation, able to form judgments from the facts observed, and exact in conclusions. Nothing surpasses laboratory training as a means of attaining this goal, and biology is a recognized laboratory science. We have but to think of the horrors of witchcraft, fanaticism, and mob violence to realize what emotions untempered by scientific knowledge will do for the race.

Biological Contributions to the Understanding of Man. We are organisms and have much in common with other living things, particularly other members of the animal kingdom. Evidence points to a common ancestry for man and the animals that most closely resemble him. Not only the structure of the human body but the activities and behavior of man have resulted from evolution; hence biology is the logical approach to the study of human behavior. Mental disease was once attributed to demoniac possession, but now it is treated in the light of knowledge of the structure and function of the brain and nervous system. Biology has a direct bearing upon such subjects as psychology, history, economics, sociology, language, art, education, and religion, for they all deal with certain aspects of human behavior; hence the foundations laid in an elementary course in biology help greatly in understanding the humanities. Wise management of social problems has its basis in knowledge of biological truths. Since we know that man is subject to the same laws of heredity that prevail for other organisms, we have what neither we nor any other species ever before possessed—the ability to control our own evolution. We are frequently reminded that the human race is deteriorating because the ignorant and incompetent are breeding more rapidly than the intelligent and capable. The appreciation of the existence of this condition and the possible remedies lie within the scope of biology.

Biology Divided as to Point of View. Our first question regarding an organism new to us is generally "What is it?" The answer to this question is the province of the subdivision *taxonomy* (Gr. "arrangement law"), the science of classification. But before we can classify we must know something of the form and structure; hence biologists have given much attention to *morphology* (Gr. "form science"). This subdivision includes *anatomy* (Gr. "cutting up"), the study of the grosser structures; *histology* (Gr. "tissue science"), the microscopic study of tissues; and *cytology* (Gr. "cell science"), the study of the living units or cells. Another subdivision, *physiology*, deals with the functions or activities of organisms and their organs. *Ecology* (Gr. "house, or habitat, science") considers the relations of organisms to their environment. There are specialists not only in each of the many groups of plants and animals but also in the various subdivisions representing these points of view. The course in general biology can hope only to pick out a few of the more significant and useful groups, fields, and principles from the wealth of material in this vast subject.

EXERCISES

1. In the study of any group of animals or plants, what would you call the phase of biology devoted to (a) the finding and classifying of the different species and varieties; (b) the study of the body and its parts as revealed by dissection; (c) the study of the organism's digestion, respiration, and excretion; (d) the study of the adjustment of its body structure and its mode of life to its natural surroundings?
2. Name three improved plant and animal types which have been developed as the result of biological research.
3. Name three diseases of animals and plants that have been conquered by biology, and state the nature of the conquest.
4. State three biological processes which represent physical changes; three which represent chemical changes.
5. Name three persons whom you consider to have made noteworthy contributions to the development of biology.
6. Who are some of the outstanding biologists now living, and in what fields have they worked?

REFERENCES

Beebe, W., *Half Mile Down*, Harcourt, Brace & Company, Inc., 1934; also articles in *Nat. Geog. Mag.*, 1931–1934; *Popular Mechanics*, October, 1949.
Byrd, R. E., *Nat. Geog. Mag.*, 68:399, 1935.
Conant, J. B., *Science and Common Sense*, Yale University Press, 1951.

Davis, W., *The Advance of Science*, Doubleday & Co., Inc., 1934.
De Kruif, Paul, *Men Against Death*, Harcourt, Brace & Company, Inc., 1932.
Hylander, C. J., *The World of Plant Life*, The Macmillan Company, 1939.
Meier, F. C., *Sci. Mo.*, 40:5, 1935. (On Lindbergh's work.)
Moulton, F. R., *The World and Man*, Univ. of Chicago Press, 1937.
Singer, C., *A History of Biology*, Henry Schuman, Inc., rev. ed., 1950.

Chapter II

THE CELLULAR STRUCTURE OF ORGANISMS

Introduction. An outstanding characteristic of living things is the fact that they generally consist of tiny living units called *cells*. Microscopic examination shows the presence of these units in the substance of most plants and animals. According to one estimate, the newborn human infant consists of fifteen million million cells, the adult of 240 million million. Moreover, these small units have features in common in the various tissues of an organism and in different kinds of organisms. In this chapter and the next, some aspects of cells will be considered, particularly their structure and propagation.

Use of Microscopes in Biology. The unaided eye can see objects as small as one-tenth of a millimeter in diameter (a millimeter is about one twenty-fifth of an inch). A few cells, e.g., the yolk of a bird's egg, can be seen without magnification, but for investigation of most of them a microscope is required. Ordinary microscopes make use of visible light which is refracted by means of lenses in such a way as to form enlarged images of tiny objects. A *simple microscope* consists of a single lens, such as an ordinary reading glass, or of two or more lenses which act as one in forming an erect image. A *compound microscope*, which usually gives much greater magnification, consists of one set of lenses, the *objective*, which forms an inverted image of the object, and another set of lenses, the *eyepiece*, which magnifies this inverted image. Most cells range in diameter from one to one hundred microns (a micron is one thousandth of a millimeter); hence compound microscopes reveal much of their detail. Because of the physical nature of light, the lower limit of visibility of ordinary microscopes is about one-tenth of a micron. This limit can be extended somewhat by using invisible short-wave ultraviolet light and making a photograph of the object. It can be extended much further by means of the *electron microscope* (Fig. 269), which instead of light employs beams of the subatomic particles called electrons.

14

Beginnings of Microscopy.   Simple lenses were known in ancient times. The compound microscope was developed more recently, about the 16th century A.D., but the inventor is not known with certainty. By the 17th century several investigators were making extensive application of micros-

FIG. 7. Anton van Leeuwenhoek holding one of the microscopes with which he investigated bacteria and many other biological subjects. The microscope is a simple lens mounted in a metal plate to which are attached a handle and an object holder. (Courtesy of the Bausch & Lomb Optical Co.)

copy to plant and animal material. Outstanding among these early microscopists were van Leeuwenhoek, a Dutchman, and Hooke, an Englishman.

Anton van Leeuwenhoek (1632–1723) (Fig. 7) was a minor public official who ground lenses and made microscopic observations as a hobby. He was not widely educated, but he developed astonishing skill in the construction of simple microscopes of considerable magnifying power and in the examination of almost every minute object he could find. He is said to have constructed more than 400 microscopes. With these he observed in drops of water bacteria and one-celled animals, minute creatures that had never been seen before. He also saw blood circulating in the tail of a tadpole and studied various other details of larger organisms. He wrote many letters to scientific societies describing his observations, for which he received wide recognition. His work stirred the imagination of many others, who carried on the study of the various subjects of his observations.

Robert Hooke (1635–1703), an English mathematician and physicist, published in 1665 a book entitled *Micrographia* which described things

FIG. 8. Reduced copy of Robert Hooke's illustration of cork cells, showing longitudinal section at left, cross section at right. (From Holman and Robins, *Textbook of General Botany;* copyright, Wiley.)

he had observed with a compound microscope of his own construction. In a thin slice of cork he saw innumerable pores which, since they reminded him of the cells of a honeycomb, he referred to as *cells* (Fig. 8). His sketches of them were the first published illustrations of cellular structure. However, cork, which is derived from the bark of a kind of oak tree, is dead tissue in which remain only the nonliving walls of the living units that formerly composed it. In examining green plant tissue, Hooke noticed that a liquid was contained in each space enclosed by the walls, but he did not make out the structure of this liquid or appreciate the fact that it, not the walls, constitutes the living material. Nevertheless, the term *cell*, originally used by Hooke for one of the tiny cavities in cork, has been retained and is now applied to the unit, including the wall and its living contents.

The Cell Theory. Few generalizations have done more toward stimulating further study and hastening progress in biology than has the *cell theory*, which is the idea that living things are generally made of basically similar units called cells. Like many such ideas it was anticipated by investigators long before it was generally accepted. Even by the ancient Greeks and Romans it had been suggested that all plants and animals, though appearing to be quite complex, must be made up of but a few kinds of small units multiplied many times. However, there is no evidence of any observation of such structures before Hooke's account. With continued improvements in microscopes after his time, and with the application of microscopy to different kinds of living things, the fundamental cellular structure of organisms became apparent.

A number of investigators toward the end of the 18th century and early in the 19th suggested that living things in general are made up of tiny units of essentially similar structure. Credit for this generalization has been largely given to a German botanist, Matthias Schleiden (1804–1881), and his zoological colleague, Theodor Schwann (1810–1882), who published their pronouncements in 1838 and 1839 respectively. According to their statements, plants and animals are composed entirely of cells and of their secretions or products, the cells of all organisms are fundamentally alike in structure and mode of origin, and the activity of an organism is the sum of the activities of its cells. With the further development of the science of *cytology*, this theory has been well supported by additional discoveries.

Protoplasm. The early observers of cells, like Hooke, attached but little importance to the "liquid" contained within them. However, study of this substance revealed its special structure and remarkably constant nature. An important observation that contributed greatly to appreciation of the regularity of cell contents was the discovery of the cell *nucleus* (Lat. "kernel"), a relatively large body found embedded in the substance of practically all cells (Figs. 10, 11, 12). This discovery was made by Robert Brown (1773–1858), an English botanist, who reported in 1831 that he had observed this structure in the leaf cells of orchids. Further observation of plant and animal cells showed that the jelly-like contents (of which the nucleus is a part) must be a fundamental substance of living things—perhaps the very substance of life. To designate this the term *protoplasm* (Gr. "original forming material") was proposed in 1846 by Hugo von Mohl (1805–1872), a German student of plant cells. Thus, each living unit, or cell, may be interpreted as being a mass of protoplasm. The term *protoplast* has been suggested for the protoplasm of a single cell.

Preparation of Living Material for Observation of Cells. In order to study cells effectively with a microscope, the material containing them must meet certain requirements. For one thing, microscopic observation generally requires that light pass through the object to be examined, so the object must be rather thin and relatively transparent. For another, the parts of the object must be somewhat differentiated with regard to color or refractiveness in order that they may be distinguished from each other.

Certain living cells lend themselves to microscopic study better than others. For example, tiny plants and animals consisting of but one or a few cells are often sufficiently thin and transparent to be viewed in this way. Even parts of many-celled plants and animals are sometimes favorable. The water plant *Elodea*, for instance, has thin leaves consisting of only two cell layers and is often used to demonstrate living cells. Special techniques have made it possible also to separate a few cells from a many-celled organism and keep them alive in a nutrient medium. This procedure is called *tissue culture*. If properly treated, these isolated cells grow and give rise to new cells, and since these exist in rather thin aggregations, they lend themselves well to microscopic observations. Such a method is used, for example, in studying cells of cancerous growths. A definite

Fig. 9. A rotary microtome. The material to be sectioned is embedded in the block of paraffin above the knife. With each turn of the crank (opposite side) the block is automatically shifted forward, then brought down against the knife. This results in a series of sections of the embedded material. (Photo, courtesy of the American Optical Co.)

disadvantage of the observation of living cells is the lack of differentiation of cell parts, which are likely to be colorless and to differ only slightly in refractiveness. Of great use for the study of living cells is the *phase contrast microscope*, which translates differences of thickness and refractiveness of substances into differences of lightness and darkness. When applied to living cells, phase contrast microscopy distinctly reveals various structures otherwise scarcely discernible (Fig. 12).

Cells subjected to microscopic study are usually dead cells which have been killed quickly so as to preserve their structure as accurately as possible and colored with staining substances to cause obvious differentiation of their parts. Different methods of preparation are used in different situations, depending on the source of the material and the kind of cell structures to be studied. The following is a general outline of a commonly used procedure. Killing of the cells is accomplished by means of a quickly penetrating fluid applied to a small cell mass (a small organism or a tiny bit of a large one). This is called *fixation*, and the fluid is a *fixative*. In order to make thin preparations, the material is embedded in paraffin and then cut by means of a *microtome* (Gr. "small cutting"), an instrument which enables a very sharp razor blade to cut from the embedded material a succession of very thin slices of uniform thickness (Fig. 9). Afterwards, the slices (*sections*) are attached to glass microscope *slides*, and the paraffin is dissolved; they are then stained. Often more than one stain is used to give different colors to different cell parts (or types). Finally, some transparent solidifying substance (*mounting medium*) is added to the sections on the slide, which is then covered with a thin glass *cover slip*.

CELL STRUCTURES

Numerous details have been observed in cells and associated substances. Some of these features have been found to be very widespread, others to be relatively restricted to certain organisms or to certain kinds of cells. It has, moreover, been found that special techniques are required to make certain structures visible. Consequently, we may not observe in a single preparation all the various features known to exist in cells. Nevertheless, for convenient reference we may illustrate the different cell structures in a diagram of a cell, such as that in Fig. 10, which represents an animal cell. Fig. 11 shows a number of typical plant cells, in which the outstanding features differentiating these cells from those of animals are presented. Special attention will be given to these cell structures in succeeding paragraphs.

Nucleus and Cytoplasm. A general feature of cells is the differentiation of the protoplast into a specialized internal portion called the *nucleus* and an outer part called the *cytoplasm* (Gr. "cell substance"). Both of these are translucent and colorless in living cells and differ but slightly in refractiveness; hence the nucleus may be scarcely discernible within the cytoplasm. However, they are sufficiently different to be made clearly distinct with the phase contrast microscope (Fig. 12). In dead, stained material, the nucleus is generally very conspicuous, since in preparing such material use is made of a stain which is taken up by the nucleus more readily than by the cytoplasm. Both cytoplasm and nucleus contain various special structures.

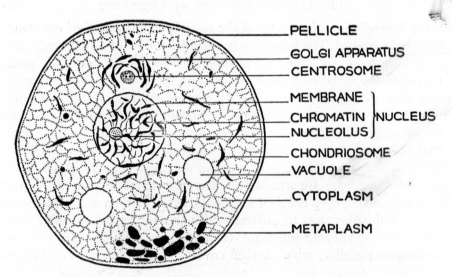

PELLICLE

GOLGI APPARATUS

CENTROSOME

MEMBRANE ⎫
CHROMATIN ⎬ NUCLEUS
NUCLEOLUS ⎭

CHONDRIOSOME

VACUOLE

CYTOPLASM

METAPLASM

FIG. 10. A generalized animal cell, showing the structures commonly found. The two small dots in the centrosome are centrioles.

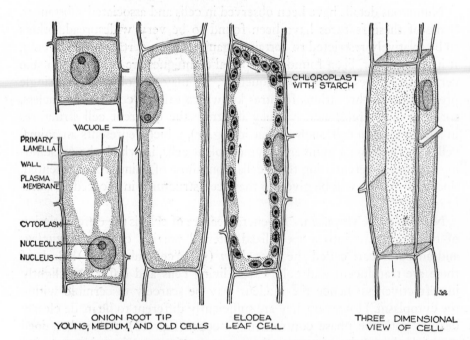

CHLOROPLAST WITH STARCH

VACUOLE

PRIMARY LAMELLA

WALL

PLASMA MEMBRANE

CYTOPLASM

NUCLEOLUS

NUCLEUS

ONION ROOT TIP
YOUNG, MEDIUM, AND OLD CELLS

ELODEA
LEAF CELL

THREE DIMENSIONAL
VIEW OF CELL

FIG. 11. Typical plant cells. Note (left) that as the cell enlarges, several vacuoles appear in the cytoplasm, to merge later into one large vacuole; the nucleus, remaining about the same size, is pressed against the wall. The arrows in the *Elodea* leaf cell indicate movement of the cytoplasm, a rather common phenomenon, but more evident in certain plants than in others. Cells are three-dimensional bodies, as shown in the figure at the right.

The Cytoplasm. The surface of the cytoplasm (which is the outermost part of the protoplast) is bounded by an exceedingly thin membrane, the *plasma membrane* (too thin to be visible with ordinary microscopes). This membrane has the important function of regulating the passage of substances into and out of the protoplast. Inside the cytoplasm there are often found apparently empty cavities called *vacuoles,* which in reality contain watery solutions of various substances. In a mature plant cell the greater part of the volume is usually occupied by a prominent vacuole

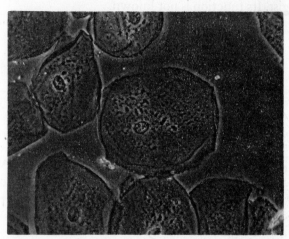

Fig. 12. Unstained human epithelial cells as viewed by the phase contrast microscope. (× 600). These were obtained by gently scraping the inside of the cheek. The oval body visible in several of the cells is the nucleus. (Photomicrograph by Dr. O. W. Richards. Courtesy of the American Optical Company, Research Laboratory.)

(Fig. 11). Granules and other suspended bodies are frequently found in the cytoplasm. Among these are the *chondriosomes* (Gr. "granular bodies"), tiny particles of various shapes which are generally found in cells (Fig. 10). The function of these is not well known, though certain enzymes (p. 48) have been found to be associated with them. In many plant cells, but rarely in the cells of animals, the cytoplasm contains additional bodies called *plastids* (Fig. 11). These are generally larger than chondriosomes. Outstanding among these are the green plastids, *chloroplasts* (Gr. "green plastids"), which contain *chlorophyll* (Gr. "leaf green"), a substance important in the manufacture of carbohydrate foods in the presence of light (*photosynthesis*), a vital process in green plants. Red, orange, or yellow plastids (*chromoplasts*) give color to certain flowers and fruits. In animal cells of certain kinds may be found cytoplasmic structures that are rarely, if ever, found in plant cells. An example is the *centrosome*, a small body lying close to the nucleus and containing dot-like *centrioles* (Fig. 10). This is found in many kinds of animal cells but only in cells of some of the lower plants. As will be seen in the next chapter, the centrosome appears to play an important role at the time of cell division. A cytoplasmic feature very widespread among animals but apparently not present in plants is the *Golgi apparatus* (Fig. 10), a localized system of granules and threads first described by Camillo Golgi, an Italian cytologist. Its function is not known.

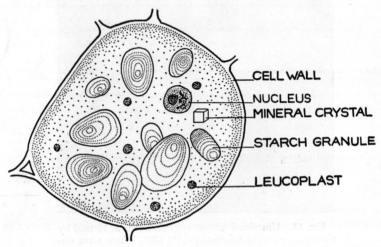

CELL WALL

NUCLEUS

MINERAL CRYSTAL

STARCH GRANULE

LEUCOPLAST

Fig. 13. Cell of a potato tuber showing metaplasmic content—starch granules and a mineral crystal. Leucoplasts are colorless plastids.

Although it may be difficult to decide whether a given cytoplasmic inclusion is alive or not, some substances and structures of the cytoplasm seem definitely nonliving. These are collectively termed *metaplasm*. Conspicuous in many plant cells are granules which are accumulations of the food substance *starch* (Fig. 13); these are formed in association with plastids. A somewhat similar substance, *glycogen*, may be found in certain animal cells. Other examples of metaplasm are *oil droplets*, *protein granules*, and *crystals* of various organic salts.

The Nucleus. The outer surface of the nucleus, like that of the cytoplasm, is bounded by a very thin membrane, the *nuclear membrane*. Within lies an apparent network of material which is readily colored by various biological stains. This substance is called *chromatin* (Gr. "color"), and study of it has shown that it is associated with a number of separate thread-like bodies, the *chromosomes* (Gr. "color bodies"), which are entangled with each other inside the nucleus to give the impression of a network. The chromosomes become quite distinct and are released from the confines of the nucleus at the time of cell division, as will be shown in the next chapter. Various kinds of evidence have shown that the chromosomes are of primary importance in the life of cells and of living things in general. The science of genetics has accumulated much evidence show-

ing that the chromosomes contain minute particles, the *genes*, which govern the development of organisms. Some of this evidence will be considered in Chapter XXVIII. Also contained within the nucleus is a body (or bodies), the *nucleolus*, sharply distinguished from the chromatin by its reaction to stains. The function of this is uncertain. The nucleus also contains a liquid called *nuclear sap*.

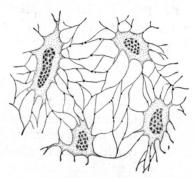

Fig. 14. Cells of a membrane bone of a mouse (greatly magnified). These cells are separated from each other by the hard substance of the bone except for thin protoplasmic strands which lie in tiny canals in this substance. (Redrawn from Maximow and Bloom, *A Textbook of Histology,* copyright, 1930, W. B. Saunders Company.)

Extraprotoplasmic Material. Around the protoplast, but not part of it, there is often a wall or membrane of appreciable thickness. This is a nonliving product of cell activity. In plants there is usually a thick, durable cell wall made of *cellulose*. Occasionally in plants and frequently in animals the plasma membrane seems to constitute the only cell boundary, but in some animal cells there is a thin nonliving sheath, the pellicle (called a wall by some biologists), that lies just outside the membrane. Some kinds of cells produce a great deal of extracellular material which accumulates and tends to separate the protoplasts. In vertebrate animals this extracellular material is exemplified by the hard substance of bone. This is secreted by bone cells, which lie separate from each other in little cavities in the hard material (Fig. 14).

SUMMARY OF CELL STRUCTURES

I. Nonliving:
  A. *Cell wall* (and other extraprotoplasmic material): made externally by the protoplast and serving to support and protect it.
  B. *Vacuoles:* cytoplasmic cavities containing water with dissolved substances.
  C. *Metaplasm:* granules or droplets suspended in the cytoplasm.

II. Living:
- A. *Cytoplasm:* the outer portion of the protoplast.
    1. *Plasma membrane:* exceedingly thin outermost layer of cytoplasm.
    2. *Chondriosomes:* tiny bodies of various shapes scattered throughout the cytoplasm.
    3. *Plastids:* special bodies often found in the cytoplasm of plant cells, such as *chloroplasts*.
    4. *Centrosome:* small body lying close to the nucleus in many animal cells and in the cells of some lower plants.
    5. *Golgi apparatus:* system of granules and threads found in many animal cells.
- B. *Nucleus:* specialized internal portion of the protoplast.
    1. *Nuclear membrane:* thin outermost layer of the nucleus.
    2. *Chromatin:* characteristically heavy-staining substance associated with the *chromosomes*.
    3. *Nucleolus:* distinct body found in the nucleus.
    4. *Nuclear sap:* relatively liquid substance of the nucleus.

Fig. 15. A striated muscle fiber of man (greatly magnified). This has been partly crushed and spread out. The cross-striations and numerous nuclei characteristic of this muscle may be noted. (Redrawn from Maximow and Bloom, *A Textbook of Histology,* copyright, 1930, W. B. Saunders Company.)

Variation Concerning Nuclei. Although organisms generally consist of cells in which a single nucleus is surrounded by cytoplasm, deviations from this plan are known. Some masses of protoplasm contain no nucleus. In man and other mammals the red blood cells lack a nucleus when mature, though similar blood cells in lower vertebrates (e.g., the frog) are nucleated. In certain microorganisms (bacteria and blue-green algae) there is no clearly defined nucleus, though material comparable to chromatin has been recognized in some of them. In still other cases there are no membranes enclosing individual cells; hence many nuclei exist in a continuous mass of protoplasm forming a *coenocyte* (Gr. "cell in common"). This condition is illustrated by the type of human muscle attached to the large bones (*skeletal muscle*), which is also exceptional in having a peculiar striped (*striated*) aspect under the microscope (Fig. 15). The coenocytic condition is also present in various other organisms, such as some of the simple plants (certain green algae, such as *Vaucheria,* the green felt plant. and the Class PHYCOMYCETES of the fungi).

TISSUES AND ORGANS

In many-celled organisms there are definite aggregations of cells of different kinds, and the cells of an individual (along with extracellular materials) may be classified into main categories called *tissues*. The cells of the same tissue are not necessarily exactly like each other, but they have certain characteristics in common that set them apart from other cells. These features include functional as well as structural peculiarities. The main kinds of tissue found in the higher animals are (1) *epithelial tissue*, which consists of cells that cover surfaces and line cavities; (2) *muscular tissue*, made up of cells adapted to contract and cause pronounced movement; (3) *nervous tissue*, with cells capable of transmitting nerve impulses; and (4) *supporting and connective tissue*, which includes bone, cartilage, and other supporting material and also the blood. Further consideration of these tissues will be given in Chapter VIII. The tissues are in turn grouped into *organs* which are capable of performing certain functions. The human hand may be used as an example of an organ. It consists of bone, muscle, nerve, blood, epithelial, and cells of still other kinds. Its work is the grasping and handling of objects.

EXERCISES

1. What is the basis for the lower limit of visibility of a microscope employing ordinary light? Of what advantage should be the use of ultraviolet light?
2. Name other 17th-century microscopists besides van Leeuwenhoek and Hooke and tell something about their investigations.
3. Describe a method for culturing cells *in vitro* (Lat. "in glass"—i.e., in glass containers).
4. What criteria may be used to decide whether a cellular inclusion is alive?
5. Name additional examples of metaplasm besides those given in the text.

REFERENCES

Allen, R. M., *The Microscope*, D. Van Nostrand Company, 1940.

Bennett, A. H., *Phase Microscopy; Principles and Applications*, John Wiley & Sons, Inc., 1951.

DeRobertis, E. D. P., Nowinski, W. W., and Saez, F. A., *General Cytology*, W. B. Saunders Company, 1948.

Maximow, A. A., and Bloom, W., *A Textbook of Histology*, W. B. Saunders Company, 1942.

Sharp, L. W., *Introduction to Cytology*, McGraw-Hill Book Company, 1934.

Sharp, L. W., *Fundamentals of Cytology*, McGraw-Hill Book Company, 1943.

Chapter III

THE FORMATION OF NEW CELLS
FROM OLD CELLS

Cell Division. New cells generally form by the division of previously existing cells. That this is the case was not apparent to the early observers of cells and was not clearly understood even at the time of the formulation of the cell theory. Von Mohl, already mentioned as the originator of the term protoplasm, was among the first to observe cell division and to describe it in some detail. Cell division, as well as cell enlargement, generally accompanies increase in size (i.e., growth) in many-celled plants and animals. Cell division is also important in the reproduction of organisms.

Mitosis. When a cell divides, the nucleus undergoes a striking transformation. The *chromosomes*, which have been concealed in the nucleus, come clearly into view, are divided, and are distributed equally to the two parts of the dividing cell. This nuclear process is called *mitosis* (Gr. "thread," because of the thread-like nature of the chromosomes). In practically all living things cell division is accompanied by mitosis. Moreover, the process is essentially the same in the various organisms. Only relatively minor variation is ordinarily encountered, though there are rather regular differences between plants and animals and among some of their subgroups. This regularity of mitosis is additional evidence supporting the contention of the cell theory that all cells are fundamentally similar.

Mitosis may most profitably be studied where cells are dividing frequently—for example, in the embryos of many-celled animals and in the root tips of higher plants. The methods of preparing cells for the study of mitosis are similar to those already described for the observation of cells. Mitosis may sometimes be seen in living cells; the phase contrast microscope is proving to be most useful for such observations. However, this process has usually been studied in fixed, stained material. In such material, cells are observed which have been arrested at various stages of mitosis (Fig. 16). From these a picture of the process is constructed, as, for in-

26

stance, one might reconstruct an event from a group of snapshots taken during its progress.

Outline of Mitosis. Although mitosis is a continuous process, it is convenient to consider it as a series of stages, each characterized by certain features. A cell which is not in process of division is said to be at *interphase*

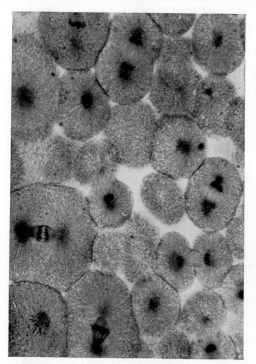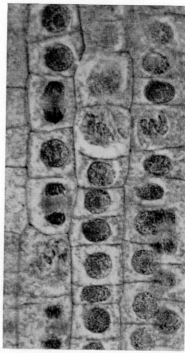

Fig. 16. Rapidly growing animal and plant tissues killed, embedded, sectioned and stained to show cells arrested at various stages of mitosis. Left, young embryo of white-fish; right, zone of cell division in an onion root tip. See Figs. 17 and 18 for the stages included. (Photomicrographs, courtesy of General Biological Supply House, Chicago.)

(Gr. "between phase"), or the *growth stage*. The structure of such a cell was described in the preceding chapter. The following is an outline of the stages of mitosis as they usually appear (Fig. 17).

I. *Prophase* (Gr. "before phase"). This is the early part of mitosis, during which the chromosomes make their appearance and become progressively more distinct.

 A. The chromosomes appear as long, slender threads.

   1. These threads are seen to be double.

   2. Somewhere along the length of each chromosome there may be seen a small body of special nature, the *spindle attachment*. The

movements that a chromosome undergoes during mitosis appear to be directed through this body.

B. The chromosomes become shorter and thicker. This is accomplished through the coiling of the chromosome strands and the addition of a heavily staining envelope, the *matrix*.

C. The nuclear membrane disintegrates, releasing the chromosomes, and the nucleolus disappears. The chromosomes come to be associated by their spindle attachments with a spindle, apparently of fine fibers.

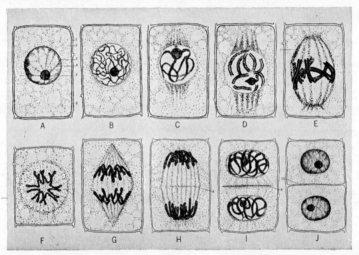

Fig. 17. Principal stages in mitosis, as seen in dividing cells of a root tip. *A. Interphase* (1, wall; 2, cytoplasm; 3, nuclear membrane; 4, chromatin; 5, nucleolus; 6, plasma membrane). *B, Early prophase;* chromosomes long and narrow. *C, Middle prophase;* chromosomes shorter, sometimes apparently joined end to end, spindle beginning to appear. *D. Late prophase;* chromosomes beginning to split. *E, Metaphase;* chromosomes gathering along equatorial plane, spindle evident. *F,* Polar view of *early anaphase* showing chromosome halves. *G, Anaphase,* chromosome halves separating. *H, Early telophase;* the partition membrane beginning to form. *I, Late telophase,* with partition membrane. *J, Daughter cells* separated by a wall. (From *General Biology Charts,* edited by Goddard, Kenoyer, and Hinds, published by the Denoyer-Geppert Company, Chicago; courtesy of the publishers.)

II. *Metaphase* (Gr. "after phase").

A. The chromosomes move so that their spindle attachments lie together in a plane halfway between the poles of the spindle (the *equatorial plate*). Observation of the chromosomes along the axis of the spindle (polar view) may reveal them to be quite distinct from each other, so they may readily be counted. The number of chromosomes observable at mitosis is practically constant for all the cells of an individual and, moreover, for all individuals of the same *species* of plant or animal, though definite exceptions are sometimes encountered.

    B. Each chromosome, which has already shown itself to be split lengthwise, separates completely into halves.

III. *Anaphase* (Gr. "apart phase"). As metaphase passes into anaphase, the halves of each chromosome move apart from each other toward the poles of the spindle, one toward each pole. In this process the chromosomes often give the appearance of being dragged by the spindle attachment, but the mechanism of this movement is not known.

IV. *Telophase* (Gr. "end phase").

    A. Each group of chromosomes (halves of the original chromosomes) has reached a pole of the spindle, where it forms a rather compact mass.

    B. A nuclear membrane forms about each mass, nucleoli appear, and the chromosomes become less and less distinct, taking on the appearance of a network. Interphase nuclei are formed.

    C. The spindle disappears and division of the cytoplasm takes place, with each new nucleus being enclosed in part of the cytoplasm of the original cell. Thus, two new cells take the place of the old one.

Significance of Mitosis. Evidence has accumulated to show that the *hereditary factors* or *genes* are located in linear order on the chromosomes, each chromosome having a different group. The longitudinal splitting of the chromosomes in the metaphase and the separation of the halves of each in the anaphase therefore insures the transmission of all the genes of the old cell to both of the new ones and hence keeps the gene (or hereditary) combination constant. This will be discussed more fully in Chapter XXVIII.

Variations in Mitosis. There are certain general differences between plants and animals as regards mitosis. Fig. 18 illustrates mitosis in an animal. The centrosome seems to play a part in the formation of the spindle. In early prophase the centrosome liberates two small particles, the *centrioles*, and these move slowly apart. About each of these a system of radiating lines, an *aster* (Gr. "star"), develops. A portion of each aster extends to the equatorial plate, forming the spindle, so that the centrioles come to occupy positions at the poles of the spindle. The asters are very striking features of dividing animal cells and persist through the process. Like the centrosome itself, centrioles and asters are also found in some of the simple plants.

Another feature in which plants and animals often differ is the manner in which the cytoplasm is divided. In plants, the cytoplasm of the new cells is usually separated by a *cell plate*, a partition which forms across the center of the spindle and spreads so as to divide the cell completely. This partition then develops into the cell wall characteristic of plants. In animals on the other hand, division of the cytoplasm is usually achieved through *constriction*. In a plane passing between the daughter nuclei a furrow forms about the cell, and this deepens until the protoplasmic mass is cut in two.

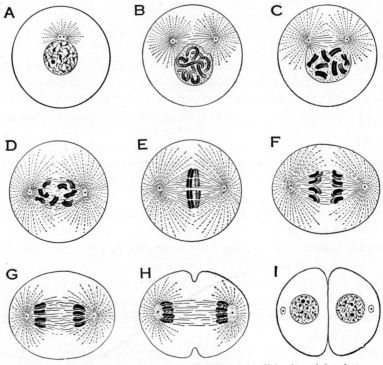

Fig. 18. Typical stages in mitosis of an animal cell having eight chromosomes. *A, Interphase,* with dividing centrosome surrounded by the aster. *B, Early prophase. C* and *D, Later prophases. E, Metaphase,* chromosomes on equatorial plane, each splitting longitudinally. *F* and *G, Anaphases,* chromosome halves separating. *H, Telophase,* chromosomes merging to form new nuclei and spindle disappearing as constriction appears in cytoplasm. *I,* Division completed. (From Woodruff, *Animal Biology;* copyright, Macmillan.)

Some features of mitosis are peculiar to certain groups of organisms, or even to parts of organisms or to stages in their development. For example, among the little animals called protozoans, the mitotic figure, including spindle as well as chromosomes, is often entirely enclosed in the nuclear membrane during a large part of mitosis. Another example is coenocytic organisms and tissues; here nuclear division is regularly not accompanied by cytoplasmic division.

In a very few situations, cell division takes place without mitosis. The nucleus merely divides by a sort of constriction. This is called *amitosis*

(Gr. "not mitosis"). Such a process has been reported, for example, in degenerating or pathological tissues, as in certain cancers.

Cells and Reproduction. A fundamental characteristic of living things is their ability to reproduce themselves. This involves the separation of living material from an organism and the organization of this material into a new individual. Cell division plays an important part. Single-celled organisms usually reproduce by simply dividing in two. Many-celled plants and animals ordinarily give rise to cells or groups of cells which separate from the parent and are capable, through repeated division, of producing new multicellular individuals. Reproduction is often complicated by an additional cellular process, *fertilization*, in which a new cell is formed by the *fusion* of two previously existing ones. This is an essential feature of *sexual reproduction*, a widespread phenomenon among both animals and plants. All other kinds of reproduction, such as the division of single-celled creatures into two, are termed *asexual*. The cells coming together at fertiliza-

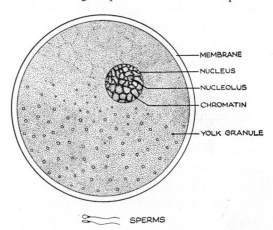

Fig. 19.   Human egg and sperms ($\times$ 250). The egg has about 50,000 times the volume of the sperm, yet the two have equivalent contributions to the heredity of the offspring. The sperm consists of the head (nucleus, shown in side and edge views), the middle piece (containing the centrosome), and the tail (cytoplasm).

tion are called *gametes* (Gr. "spouse," Fig. 19), and the resulting cell is a *zygote* (Gr. "yoked"). The zygote gives rise to a new individual, either single-celled, or, through repeated division, a many-celled organism.

Chromosome Numbers.   It has already been pointed out that the number of chromosomes appearing at mitosis is practically constant for all individuals of the same species. Chromosome numbers have been determined for many species. For example, 48 chromosomes are found in the human cell, 40 in the mouse, 20 in corn, 16 in the onion. No great importance can be attached to the numbers themselves; though similar species often have similar chromosome numbers, very different species may have the same number; for instance, the potato plant, like man, has 48 chromosomes.

Maintenance of a Constant Chromosome Number.   Since mitosis involves the division of each chromosome into two equal parts and the distribution of a half to each new cell, it is evident that cell division accompanied by mitosis should normally produce new cells with the same chromosome number as the old one. Each cell of an individual's body should receive the same number of chromosomes as was present in the original cell. Moreover, with asexual reproduction, different individuals should also have the same chromosome number in all their cells. Thus, we may explain the regularity of chromosome numbers observed in mitosis. On the other hand, since sexual reproduction involves the fusion of cells (with their nuclei and chromosomes), we might expect this process to be associated with an increase of chromosome number. Observations of numbers of chromosomes in gametes and zygotes have shown that such an increase does take place; the number of chromosomes present in the zygote is the sum of the chromosomes in the gametes. However, the increase in chromosome number accompanying fertilization does not result in a continuous increase generation after generation. This is prevented by a reduction of the number of chromosomes to one-half (or approximately one-half, in case there is an odd chromosome) prior to the formation of gametes. This process, a special modification of mitosis, is called *meiosis* (Gr. "making smaller"). A general outline of meiosis with some of its details will be presented later (Chap. XXVII).

The changes in chromosome number accompanying reproduction may be illustrated in the human species. Because of meiosis, the gametes of man (tiny cells called *eggs*, produced by the female, and much smaller ones called *sperms*, produced by the male) have only 24 chromosomes each. Fertilization results in the combination of the 24 chromosomes of the egg with the 24 of the sperm to give 48 chromosomes altogether, the number characteristically exhibited by cells during mitosis (although irregularities of mitosis sometimes cause deviations from this number[1]). The number 24 is called the *haploid number* (Gr. "simple number"), 48 the *diploid number* (Gr. "double number"). Later, when the new individual has matured, gametes are produced which, because of meiosis, have only 24 chromosomes each.

Summary. Continued study of cells and cell propagation has supported the generalization that all cells come from previously existing ones. Cells are usually derived by cell division, and this is ordinarily accompanied by mitosis, in which the chromosomes of the nucleus are precisely

---

[1] Recent studies of human mitosis have shown considerable variation of chromosome number in certain tissues; nevertheless, the tissues producing the gametes would seem regularly to have 48 chromosomes per cell, while the gametes have but 24.

divided and distributed equally to the forming cells. The reproduction of plants and animals regularly involves cell division. However, sexual reproduction requires that cells also come into existence through fertilization, which is the fusion of cells called gametes. Mitosis tends to keep the number of chromosomes constant from cell to cell. Fertilization, on the other hand, causes an increase in the number of chromosomes. This is counterbalanced by meiosis, which reduces the chromosome number. Because of meiosis, gametes regularly have the haploid number of chromosomes, the diploid number being restored at fertilization.

EXERCISES

1. William Harvey made the biological generalization, *Omne vivum ex ovo*. It was modified by Virchow into *Omnis cellula e cellula*. Explain.
2. Why would it be difficult to count the chromosomes in dividing cells observed in a longitudinal section of a root tip (as in Fig. 16)?
3. Suppose a cell has the shape of a sphere. As the cell grows larger, how would the relationship between its volume and its surface area change? What might this have to do with cell division?
4. Enumerate the more general differences between plant and animal cells.
5. Name some examples of asexual reproduction in familiar organisms.
6. Which would be more likely to maintain in the new cells the hereditary factors of the old, mitosis or amitosis? Explain.

REFERENCES

Darlington, C. D., *Recent Advances in Cytology*, J. & A. Churchill, Ltd., 1937.
Darlington, C. D., and LaCour, L. F., *The Handling of Chromosomes*, George Allen & Unwin, Ltd., 2nd ed., 1947.
Sharp, L. W., *Fundamentals of Cytology*, McGraw-Hill Book Company, 1943.
White, M. J. D., *The Chromosomes*, Methuen & Co., Ltd., 4th ed., 1950.

Chapter IV

CHEMICAL AND PHYSICAL ASPECTS
OF LIVING THINGS

It is important that the student of biology acquire a few of the fundamental concepts of chemistry and physics, since an approach to understanding the characteristics of living things may be made through the application of these principles. In this chapter some of the basic ideas of these
sciences will be discussed, and some application of them will be made to
the composition of living things. Chemical and physical processes that occur in organisms will be considered in the next chapter.

Matter and Energy. Anything which occupies space and has mass
(determinable as weight) is *matter*. There are many kinds of matter, or
substances. Moreover, substances exist in any of three different states:
solid, liquid, and *gas*. For example, water is a substance which may exist as
ice (a solid), ordinary water (a liquid), or water vapor (a gas). Chemical
changes involve alteration of the kinds of substances. Physical changes
leave the substances the same but alter their state or the relations of their
parts. Thus the melting of ice and the evaporation of water are physical
changes. When matter is caused to move against an opposing force (as
when an object is lifted against gravity), work is accomplished. *Energy* is
the capacity to do work. There are various manifestations of energy. In
addition to that which is evident through the movement of large objects,
there are heat, light, electricity, etc. Energy may also be classified according to whether it is immediately associated with movement (*kinetic energy*) or is latent (stored) in a situation (*potential energy*). For example,
water that is flowing exhibits kinetic energy, but water that is impounded
behind a dam (but is capable of flowing when released) has potential
energy. Energy may be transformed from one kind to another, and such
transformations accompany chemical and physical changes. Of great importance to living things is the fact that potential energy may reside in

chemical substances, capable of being stored or released by the activities of organisms.

Elements. Analysis of matter has shown it to be made up of more than 90 different substances which are not decomposed into simpler substances by ordinary chemical means. These are called *elements*, and they include such substances as the gases oxygen and nitrogen, the metallic solid gold, and the nonmetallic solid carbon (to name a few that occur appreciably in the uncombined state). Each element is characterized by certain properties. For example, carbon, which is a solid under ordinary conditions, usually exists in the uncombined form as black crystals or as an apparently noncrystalline material (graphite, coal, soot, etc.), rarely as very hard, transparent crystals (diamond).

Compounds. A *compound* is a substance in which two or more elements are chemically combined. The properties of a compound are likely to be greatly different from those of its component elements. Moreover, the elements of a compound are always present in definite proportions by weight. An example of a simple compound is water, a liquid at ordinary temperatures, in which the gases hydrogen and oxygen are combined in a ratio of weights of about 1:8. A somewhat more complex compound is common sugar, which contains carbon united with hydrogen and oxygen. The element carbon is capable of forming a very large number of different compounds, and these, generally speaking, occur in nature only through the activities of living organisms. Consequently, these substances are called *organic compounds*, and the study of them is *organic chemistry*. Compounds that do not contain carbon (as well as a few simple ones that do) are called *inorganic*. Common sugar is an example of an organic compound. It is produced through the activities of certain plants—sugar cane and sugar beets, for instance. It was once believed that organic compounds could be formed only through the agency of life processes. However, it has since been found possible to manufacture many of them in chemical laboratories.

Elements and Compounds in Living Things. Chemical analysis of organisms has shown four of the elements to be invariably present in appreciable amounts: carbon, hydrogen, oxygen, and nitrogen. Analyses of protoplasm (which have been made on certain simple organisms and parts of many-celled ones) have shown that these elements constitute about 99 percent of it by weight. Practically always found in living things, but generally in very small amounts, are eight others: sulfur, phosphorus, potassium, iron, magnesium, calcium, sodium, and chlorine. Traces of still other elements are sometimes found, and some of these are known to be essential for the survival of certain organisms—for example, iodine, boron, copper, cobalt, manganese, and zinc.

Outstanding among the inorganic compounds of living things is water. The amount of this substance is variable, but it is frequently very high; for instance, the human body is about 65 percent water. Other inorganic compounds are largely substances called salts, which include various elements in their composition.

The organic compounds of organisms fall largely into three categories: *carbohydrates, fats* (and fat-like compounds), and *proteins* (these are also the main categories of *foods* and will be considered as such in the next chapter). Carbohydrates contain the elements carbon, hydrogen, and oxygen in various amounts. Several examples of carbohydrates have already been mentioned: common sugar (or *sucrose*); starch, which is stored as granules in plant cells; cellulose, the building material of plant cell walls. Fats and fat-like compounds also contain carbon, hydrogen, and oxygen; but the amount of oxygen is relatively much smaller in them than in carbohydrates, and some of the fat-like compounds contain other elements besides these three. As has already been mentioned, fat droplets are sometimes prominent features of cells. Proteins contain carbon, hydrogen, oxygen, nitrogen, almost always sulfur, and usually phosphorus; and still other elements may be present. Proteins are exceedingly complex compounds that may be very intimately associated with protoplasm. The chromatin of cell nuclei and of chromosomes, for instance, is a complex of *nucleoproteins*, consisting of proteins combined with phosphorus-containing substances called nucleic acids.

Atoms and Molecules. Matter consists of very small particles known as *atoms*. Each element consists of atoms of a certain kind. Still smaller particles—electrons, neutrons, protons, etc.—are contained in atoms, and the number of them varies from one element to another. The atoms of the various elements also differ as to weight. Although the individual atoms must have exceedingly small weights, the *atomic weights* of the elements may be represented by appreciably large numbers relating these weights to each other. As the basis for assigning atomic weights, oxygen is given a value of 16. Hydrogen, the lightest of the elements, then has an atomic weight of about 1 (i.e., about $\frac{1}{16}$ that of oxygen). Additional examples of atomic weights (approximate) are: carbon, 12; nitrogen, 14; phosphorus, 31; and sulfur, 32.

Atoms are joined together in close union to form *molecules*. A molecule of an element consists only of atoms of that element, but a molecule of a compound contains atoms of more than one kind. For example, a molecule of hydrogen has two atoms of hydrogen joined together; a molecule of water has two hydrogen atoms combined with one of oxygen. The *molecular weight* of a substance is the sum of the weights of its component atoms. A molecule of hydrogen has the weight $2 \times 1 = 2$; the weight of a molecule of water is $2 \times 1 + 16 = 18$. The molecular weights of organic compounds are often much greater. For instance, common sugar, or sucrose, has a molecular weight of approximately 342. Complex organic compounds, especially the proteins, have molecular weights running into the thousands and even the millions.

Atoms and molecules are exceedingly small and are generally invisible, even with the most powerful microscopes. The dimensions of atoms and molecules have been determined by indirect means. Thus atoms must have diameters of about one ten-thousandth of a micron, and molecules range in diameter from scarcely more than this (as in the hydrogen molecule) to somewhat more than one hundredth of a micron. With the electron microscope, which is capable of revealing dimensions of the order of one thousandth of a micron, some of the largest of the molecules (protein molecules) have been made visible.

Chemical Symbols and Formulas.   Each element is symbolized by a letter or combination of letters derived from its Latin name. Sometimes the symbol is the initial letter of the English name of the element; thus carbon, hydrogen, oxygen, nitrogen, sulfur, and phosphorus are represented by the letters C, H, O, N, S, and P respectively. Two letters are used for some —Mg for magnesium, Ca for calcium, and Cl for chlorine. The letter or letters may come from a Latin name quite different from the corresponding English name, as in K for potassium (from Latin "kalium"), Fe for iron (from "ferrum"), and Na for sodium (from "natrium").

An element or compound may be represented by a molecular formula showing the kinds and numbers of atoms present in one of its molecules. Such a formula is a series of element symbols to which subscripts are appended to show how many atoms of each element are present (except that no subscript is used when there is only one atom). If the substance is an element, only one symbol is needed; thus the gases hydrogen, oxygen, and nitrogen have the molecular formulas H_2, O_2, and N_2, since each of them has a molecule made of two atoms. Water has the molecular formula H_2O. Sucrose has the molecular formula $C_{12}H_{22}O_{11}$, indicating the presence in each molecule of 12 carbon atoms, 22 atoms of hydrogen, and 11 of oxygen. Though the component elements may have been determined, the molecular formulas of many of the very complex compounds of living things are known only approximately if at all.

Arrangements of Atoms in Molecules. Although molecules are very small, ways have been found to determine the arrangement of the atoms in many of them. In relatively simple compounds no more than one arrangement ordinarily exists. However, in more complex ones (such as are frequently encountered among the organic compounds), two or more arrangements are often possible, and these may be associated with different properties. Because of the importance of atomic arrangement, organic compounds are often represented by *graphic* (or *structural*) *formulas*.

In a *graphic formula*, each symbol is connected to other symbols by a certain number of lines. The number of lines represents the *valence*, or combining capacity, of the element. The valence of hydrogen is 1; oxygen, nitrogen, and carbon have valences of 2, 3, and 4 respectively. This is shown in the following manner:

$$H— \qquad —O— \qquad \overset{\displaystyle |}{\underset{\displaystyle |}{—N—}} \qquad \overset{\displaystyle |}{\underset{\displaystyle |}{—C—}}$$

In a graphic formula, each line connects two symbols and represents a *bond* between the atoms. Sometimes two atoms are joined by a double bond, shown by two parallel lines. To illustrate these formulas, the following relatively simple organic compounds are shown: methyl alcohol (wood alcohol), which has the molecular formula CH_4O; acetic acid (present in vinegar), with the molecular formula $C_2H_4O_2$; and the amino acid glycine (amino acids are derived from proteins), with the molecular formula $C_2H_5O_2N$.

$$
\begin{array}{ccc}
\text{H} & \text{H} \quad \text{O} & \text{H—N—H} \qquad \text{O}\\
| & | \quad \diagup\!\!\diagup & | \qquad \diagup\!\!\diagup\\
\text{H—C—O—H} & \text{H—C—C} & \text{H—C—C}\\
| & | \quad \diagdown & | \qquad \diagdown\\
\text{H} & \text{H} \quad \text{O—H} & \text{H} \qquad \text{O—H}\\
\text{Methyl alcohol} & \text{Acetic acid} & \text{Glycine}
\end{array}
$$

These examples show the presence of certain atomic groups that are found repeatedly in organic compounds and may confer definite properties on these substances. Illustrated here are the methyl, carboxyl, and amino groups:

$$
\begin{array}{ccc}
\text{H} & \text{O} & \\
| & \diagup\!\!\diagup & \\
\text{H—C—} & —\text{C} & \text{H—N—H}\\
| & \diagdown & \text{Amino}\\
\text{H} & \text{O—H} & \\
\text{Methyl} & \text{Carboxyl} &
\end{array}
$$

The methyl group is present in many different organic compounds, the carboxyl group in all organic acids, and the amino group in the so-called amino acids (which also have the carboxyl group) and in certain other compounds.

For convenience in printing, molecular structures are often shown by a *semigraphic formula*, in which groups of atoms are given in a series. The frequently encountered atomic groups methyl, carboxyl, and amino then become $-CH_3$, $-COOH$, and $-NH_2$ respectively (the dash indicating the attaching bond is regularly included when these groups are printed by themselves). According to this system, methyl alcohol is CH_3OH, acetic acid CH_3COOH, and glycine CH_2NH_2COOH.

In very complex organic compounds, even though the molecular formula may be known (at least approximately), the structure of the molecule may be in doubt. Consequently, these compounds must be designated by their molecular formulas, their names being given to distinguish them from other substances with the same molecular formula. Even when the molecular structure is known, it may be so complex that it is ordinarily inconvenient to represent the substance by a graphic or even semigraphic formula. Here also the molecular formula may be used, the name of the compound being given to identify it. For example, common sugar is usually given as $C_{12}H_{22}O_{11}$ and referred to as sucrose, because its molecule is fairly complex.

Chemical Reactions and Chemical Equations. A *chemical reaction* is a process in which atoms enter into new associations with other atoms. This may involve the combination of elements to form compounds, exchanges of atoms between compounds, the breakdown of compounds to form simpler substances (including the release of elements). Such reactions regularly involve energy transformations, energy either being taken up from the surroundings or being liberated. These reactions are reversible; that is, the products may react to form the original substances (though a reaction may proceed much more readily in one direction than the other). As an example of a chemical reaction let us take the burning (or explosion) of hydrogen. This represents a reaction of hydrogen with the oxygen of the air; during the process water is formed, along with the liberation of energy as light and heat. That this reaction is reversible is shown by *electrolysis*, the process in which water is decomposed into the gases hydrogen and oxygen by passing an electric current through it (a way of supplying energy).

Chemical reactions are represented by *chemical equations*. Let us represent the burning of hydrogen by an equation.

$$2H_2 \quad + \quad O_2 \quad \rightarrow \quad 2H_2O$$
$$\text{Hydrogen} \qquad\qquad \text{Oxygen} \qquad\qquad \text{Water}$$

As in an algebraic equation, there are left and right members, the left member representing the mixture of hydrogen and oxygen, the right one water. The number of molecules of each kind is shown by the coefficient of each molecular formula (when the number is greater than 1). In this case, two molecules of hydrogen react with each molecule of oxygen to form two molecules of water. During an ordinary chemical reaction the quantity of an element remains the same. Consequently, each atom in the left member of the equation must be accounted for in the right member. In the example, we see that each member contains four atoms of hydrogen and two of oxygen. The reversibility of the reaction is shown by using an arrow pointing from right to left to indicate the decomposition of water by electrolysis.

$$2H_2 \quad + \quad O_2 \quad \rightleftarrows \quad 2H_2O$$

Finally, the liberation of energy with the formation of water and the use of energy in its decomposition is indicated by adding the word "energy" to the right member.

$$2H_2 \quad + \quad O_2 \quad \rightleftarrows \quad 2H_2O \quad + \quad \text{Energy}$$

The quantity of energy likewise does not change during a chemical reaction, though the equation shows only the kinetic energy (light, heat, or electricity) of the right member. Hydrogen and oxygen when separate possess potential energy, which is liberated when the hydrogen and oxygen react and which is stored when water is decomposed into these two gases.

Through ordinary chemical reactions elements maintain their identities. However, reactions are known in which the transformation of one element into another does take place, e.g., the decomposition of the radioactive elements uranium and radium into lead. Such transformations involve enormous energy changes and are, generally speaking, outside the realm of biological phenomena. However, the high energy radiations associated with them, when applied artificially to living things, are known to have definite effects on chromosomes and other parts of cells (see page 492).

Ionization. The molecules of certain substances called *electrolytes* dissociate rather readily into electrically charged particles known as ions. An *ion* may be considered to be an atom or a group of atoms with either a positive or a negative electrical charge. Electrolytes include acids, bases, and salts. Although these substances are of various kinds and differ among themselves regarding the extent of their ionization, they have certain special properties in common. For example, their solutions conduct electricity, and their chemical reactions occur with considerable rapidity.

Acids are characterized by a sour taste, *bases* by a bitter taste. Certain substances called *indicators* react with acids and bases and undergo color changes. An example of an indicator is litmus, which is derived from a species of lichen (a simple plant). Acids are capable of changing litmus from blue to red, and bases can change it from red to blue. Acids regularly liberate positively charged hydrogen ions (H^+) when in solution. Bases yield negatively charged hydroxyl ions (OH^-). Acids react with bases to form *salts* and water. This is called *neutralization*. For example, hydrochloric acid, a strong acid, reacts with sodium hydroxide, a strong base, to form common salt (sodium chloride) and water. This may be shown by an equation (the ionization of the acid, base, and salt is not shown):

$$\underset{\text{Sodium hydroxide}}{\text{NaOH}} \quad + \quad \underset{\text{Hydrochloric acid}}{\text{HCl}} \quad \rightarrow \quad \underset{\text{Sodium chloride}}{\text{NaCl}} \quad + \quad \underset{\text{Water}}{\text{H}_2\text{O}}$$

In this process the hydrogen and hydroxyl ions are united to form water, which is scarcely ionized. Consequently, these ions are practically eliminated from the mixture.

As previously mentioned, inorganic salts occur in living things. These salts must exist there largely as ions. Acids and bases sometimes also occur in small quantities. For example, hydrochloric acid is normally present in small amounts in the human stomach during digestion. However, high concentrations of either hydrogen or hydroxyl ions are markedly injurious to organisms. Living creatures tend to avoid places of high concentrations of these ions, and they contain mechanisms within themselves to prevent too great concentrations of them. Certain substances which are themselves neither strong acids nor strong bases are capable of reacting so as to reduce the concentration of hydrogen and hydroxyl ions. These are called *buffers* and are extensively employed by living things to keep protoplasm and the substances associated with it nearly neutral.

Mixtures. A substance consisting of molecules (or ions) of more than one kind is called a *mixture*. A mixture may thus be made up of different elements, or of different compounds, or of both. Moreover, the same components may be present in a mixture in various proportions and various ways. Air is an example of a mixture of gases. About four-fifths of air is nitrogen, about one-fifth oxygen. In addition, there are small amounts of inert gases such as argon, of compounds such as carbon dioxide (0.03 percent), and water vapor (varying amounts). As must already be evident, living things themselves are complex mixtures of substances.

Solutions. Mixtures in which molecules (or ions) of one substance are dispersed in another are called *solutions* (except when the dispersed molecules are very large). Usually the term is restricted to cases in which one of the substances is a liquid; the dissolved substance is then called the *solute*, the dissolving liquid the *solvent*. Examples of solutions are water containing sodium chloride (which ionizes) and water containing sucrose (which does not). A solution regularly has a clear, homogeneous appearance, even under the most powerful microscopes. The water in living things serves as a medium in which many substances (inorganic salts, simple organic compounds) are in solution.

Colloidal Dispersions. Mixtures having small particles which are either very large molecules or clumps of smaller ones dispersed in a different substance are called *colloidal* (Gr. "glue-like," because such mixtures sometimes have a glue-like appearance). All three states of matter may be involved. Of special biological interest, however, are mixtures in which one or both of the substances is a liquid. Compared with solutions, colloidal dispersions appear "milky" rather than clear, though they may seem quite homogeneous. The dispersed particles are sometimes visible microscopically (Fig. 20).

A striking feature of these particles is the fact that they may be seen to be in continuous, erratic movement (Fig. 21). This is called *Brownian movement*, after the English botanist Robert Brown (discoverer of the cell nucleus), who first described it. The movement of these colloidal particles is explained as being due to the ceaseless motion of the molecules of the *dispersion medium* which bombard the dispersed particles in such a way as to cause them to move about. Colloidal dispersions are formed in water by such substances as the complex carbohydrate starch and the proteins gelatin and egg albumin. In these cases the dispersed particles are too small to be seen microscopically. On the other hand, milk consists of tiny granules and droplets suspended in a watery medium; the larger particles may be seen with a microscope and their Brownian movement observed.

A colloidal dispersion may be relatively fluid, a *sol*, or relatively solid, a *gel*. Such a mixture may be changed from one of these states to the other, and sometimes the change is reversible. For example, a mixture of gelatin and water may be a sol when warmed, a gel when cold; and the transformation from one form to the other may be repeated again and again. If both the dispersed particles and the dispersion medium of a colloidal dispersion are liquids, the mixture is a *colloidal emulsion*. Milk and cream are colloidal emulsions in which fat droplets are dispersed in a water medium; and since they are relatively fluid, they may be called sols. Butter is likewise a colloidal emulsion consisting of watery material and fat, but this mixture may be considered a gel, with the relatively solid fat forming the dispersion medium.

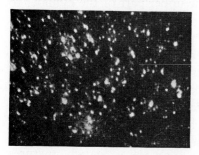

FIG. 20. Colloidal suspension as viewed by the ultramicroscope (very highly magnified). The particles are made luminous by reflected light. (From Gerard, *Unresting Cells*, copyright, Harper & Brothers.)

FIG. 21. Actual path of a colloidal particle in Brownian movement. (From Gerard, *Unresting Cells*, copyright, Harper & Brothers.)

Although protoplasm presents many different aspects under the microscope—variously described as *reticular* (like a network), *fibrillar* (with little fibers), *granular*, or *alveolar* (foam-like)—it generally incorporates the features of a colloidal dispersion. In living preparations protoplasm is nearly colorless, translucent, and somewhat denser than water. Tiny granules and droplets may be seen suspended in it, and these may be observed in Brownian movement. Protoplasm seems sometimes to be a sol, sometimes a gel. For example, in the tiny water animal called the ameba (a protozoan), the cytoplasm is sometimes rather dense and sometimes rather fluid, and there appears to be transformation from one form to the other.

Diffusion.   In liquids and gases, molecules are in constant, relatively free motion. The Brownian movement of tiny visible particles is one manifestation of this. Because of the randomness of this motion, molecules tend to scatter and distribute themselves evenly throughout the space available to them. Consequently, even though the movement of the individual particles is undirected, there is a tendency for them to drift away from places where they are concentrated to places of low concentration. This scattering of molecules (and other small particles) is called *diffusion* (Lat. "pouring apart"). The phenomenon may be illustrated by placing a crystal of potassium permanganate in the bottom of a cylinder filled with water (Fig. 22). This substance is a salt which forms an intensely purple solution. Ions of the salt scatter throughout the water, as may be noted by the gradual rise of the color from the bottom toward the top of the container. At the same time water molecules diffuse from the upper part of the cylinder to the part occupied by the salt. Thus, each of the two substances diffuses from the place where it is more concentrated to the place where it is less concentrated.

Osmosis. Certain membranes, such as pig bladder, allow some diffusing substances to pass through but prevent or retard others. They are called *differentially permeable membranes*. If such a membrane is sealed over the mouth of a thistle tube, the bowl of which contains a concentrated solution of sugar, and the tube is then inverted in a vessel of water (Fig. 23), the level of the sugar solution may be observed to rise inside the thistle tube. This phenomenon is attributed to the more rapid diffusion of water into the solution than out of it. This may be explained by the differential permeability of the membrane, which permits the passage of water molecules but restricts the movement of the sugar molecules. Water molecules are more concentrated in the pure water than they are in the sugar solution, where they are mixed with molecules of sugar. Thus, the tendency of the sugar solution to rise may be interpreted as an example of the tendency of a diffusing substance to distribute itself evenly throughout the space available to it. A corresponding tendency of the sugar to move in the opposite direction is prevented by the membrane. Thus, there is an increase in volume of the liquid on the side of the sugar solution. Diffusion through a differentially permeable membrane is called *osmosis* (Gr. "pushing"); the pressure associated with it (such as causes the rise of the sugar solution), *osmotic pressure*.

Fig. 22. Diagram to illustrate diffusion. A soluble solid such as potassium permanganate, placed in the bottom of a vessel filled with water, diffuses to all parts of the water. The concentration of the dissolved solid will in time become equal throughout.

Differential Permeability in Living Things. The fact that cell membranes are differentially permeable may be demonstrated by changing the concentration of solutes in the liquid surrounding the cell. For example, the cells of plants supplied with an abundance of fresh water are regularly in a distended condition, called a state of *turgor*, with the protoplast in close contact with the cell wall and pressing against it, just as the rubber bag of an inflated football pushes against the leather casing. If the plant material is transferred to a solution of some substance which does not pass readily through the cell membranes and which has a fairly high concentration in the solution, the cells may be observed to lose their distended appearance and the protoplasts to shrink away from the cell walls (Fig. 24). This process is known as *plasmolysis*. If the cells are returned to water while still alive, a reversal of the process will be seen, with the normal turgid condition of the cells being resumed. Such cells as these are ordinarily in contact with water containing only little if any solutes. Because of the solutes within the cells, water diffuses into them until the osmotic pressure is balanced by the resistance of the cell walls (the condition of turgor). When the cells are transferred to a solution in which water is even less concentrated than in their protoplasts, they tend to lose water to their surroundings (exhibiting the symptoms of plasmolysis). The effect of osmotic pressure due to water entering cells is even more strikingly shown in cells not ordinarily exposed to pure water. Human red blood cells are normally surrounded by a fluid called plasma, in which various substances (salts, etc.) are dissolved. Transfer of these cells to distilled water quickly causes them to swell and burst, the cell membranes not being able to withstand the very considerable osmotic pressure that develops. The opposite phenomenon, shrinkage of the protoplast (accompanied by wrinkling of the outer membrane), may also be observed

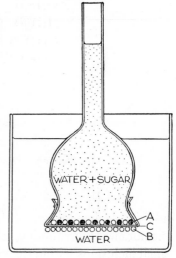

Fig. 23. Diagram to illustrate osmosis. A differentially permeable membrane is stretched and sealed across the bowl of a thistle tube, which is filled with sugar solution and inverted in a vessel of water. The black dots represent sugar molecules, the white ones water molecules. The sugar dilutes the water, leaving fewer water molecules in contact with the inside than with the outside of the membrane. Hence water moves more rapidly in an inward direction, and the fluid level of the liquid rises within the tube. (From Transeau, Sampson, and Tiffany, *General Botany*, Harper & Brothers; courtesy of the authors.)

in these cells when they are placed in concentrated solutions (Fig. 25).

Because of the partitions and membranes of living things, there is thoroughgoing regulation of the distribution of substances within organisms. The cell wall and the plasma membrane of a cell are important factors in this regulation. Appreciably large particles, such as starch granules and fat droplets, are obviously not free to move from cell to cell.

Similarly restricted must be the various large molecules that cells contain. Small molecules (and ions) are capable of penetrating the plasma membrane, but even among them there must be differences with regard to the ease with which they can traverse this membrane. There is evidence of

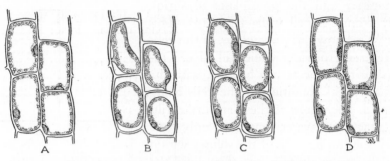

Fig. 24. Plasmolysis and recovery in leaf cells of *Elodea*. *A*, Cells in water, showing normal turgor; *B*, after two minutes in 5 percent salt solution, plasmolyzed; *C*, shortly after replacement of the salt solution with water; *D*, after a half hour, showing complete recovery.

additional membranes within cells—the nuclear membrane, vacuolar membranes (surrounding the vacuoles), and even membranes around small inclusions within the cytoplasm (e.g., chondriosomes). Thus, protoplasm is subdivided by numerous membranes, thereby considerably in-

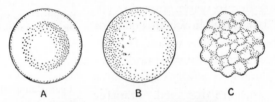

Fig. 25. Effect of varying concentrations of the surrounding medium on the red cells of human blood. *A*, Normal shape, as in the blood plasma; *B*, in distilled water, swollen by water that has entered through osmosis; *C*, in concentrated salt solution, shrunken by loss of water. (Based on Buchanan, *Elements of Biology;* copyright, Harper.)

creasing its complexity beyond that of a simple solution or colloidal dispersion.

EXERCISES

1. To aid the student in remembering the chemical elements usually present in protoplasm, the following mnemonic "sentence" has been suggested, "C. HOPKINS CaFe Mg NaCl." It may be read, "C. Hopkins' Cafe is

mighty good if taken with a grain of salt." The symbols of what thirteen elements are included in this "sentence"?

2. The formula of starch is given as $(C_6H_{10}O_5)_n$, n being an undetermined number. If n were equal to 30, what would be the molecular weight of starch?

3. Write the chemical equation to illustrate the formation of the white precipitate, calcium carbonate, $CaCO_3$, by bubbling carbon dioxide through lime water, $Ca(OH)_2$.

4. If the thistle tube of the osmosis apparatus were filled with pure water and the beaker with sugar solution, what would happen?

5. What effect has varying temperature on rates of diffusion and osmosis?

6. What are isotopes? Of what importance are certain rare isotopes in biological research?

REFERENCES

Gerard, R. W., *Unresting Cells*, Harper & Brothers, 1949.

Glasstone, S., *Sourcebook of Atomic Energy*, D. Van Nostrand Company, Inc., 1950.

Marsland, D., *Principles of Modern Biology*, Henry Holt & Company, Inc., rev. ed., 1951.

Mitchell, P. H., *A Textbook of General Physiology*, McGraw-Hill Book Company, Inc., 1948.

Chapter V

METABOLISM

Definition of Metabolism. The life of an organism involves continuous chemical and physical change. Matter is taken up from the surroundings, transformed, retained a while, and then released to the outside. Energy likewise is derived from the environment, is stored, changed, and liberated. The sum of all these matter- and energy-converting processes is called *metabolism* (Gr. "throwing beyond," hence "change"). Included under this term are the manufacture and consumption of food substances, the building up of protoplasm and extraprotoplasmic materials, the chemical transformations that yield appreciable energy (used in all the various activities of living things) and that produce useful substances, and the disposal of wastes. Metabolism may be subdivided into *anabolism* (Gr. "heaping up"), which covers the construction of the substance of an organism's body, and *catabolism* (Gr. "throwing down"), the tearing down of this material.

Enzymes. The chemical reactions of living things would generally take place only slowly if at all were it not for the presence of substances called *enzymes*. These are complex organic compounds produced by protoplasm, sometimes acting within the cells that produce them and sometimes passing to the outside of these cells (or even of the organism itself) to bring about their changes. Enzymes constitute a special class of the agencies known as *catalysts*, which influence the rate of chemical reactions without being themselves consumed in the process. The first of the enzymes to be clearly recognized was the one produced by the microscopic plants called yeasts, which promotes the process of alcoholic fermentation. It was first believed that this process required the presence of living yeast cells; however, it was found that the active substance of these organisms could be separated from the cells and made to promote fermentation in their absence. Because of this substance, the term *enzyme* (Gr. "in yeast") has come to be applied to the catalysts of living things in general.

48

As an example of a chemical reaction that is greatly speeded up by an enzyme, let us take the *hydrolysis* (Gr. "splitting by water") of common sugar, or sucrose. If sucrose is mixed with water, scarcely any reaction takes place, even if the mixture is heated to boiling or permitted to stand a long time. However, there is an enzyme called *sucrase* which will cause the sucrose to react with water at ordinary temperatures in a rather short while. This enzyme may be found in many different living things (including man, other animals, various plants), and it may be extracted from them (usually from fungus plants) and caused to produce its effect *in vitro* (Lat. "in glass"—i.e., in glass containers). If a small amount of sucrase is added to a mixture of sucrose and water, there occurs an appreciable transformation of the sucrose to a mixture of two simple sugars, glucose and fructose. These products both have the molecular formula $C_6H_{12}O_6$ (though their structures are different), and the reaction that produces them may be represented by the following equation:

$$C_{12}H_{22}O_{11} + H_2O \xrightarrow{\text{Sucrase}} C_6H_{12}O_6 + C_6H_{12}O_6$$

Sucrose   Water   Glucose   Fructose

It is not necessary to include the enzyme in either member of the equation, since this substance is not incorporated in the final products of the reaction (though it may participate in intermediate steps which are not shown). The fact that the reaction is promoted by this enzyme is shown by putting its name above the arrow. The hydrolysis of sucrose in the presence of sucrase is carried on by many different organisms. It is the process whereby this sugar is digested in the human body.

Numerous enzymes have been separated from living things and their properties studied. Some of them have been obtained in crystalline—i.e., pure, or nearly pure—form, and these have been found to be protein substances. Perhaps all enzymes are proteins. A remarkable feature of enzymes is the fact that they are rather specific with regard to the chemical reactions they influence. For instance, sucrase, as its name suggests, has a special relationship to sucrose; this enzyme causes the decomposition of sucrose but fails to affect other sugars similar to sucrose (including some with the same molecular formula). Other enzymes are not so specific but are able to affect whole groups of substances rather than just one or a few of them; examples are the enzymes that cause protein hydrolysis. Enzymes are quite sensitive to changes in their environment. Temperature extremes may affect them adversely; high temperatures may cause their irreversible inactivation. Some substances, for example certain metallic ions, inhibit or destroy them. Different enzymes have different conditions favoring their activities. Moreover, with changes of conditions, an enzyme sometimes promotes the reverse of the reaction which it otherwise speeds up.

FOODS AND FOOD ACCESSORIES

Definitions. Substances that contribute matter and/or energy to an organism are usually called *foods*. However, the term is generally restricted to those substances that are most important in building protoplasm and contributing energy, i.e., the carbohydrates, fats, and proteins. Certain living things manufacture such substances, using simple materials to make them. Outstanding among these are the green plants, which, through the process of photosynthesis, combine the carbon dioxide of the air with water to make organic compounds, in which the energy of light is stored. On the other hand, the nongreen plants and all animals require organic foods, which it is necessary that they seek and consume. Though the term "foods" is more or less restricted to carbohydrates, fats, and proteins, there are other substances which are necessary for the life of the organism and which may have to be taken up from the surroundings. These are called *food accessories*.

Classification of Foods and Food Accessories. Foods and food accessories may be classified as follows:

I. *Foods:* complex organic compounds, useful to organisms because of their stored energy as well as their ability to contribute to the substances of the organisms.
   A. *Carbohydrates:* compounds of carbon, hydrogen, and oxygen, the atomic ratio being either exactly or approximately 1:2:1. A molecule usually consists either of one simple sugar unit or of more than one of these units bound together through the elimination of water. Carbohydrates are largely the following:
   1. *Monosaccharids* or *simple sugars*, mainly $C_6H_{12}O_6$, such as glucose (dextrose, grape sugar) and fructose (levulose, fruit sugar).
   2. *Disaccharids* or *double sugars*, mainly $C_{12}H_{22}O_{11}$, such as sucrose (cane sugar, beet sugar), maltose (malt sugar), lactose (milk sugar).
   3. *Polysaccharids* or *multiple sugars*, mainly $(C_6H_{10}O_5)_n$, such as starch, glycogen (animal starch), cellulose, hemicellulose.
   B. *Fats:* compounds of carbon, hydrogen, and oxygen, the proportion of oxygen being much less than in carbohydrates. Fat molecules consist of *fatty acids* united with *glycerol* (glycerin) through the elimination of water. Example: olein, the chief fat of olive oil, with the molecular formula $C_{57}H_{104}O_6$.

C. *Proteins:* compounds containing carbon, hydrogen, oxygen, nitrogen, usually sulfur, and frequently phosphorus and still other elements. A protein molecule consists of numerous *amino acid* molecules bound together through the elimination of water. Example: egg albumin, which has a molecular weight of about 40,000.

II. *Food accessories:* substances entering into protoplasm but not serving as appreciable energy sources.

A. *Water:* important as a solvent and as a participant in many of the chemical reactions of living things.

B. *Inorganic salts:* such as sulfates, phosphates, and chlorides of potassium, sodium, calcium, and iron. These contribute various necessary elements used for many different purposes.

C. *Vitamins:* organic compounds which act in relatively small quantities to promote growth, regulate various metabolic processes, and maintain health.

Carbohydrates. The simple sugars glucose and fructose are widely distributed in plants and animals, particularly glucose, which is among the first products of photosynthesis in plants. These compounds both have the molecular formula $C_6H_{12}O_6$. The structures of their molecules are shown in the following graphic formulas: Both of these sugars have the power

$$
\begin{array}{cc}
 & H \\
 & | \\
H-C=O & H-C-OH \\
| & | \\
H-C-OH & C=O \\
| & | \\
HO-C-H & H-C-OH \\
| & | \\
H-C-OH & H-C-OH \\
| & | \\
H-C-OH & H-C-OH \\
| & | \\
H-C-OH & H-C-OH \\
| & | \\
H & H \\
\text{Glucose} & \text{Fructose}
\end{array}
$$

to react with *Fehling's solution* (an alkaline solution of copper sulfate mixed with Rochelle salts) to form a brick-red precipitate. Since this involves a *reduction* process (removal of oxygen or addition of hydrogen), these compounds are called *reducing sugars.* The two substances have somewhat different properties. For example, fructose is much sweeter than glucose. Also, when light has been *polarized* (i.e., "filtered" in such a way that its waves are in parallel planes), its passage through a solution of glucose causes the planes of polarization to twist to the right, and passage through a fructose solution causes them to twist to the left. Because of this, these sugars are called respectively *dextrose* (Lat. "right") and *levulose* (Lat. "left").

Disaccharids contain two simple sugar units joined together with the subtraction of a water molecule. For example, a molecule of sucrose contains a glucose molecule joined to a fructose molecule with the elimination of two atoms of hydrogen and one of oxygen. Sucrose differs from these simple sugars in a number of ways. For instance, it does not react with Fehling's solution to give a red precipitate. Other disaccharids are maltose, consisting of two glucose molecules joined together; and lactose, containing a molecule of glucose joined to one of galactose.

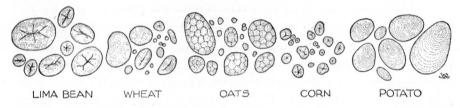

LIMA BEAN   WHEAT   OATS   CORN   POTATO

Fig. 26. Starch granules of various food plants as seen under high power. Note differences in form and size. The granule of oat starch is compound. The dotted lines, concentric on the granules from the bean and eccentric on those from the potato, indicate layers of successive starch deposition.

Starch, which accumulates as insoluble granules in various plant cells, is the most abundant storage carbohydrate of plants. It is far more complex than the disaccharids, consisting of many glucose molecules bound together. The n in the formula $(C_6H_{10}O_5)_n$ is an undetermined number, but it is thought to be at least 30. Thus the molecular weight of starch must at the minimum be almost 5000. Starch from different plants varies in its granule structure, as the microscope clearly reveals (Fig. 26), and probably also in its chemical structure. Starch may be identified by its reaction with iodine to form *starch iodide*, a compound with a striking violet-blue color. Another storage carbohydrate is hemicellulose, which is stored in the thick walls of certain plant cells, such as those of the date seed. Cellulose is almost universally present in a pure or modified form in the cell walls of plants. However, its importance lies largely in its value as a structural substance, rather than as a food reserve. In many animals, including man, simple sugars are combined to form glycogen (animal starch) which is stored, for example, in the cells of the liver.

Fats. We have noted that an acid and a base unite to form a salt. A similar compound of an organic acid and an alcohol is known as an *ester*.

A fat is an ester of which the acid part is a *fatty acid* (e.g., oleic acid, present in the olein of olive oil) and the alcohol is *glycerol* (glycerin). These are joined through the elimination of water molecules, as shown in the following equation:

$$
\begin{array}{ccccccc}
\text{H} & & & & \text{H} & & \\
| & & & & | & & \\
\text{H—C—OH} & + & \text{HOOCC}_{17}\text{H}_{33} & & \text{H—C—OOCC}_{17}\text{H}_{33} & & \\
| & & & & | & & \\
\text{H—C—OH} & + & \text{HOOCC}_{17}\text{H}_{33} & \rightleftarrows & \text{H—C—OOCC}_{17}\text{H}_{33} & + & 3\text{H}_2\text{O} \\
| & & & & | & & \\
\text{H—C—OH} & + & \text{HOOCC}_{17}\text{H}_{33} & & \text{H—C—OOCC}_{17}\text{H}_{33} & & \\
| & & & & | & & \\
\text{H} & & & & \text{H} & & \\
\text{Glycerol} & & \text{3 molecules of} & & \text{Olein (a fat)} & & \text{Water} \\
& & \text{oleic acid} & & & &
\end{array}
$$

Fats may be either solid or liquid at ordinary temperatures, the latter type being generally designated as *oils* (though there are oils of other kinds). Fats are a prominent storage form of food in various organisms, particularly in the animal tissue referred to as "fat."

Proteins. Proteins are chemically the most complex of the foods. They contain nitrogen and a number of other elements besides carbon, hydrogen, and oxygen. Amino acids are the basic structural units of protein molecules. About twenty-five different amino acids are known to occur in proteins, and molecules of these are joined together (through the elimination of water) in large numbers and in many different combinations. The exact molecular structure is not known. Molecular weights in the thousands, and even in the millions, are frequently found in these compounds. Glycine (CH_2NH_2COOH), a simple amino acid, was given as an example of an organic compound in the preceding chapter. A slightly more complex amino acid is cysteine, which contains sulfur as well as carbon, hydrogen, oxygen, and nitrogen.

$$
\begin{array}{ccc}
& \text{H} \quad \text{H—N—H} \quad \text{O} & \\
& | \qquad | \qquad \diagup & \\
\text{H—S—C} & \text{———C—C} & \\
& | \qquad | \qquad \diagdown & \\
& \text{H} \qquad \text{H} \qquad \text{OH} &
\end{array}
$$

Proteins are found in the white of egg (albumin), in milk and cheese (casein), in lean meat (myosin), in wheat flour (glutin), in cartilage (gelatin), and in various other foods. In plants, proteins may be stored as *aleurone granules*, such as occur in certain cells of a grain of wheat (Fig. 27). Though protein contributes extensively to the substance of an animal's body and may be broken down with the release of energy, there are no such clearly recognizable storage forms of proteins in these organisms.

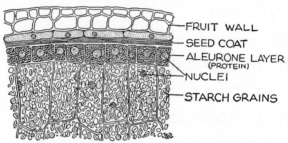

FIG. 27. Portion of cross section of a grain of wheat, showing regions of protein and starch storage in the form of granules. The wheat grain is really a fruit (ripened ovary). The fruit wall and seed coat together constitute the bran.

Water. Water constitutes a very important food accessory, though living things vary in their requirements of this substance. Many insects seem to require very little, and some plants can survive very dry conditions. As will be seen in the section on respiration (page 62), water is released with the decomposition of foods, and may thus be made available to organisms. However, living things generally require that water be supplied them in addition to the water released by their food. Water serves as a solvent for the various substances of living organisms. Moreover, it enters into chemical reactions with other substances and may become bound to certain compounds in the bodies of organisms.

Inorganic Salts. Various important elements are brought into living things in the form of inorganic salts. A frequent accessory of human food is common salt (sodium chloride). Other salts are supplied with vegetable and animal foods and in drinking water. An example of an element in which the human diet is sometimes deficient is iodine. This is abundant in sea water and may be secured through the eating of sea foods. It is often present in drinking water. However, where there is a deficiency of it, this element may readily be obtained by using common salt to which a small amount of potassium iodide has been added. Iodine deficiency sometimes becomes apparent through the occurrence of the pathological condition known as *goiter*, in which the *thyroid gland* of the throat region becomes greatly enlarged.

The mineral requirements of certain plants have been determined by experiments in which these plants were grown in carefully purified solutions containing known substances. It has been shown that such elements as iron, manganese, boron, copper, and zinc may be essential for plant growth, and in exceedingly low concentrations. Various animals are known similarly to require traces of certain elements.

Vitamins. Experiments carried on near the beginning of the present century indicated that the lack of certain organic compounds in the rations of experimental animals led to symptoms of specific diseases, from which the animals recovered only when the lacking substances were supplied. These important substances were called *vitamins* (Lat. "life amines," because it was once erroneously believed that they were all compounds of the kind called amines). The early investigators designated them by the letters of the alphabet, but the discovery that some of them are actually mixtures of different compounds (particularly the B complex) has necessitated the use of subscripts as well. Alternative names, based on the deficiency diseases which the vitamins prevent and on their chemical nature, have also been given most of these compounds. The vitamins are effective in such small quantities that their function is evidently not to supply energy. It has been calculated that one drop of a 1 percent solution of vitamin A would be sufficient to maintain the health of fifty rats throughout their lifetime. Vitamins are believed to function as catalysts in certain vital processes; some of them are known to contribute to the formation of important enzymes.

The term "vitamin" is generally restricted to a substance that must be supplied to an organism by its surroundings; if the substance is manufactured by the organism, it may be called an *endocrine*. However, this distinction cannot always be maintained, for vitamin A can be made in the organism by splitting the carotene molecule, and vitamin D may be produced in our bodies by the action of ultraviolet light on ergosterol, a substance in the fatty layer beneath the skin. Though the vitamins not manufactured by the body ordinarily must be consumed with the food, some of these substances (e.g., the B vitamins) may be produced by bacteria living in the digestive tract and may thus be made available to the individual.

The accompanying table includes outstanding representatives of vitamins essential to man's health, the deficiency diseases they prevent, and some important food sources of them.

Vitamin A is found in concentrated form in the liver of fishes, especially sharks, also in the liver of mammals, in butter, and in egg yolk. Carotene, the yellow pigment associated with chlorophyll in green vegetables and occurring also in yellow vegetables such as the carrot, is readily converted into vitamin A by the addition of water to its molecule. Reserves of the vitamin are stored in the liver of the consumer. When these are exhausted, children in particular suffer from *xerophthalmia*, an inflammation and drying of the eyes that often leads to blindness. *Night blindness* may also be produced by a shortage of vitamin A.

Vitamin	Deficiency May Cause	Important Food Sources
A (Activated carotene)	Night blindness; xerophthalmia	Butter, egg yolk, yellow and green vegetables, fish liver oils
B₁ (Thiamine)	Beriberi	Bran of grains, wheat germ, yeast
B₂, G (Riboflavin)	Soreness of lips	Liver, yeast
Niacin	Pellagra	Yeast, vegetables
B₁₂	Pernicious anemia	Liver
C (Ascorbic acid)	Scurvy	Citrus fruits, tomato, cabbage
D (Calciferol)	Rickets	Fish liver oils, irradiated milk
K	Hemorrhage	Green vegetables

The *vitamin B group*, originally regarded as one substance, has been separated into no less than ten different substances, several of which have been analyzed. Most of them are essentially dietary factors in experimental animals. *Vitamin B₁*, or *thiamine*, is found in bran, or the outer portion of the grain (hence the value of whole-wheat bread), in yeast, and in such vegetables as lettuce, cabbage, beans, and asparagus. Experimental animals deprived of it are retarded in growth and suffer nervous disturbances (Fig. 28 A). Its deficiency in man may cause *beriberi*, a nervous disease prevalent in the Orient where polished rice is the staple diet. Thiamine when applied to seeds and roots of plants has been found to be instrumental in hastening growth; hence commercial preparations of it are being used by plant growers for this purpose. A root removed from a certain plant may grow in a culture solution if supplied with this vitamin but not if it is absent, indicating that the vitamin is produced normally by the parts of the plant above the ground. Another member of the B complex, *riboflavin*, increases vitality and disease resistance in rats and probably also in man, in whom deficiencies of this substance have been associated with various symptoms, e.g., soreness of the lips. *Niacin* is a preventive of *pellagra*, a disease common among the poorer people of the southern states where the prevailing diet is practically limited to corn bread, molasses, and salt pork. *Vitamin B₁₂* has been isolated from liver and has been found to be highly active in the treatment of *pernicious anemia*, a disease characterized by a deficiency of red blood cells and hence of hemoglobin.

A

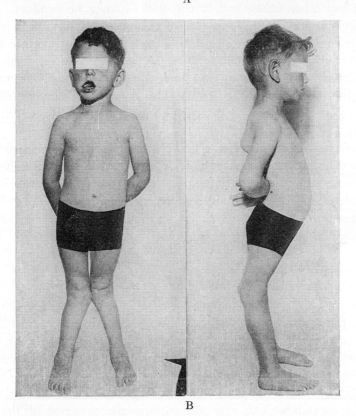

B

Fig. 28. Effects of vitamin deficiencies. *A*, Normally fed rat, used as a control, at left; a rat of the same age given the same food but without vitamin B₁ at right. Note the retarded growth and nervous impairment of the latter. *B*, Two views of a child suffering from rickets, a disease due to vitamin D deficiency. Failure in the utilization of calcium and phosphorus has resulted in improper hardening of the bones and teeth; symptoms are knock-knees, enlarged joints, and other skeletal deformities accompanied by very poor posture. (Photos, courtesy of Wisconsin Alumni Research Foundation.)

Vitamin C, now known as *ascorbic acid*, is probably the oldest known remedy for a deficiency disease. About 350 years ago Sir Richard Hawkins, a British naval commander, recognized that oranges and lemons were capable of preventing and curing *scurvy*, a disease prevalent among seamen on prolonged voyages. Scurvy is characterized by the destruction of the walls of the tiny blood vessels, causing blood spots to appear just beneath the skin, and by withdrawal of calcium from teeth and bones, resulting in a spongy condition of these structures. Orange juice is the most potent source of vitamin C, but grapefruit juice, tomato juice, and various other fruits and vegetables are also of value.

Vitamin D, or *calciferol*, is found naturally in the liver oils of the cod, halibut, and other fishes, and in egg yolk. It may be produced in our bodies by sun baths or by exposure to the ultraviolet rays of a mercury vapor lamp; this causes ergosterol to be activated, or turned into vitamin D. Lack of the vitamin leads to *rickets*, a condition resulting from failure of calcium deposition in the bones; consequently the bones are softened and the limbs deformed (Fig. 28 B). This disease is usually restricted to children, particularly poorly nourished ones in slum areas that have little sunlight.

Vitamin K, which occurs in several chemical forms, is necessary to give the blood the proper composition for clotting. Without this vitamin the blood does not clot sufficiently rapidly after a wound. Vitamin K is rather widely distributed among foods; it is present in all green plants. It is often administered to expectant mothers as a precaution against excessive bleeding during childbirth.

MANUFACTURE OF FOODS

Photosynthesis. Through the process of *photosynthesis*, green plants combine the carbon dioxide of the air with water to make organic compounds (e.g., glucose); oxygen is released during the process. Photosynthesis takes place in the presence of light (hence its name, derived from the Greek, meaning "putting together by light"). The kinetic energy of the light is transformed into potential energy (chemical energy) in the organic compounds. This reaction requires the presence of the green substance *chlorophyll*, which is ordinarily contained in *chloroplasts*. However, although chlorophyll may be extracted from green plant material, photosynthesis will not take place in the presence of an extract of chlorophyll, hence the plant probably carries on one or more enzymatic reactions which complete the process. Since glucose is among the early products of photosynthesis and oxygen is given off, the chemical change may be represented by the following equation, in which the energy of light is given in the left member and chlorophyll is represented as a substance promoting the process:

$$6CO_2 + 6H_2O + Energy \xrightarrow{\text{Chlorophyll}} C_6H_{12}O_6 + 6O_2$$

Carbon dioxide   Water   Glucose   Oxygen

Further discussion of the process of photosynthesis will be presented in Chapter XIX.

This is a most important process for living things in general, because practically all the energy used by organisms is made available by it. Green plants make use of a portion of the energy which they store in this manner. Nongreen plants and animals generally derive some of this energy from "feeding" on green plants, either directly or indirectly. In addition, besides using this energy in metabolism, man employs it extensively in various activities; for example, coal and petroleum, widely used as fuel, are derived from ancient forms of life which carried on photosynthesis. Practically the only exception to the derivation of the energy for metabolism from this process is the fact that certain bacteria are able to obtain energy by the oxidation of certain inorganic compounds—a process known as *chemosynthesis*.

Other Food Manufacture. Most plants convert the glucose derived from photosynthesis into starch, which is stored in certain cells. Still other complex organic compounds are manufactured by green plants—fats, proteins, and a number of others (e.g., vitamins); and these are derived wholly or in part from the glucose obtained from photosynthesis. Plants are capable of manufacturing proteins from relatively simple substances by adding nitrogen-containing salts and other minerals of the soil to the elements contained in sugar. Animals, including man, also manufacture complex food substances, though these may have to be made from already fairly complex compounds. Glucose is converted into glycogen. Carbohydrates may also be converted into fats. Proteins are built up from amino acids rather than from the simpler nitrogen-containing compounds utilized by plants.

TRANSPORT OF FOODS WITHIN THE BODY OF THE ORGANISM

Ingestion. The taking of masses of food substances into the body or into a digestive cavity or tube is called *ingestion*. This is practically equivalent to the common term eating. This process is characteristic of animals but is seldom found in plants, for the latter either manufacture their own foods within themselves or absorb food substances through their outer surfaces. There are, however, some plants that "feed" on insects (*insectivorous plants*, such as the pitcher plant and sundew, Fig. 418).

Digestion. Food materials frequently are insoluble or have relatively large molecules which cannot readily diffuse through the cell membranes of an organism. This is often true of food that has been ingested, and it is also generally true of stored foods, such as starch granules in a plant cell. The reduction of these food substances to simpler compounds with rather small molecules capable of diffusing readily is called *digestion*. It

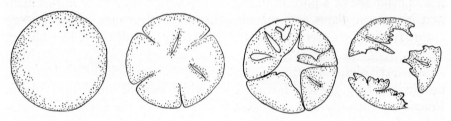

Fig. 29. Stages of disintegration of a starch granule in corn by action of the enzyme amylase.

has already been pointed out that complex carbohydrates, fats, and proteins have molecules consisting of simpler molecules bound together through the elimination of water. The digestion of these substances involves their reaction with water (*hydrolysis*) so that the simpler molecules in them become separated from each other. *Carbohydrates* are generally digested to form *glucose* and other *monosaccharids*. *Fats* become *fatty acids* and *glycerol*. *Proteins* break down into *amino acids*. These transformations, which may be accomplished in a number of steps, are promoted by various *digestive* (*hydrolyzing*) *enzymes*, of which sucrase has already been presented as an example.

Digestion takes place in various situations. It may occur within cells. For example, germinating seeds show evidence of the digestion of their starch granules, microscopic examination revealing the eroding away of these granules in the cells (Fig. 29). Here starch is being decomposed to yield glucose, which is needed during the growth of the young plant. Certain simple animals (protozoans, for example) ingest food directly into their cells, and digestion of this material takes place in special vacuoles called food vacuoles. Digestion may also take place outside the body of an organism. A bread mold, for instance, secretes digestive enzymes into the bread on which it grows, causing the bread to be digested. In the many-celled animals, digestion of food material that has been ingested generally takes place in a special cavity or a tube, into which digestive enzymes are secreted. In the human body, for example, various enzymes are secreted and poured into different parts of the alimentary canal (Fig. 30) —the mouth, stomach, and small intestines. As in plants, digestion of the stored foods of animals occurs in the storage cells, e.g., digestion of glycogen in the liver cells of man.

Absorption. Absorption of digested food takes place through the membranes adjacent to or surrounding the site of digestion. The small molecules resulting from digestion are absorbed through the wall of the small intestine of man. The surface of this wall is enormously increased by folds in the lining and by the presence of many tiny finger-like projections called *villi* (Fig. 31) which greatly facilitate absorption. In the simple plants that secrete digestive enzymes into the surrounding medium (e.g., bread mold), absorption of the digested food takes place through their outer surface.

Circulation. Following absorption, food is transported in the body fluid of the organism from the place of absorption to the place of its storage or utilization. This is accom-

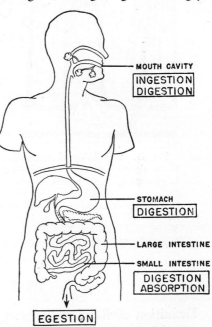

Fig. 30. Diagram illustrating the human digestive system. A few of the parts have been labeled and their functions indicated. (For a more complete illustration, see Fig. 222.)

plished in various ways in different living things. In small, relatively simple forms, circulation may depend largely on the diffusion of food molecules from place to place within the cell, or from cell to cell. Movements of the protoplasm may also help. In more complex plants and animals, a circulating fluid (sap, blood, lymph) may greatly assist in circulation. In the human body, the blood circulates through a system of vessels, propelled by the action of a muscular pump, the heart.

Assimilation. The taking of food substance into protoplasm is called *assimilation.* Here it may be retained a while as a distinctly separate substance (i.e., stored), or it may be incorporated into the protoplasm or changed into other substances.

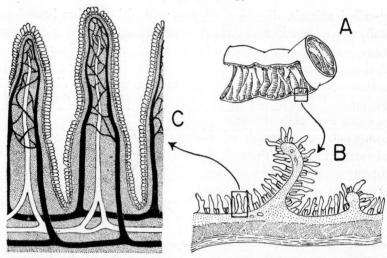

F<small>IG</small>. 31. The lining of the human small intestine shown at three magnifications. *A*, Short piece of intestine cut open to show folds in the lining. *B*, Enlargement of section through two of the folds, showing the villi, the minute projections which increase still further the surface area of the intestinal lining. *C*, Greater enlargement of villi, showing the tiny blood vessels (black) and the lacteals (white) into which absorbed foods are taken. (Redrawn from Young and Stebbins, *The Human Organism and the World of Life*, rev. ed. copyright, 1951, Harper & Brothers.)

RESPIRATION

Definition of Respiration. Organisms cause the energy-releasing decomposition of food substances through *respiration*, which is the reaction of these substances with oxygen (directly or indirectly) and the liberation of carbon dioxide and water. Respiration may be represented by an equation that is the reverse of the one already given for photosynthesis.

$$C_6H_{12}O_6 \;+\; 6O_2 \;\rightarrow\; 6CO_2 \;+\; 6H_2O \;+\; \text{Energy}$$

Glucose   Oxygen   Carbon dioxide   Water

The potential energy of the glucose is converted into kinetic energy, and this may take various forms—the movement of muscle cells, the transmission of impulses by nerve cells, the manufacture of numerous chemical compounds, even electrical discharges or flashes of light. Like photosynthesis, respiration is a complex process. Actually, there are numerous steps, promoted by various enzymes. However, these steps are not simply the reverse of those that occur during photosynthesis.

Respiration is characteristic of living things in general. Since animals and nongreen plants carry on respiration but not photosynthesis, they regularly consume oxygen and give off carbon dioxide. Respiration also occurs in green plants; but during the daylight hours the process of photosynthesis completely masks respiration, because photosynthesis gives off much more oxygen than respiration requires and uses more carbon dioxide than respiration yields. In darkness, however, when photosynthesis cannot take place, green plants, like nongreen plants and animals, take in oxygen and give off carbon dioxide.

As defined above, respiration takes place in the cells of an organism. But the term is often used in a broad sense to include the bringing of oxygen to the cells and the carrying away of carbon dioxide. The parts of an organism that are especially concerned with oxygen and carbon dioxide transport are said to have a *respiratory function*. In man, for example, the lungs and the passages leading to them constitute the *respiratory system* (Fig. 32).

Organs of Respiration. In many of the smaller animals, such as the earthworm, the exchange of oxygen and carbon dioxide takes place through the body surface. In the larger forms, as well as the more active small forms, the surface is not sufficient to supply the needs

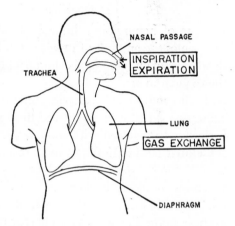

Fig. 32. Diagram illustrating the human respiratory system. Some of the parts and functions have been labeled (additional details are shown in Fig. 224).

of the body. Hence, we find in many aquatic animals *gills* that present a considerable surface for the diffusion of oxygen from solution in water. In terrestial forms, air is taken into branching tubes (*tracheae*) that reach all portions of the body or into *lungs* from which it diffuses into the blood stream to be carried to the body tissues. The movement of air into lungs or tracheae is called *inspiration*, its movement from them *expiration*. Together these movements constitute *breathing*.

Transport of Oxygen and Carbon Dioxide. From its place of diffusion from the surrounding medium into the organism's body, oxygen is transported by the body fluid to the places where it is used. This is an additional function of circulation. It may be accomplished simply by the diffusion of oxygen molecules through the substance of a cell or from cell to cell, or it may be greatly aided by a circulating body fluid. In many animals the body fluid, or blood, contains a *respiratory pigment* that is capable of entering into a loose combination with oxygen and of carrying it from place to place. An example is the substance called *hemoglobin*, which is present in the red cells of human blood. This is a complex iron-containing compound of a protein nature. In places of high oxygen concentration (the lining of the lungs), hemoglobin unites with oxygen to form oxyhemoglobin; but where oxygen has a low concentration (as in various tissues deep within the body), the oxyhemoglobin tends to lose oxygen, which thus becomes available to the cells of the region. This may be shown in an equation:

$$\text{Hemoglobin} + O_2 \rightleftarrows \text{Oxyhemoglobin}$$

Because of hemoglobin, human blood is capable of transporting at least fifty times the amount of oxygen it could carry if it depended only on the dissolving of oxygen in the liquid part of the blood (since 98 percent of the oxygen in arterial blood is combined with hemoglobin). In the human body, hemoglobin also carries some carbon dioxide, though much of this substance is transported by the fluid portion of the blood (in a modified form due to reaction with sodium and potassium).

Cellular Respiration. When "respiration" is used in its broad sense, the term *cellular respiration* may be employed to designate the process in cells whereby foods are broken down to liberate energy. As has already been said, a number of steps are involved, and different enzymes are concerned in these steps. These enzymes perform such various functions as removing hydrogen from food molecules, combining with free oxygen, and putting the hydrogen and oxygen together to form water. More than twenty such steps have been recognized in the breakdown of a sugar molecule. The properties of a number of these respiratory enzymes have been studied. It is known, for example, that some of them are sensitive to poisonous compounds such as hydrogen cyanide (HCN); much of the ill effects of these substances may be attributed to their influence on these vitally important cellular enzymes.

Anaerobic Respiration. Though respiration has been defined as a reaction involving oxygen, certain energy-releasing processes that take place in the absence of free oxygen are sufficiently allied to respiration to be called *anaerobic* (Gr. "living without air") *respiration*.

Anaerobic respiration takes place during muscle activity in animals (including man). At this time, glucose is broken down into lactic acid (molecular formula: $C_3H_6O_3$), a process which yields energy that sustains the activity. This process is shown by the following equation:

$$\underset{\text{Glucose}}{C_6H_{12}O_6} \rightleftarrows \underset{\text{Lactic acid}}{2C_3H_6O_3} + \text{Energy}$$

During the rest period following muscular contraction, part of the lactic acid combines with oxygen to form carbon dioxide and water and to produce sufficient energy to reconvert the remaining lactic acid to glucose.

$$C_3H_6O_3 \quad + \quad 3O_2 \quad \rightarrow \quad 3CO_2 \quad + \quad 3H_2O \quad + \quad \text{Energy}$$

Lactic acid   Oxygen   Carbon dioxide   Water

The anaerobic process indicated by the first of these two equations yields only about one-tenth the amount of energy that would result from the direct decomposition of glucose to carbon dioxide and water. Nevertheless, because of this process, muscular activity can proceed much more readily than if it had to wait for free oxygen to be supplied. With the reconversion of part of the lactic acid to glucose, the muscle again becomes capable of carrying on activity. It is as though, for the emergency of contraction, the muscle borrows a certain amount of fuel value, which it repays when it has the leisure to secure sufficient oxygen.

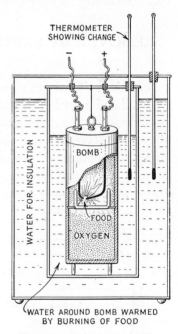

The alcoholic fermentation of yeasts may also be considered anaerobic respiration. The chemical reaction involved is represented by the following equation:

$$C_6H_{12}O_6 \rightarrow 2C_2H_5OH + 2CO_2 + \text{Energy}$$

Glucose   Ethyl alcohol   Carbon dioxide

Here also, less energy is provided than would be produced by the direct transformation of glucose to carbon dioxide and water in aerobic respiration—about one twenty-fifth as much. However, ability to carry on this process enables these little plants to live in situations that are not capable of supporting many other forms of life.

Fig. 33. Calorimeter. (From Hunter, *Life Science*; copyright, American Book Company.)

Energy Values of Different Foods. The amounts of energy which different foods make available can be determined by means of an instrument called a *calorimeter* (Fig. 33), which measures the energy released when these foods react with oxygen. The *direct method* involves simply the burning of the food substance in the calorimeter. In the *indirect method*, the food is oxidized in a living organism kept inside the instrument and the liberated energy is measured. A unit of energy is the *kilocalorie* (or large Calorie, equal to 1000 small calories), which is the energy necessary to raise the temperature of one kilogram of water (a little more than two pounds) one degree Centigrade (1.8°F.). It has been determined by the direct method that one gram of carbohydrate (between three and four hundredths of an ounce) yields 4.1 kilocalories of energy, and one gram of protein (incompletely oxidized, as in an animal's body) about the same, but that one gram of fat gives 9.3 kilocalories, well over twice as much as either of the others. Thus fats may be called "high-energy foods." However, there is evidence that in human metabolism the breakdown of fats is incomplete unless there is also oxidation of carbohydrates; consequently, a diet containing an excess of fat may be undesirable.

REMOVAL OF SUBSTANCES FROM CELLS AND FROM ORGANISMS

Secretion. The term *secretion* is applied to a useful substance produced by a cell and passed to the outside of it. The term is also used for the process of passing the substance to the outside. Certain cells are especially adapted to secrete. These form *glands* (Fig. 34), which may be unicellular or may consist of a combination of numerous secreting cells. Glands occur in plants as single cells, such as the glandular hairs of certain leaves, and as groups of cells lining a surface, such as those that line resin canals in pine wood. In animals, glands are sometimes rather simple (e.g., the

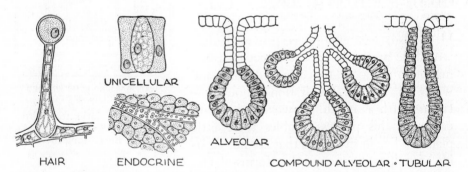

UNICELLULAR

ALVEOLAR

HAIR   ENDOCRINE   COMPOUND ALVEOLAR · TUBULAR

Fig. 34. Glands of several types. The glandular hair projecting from the surface of a cultivated geranium leaf secretes the aromatic oil that gives the plant its characteristic odor. The unicellular gland (middle cell of the three) is a mucous gland from the epidermis of the earthworm. The endocrine gland shown is a small detail of the pituitary gland, including a part of the capillary network that carries the secretion away from the gland cells. The alveolar gland is a mucous gland from frog skin. Only a small portion of the salivary gland (compound alveolar) is included in the sketch. The tubular gland is a gastric gland from the stomach of the frog.

tubular glands in the wall of the human stomach) and sometimes very complex branched or compound structures (e.g., the salivary glands, which discharge their secretions into the mouth cavity). The salivary glands secrete through tubes (or *ducts*). There are also glands which secrete directly into the body fluid or blood and which are called *endocrine* (Gr. "secreted within") *glands*, or *glands of internal secretion*. The products of these glands are called *hormones* (Gr. "exciters"), or *endocrines*. Definite endocrine glands are limited to animals, though plants also have substances called hormones which are formed in one part and produce their effects in another. An example of an endocrine gland in man is the *thyroid gland* situated in the throat region; this produces a hormone called *thyroxin* (which requires iodine for its manufacture), an important substance that controls growth and the rate of metabolism.

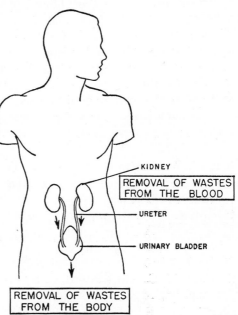

KIDNEY

REMOVAL OF WASTES FROM THE BLOOD

URETER

URINARY BLADDER

REMOVAL OF WASTES FROM THE BODY

Fig. 35. Diagram illustrating the human excretory system. Some of the parts and functions have been labeled and indicated by arrows. (Figs. 231 and 232 show further details.)

Excretion. A useless substance produced by cells and passed to the outside of them is called an *excretion*; similarly, the process of passing such a substance to the outside is called excretion. In the bodies of animals, certain structures may be specialized as organs of excretion. Outstanding examples of *excretory organs* in man and similar animals are the kidneys (Fig. 35), which separate various wastes of metabolism from the blood as it passes through them (for instance, urea, a product of protein breakdown), and collect these wastes together in the mixture called urine, which eventually passes from the body.

Egestion. The passing of unabsorbed material from an organism's body or from its digestive cavity or canal is called *egestion*. Egested material has not been incorporated into the organism's protoplasm. For example, cellulose, a prominent component of many vegetable foods eaten by man, cannot be digested by the human body and hence is not absorbed but passes from the body chemically unchanged. Egestion, like ingestion, is a characteristic of animals, not plants.

EXERCISES

1. Give examples of industrial uses of enzymes, naming the source of the enzyme in each case.
2. What is *basal metabolism?* How is it determined?
3. What interchange of gases takes place between green plants and the air at night? What is responsible for this?
4. Obtain from a text on hygiene or nutrition the fuel value (in kilocalories) of the various common foods, and calculate the fuel value of your own food intake for a day.
5. Tabulate the outstanding differences between plant and animal metabolism. In which is anabolism more pronounced? Catabolism?

REFERENCES

Butler, J. A. V., *Man Is a Microcosm,* The Macmillan Company, 1951.

Carlson, A. J., and Johnson, V., *The Machinery of the Body,* Univ. of Chicago Press, 3rd ed., 1948.

Gerard, R. W., *Unresting Cells,* Harper & Brothers, 1949.

Maximov, N. A., *Textbook of Plant Physiology* (translated), McGraw-Hill Book Company, Inc., 2nd ed., 1938.

Shafar, J., *The Vitamins in Medical Practice,* Staples Press, 1949.

Sherman, H. C., and Lanford, C. S., *Essentials of Nutrition,* The Macmillan Company, 3rd ed., 1951.

Chapter VI

THE ANIMAL KINGDOM

Though animals and plants have many similar characteristics (e.g., in cellular structure, physical and chemical nature), it is convenient to study them separately. In this chapter the classification and naming of animals are presented, together with an introduction to the main divisions of the animal kingdom. In succeeding chapters the various animal groups are given more detailed treatment. Chapter XIX serves as a similar introduction to the plant kingdom, and it is followed by chapters devoted to different groups of plants. However, since variation and the systems of classification and nomenclature are similar in both kingdoms, much of the material in the present chapter applies to plants as well as to animals.

Natural Groups of Animals. An obvious feature of the variation of animals is their existence in groups of similar individuals, e.g., men, dogs, honeybees, earthworms. Members of the same kind, though varying somewhat among themselves (extensively at times; as in the case of people and dogs), have features in common which set them apart from all other organisms. Moreover, the various kinds themselves exist naturally in larger groups. For example, wolves, coyotes, and jackals are different from domestic dogs and from each other, and yet they all seem to constitute a group of definitely similar kinds. Even these larger groups are capable of being themselves grouped into larger and larger categories. Although there is sometimes doubt on the part of zoologists as to how to determine the limits of these groups, the fact that animals can naturally be grouped on the basis of their similarities and differences is very evident.

Evolution. A generalization of outstanding importance in biology is the principle of evolution. According to this idea, the various kinds of animals and plants have been derived from previously existing different kinds by a process of descent with modification. The evolution idea was suggested even in early times. Aristotle (384–322 B.C.), the ancient Greek naturalist and philosopher (Fig. 36), upheld an idea of progress in the world of living things from simple forms through more and more

69

complex kinds to man himself. However, it was not until the 18th and 19th centuries A.D. that the idea began to receive wide attention and acceptance on the part of biologists and others. The French biologist Lamarck (1744–1829) advanced the idea of evolution and sought an explanation of the gradual modification of organisms in terms of their inter-actions with their environments. The greatest exponent of evolution was the Englishman Charles Darwin (1809–1882), whose widely ex-tended observations and theory of evolution by natural selection have profoundly influenced biologi-cal thought. Today evolution is generally accepted by biologists. This acceptance is based on vari-ous kinds of evidence, some of which will be considered in Chapter XXIX.

FIG. 36. Aristotle, the leading scientist and philosopher of ancient Greece. (Photo from Science Service.)

Phylogenetic Trees. It is a matter of common observation that individuals related to each other tend to be rather similar. This phenomenon is called *he-redity* and is especially apparent in human families and among re-lated individuals in the domestic animals and cultivated plants. According to evolution, animals that are enough alike to be placed in the same species (or larger group) owe these similar-ities to descent from common ancestors. The various degrees of similarity found between groups are largely due to different degrees of relationship. Since one kind of animal that lived in the distant past may have given rise to a number of different kinds of descendants, and these in turn may have produced still more kinds, the relationship of a number of animal groups may be represented by a branching, tree-like diagram, a *phylogenetic* (Gr. "origin of kind") *tree*. Largely on the basis of *paleontology* (Gr. "study of ancient beings") attempts have been made to construct phylogenetic trees for the different kinds of animals. The paleontologist studies *fossils* (Lat. "that which is dug up"), the remains of organisms that existed long ago. Fossils frequently exhibit sufficient similarity to modern forms to suggest that they represent organisms ancestral to the kinds found today. By putting together such evidence we can obtain an idea of the course and duration of evolution in groups of animal kinds and show this by phylogenetic trees. For example, there is evidence that the various carnivorous animals —dogs, cats, bears, weasels, etc.—have all descended from common ancestors that lived about fifty million years ago (Fig. 37).

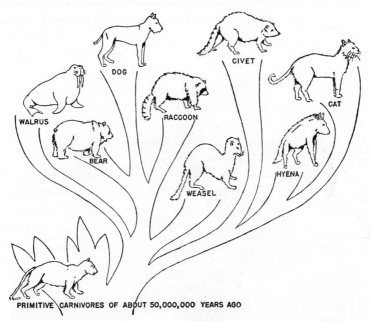

Fig. 37. Simplified family tree of carnivorous animals (carnivores). (Redrawn, with modification, from Romer, *Man and the Vertebrates*, 3rd ed., copyright 1941, University of Chicago Press.)

A Natural System of Classification. With evolution in mind, zoologists seek to devise a *natural system of classification* of animals that reflects the relationships believed to exist between the various kinds. According to such a system, members of the same category are more closely related to each other than to members of other groups, and the characteristics used in classification are those considered most likely to reveal relationships. The construction of such a system has required and continues to require the combined efforts of numerous zoologists (called *animal taxonomists*). Many of the details of this system are still under investigation as new kinds of animals and new characteristics for classifying them are discovered.

Species. An important category of classification is the *species* (plural, *species*). This corresponds very roughly to "kind" used in common language. For example, man, dog, and honeybee each represents a species to the zoologist. However, several species of earthworms are recognized. Although the existence of different kinds of organisms is evident, there is some disagreement among biologists as to what constitutes a species, and it has not been possible to devise a universally acceptable definition of this term. A definition which seems to fit many cases is as follows: *A species is a group of similar organisms which are capable of breeding with each other but which do not interbreed freely with members of other groups.* It will be noted that this definition does not make clear how simi-

Fig. 38. The honeybee (*Apis mellifica* Linnaeus 1758). (Courtesy of *Nature Magazine*, Washington, D.C.)

lar the organisms must be or how readily they must interbreed in order for them to be included in the same species. It is difficult to define such matters precisely. Consequently, decisions as to the recognition of species (as with the other categories to be discussed) depend on the judgments of qualified investigators.

Genus. There are many natural groups of similar species. Such a group is called a *genus* (plural, *genera*). For example, the common honeybee appears to be closely related to several oriental wild species of bees that are similar to it; hence the familiar honeybee is included with these others in the same genus.

Scientific Name. A genus is given a name, a noun that is frequently of Greek or Latin origin and is regularly written with a capital letter. For example, the genus that includes the common honeybee and similar bees is called *Apis* (Lat. "bee"). Each species is given a name which is an adjective modifying the genus name or a noun in apposition with it. This is also often of Greek or Latin origin, but it is usually written with a small letter. For instance, the species of the common honeybee has been given the name *mellifica* (Lat. "honey-making"). The *scientific name* of an organism consists of the genus name followed by the name of the species. Thus, the familiar honeybee is *Apis mellifica*. The scientific name is generally italicized, and frequently there are appended to it the name of the investigator who described and named the species and the date of his published description. The common honeybee (Fig. 38) may be designated *Apis mellifica* Linnaeus 1758.

The system of *binomial nomenclature* of living things developed from the work of Carolus Linnaeus (1707–1778), 18th-century Swedish naturalist (Fig. 39), and the assigning of scientific names according to this system begins with his publications. Linnaeus was greatly interested in collecting and classifying animals and plants. However, he found much con-

Fig. 39. Linnaeus, establisher of the binomial system of naming organisms. The plant in his hand is the twinflower (*Linnaea borealis*), which was named in his honor. (Photo from Science Service.)

fusion in the systems then in use for the identification of living things. No plan of classification had been fully organized or generally accepted, and there was lack of agreement as to the names to be applied to organisms. Linnaeus attempted both the construction of a system of classification and the assignment of descriptive names (in Latin) to the various kinds of animals and plants. Although his system of classification has been greatly changed by later biologists, the binomial system of nomenclature, which developed on the basis of his descriptive names, is still an invaluable tool for any treatment of biological subject matter.

Scientific Names and Common Names. Scientific names have the defi-

nite advantages over common names of being universally accepted by
biologists and of being precise with regard to the organisms so designated
(though adjustments in the use of these names are sometimes necessary
as our knowledge of organisms increases). Often more than one common

FIG. 40. *Felis concolor.* A wild specimen photographed in a forest in
the state of Washington. (Photo by O. J. Murie, Fish and Wildlife
Service.)

name is applied to the same organism, even in the same language. Moreover, the same common name may be used indiscriminately for various
different species. For example, in North and South America there lives
a large carnivorous animal of the cat family to which the scientific name
Felis concolor (Lat. "uniformly colored cat") has been given (Fig. 40).
However, this animal has variously been called by such common names
as cougar, puma, panther, catamount, mountain lion, and American lion.
Not only does this multiplicity of names lead to some confusion, but cer-

tain of these names are often misleading because they have also been applied to quite different animals living in other parts of the world. For instance, the name "panther" has been given to one or more kinds of leopards, which are spotted cat-like animals found in Asia and Africa.

On the other hand, common names have the advantages of being relatively brief and easy to pronounce and often of being already familiar to many people. Because of these advantages, common names are sometimes used in biological publications, though they are usually accompanied by scientific names to make clear the species under consideration. Common names will frequently be used in this book, but scientific names will also be given when references to certain genera and species are necessary.

Higher Categories of Classification. A group of similar genera constitutes a *family* (this term is, of course, used in a special sense quite different from its ordinary meaning). For example, the Family APIDAE (Lat. "bees") has been set up to include all true bees—carpenter bees and bumblebees, as well as bees of the genus *Apis*. An *order* consists of a group of similar families. The Order HYMENOPTERA (Gr. "membrane-winged") includes the Family APIDAE and numerous other families containing such insects as wasps and ants. A group of similar orders constitutes a *class*. The Class INSECTA (Lat. "cut into," because the bodies of these animals are more or less deeply constricted) includes all the various creatures to which the name "insect" is properly applied; besides the Order HYMENOPTERA, it includes other orders consisting of beetles, flies, butterflies and moths, grasshoppers, true bugs, etc. A still larger category is the *phylum* (plural, *phyla*), consisting of a number of classes. The Class INSECTA belongs to the Phylum ARTHROPODA (Gr. "jointed feet"), which also includes classes containing such animals as lobsters, centipedes, and spiders. The phylum is the largest subdivision of the ANIMAL KINGDOM that is ordinarily used. The relations of these categories of classification are summarized in the following classification of the common honeybee:

Kingdom: ANIMAL
  Phylum: ARTHROPODA
    Class: INSECTA
      Order: HYMENOPTERA
        Family: APIDAE
          Genus: *Apis*
            Species: *mellifica*
              Scientific name: *Apis mellifica* Linnaeus 1758

Additional Categories. Investigations of the various groups of animals have sometimes shown the need for still other categories besides those given above. In a single group of one of the kinds already mentioned, the component categories may seem to exist in more than one natural group. Consequently, "sub-" categories have also been set up: subkingdoms, subphyla, subclasses, suborders, subfamilies, subgenera, and even subspecies. An outstanding example of a "sub-" category is the group to which all animals with backbones have been assigned, the Subphylum VERTEBRATA, which is part (the major part) of the Phylum CHORDATA. Man himself and most of the familiar animals are members of this subphylum.

The Animal Kingdom. In the chapters following this one (Chapters VII through XVIII), various representatives of the animal kingdom will be considered. A brief introduction to the phyla of this large division of living things is presented here. The more than one million species of animals that are known have been grouped into about thirty phyla. However, some of these are far more prominent and important to man than are the others. Most of our attention will be devoted to ten animal phyla that are especially outstanding, but a number of the others will be given brief consideration.

The ten outstanding phyla are (numbers of species are approximate):

1. PROTOZOA (protozoans, 29,000 species). Protozoans, the one-celled animals, are exceedingly abundant in water containing organic matter, in soil, and in the bodies of other animals. They are so small that they remained unknown until the investigations of the early microscopists (e.g., van Leeuwenhoek). Since the single-celled condition is a fundamental characteristic that sets the protozoans apart from all the other animals, these creatures have also been placed in the Subkingdom PROTOZOA (Gr. "first animals"), which contains the single Phylum PROTOZOA. The remaining phyla of animals, which are all many-celled, constitute the Subkingdom METAZOA (Gr. "beyond animals").

2. PORIFERA (sponges, 5000 species). The organisms in this group are attached, as are plants. They consist of many cells which are very loosely organized. This group includes a few fresh-water and many *marine* (Lat. "sea") forms.

3. COELENTERATA (coelenterates, 10,000 species). These are multicellular animals, consisting of comparatively few cells arranged in two layers. They are attached, or slow-moving, or adapted for drifting in the water. Their bodies are radially arranged and often somewhat plant-like in appearance. The almost microscopic Hydra of fresh water, and the jellyfishes, sea anemones, and corals of the oceans belong in this phylum.

4. PLATYHELMINTHES (flatworms, 6500 species). These usually have elongated, forward-moving bodies built up from three cell layers of the

embryo and showing more complexity than do the coelenterates. There are free-living and parasitic forms, the better known of the latter being flukes and tapeworms.

5. Nemathelminthes (roundworms, 10,000 species). The bodies of this group are cylindrical and elongated, and built on the tube-within-a-tube plan. The group includes the tiny vinegar eels, numerous fresh-water forms, and a host of parasitic forms, such as hookworms and trichina worms. Many of them are small and thread-like, and hence are called threadworms.

6. Annelida (segmented worms, 7500 species). The body wall of these elongated animals is made up of a series of ring-like segments. Here belong the earthworms, the leeches, and other fresh-water forms, and numerous marine species such as clamworms.

7. Mollusca (mollusks, 90,000 species). These animals ordinarily have skeletons consisting of a calcareous shell of one or more parts. The group includes the familiar clams, the snails of fresh water and land, and many of the numerous "shellfish" of the sea.

8. Arthropoda (arthropods, 770,000 species). These animals have jointed bodies with external skeletons and are provided with jointed appendages. This group is represented by insects, crustaceans (such as the crayfish), centipedes, millipedes, and spiders. This phylum is by far the largest of the animal phyla; it contains more than three-fourths of all known species of animals.

9. Echinodermata (echinoderms, 6000 species). These are slow-moving animals that for the most part have radial symmetry (like the coelenterates). They inhabit the shore and bottom of the sea. Representatives are starfish, sea urchin, sea cucumber, and sea lily.

10. Chordata (chordates, 102,000 species). This group includes the backboned animals (Subphylum Vertebrata) and a few others which have a mere suggestion of a backbone called a notochord. These animals, because of their structural and functional similarity to man (included in this group), are the most significant to the student of general biology.

Less prominent than the above groups are such phyla as the Acanthocephala (spiny-headed worms), Brachiopoda (lamp shells), Bryozoa (moss animals), Chaetognatha (arrow worms), Ctenophora (comb jellies), Gastrotricha (gastrotrichs), Nemertea (proboscis worms), and Rotifera (wheel animalcules).

The ten outstanding animal phyla and a few of the less prominent ones are shown in Fig. 41, according to their supposed phylogenetic relationships.

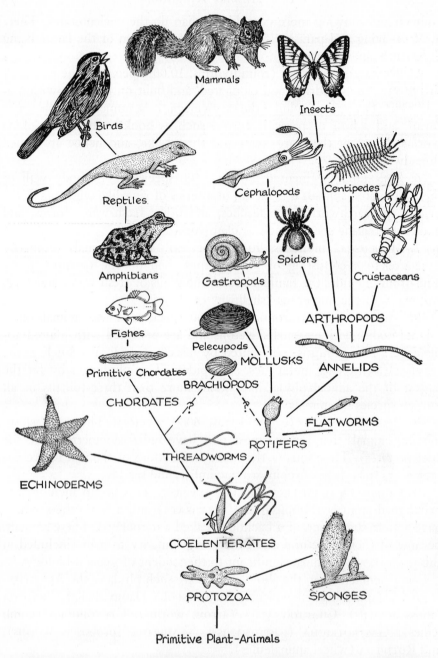

Mammals

Birds

Insects

Reptiles

Cephalopods

Centipedes

Spiders

Amphibians

Gastropods

Crustaceans

ARTHROPODS

Fishes

Pelecypods

MOLLUSKS

Primitive Chordates

ANNELIDS

CHORDATES

BRACHIOPODS

FLATWORMS

ROTIFERS

THREADWORMS

ECHINODERMS

COELENTERATES

PROTOZOA

SPONGES

Primitive Plant-Animals

Fig. 41. The principal groups of the animal kingdom, showing probable relationships by descent from the more primitive (below) to the more advanced. Groups of phylum rank are printed in capitals; the classes (phylum subdivisions) of mollusks, arthropods, and chordates are indicated in small letters.

EXERCISES

1. What are the scientific names of the cat, horse, cow, sheep, chicken, duck? What is the smallest classification category in which all these animals are included?
2. List as many phyla as possible that are represented by animals native to the locality in which you live; give examples.
3. Name several animals and plants for which the genus name is also the common name.

REFERENCES

Calman, W. T., *The Classification of Animals*, Methuen & Co., Ltd., 1949.

Carter, G. W., *Animal Evolution*, Sidgwick and Jackson, Ltd., 1951.

Hegner, R. W., and Stiles, K. A., *College Zoology*, The Macmillan Company, 6th ed., 1951.

Jaeger, E. C., *A Source-book of Biological Names and Terms*, Charles C. Thomas Publisher, 2nd ed., 1950.

Ley, Willy, *The Lungfish, the Dodo, and the Unicorn*, Viking Press, 2nd ed., 1948.

Pearse, A. S. (ed.), *Zoological Names: A List of Phyla, Classes, and Orders*, prepared for Section F of the American Association for the Advancement of Science, 4th ed., 1949.

Chapter VII

PROTOZOA: ONE-CELLED ANIMALS

PROTOZOA (Gr. "first animals") are animals in which the individual consists of a single cell; the cells are ordinarily separate, but sometimes they are grouped into colonies. Protozoans are of wide distribution in fresh and salt water, in soil moisture, and as parasites in the bodies of animals. Each cell is fitted with essential structures and is not dependent upon other cells.

The four classes of Protozoa, with representative genera, are as follows:

1. RHIZOPODA (Gr. "root-footed"): with temporary processes known as pseudopods for locomotion; *Amoeba*.
2. FLAGELLATA (Lat. "with small whips"): with one or a few whip-like flagella; *Euglena*.
3. SPOROZOA (Gr. "spore animals"): parasitic, and without definite locomotor organs; *Plasmodium*.
4. CILIATA (provided with cilia): with numerous cilia (hair-like processes) for locomotion; *Paramecium*.

RHIZOPODA

Ameba (Gr. "change"). The ever-changing bits of colorless protoplasm known as amebas are among the simplest representatives of the animal kingdom (Fig. 42). A species often studied is *Amoeba proteus*, which lives in fresh-water ponds and streams; it is about 0.25 mm. across, and therefore visible to the unaided eye as a tiny white speck. Although less specialized than the other protozoans, the cell has several distinct parts. The definite but thin and flexible outer boundary is the *plasma membrane*. The cytoplasm consists of two distinct regions—a transparent *ectoplasm* (Gr. "outside plasm") just within the plasma membrane, and a granular *endoplasm* (Gr. "inside plasm") that occupies the center of the cell. In the cytoplasm is a comparatively firm, disk-shaped *nucleus*.

Movement. All protoplasm has the power of motility in some degree. In the ameba this power is equally distributed through the whole of the cytoplasm, instead of being localized in certain parts, as is generally true of the more complex animals. When relatively inactive, this organism may

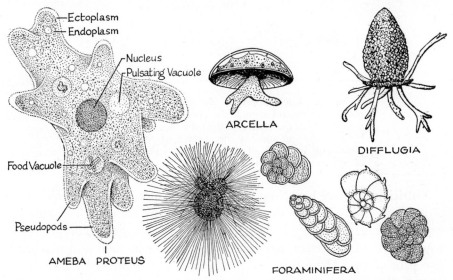

Fig. 42. *Amoeba proteus* and other *Rhizopoda. Amoeba* is a typical naked rhizopod; *Diffugia* constructs an enclosing case of sand grains; *Arcella* secretes a shell of chitin; and the various members of the group Foraminifera secrete shells of calcium carbonate. The left figure in the last group represents the living animal, with thread-like pseudopods; the others represent empty shells. It is of such shells that chalk is formed.

be roughly globular, but when moving or searching for food it puts out one or more processes known as *pseudopods* (Gr. "false feet") into which the protoplasm gradually flows. Frequently the ameba itself seems to flow along with the extension of its pseudopods, though it has some-times been reported to "walk" on stiff pseudopods. A widely recognized theory to account for the "flowing" type of locomotion is as follows. The outer part of the endoplasm is in the rigid (gel) state and the inner part in the fluid (sol) state (Fig. 43). The advancing tip is fluid, and the central sol flows forward as if through a tube, the contraction of the gel tending to push it along. The lateral portions of the advancing pseudopod again harden to gel. The friction of the plasma membrane on the substratum enables this flow to carry the entire organism along. Similar movement, known as ameboid movement, is found in higher animal groups. Examples are certain wandering cells in a sponge, and the white blood cells in man and other vertebrates.

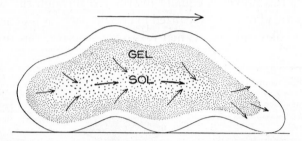

Fig. 43. Locomotion of *Amoeba*. The protoplasm changes to the sol state at the posterior end, flows forward through the center of the tube of gel, and changes back to the gel state at the surface of the advancing pseudopod just back of the tip. Arrows show direction of movement. (Modified from Mast.)

Nutrition. As we have seen, an organism requires food to build up its protoplasm and to replace the wastes which result from the constant destruction made necessary by organic activities. Nutrition comprises the whole series of processes that accompany taking in food and making it into protoplasm. These processes, indicated diagrammatically in Fig. 44, are as follows:

1. *Ingestion*, or the taking in of food. The food of the ameba consists of one-celled animals or plants, or of small particles of organic matter. Ingestion takes place anywhere on the surface of the plasma membrane, for there is no mouth. The protoplasm pushes past a food particle on all sides, causing it to be immersed in a cup-like depression and then, with a little water, to be completely enclosed as a *food vacuole*. Several of these vacuoles, which may be regarded as temporary stomachs, can often be seen in the cell at one time.

2. *Digestion*, or the bringing of the solid parts of the food into solution by the action of enzymes which are secreted by the protoplasm and flow through the vacuolar membrane into the food vacuole. Proteins, and probably also fats, starches, and sugars are digested, each being acted upon by a specific enzyme.

3. *Absorption*, or the passage of the digested food into the protoplasm by diffusion through the membrane of the vacuole.

4. *Circulation*, or the distribution of the digested food to the various

parts of the organism. This is accomplished by protoplasmic movements which result in changes in the position of the food vacuole itself, and also in the substances absorbed from it.

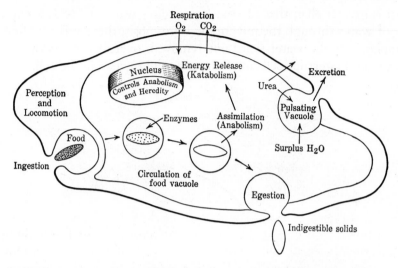

Fig. 44. Diagram showing the leading physiological processes in *Amoeba*. (Modified from Plunkett.)

5. *Assimilation,* or the building of food into the complex protoplasmic system.

6. *Egestion,* or the removal of the indigestible portions of the food from the body. This is the reverse of ingestion. The cell gradually moves away from these particles and the surrounding vacuole fluid, leaving them behind.

Respiration and Energy Liberation. Oxygen, always in solution in the water in which the ameba lives, diffuses through any part of the plasma membrane; part of the protoplasm is oxidized into simple substances and its stored energy is thereby liberated. Part of these simple substances, notably carbon dioxide and ammonia, diffuse out into the surrounding water. The liberated energy is used for carrying on both the complicated chemical processes involved in assimilation and the general activities of the organism.

Excretion and Control of Water Content. Near the outer part of the endoplasm is a transparent, fluid-filled *pulsating vacuole,* which gradually enlarges, suddenly collapses to discharge its contents to the exterior, then reappears and repeats the process. It was formerly considered an organ of *excretion*. Later research has shown that the nitrogenous wastes, largely ammonia, diffuse through the bounding plasma membrane as well as into the vacuole. The main function of the vacuole is thought to be the removal of surplus water. Since the concentration of solutes in the protoplasm is greater than that of the surrounding water, there is a constant flow of water through the membrane by osmosis; this tends to dilute the protoplasm. If the water were not removed, overdilution of the protoplasm would interrupt cell functions and might even kill the cell.

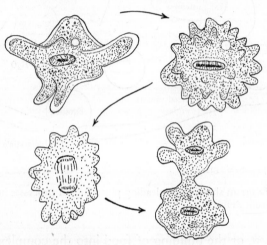

Fig. 45. Stages in nuclear and cell division (asexual reproduction) of *Amoeba*. The chromosomes are very small and the nuclear membrane persists through much of the process.

Response. Response to stimuli is a characteristic of even the simplest of organisms. Responses involving orientation, known as *tropisms* (Gr. "turnings"), are *positive* if directed toward, and *negative*, if directed from, the stimulus in question. A floating ameba responds positively to a solid object which it happens to reach with the tip of a pseudopod, and draws its entire body toward the object. The organism engulfs food but disregards grains of sand, which implies an ability to distinguish between the two by some sense akin to our sense of taste. It reacts negatively to certain chemicals that would endanger its existence, to unfavorable temperature, and to a beam of intense light; i.e., it moves away from these stimuli. In general, tropisms are positive to stimuli that favor the welfare of the cell, and negative to those that are injurious or destructive. It is interesting to note that perception, transmission of the influence of perception, and movement in response occur in an organism that possesses no sense organs, nerves, or muscles.

Role of the Nucleus. It is possible, by means of delicate needles carefully manipulated, to divide an ameba into two parts, one with and one without a nucleus. Each piece soon constructs a new plasma membrane to cover the surface where the separation was made, and both continue their activity. The piece with the nucleus continues to digest food, grow, and reproduce; the enucleated piece continues active for a time at the expense of protoplasm already present, then dies. Without a nucleus the power

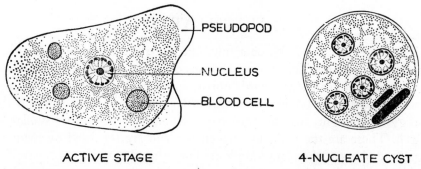

ACTIVE STAGE   4-NUCLEATE CYST

Fig. 46. *Endamoeba histolytica*, the intestinal parasite responsible for amebic dysentery, in active and encysted stages.

of constructive metabolism is impaired. Thus, the importance of the nucleus for metabolism may be demonstrated. Reproduction is asexual, the division of the nucleus preceding that of the cell (Fig. 45). As is usual among organisms, the nucleus divides mitotically, maintaining a constancy of hereditary factors. But since the chromosomes are small and are retained within the nuclear membrane during a large part of mitosis, they are difficult to demonstrate.

Parasitic Types. A *parasite* is an organism that lives and feeds upon a living organism of another species, the *host*. Several of the RHIZOPODA are parasites on man. *Endamoeba gingivalis* is found in the mouths of the majority of people, where it feeds on bacteria and epithelial cells. It is probably not *pathogenic* (disease producing). *Amebic dysentery* is a serious disease caused by *Endamoeba histolytica* (Fig. 46), which lives in the large intestine, feeding on blood and other tissues and producing large ulcers. Like numerous other protozoans, this species has the power of *encystment*, or *cyst formation*. This is accomplished by withdrawing much of the water from the cell and secreting a gelatinous covering which hardens into a firm coat that protects the cell while it remains in an inactive condition. *Endamoeba histolytica* is transmitted to new victims in the form of a four-nucleate cyst which passes from the intestine of the infected individual and may contaminate food or water. In one of our large city hotels, the presence of "carrier" employees and an antiquated plumbing system which mixed drain water with the drinking water led to a widespread epidemic resulting in 1500 cases and 100 deaths. About 10 percent of the people of the United States are said to be infected, but in many of them the symptoms are mild. A number of drugs have been found valuable for treatment of the disease.

FLAGELLATA

The flagellates have one or a few, occasionally many, long whip-like processes, *flagella*, which serve as a means of locomotion. These organisms consist of two groups as regards nutrition. One includes forms that possess *chlorophyll* in bodies known as *chloroplasts* and that, through the energy of sunlight, manufacture *paramylum*, a carbohydrate similar to starch. These are the plant-like flagellates, and are regarded by many as algae, members of the plant kingdom. The other is made up of forms that lack chlorophyll and ingest solid food particles through a mouth. These are definitely animals. Since the groups are so much alike in respects other than nutrition, it is convenient to consider them together.

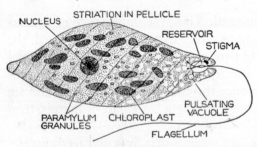

FIG. 47. *Euglena viridis.*

Euglena. The genus *Euglena* (Fig. 47) contains several species of plant-like flagellates with spindle-shaped bodies. They often accumulate in such numbers as to form a distinct green scum on water. Like true animals, they lack a cell wall and are very flexible. Also, like the animal flagellates, the cell has a *mouth*, a depression at the anterior end that leads into a tubular *gullet*, though these structures seem to have no connection with nutrition in the plant-like forms. From the mouth projects a long, delicate *flagellum*. Movement is achieved not only by the lashing of the flagellum, but by writhing and wave-like contortions of the entire body. Near the *pulsating vacuole*, which discharges into a *reservoir* at the rear end of the gullet, is a red eyespot or *stigma* which enables the organism to perceive the direction of light and orient itself accordingly. Reproduction is by longitudinal fission, which often takes place when the cell is in an encysted or resting condition. Thus, as in *Amoeba*, reproduction is asexual.

Flagellates and Disease. *Trypanosoma* (Fig. 48) is a genus of flagellates which live in the blood plasma of various mammals, causing disease in cattle, horses, and game animals, and Chagas' disease (South America)

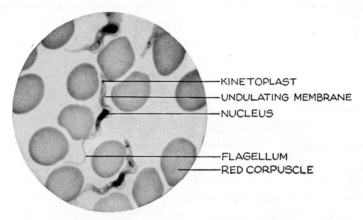

KINETOPLAST
UNDULATING MEMBRANE
NUCLEUS

FLAGELLUM
RED CORPUSCLE

Fig. 48. *Trypanosoma gambiense*, a flagellate that lives in human blood and causes one of the types of African sleeping sickness ($\times$ 1500). (Photomicrograph, copyright, General Biological Supply House, Inc., Chicago.)

and African sleeping sickness[1] in man. Sleeping sickness is transmitted by the bite of the tsetse fly. In sucking the blood of a diseased person the fly ingests the flagellates which, after undergoing certain phases in the insect's digestive tract, invade the salivary glands to be injected into the blood stream of the next human victim. This disease produces weakness and anemia, and, unless treated in its early stages, leads to unconsciousness and death. Control of the disease, which has been prevalent over a large part of central Africa, involves the restriction of the tsetse fly (e.g., through the elimination of vegetation in which it breeds) and the use of certain drugs, such as Bayer 205.

SPOROZOA

Plasmodium, the Malaria Organism. SPOROZOA get their name from the division of the protoplast, at certain intervals in the life history, into numerous reproductive bodies called *spores*. Malaria is caused by organisms of the genus *Plasmodium*, which is parasitic in the blood stream of

[1] Not to be confused with encephalitis, a virus disease, also known as sleeping sickness.

certain vertebrates, including man. It is transmitted to the vertebrate by
the bite of a female mosquito of the genus *Anopheles* (Fig. 143), upon
which it is parasitic during a portion of its life cycle (Figs. 49, 50). Into

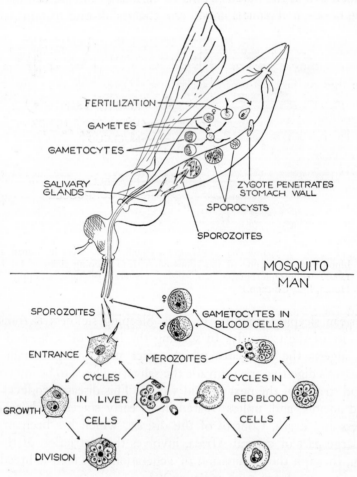

FIG. 49. Life history of *Plasmodium vivax*, the organism causing
benign tertian malaria, a common type of this disease in man. Asexual
cycles take place in the human body, in cells of the liver and in red
blood cells. The cycle in the blood is completed every two days,
causing chills and fever in the patient at two-day intervals. The sexual
cycle in *Anopheles* requires about twelve days.

the blood stream of her victim the mosquito injects saliva which prevents
the coagulation of the blood; if she happens to have been infected with
Plasmodium, she may inject many elongated spores (*sporozoites*), which
have migrated from cysts on her stomach wall. These spores do not remain

in the blood, but enter the cells of the liver, where they grow and later divide into spores of another sort, *merozoites*, which again enter liver cells. On completing two or three of these cycles in the liver, the merozoites enter red blood cells. Here they grow until they fill the cell; then they divide into new merozoites, which are liberated with the rupture of the cell membrane. After a few such cycles these parasites become numerous enough to produce the symptoms of the disease—anemia caused by destruction of red blood cells, and a chill followed by a fever at each liberation of merozoites, which occurs every two or three days, according to the type of malaria. The body apparently reacts to some poison liberated with the merozoites. Continued harboring of the parasites in the cells of the liver and their release later into the blood stream proba-

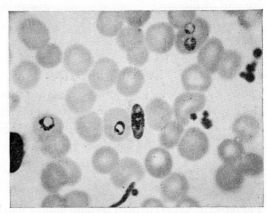

Fig. 50. Organism of malignant malaria (*Plasmodium falciparum*) in human blood (× 1000). Three of the corpuscles contain trophozoites in the ring stage. Gametocytes are sausage-shaped in this species. A female gametocyte may be seen near the center. (Photomicrograph, copyright, General Biological Supply House, Inc., Chicago.)

bly accounts for the relapse of many patients after they seem to have recovered from some kinds of malaria (but apparently not malignant malaria).

Cycle in the Mosquito. *Plasmodium* has a sexual phase in its life cycle. This is initiated in man and completed in the mosquito. Some of the bodies in the red blood cells, instead of dividing into spores, form *gametocytes* (Gr. "gamete-forming cells"). These undergo no further development unless they are swallowed by an *Anopheles* that bites the malaria victim. Gametocytes are of both sexes. In the stomach of *Anopheles* the female gametocyte throws off a mass of surplus chromatin and becomes an *egg;* the male divides into four to eight elongated *sperms*. The sperm unites with the egg to form a *zygote*, which immediately becomes active, bores its way through the stomach wall, and becomes encysted just outside the wall. After enlarging for about a week, the cyst divides into hundreds of spindle-shaped *sporozoites*. The rupture of the cyst liberates them into the blood cavity, through which they are carried to the salivary gland. On penetrating to its hollow center they are ready to be injected into a person bitten by the mosquito. The life cycle in the mosquito usually requires from ten to eighteen days, and it is only after this period that the infected mosquito can transmit the disease.

Importance and Types of Malaria. Malaria is one of the most important human diseases. It produces suffering, inability to work, and lack of vitality and of disease resistance among vast numbers of people, particularly in the warmer parts of the world; it prevents the cultivation of wide areas of fertile land; it has contributed to the destruction of ancient civilizations, such as those of Greece and Rome and the Mayan culture of Yucatán. Its name (Gr. "bad air") expresses an old misconception regarding the cause of the disease, for it was thought to be due to breathing, particularly during the night, the poisonous vapors arising from swampy land. The discovery of its mode of transmission was completed about 1898 by Ross, an Englishman, and Grassi, an Italian.

The species of *Plasmodium* with the types of malaria and their distribution are:

Plasmodium vivax: benign tertian; almost world-wide.
Plasmodium ovale: benign tertian, Philippines and Africa.
Plasmodium malariae: quartan; widely distributed, but less common than *vivax.*
Plasmodium falciparum: malignant subtertian; widespread in the tropics.

The terms tertian and quartan are based on an old method of reckoning time, in which the first and last days of the time interval are counted. The tertian types complete the asexual cycle in man "every third day" (48-hour intervals), the quartan "every fourth day" (72-hour intervals); the subtertian is somewhat irregular in the length of its cycle. The benign types are generally not immediately fatal; the malignant disease often ends in death.

Control of Malaria. The following are important measures in the control of the disease:

1. Suppressing mosquitoes by draining swamps to destroy the breeding places, by spraying ponds with oil or poisons to kill the larvae when they come to the surface to breathe, or by introducing minnows to feed upon the larvae.
2. Protecting living quarters and especially sleeping rooms with screens. *Anopheles* is nocturnal; usually it has to continue biting for some time to inject the spores, and hence it is especially likely to infect sleeping persons.
3. Using drugs. The old standby is *quinine*, obtained from the bark of the *cinchona*, a tree native to South America but grown mainly in the East Indies. The cutting off of the quinine supply during World War II intensified the search for synthetic substitutes, some of which have proved to be

superior to quinine. *Atabrine* and *chloroquin* are now the favorites for kill-ing the merozoites, *plasmochin* for killing the gametocytes.

The increasing use of airplanes heightens the danger of mosquito stowa-ways spreading serious types of malaria and other diseases. Since species of *Anopheles* are distributed over most of the United States there is always danger that they may become infected by human carriers of malaria and start new epidemics. Therefore the control of malaria is a biological prob-lem of the first magnitude.

Pebrine. Another of the SPOROZOA is responsible for the silkworm dis-ease, *pebrine*, which once threatened the silk industry of France. One of the outstanding achievements of Pasteur (Fig. 272) was the discovery of the parasitic nature of this disease and the development of an effective control.

CILIATA

Paramecium, the Slipper Animalcule. The class CILIATA is charac-terized by hair-like cilia that cover all or a considerable portion of the

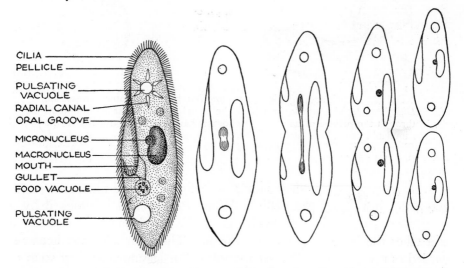

CILIA
PELLICLE
PULSATING VACUOLE
RADIAL CANAL
ORAL GROOVE
MICRONUCLEUS
MACRONUCLEUS
MOUTH
GULLET
FOOD VACUOLE
PULSATING VACUOLE

FIG. 51. *Paramecium caudatum*, structural detail and outline of successive steps in fission. The macronucleus divides by amitosis, the micronucleus by a modification of mitosis in which the chromosomes remain within the nuclear membrane.

body. *Paramecium*, one of the best-known genera, may be used to show the characteristics of the class (Fig. 51). As compared with such forms as the ameba, it shows a high degree of specialization within the cell.

1. The body has a definite form, roughly that of a slipper, with the heel

end directed anteriorly. This form is maintained by a firm pellicle just outside the plasma membrane.

2. The body is covered by *cilia* which serve as locomotor appendages.

3. There is a definite *mouth*, that serves for ingestion of food, and a definite *anus*, that serves for the egestion of undigested residues.

4. There are specialized protoplasmic *fibrils*, more sensitive than the surrounding protoplasm, that serve to coordinate the beating of the cilia.

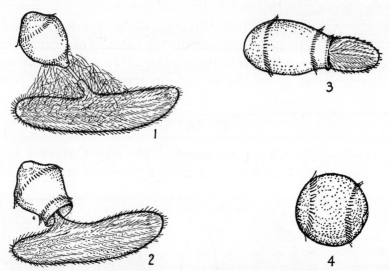

FIG. 52. Attack and ingestion of *Paramecium* by the predatory protozoan, *Didinium*. *1*, The attack, in which the attacker has thrust its proboscis through the pellicle of its prey. Trichocysts have been discharged from the stimulated part of the latter. *2, 3*, Steps in ingestion. *4*, Ingestion completed. (Based on Buchsbaum, *Animals Without Backbones;* Univ. of Chicago Press.)

5. *Trichocysts* (Gr. "hair sacs") are ellipsoidal fluid-filled sacs in the ectoplasm just under the pellicle. When *Paramecium* is attacked by a predator or irritated by certain chemicals, the fluid is suddenly discharged and takes the form of gelatinous threads. These threads have been regarded as useful in repelling an aggressor, but inasmuch as they seem to cause only a slight delay in the seizure and destruction of *Paramecium* by *Didinium* (Fig. 52), their real function may be regarded as doubtful.

6. The *pulsating vacuoles*, of which *Paramecium* usually has two, are in a fixed location and are surrounded by several *radiating canals* which conduct water into them. As the vacuole is emptied, the canals begin to fill; as the canals empty, the vacuole enlarges.

7. *Paramecium* reproduces by *sexual* as well as *asexual* means.

Nutritive Processes. Food vacuoles, which gradually form at the narrow end of the funnel-shaped gullet, are water droplets containing the food particles, important among which are bacteria. These vacuoles circulate around the center of the body and gradually grow smaller as digestion proceeds. The undigested debris is then extruded at the anus, a small opening near the mouth that is seen only when wastes are egested.

Locomotion and Behavior. The cilia, which normally extend perpendicularly from the surface of the body, beat back to an oblique position and propel the organism much as the stroke of the oars propels a boat. The more rapid beating of the cilia along the oblique oral groove produces

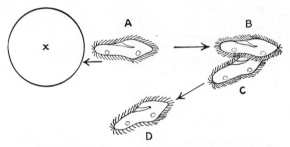

Fig. 53. Trial-and-error behavior in *Paramecium. A* to *D,* Successive positions assumed by the organism in avoiding a solid object or irritating substance represented by *x.* Arrows show the direction of movement. Rotation on the long axis also occurs but is not shown in the diagram. (After Jennings.)

a spiral movement accompanied by rotation on the long axis. When the cell strikes an obstruction, its cilia suddenly change the direction of their beat, causing the cell to move backward for a little distance; then, turning on the thicker end of its body, the organism starts forward at a slightly different angle. This process is continued until it finds its way past the obstacle by a trial-and-error method (Fig. 53).

Reproduction. The nucleus of *Paramecium* is in two or more parts, a large ovoid *macronucleus* and one or more small globular *micronuclei.* Asexual reproduction is by *fission.* Both kinds of nuclei divide into halves, the micronucleus by mitosis, the macronucleus merely by pinching in two (amitosis). The gullet then splits, and a constriction in the cytoplasm gradually divides the organism (Fig. 51). The entire process is completed in from half an hour to two hours. About a day later the daughter organisms may be ready for another division.

At certain times, especially when different strains are present in a culture, numerous individuals undergo a *sexual* process, *conjugation* (Fig.

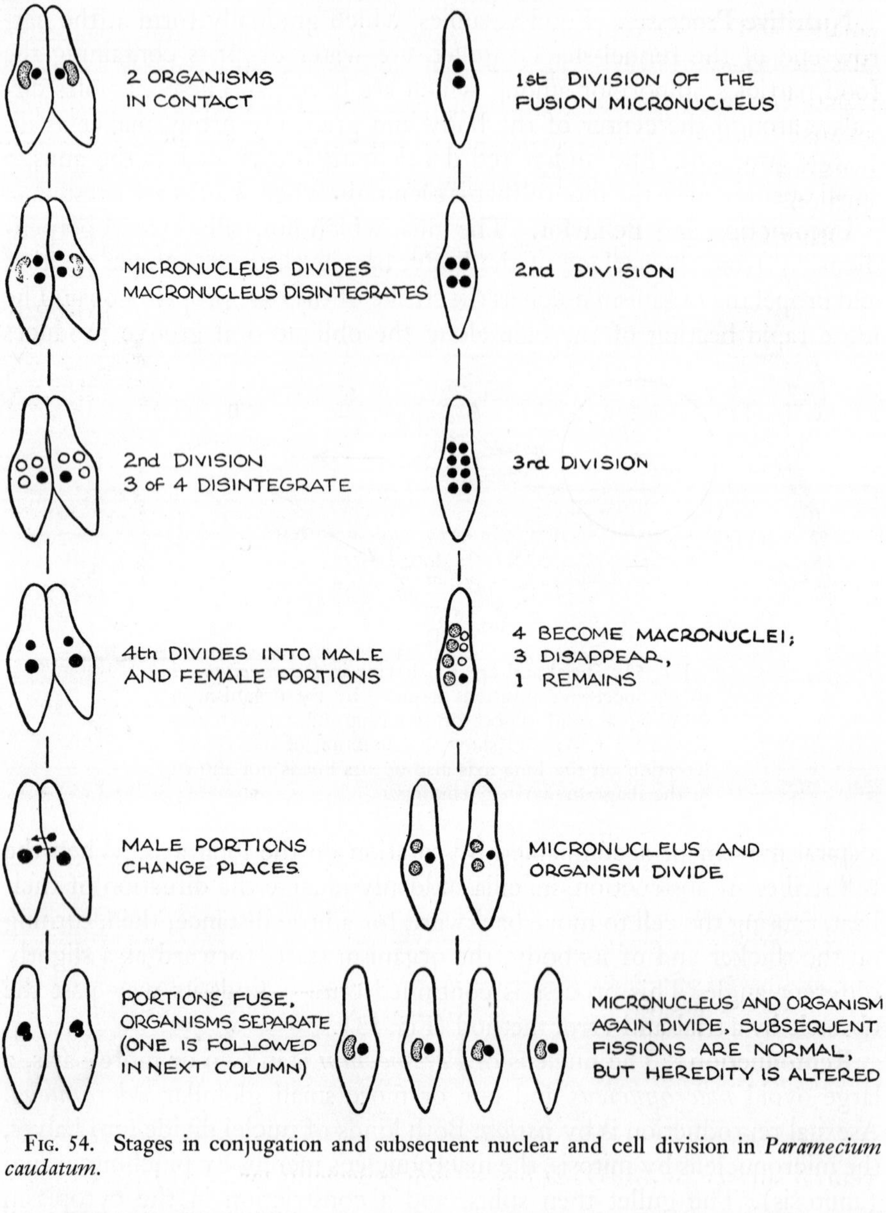

2 ORGANISMS
IN CONTACT

1st DIVISION OF THE
FUSION MICRONUCLEUS

MICRONUCLEUS DIVIDES
MACRONUCLEUS DISINTEGRATES

2nd DIVISION

2nd DIVISION
3 of 4 DISINTEGRATE

3rd DIVISION

4th DIVIDES INTO MALE
AND FEMALE PORTIONS

4 BECOME MACRONUCLEI;
3 DISAPPEAR,
1 REMAINS

MALE PORTIONS
CHANGE PLACES

MICRONUCLEUS AND
ORGANISM DIVIDE

PORTIONS FUSE,
ORGANISMS SEPARATE
(ONE IS FOLLOWED
IN NEXT COLUMN)

MICRONUCLEUS AND ORGANISM
AGAIN DIVIDE, SUBSEQUENT
FISSIONS ARE NORMAL,
BUT HEREDITY IS ALTERED

FIG. 54. Stages in conjugation and subsequent nuclear and cell division in *Paramecium caudatum*.

54). They adhere in pairs, the contact being along an area near the oral groove of each. The micronuclei then undergo a series of divisions which result in the discarding of part of the chromatin. Eventually the micro-nuclear material consists of two parts. One of these, which is somewhat smaller and is regarded as the male portion, passes through the protoplasmic bridge between the cells and fuses with the female portion of the other. Hereupon the two cells separate, and each undergoes a series of asexual divisions. Neither is genetically the same as it was before, for each has given up a portion of its old nuclear material and has received a new portion.

Other Ciliates. There are many genera of ciliates (Fig. 55). On some

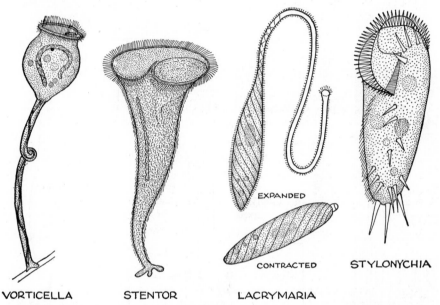

VORTICELLA   STENTOR   LACRYMARIA   STYLONYCHIA

Fig. 55. Several genera of ciliates. *Vorticella* is anchored to water vegetation by a stalk containing contractile fibers. When it is disturbed, the stalk coils, suddenly withdrawing the cell body from danger. While feeding, *Stentor*, the trumpet animalcule, attaches itself by the small end, drawing the food particles to its mouth by a current produced by the vibration of the cilia at the broad end. In *Lacrymaria*, the mouth is at the end of a long, snake-like neck which enables the organism to explore widely for food. In *Stylonychia* the cilia are unequally distributed, part of those on the lower surface being fused in groups and serving as legs by means of which the animal crawls. (Redrawn from various sources.)

the cilia are more or less restricted to the region of the mouth. On its ventral surface *Stylonychia* has several especially large cilia by which it crawls on the substratum. *Stentor*, the trumpet animalcule, attaches itself temporarily by the small end of its funnel-shaped body; the fringe of cilia at the broad end sweeps food into the gullet. *Vorticella*, the bell animalcule, has a long, permanently attached stalk containing elastic fibrils that contract when the organism is threatened with danger.

GENERAL REMARKS

Protozoa are eaten in great numbers by somewhat larger aquatic animals, which in turn are eaten by still larger forms; hence they constitute an important link in the chain of life. Some of the RHIZOPODA of sea water

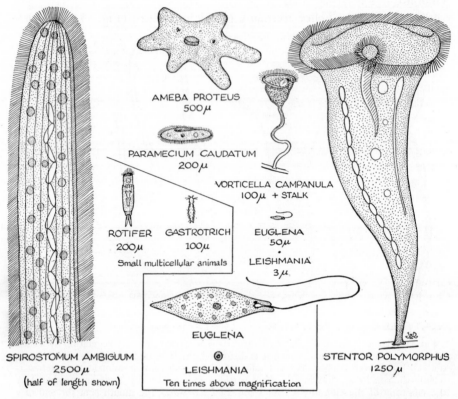

FIG. 56. Comparative sizes of *Protozoa*. Species of this group vary about as much as do those of any phylum of multicellular animals. Several are drawn here to scale. Measurements given are of the longest dimension in microns (thousandths of a millimeter). A large multinucleate ameba (*Chaos chaos*) has been reported to attain a length of 5 mm., about four times the length of the *Stentor* shown in this figure. Two of the smaller multicellular animals (a rotifer and a gastrotrich) are included on the same scale for comparison. In the lower box, the linear scale is increased ten times. Note the chain-like macronuclei in *Spirostomum* and *Stentor*.

secrete external skeletons of calcium carbonate (Fig. 42). The accumulation of untold numbers of their cast-off shells produces the white ooze that covers much of the ocean bottom and becomes consolidated to form beds of chalk, such as those that are a striking feature of the southeast coast of England. Ameba-like protozoans that live in the soil destroy soil fertility by devouring the bacteria which would otherwise bring about the desirable conversion of ammonia to nitrates. Baking such soil kills the protozoans so that subsequently introduced useful bacteria may survive.

Although the PROTOZOA are all of microscopic dimensions, there is a vast difference in size between the smallest and the largest (Fig. 56). Some are much larger than the smallest METAZOA, such as rotifers, gastrotrichs, and the smaller roundworms. Some are even more complex in structure than a simple metazoan like the hydra.

EXERCISES

1. In what respects is the cell of *Amoeba* more highly specialized than the cells of most human tissues? In what respects is *Paramecium* more highly specialized than *Amoeba?*
2. What physiological processes are common to *Amoeba* and to man? How do the two compare regarding specialization of structures for carrying out these processes?
3. In what respects are the flagellate protozoans plant-like? In what respects animal-like?

REFERENCES

Brown, F. A., Jr. (ed.), *Selected Invertebrate Types,* John Wiley & Sons, Inc., 1950.

Calkins G. N., *Biology of Protozoa,* Lea & Febiger, 2nd ed., 1933.

Chandler, A. C., *Introduction to Parasitology,* John Wiley & Sons, Inc., 8th ed., 1949.

Craig, C. F., and Faust, E. C., *Clinical Parasitology,* Lea & Febiger, 5th ed., 1951.

Culbertson, J. T., *Medical Parasitology,* Columbia Univ. Press, 1942.

de Kruif, P., *Microbe Hunters,* Harcourt, Brace and Company, Inc., 1925.

Hegner, R. W., and Stiles, K. A., *College Zoology,* The Macmillan Company, 6th ed., 1951.

Hyman, L. H., *The Invertebrates: Vol. I, Protozoa Through Ctenophora,* Mc-Graw-Hill Book Company, 1940.

Jahn, T. L., *How to Know the Protozoa,* William C. Brown Co., 1949.

Kudo, R. R., *Handbook of Protozoology,* Charles C. Thomas, Publisher, 1931.

Pratt, H. S., *Manual of the Common Invertebrate Animals,* The Blakiston Company, rev. ed., 1935.

Ward, H. B., and Whipple, G. C., *Fresh-water Biology,* John Wiley & Sons, Inc., 1918.

Chapter VIII

INTRODUCTION TO THE MULTICELLULAR ANIMALS

Colonial Organisms. Many kinds of unicellular organisms form colonies of cells grouped together in definite fashion. Because there is little or no division of labor we regard these organisms as unicellular rather than multicellular. But division of labor apparently came gradually in the course of evolution. As an example to illustrate this, a series of plant-like flagellates of the Order VOLVOCALES is often used (Fig. 57). Their cells are somewhat like that of *Euglena*, but are held in constant shape by a thin but rigid wall. A one-celled member of this series in *Sphaerella*. It sometimes accumulates on snow banks, giving them a reddish color due to a pigment that is suffused through the cell. A species of *Gonium* has a plate of four cells embedded in a gelatinous matrix. *Pandorina* is a spheroidal colony of 16 cells similarly embedded. The cells are all alike, and each is capable of dividing into 16 small cells which arrange themselves into a daughter colony. The 16 daughter colonies eventually break out of the old matrix and grow to adult size.

Beginnings of Differentiation. Other representatives of the series have cells that differ mainly in reproductive ability. *Pleodorina illinoisensis* is a colony of 32 cells, of which the four anterior (those that are foremost in locomotion) are smaller and are purely nutritive, whereas the other 28 become reproductive and organize daughter colonies. In *Pleodorina californica* the cells of the anterior half of the colony are smaller and are purely nutritive; those of the posterior (rear) half possess the power of reproduction. *Volvox* consists of thousands of cells that occupy the surface of a gelatinous sphere. Only a few of these (about six or eight) enlarge, then divide into many small cells that arrange themselves in a spherical daughter colony. In other colonies a restricted number of cells develop sperms or eggs, which take part in sexual reproduction. Thus, when we take reproductive activities into consideration, *Pleodorina* and

98

Volvox have taken a step away from colonial organization toward that of the multicellular individual.

Early Development of a Metazoan. The egg of any metazoan divides after fertilization into a two-celled stage, each cell again dividing to form a four-celled stage. Succeeding divisions result in eight and 16 cells. In

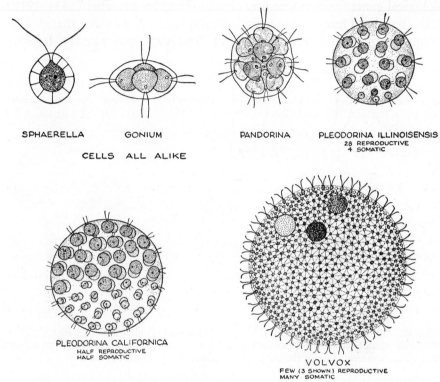

SPHAERELLA GONIUM PANDORINA PLEODORINA ILLINOISENSIS
28 REPRODUCTIVE
4 SOMATIC

CELLS ALL ALIKE

PLEODORINA CALIFORNICA
HALF REPRODUCTIVE
HALF SOMATIC

VOLVOX
FEW (3 SHOWN) REPRODUCTIVE
MANY SOMATIC

Fig. 57. Colonial protozoans, showing transition from the typical colony, with cells all alike, to colonies that approach the multicellular individual by having some cells that are capable of daughter colony formation and others that are purely nutritive (somatic). Each cell has two flagella and an eyespot.

many of them further development occurs as follows: As divisions continue, the cells push one another away from the center; this results in a hollow sphere, the *blastula*. Up to this point there has been no essential differentiation in cells. Shortly afterward, the embryo becomes two-layered, the *gastrula*. This change occurs in various ways; a common method is for the cells to grow in such a manner that one side of the sphere comes to be indented toward the other, forming a two-layered cup. The outer layer is known as the *ectoderm* (Gr. "outer skin"), and the inner as the *endoderm* (Gr. "inner skin"). In the coelenterates these are the only layers which ordinarily develop, so these animals are called *diploblastic* (Gr. "double bud"). In most of the remaining Metazoa a *mesoderm* (Gr. "middle skin") appears between the ectoderm and endoderm; hence these forms are called *triploblastic* (Gr. "triple bud").

Resemblance of Embryonic Stages to Existing Forms. An important biological generalization was first clearly stated by Haeckel (1834–1919) in the words, "Ontogeny recapitulates phylogeny," meaning that the development of the individual summarizes briefly the evolutionary develop-

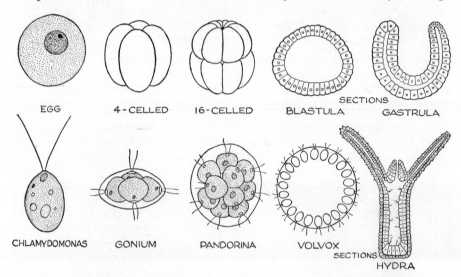

FIG. 58. "Ontogeny recapitulates phylogeny." The embryonic stages of a higher animal (the lancelet, a chordate), shown in the upper row, bear a general resemblance to mature colonies or organisms low in the evolutionary scale, shown in the lower row.

ment of the species. The fact that the stages of development of higher animals have some similarity to existing lower forms is regarded as evidence of this principle (Fig. 58). The egg of a multicellular organism resembles a unicellular protozoan; a four-celled embryo resembles *Gonium;* a 16-celled embryo, *Pandorina;* a blastula, *Pleodorina* or *Volvox;* a gastrula, a hydra (though this animal has progressed somewhat beyond the gastrula stage). We might regard these organisms as having gone along the evolutionary path in company with their fellows in the higher groups and having become stranded at various intervals along the path.

Tissues of a Multicellular Animal. The colonial protozoans are regarded as unicellular, for there is little if any differentiation among nutritive cells. Multicellular animals, as we shall see in the following chapters, range widely in differentiation, from the hydra, which has two cell layers with ten or twelve types of cells hardly organized into tissues, to the higher vertebrates, which have many kinds of cells organized into tissues that in turn make up the various organs. In the early stages of its development the cells of the individual are scarcely distinguishable from one another; but as growth proceeds, an orderly course of differentiation brings about the highly complicated structure of the mature organism.

Types of Animal Tissue. As was pointed out in Chapter II, the many kinds of tissue found in the higher animals may be grouped into four main types: *epithelial, supporting* or *connective, muscular,* and *nervous.* Some of their characteristics, as they are found in man and other vertebrates, are presented here.

1. *Epithelial tissues:* Such tissues form the covering for the outside surface of the body or the lining of any of its cavities or passages (Fig. 59). They protect the body against mechanical injury and microbial infection (Chapter

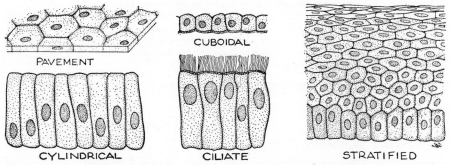

PAVEMENT CUBOIDAL

CYLINDRICAL CILIATE STRATIFIED

FIG. 59. Types of epithelial tissue which serve as a covering for the body or a lining for its cavities.

XX), and serve as the passageway for whatever enters or leaves the cells of the body. Some epithelia consist of a single layer of cells; here the individual cells may be *flat, cuboidal,* or *columnar.* Flat, thin cells make up the walls of the air sacs of the lungs and of the blood capillaries, enabling the rapid interchange of oxygen and carbon dioxide. Cuboidal cells are found in the walls of the kidney tubules. Cells of the columnar type make up the walls of the stomach and intestine; their function is the secretion of enzymes and the absorption of digested food. Other epithelia are stratified, i.e., made up of several layers. The outer skin (epidermis) and the mucous membrane of the mouth are of this type. In many animals some of the epithelial cells become hard and horny and form scales, feathers, hair, nails hoofs, and horns.

2. *Supporting or connective tissues:* In general, these tissues give form to the body, bind its parts together, or serve as a medium of transportation be-

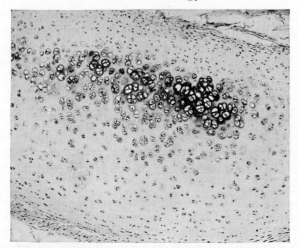

Fig. 60. Hyaline cartilage, a connective tissue (× 100). The cells are isolated or in groups of two or four, separated by a translucent intercellular matrix. The more mature cartilage is the region of the larger cells, near the center. From a developing bone (sternum) of a young rabbit. (Photomicrograph, copyright, General Biological Supply House, Inc., Chicago.)

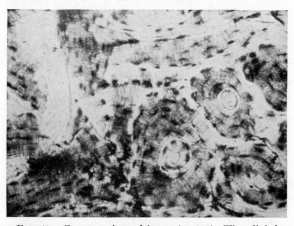

Fig. 61. Cross section of bone (× 110). The slightly elongated dark bodies (bone cells) are arranged in cylindrical layers around the canals that provide the blood supply. Minute canals permit of lymph communication between the cells. (Photomicrograph by Robert Van Voorhees.)

tween the parts. A striking characteristic of these tissues is that the cells occupy a relatively small part, the main bulk consisting of intercellular secretions. In vertebrate animals a common kind of skeletal tissue is *cartilage* (Fig. 60). Its cells are in little pockets distributed through an elastic, gelatinous intercellular substance. In most vertebrates *bone* (Fig. 61) ultimately replaces much of the cartilage or is developed from membranes. Its intercellular substance consists mainly of calcium phosphate. The intercellular material of *tendons*, which bind the ends of muscles to the bones, is composed of white inelastic fibers. *Ligaments*, which hold the bones together at the joints, must be somewhat elastic to allow freedom for bone movement; hence they are provided with yellow elastic fibers. *Blood* (Fig. 62)

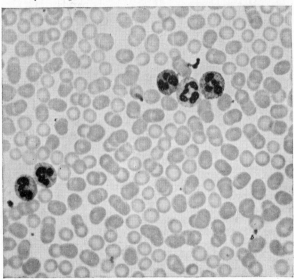

FIG. 62. Human blood (× 630). The red cells (most numerous) are biconcave and lack nuclei. Five large multinucleate white cells are included. The small dark dots are blood platelets. (Photomicrograph, copyright, General Biological Supply House, Inc., Chicago.)

is a tissue which, though quite distinctive, is often classed with the connective tissues. The intercellular substance is a liquid, the *plasma*. Its cells include *white corpuscles*, which aid in rebuilding injured tissues and destroying microorganisms, and the far more numerous *red corpuscles*, which carry oxygen. In groups below the mammals these corpuscles retain their nuclei, but in mammals they lose their nuclei before passing from the red bone marrow, where they are manufactured, into the circulation.

3. *Muscular tissues:* All protoplasm exhibits the power of movement. Muscles of animals are highly specialized for this purpose. Muscular movement is caused by the contraction or shortening of elongated cells. There are three kinds of muscle tissue (Fig. 63):

   A. *Smooth muscle* (involuntary) is found in the walls of the stomach, arteries, and other internal organs. The cells are spindle-shaped, each with an elongated nucleus, and they overlap to form extensive sheets.

B. *Striated muscle* (voluntary) brings about changes in the position of the bones, and other voluntary movements. The fibers, each of which is a multinucleate structure or coenocyte, are arranged in bundles. The tiny fibrils that constitute the fiber have alternate thick and thin portions; hence under the microscope the fiber appears cross-banded with light and dark bands.

C. *Heart muscle* makes up the walls of the heart. It is striated but involuntary, and consists of uninucleate cylindrical cells with side branches binding them into a sort of network.

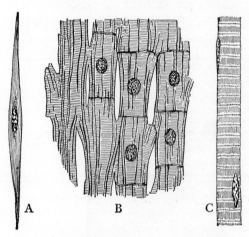

FIG. 63. *A*, Smooth muscle cell with a single elongated nucleus and tapering ends which overlap other fibers. *B*, A group of connected heart muscle cells, each with one nucleus. *C*, Portion of striated muscle, a coenocyte with many nuclei in the protoplast; two of the nuclei are shown. (Adapted from Kühn and from Schäfer.)

4. *Nervous tissues:* The nervous tissues form a system for receiving and transmitting the effects of outside stimuli, thus enabling the various parts of the body to act for the benefit of the whole; in other words, they provide for the *coordination* of the various parts of the body. A nerve cell or *neuron* (Fig. 64) consists of a nucleated cell body and two sorts of extensions, the *axon* and *dendrites*. Either may be greatly elongated. Dendrites carry nerve impulses toward the cell body, and axons carry them away. *Sensory* neurons carry impulses from special sense cells or from special sensory endings of the neuron itself to the central nervous system; *association* or intermediate neurons carry impulses from one part to another of the central nervous system; and *motor* neurons carry impulses from the central nervous system to a muscle or gland.

Gametogenesis. Very widespread among animals is the process of sexual reproduction, in which special cells called gametes unite to give rise to new individuals. In many-celled animals the gametes are produced in organs known as *gonads* (Gr. "that which generates"). Almost always there are two kinds of gonads—*ovaries*, which produce the larger food-containing reproductive cells (*eggs*); and *spermaries* or *testes*, which produce the minute motile cells (*sperms*). In *monoecious* (Gr. "one house") animals, frequent in the lower groups, spermaries and ovaries are formed in the same individual, whereas in *dioecious* (Gr. "two house") animals, common in the lower and practically universal in the higher groups, testes develop in some individuals, the *males,* and ovaries in others, the *females.*

When the testis first appears in a young animal it is made up of potential sperm-forming cells; from these, by a process called *spermatogenesis,* the sperm cells are produced (Fig. 65). The early cells divide repeatedly during the growth period, eventually giving rise to *primary spermatocytes.* Each of these divides into two *secondary spermatocytes,* which in turn divide each into two *spermatids.* The spermatid undergoes a transformation (without further division) to become a *sperm,* which in many animals is elongated, the nucleus being included in the *head* and the cytoplasm drawn out into a *tail.* By a lashing movement the tail drives the sperm along through a fluid medium (water in many aquatic species and semen in terrestrial ones), assisting it in reaching the egg, with which the sperm may fuse to form a zygote. Likewise, a young ovary contains many potential egg-forming cells. During *oogenesis* (Fig. 65) these divide repeatedly and eventually form large *primary oocytes.* Each of these divides into a large cell, the *secondary oocyte,* and a small one, the *first polar body.* The former then divides into the *egg* and a *second polar body;* the first polar body may divide into two. The polar bodies soon disintegrate. During both spermatogenesis and oogenesis meiosis occurs, i.e., the diploid chromosome number is reduced to the haploid number; this process begins in the primary spermatocyte and primary oocyte respectively and continues through the following two cell divisions. Since sperms and eggs are so distinct

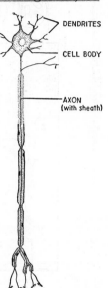

Fig. 64. Diagram of a motor nerve cell (neuron); the axon as shown is relatively too short. (Redrawn from Maximow and Bloom, *A Textbook of Histology,* copyright, 1930, W. B. Saunders Company.)

from other kinds of cells in many-celled animals, some authors consider them to constitute a special *reproductive tissue.* However, because the cells that give rise to them are similar to epithelial cells, others consider them to be simply epithelial derivatives.

Organ Systems. A distinct part of the body, such as the stomach, is made up of several tissues—epithelial, connective, muscular, nervous— and hence is called an *organ.* The several organs that do the work of pre-

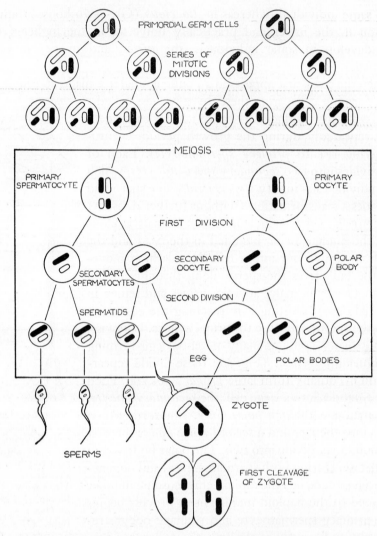

PRIMORDIAL GERM CELLS

SERIES OF MITOTIC DIVISIONS

MEIOSIS

PRIMARY SPERMATOCYTE

PRIMARY OOCYTE

FIRST DIVISION

SECONDARY SPERMATOCYTES

SECONDARY OOCYTE

POLAR BODY

SPERMATIDS

SECOND DIVISION

EGG

POLAR BODIES

SPERMS

ZYGOTE

FIRST CLEAVAGE OF ZYGOTE

FIG. 65. Diagrammatic representation of the development of gametes, sperms, and eggs. Sperm production (spermatogenesis) is shown on the left, egg production (oogenesis) on the right. One of the sperms is shown joined to the egg to form a zygote, from which a new individual develops by cleavage. Organisms differ widely in the number of chromosomes, but only two pairs are followed in this diagram. Assume that the black chromosomes in each primordial germ cell are from the mother of the organism, the white ones from the father. The segregations of these chromosomes at the first division of meiosis result in each gamete's receiving only one chromosome of each pair (either maternal or paternal). Whereas sperms arise from all four of the products of meiosis in spermatogenesis, only one of the products of meiosis in oogenesis becomes an egg, for the three polar bodies disintegrate.

paring food and delivering it—mouth, pharynx, esophagus, stomach, intestine, and digestive glands—form a *system*. The leading systems, some or all of which are found in all metazoans, are:

1. *Integumentary:* consisting of the skin, as a protective covering.
2. *Supporting:* consisting of the skeleton with its associated cartilages and ligaments, as a framework for the body.
3. *Circulatory* or *vascular:* bringing about the transportation of food, oxygen, and waste products.
4. *Respiratory:* taking in oxygen and eliminating carbon dioxide.
5. *Muscular:* for motion and locomotion.
6. *Excretory:* for throwing out the wastes of metabolism.
7. *Digestive:* for taking in the food, preparing it for absorption by the cells of the body, and eliminating the indigestible wastes.
8. *Coordinating:* for enabling the parts to work together, thereby making the body a unit. This comprises the *nervous system* and the *endocrine system.*
9. *Reproductive:* for the production of new organisms.

SYMMETRY AND SEGMENTATION

Spherical Symmetry. Inasmuch as division of an animal's body may result in similar halves, an animal is said to have *symmetry* (Fig. 66). The sun animalcule (*Actinophrys*) and some other floating PROTOZOA can be divided into similar halves by any plane passing through the central point of the body. The same is true of the colonies of certain colonial forms, such as *Pandorina* and *Volvox*. Their symmetry is said to be *spherical;* they are equally affected on all sides by the surrounding medium and present an equally organized part of the body in all directions.

Radial Symmetry. The animals that are attached or slow-moving generally have *radial symmetry*, which means that equivalent parts radiate from a central line called the *axis*, like the spokes of a wheel from its axle. This axis extends from the *oral* to the *aboral poles*, i.e., from the mouth to a point opposite it. This shape is poorly adapted to rapid locomotion but is well fitted for securing food coming from all directions and for guarding against enemies on all sides of the body. This type of symmetry is characteristic of sponges, coelenterates, and echinoderms.

Bilateral Symmetry. In the course of animal evolution, the need of searching for food and escaping enemies led to the development of forward movement in a uniform direction and often with considerable velocity. The end which is foremost in locomotion must be more amply provided with sense organs, and able to react more quickly to newly entered environments; hence there is differentiation between the *anterior* and the *posterior* parts of the body. Associated with environmental differences above and below the moving animal two surfaces may be distinguished, the *dorsal* or upper and the *ventral* or lower. (Man and a few other animals have assumed a position at right angles to the ancestral position; therefore dorsal and ventral surfaces have become respectively rear and front surfaces, and anterior and posterior ends are upper and

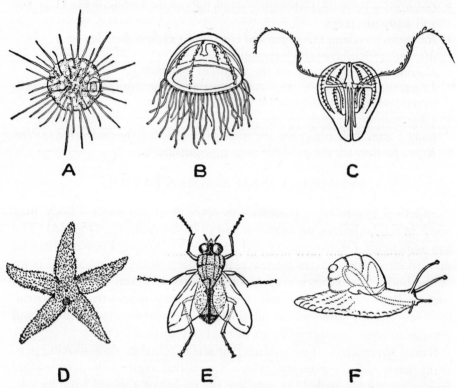

A   B   C

D   E   F

Fig. 66. Various types of symmetry. *A*, Spherical, in sun animalcule (*Actinophrys*), a protozoan; *B*, radial, in medusa stage of a hydroid, one of the coelenterates; *C*, biradial (partly radial and partly bilateral), in sea walnut, a ctenophore; *D*, secondary radial (derived from bilateral), in starfish, an echinoderm; *E*, bilateral, in housefly, an insect; *F*, distorted bilateral (or asymmetry), in snail, a mollusk.

lower.) Since a median longitudinal section through one plane only, the *plane of symmetry*, divides such an animal into equivalent *right* and *left* halves, one of which is the mirror image of the other, the animal is said to have *bilateral* (two-sided) *symmetry*. This type of symmetry is found in most animals above the coelenterates.

Many of the protozoans and sponges cannot be divided into equal halves by any plane. Such forms are said to be *asymmetrical*. In many animals symmetry is incomplete. It is well known that certain of the internal organs of a vertebrate, such as man, do not carry out the bilateral plan of symmetry. The bilateral symmetry of snails and their relatives is usually distorted by the spiral twist of the shell.

Segmentation. In certain phyla of animals the body is made up of a series of *segments*, or *metameres*, arranged in linear order. Body structures are to a certain extent repeated in these segments. The annelids (Fig. 86) and arthropods (Figs. 120, 150) have segments that are externally visible; in the chordates, including man, certain internal structures, such as vertebrae, ribs, spinal nerves, are segmentally repeated, although segments are not ordinarily visible on the outside.

EXERCISES

1. In what sense is the aggregation of cells in *Volvox* a colony? In what a multicellular individual?
2. Name the symmetry of the jellyfish, the cuttlefish, the starfish, the crayfish, and the catfish. Which of these is considered a true fish?

REFERENCES

Hegner, R. W., and Stiles, K. A., *College Zoology*, The Macmillan Company, 6th ed., 1951.
See also other zoology texts listed in the Appendix.

Chapter IX

SPONGES AND COELENTERATES

SPONGES (PHYLUM PORIFERA)

The Phylum PORIFERA (Lat. "pore-bearers") includes the *sponges* These are attached animals which have cell differentiation sufficient to place them well above the colony level of organization but which lack a nervous system and therefore cannot coordinate their activities to the extent characteristic of the typical metazoan. Most sponges are marine, but a few, which are generally green from the presence of microscopic green algae, are found in fresh water.

Structure. The simplest sponges (known as the ascon type) are hollow and vase-shaped (Fig. 67 A), and are provided at the apex with a large opening, the *osculum*. The individual consists of two continuous layers of cells, between which is a gelatinous substance containing scattered *ameboid cells, skeleton-building cells,* and the structural elements of the skeleton. The outer cell layer is protective and is made up of *epidermal cells,* which are said to be ameboid cells assembled into a single layer; the inner layer is nutritive and consists of *collar cells,* each provided with a flagellum surrounded at its base by a collar (Fig. 67 C). *Pores* extend at intervals from the outside through to the central cavity; these give the phylum its name. More complex sponges (the sycon type) have one set of canals extending from the surface almost to the cavity, and another set from the cavity almost to the surface (Fig. 67 B). Pores connect these two sets of canals. The largest and most complex sponges are provided with an intricate labyrinth of passageways lined with the characteristic cell layers which are perforated by pores. The skeleton of the simpler sponges consists of variously shaped *spicules* of silica or calcium carbonate; that of the higher sponges consists mainly of a tough, fibrous substance known as *spongin* (Fig. 68).

Activities. The constant lashing of the flagella causes water to enter the central cavity by way of the pores and to leave by way of the osculum. This water brings in oxygen and small organisms and bits of organic matter that serve as food, and carries away wastes. The lashing also drives the food particles toward the bodies of the collar cells, where they are ingested by the protoplasm just outside the collars. Part or all of the food,

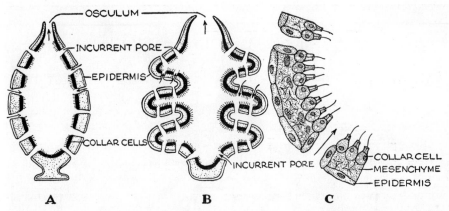

Fig. 67. *A*, Diagram showing structure of a simple sponge (ascon type); *B*, slightly more complex sponge (sycon type), with body wall folded into canals; *C*, detail of *A* as seen in highly magnified cross section.

depending on the species considered, is then transferred to the ameboid cells of the gelatinous layer. Digestion is thus *intracellular*, as it is among the Protozoa. When digested, part of the food is transferred from the ameboid cells to the epidermal layer. Many sponges have muscle cells surrounding the osculum and the pores. These cells respond slowly to changes in the environment, changing the size of the openings and therefore helping to regulate the water current through the sponge. Aside from this response there is little or no coordination of activities in a sponge. No nervous system is present to facilitate such coordination.

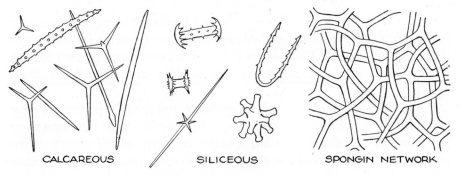

Fig. 68. Types of sponge skeletons.

General Remarks. The simple sponges may be *radially symmetrical;* in the more complex ones the individuals are commonly grouped together in irregular masses that show little symmetry. Though the simple sponges have sac-like bodies consisting of two layers of cells, they are not re-

Fig. 69. Spongin skeletons of several species of colonial sponges, the bath type. (Courtesy of Armaly Sponge and Chamois Company.)

garded as truly diploblastic because the cell layers are formed in a manner quite different from that described as *gastrulation* (gastrula formation) in the preceding chapter. Sponges are believed to constitute an early offshoot of the evolutionary tree, and one that has undergone little evolution since its origin.

Reproduction is both *asexual,* by *budding,* and *sexual.* Sperms and eggs may be produced in the same or in separate individuals. In line with their low level of cell differentiation, sponges have remarkable *regenerative* powers. The cells of some species, when pressed through bolting cloth with a mesh fine enough to separate them almost completely, gradually

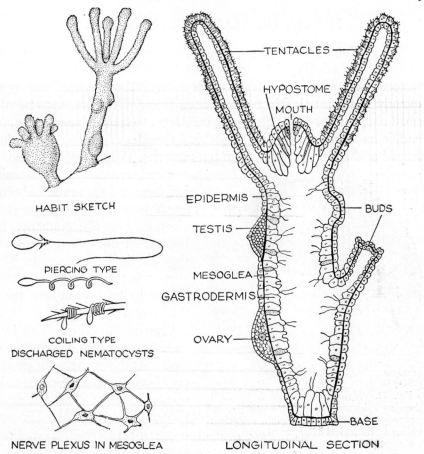

HABIT SKETCH

PIERCING TYPE

COILING TYPE
DISCHARGED NEMATOCYSTS

NERVE PLEXUS IN MESOGLEA

TENTACLES

HYPOSTOME

MOUTH

EPIDERMIS

TESTIS

MESOGLEA

GASTRODERMIS

OVARY

BUDS

BASE

LONGITUDINAL SECTION

Fig. 70. Hydra. The habit sketch shows a contracted and a partially extended individual (× 20). The coiling nematocysts grasp a hair or other projection of the prey. The nerve plexus consists of cells, the processes of which touch other cells or their processes, forming a network over which impulses can move in any direction. The hollow center (right figure) is the gastrovascular cavity.

come together again into little clumps which eventually grow into new sponges.

Commercial sponges are those with spongin skeletons that are adaptable to household and technical uses (Fig. 69). More than a thousand tons are harvested annually. They are cut loose by long hooks lowered from boats or by knives wielded by divers, and are piled so that the cellular portions will decay; then the skeletons are washed, dried, and marketed. Sponges are cultivated along the shores of Italy and Florida by planting pieces an inch square on clean, rocky bottoms. In five or six years they will be large enough for the market.

HYDRA (PHYLUM COELENTERATA)

The Phylum COELENTERATA consists of relatively simple, slow-moving or stationary animals with radial symmetry. The hydra (Gr. "a kind of water serpent," Fig. 70), a fresh-water polyp, is the coelenterate most frequently studied. It is fairly common on water plants but, because of its small size, is not readily observed. It adheres to a plant or other support and, in its expanded state, is a cylindrical thread a centimeter or two long, frayed at the free end into six to ten tentacles. When it is disturbed, the

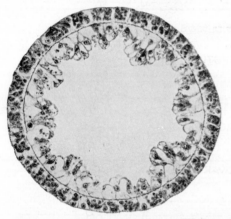

trunk contracts to an almost spherical form and the tentacles become much shortened. One common species is light brown; another is green because of one-celled green algae that live in its inner cells. These algae use carbon dioxide evolved by the hydra, and in turn furnish the latter with oxygen.

General Structure. The hydra consists essentially of a hollow cylindrical body made up of two layers of cells, each differentiated into several kinds of cells, i.e., several *tissues* (Figs. 71, 72). The outer layer, the *epidermis* (Gr. "outer skin"), is derived from the ecto-

FIG. 71. *Hydra*, cross section (× 150), showing epidermis, very thin mesoglea, and gastrodermis. (Photomicrograph, copyright, General Biological Supply House, Inc., Chicago.)

derm layer of the gastrula stage of the embryo; the thicker inner layer, the *gastrodermis* (Gr. "stomach skin"), from the endoderm. Both of these cellular layers rest on a thin, gelatinous, noncellular supporting layer, the *mesoglea* (Gr. "middle glue"). In some species the body is narrowed below into a stalk-like part. At the base of the body is the *basal disk*, which holds the organism to its temporary location by means of a sticky substance secreted by its cells. From time to time the animal moves by releasing the disk and attaching it in a new place. At the apex, within the circle of tentacles, is a cone-shaped elevation, the *hypostome* (Gr. "beneath the mouth"), at the tip of which is the mouth. The mouth opens into the *gastrovascular* (from "stomach" and "vessel") *cavity*, which is lined by the gastrodermis and has branches extending into the tentacles. The hydra reaches the gastrula stage of development (Fig. 58), then undergoes cell differentiation without acquiring a third layer, as do most of the multicellular animals. It is therefore called *diploblastic* (Gr. "double bud"). The differentiation and close interdependence of its cells put it definitely in the METAZOA.

Epithelium and Muscle. Since both epidermis and gastrodermis are continuous layers, the former covering the body and the latter lining the cavity, they are classified as *epithelium*. But they have an additional function, for extended from their bases, next to the mesoglea, are contractile (muscle) fibers. Hence the cells are called *epithelio-muscular*. The fibers of the epidermal cells run longitudinally; therefore their contraction tends

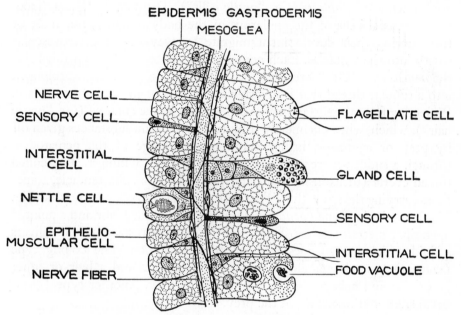

EPIDERMIS GASTRODERMIS

MESOGLEA

NERVE CELL

SENSORY CELL

INTERSTITIAL CELL

NETTLE CELL

EPITHELIO- MUSCULAR CELL

NERVE FIBER

FLAGELLATE CELL

GLAND CELL

SENSORY CELL

INTERSTITIAL CELL

FOOD VACUOLE

FIG. 72. Cell differentiation in *Hydra*, shown diagrammatically. The interstitial cells are young, undifferentiated cells capable of developing into various types.

to shorten the body or, if the contraction is localized, to bend it to one side. The gastrodermal cell fibers extend circularly and, on contracting, tend to lengthen the body.

Nervous System. It will be recalled that sponges lack a nervous system. A simple one, however, is found in the hydra (Figs. 70, 72). Instead of a controlling group of nerve cells (a brain) found in animals higher in the scale, there is a *nerve net* that spreads between the lower portions of the epidermal cells; it consists of scattered nerve cells, each with several radiating fibers which touch similar fibers from surrounding nerve cells. There is no fixed direction for the travel of impulses, as in nervous systems of the higher animal phyla; they may go from cell to cell in any direction. On both the epidermal and the gastrodermal surfaces are the free ends of sensory cells whose opposite ends join the nerve net. The impulses aroused by the stimuli of touch and taste upon this free end are carried along the nerve net to muscle fibers or gland cells; the former respond by contracting and the latter by secreting.

Offense and Defense. Distributed over most of the epidermis, particularly in elevated groups ("batteries") on the tentacles, are specialized cells that help in the capture of prey and the warding off of enemies. They are known as *cnidoblasts* (Gr. "nettle cells"). These cells originate from the interstitial cells of the epidermis of the body cylinder, but most of them during their development migrate by way of the gastrovascular cavity into the tentacles. Each contains at its outer end a fluid-filled sac, the *nematocyst* (Gr. "thread sac"), the membrane of which is prolonged into a tubular thread that is inverted and coiled in the cavity of the sac. Projecting from the surface of the cell is a bristle, the *cnidocil* (Gr. "nettle hair"), which, when chemically stimulated by certain substances given off by prey or aggressor, brings about the discharge of the nematocyst through a sudden increase of the osmotic pressure within it. The coiled thread everts (turns inside out) and protrudes from the tentacle, sometimes carrying the sac with it. There are several types of nematocysts (Fig. 70). The stinging type (*penetrant*), which has a barbed base and a pointed open tip, penetrates the exoskeleton of the smaller crustaceans and delivers a fluid which has an anesthetic or numbing action. The coiling type (*volvent*) has a larger closed tube which coils around a hair or other projection and helps to hold the prey in captivity. Another type (*glutinant*) sticks to the surface of the prey.

Nutrition and Circulation. Digestion in PROTOZOA and sponges is *intracellular* (within the cell); in the hydra it is partly intracellular and partly *extracellular* (outside the cell); in man, digestion of food that has been ingested is exclusively extracellular. A small crustacean or other aquatic animal that ventures within reach of the hydra is struck with a tentacle and stunned into insensibility by the nematocysts. It is then slowly drawn by this and the neighboring tentacles toward the hypostome. The latter secretes a slippery substance which enables the mouth to slip readily over the prey, enclosing it in the gastrovascular cavity. Certain of the gastrodermal cells are unicellular glands which secrete enzymes and discharge them into the cavity, where they act upon the food. The digested foods are absorbed into other cells of this layer. These often have flagella which, together with the body movements, produce a circulation in the cavity that is effective in distributing oxygen and digested food. Intracellular digestion occurs after small particles are engulfed by these cells much as food is engulfed by *Amoeba*. Since there is no anus, indigestible remnants of the food are egested through the mouth. There are no special organs for respiration and excretion. Oxygen comes from solution in the water into both cell layers, and carbon dioxide and other wastes are discarded into the water.

Reproduction   (Fig. 70). *Asexual reproduction* is a budding process, part of the body wall protruding as if pushed from within. The protrusion enlarges, develops a mouth and tentacles at the distal end, and finally

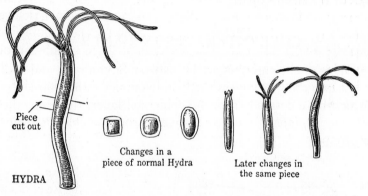

Piece cut out

Changes in a piece of normal Hydra

Later changes in the same piece

HYDRA

Fig. 73.   Regeneration in *Hydra*. A piece cut from the body undergoes the changes indicated, finally becoming a complete individual. (From Woodruff, *Animal Biology*; copyright, Macmillan; after Morgan.)

separates as a new individual. *Sexual reproduction* is brought about by sex organs developed from *interstitial cells*, undifferentiated or formative cells that lie between the bases of the ectodermal cells. These organs, the *spermaries* or *testes*, containing many sperms, and the *ovaries*, containing a single large egg in each, are borne by the same individual in some species of hydras, and by different individuals in other species. The sperms escape by the rupture of the epidermis and, if one of them chances to reach an egg, fertilization of the egg occurs. The fertilized egg undergoes several cell divisions, becoming first a sphere of cells; then, by the wandering inward of some of the cells, a solid two-layered gastrula is formed. By this time it has developed a thick covering. It now drops to the bottom of the pond and remains dormant for some months but eventually hatches into a young hydra. The ectoderm and endoderm layers of the gastrula are known as the *germ layers*, because from them all the cells of the body originate.

Regeneration. *Regeneration* means the development of a fragment into a complete animal. We have seen that sponges have this power to a high degree. A very small piece of *Hydra*, if it includes portions of both cell layers, will grow into a complete animal (Fig. 73). For the lower types of life, which are subject to great hazards, regeneration is an invaluable trait. As a rule, the higher up the scale we go the less the power of regeneration. The human body restores its injured tissues to some extent, but it cannot replace a missing member such as an arm or a finger. Apparently in man the tissues are so far removed from the undifferentiated or generalized condition that they cannot go back to it for the organization of those of the missing part.

COELENTERATES IN GENERAL

The classes of coelenterates are HYDROZOA, SCYPHOZOA, and ANTHOZOA. In the last two the mesoglea is thick and contains rather loosely arranged cells which have entered from the epidermal layer; therefore they foreshadow the *triploblastic* or three-layer structure characteristic of the higher groups.

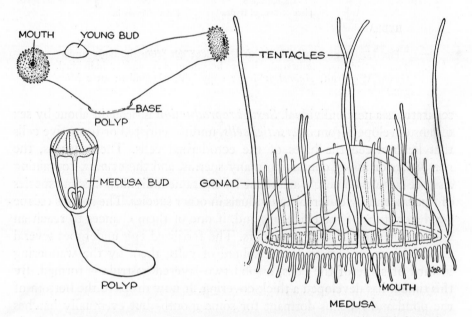

FIG. 74. A fresh-water hydroid coelenterate (*Craspedacusta sowerbii*). This form alternates between an attached, asexual hydroid polyp stage and a free-swimming, sexual medusa stage. The polyp dwindles in size as the medusa develops. (Polyps × 35, medusa × 5. Upper polyp based on photo by A. E. Woodhead; lower, on drawing by F. Payne.)

Hydrozoa (Polyps and Medusas). HYDROZOA (Gr. "hydra-like animals") includes a large number of species related to hydras. Some, like hydras, are sessile and are called *polyps* (Gr. "many feet," referring to the tentacles). Others are small free-swimming jellyfishes called *medusas* (referring to the resemblance of the tentacles to the snake-like tresses of the mythological Gorgon, Medusa). Still others, including *Obelia* and several other marine types, alternate in their life history between the polyp and

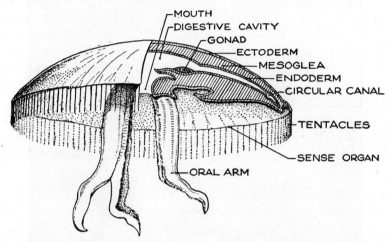

FIG. 75. A marine jellyfish (*Aurelia aurita*), with one-fourth of the body cut away on the right. Note the radial symmetry, the laterally extended digestive cavity, and the greatly thickened mesoglea. (Redrawn from Parker and Haswell.)

the medusa stages. In most of these, an attached branching structure bears many polyps with a common gastrovascular cavity, each polyp being equivalent to a hydra bud that has failed to detach itself from the parent stem. A special polyp bears a number of medusa buds, which, on developing, become detached, swim away, and reproduce sexually. The fertilized egg passes through the embryonic stages and becomes an attached polyp. Such an alternation of asexual and sexual generations is termed *metagenesis*. *Craspedacusta* (Fig. 74) is a fresh-water form with a medusa about a centimeter in diameter and a rather insignificant polyp. It occurs in many of our fresh-water streams and lakes. The Portuguese man-of-war (*Physalia*) is a conspicuous colonial hydrozoan that floats on the open sea. One polyp is enlarged into an iridescent swimming bladder which bears the nutritive, defensive, and reproductive polyps as streamers. Its defensive polyp administers a sting that is quite painful to man. The occurrence of widely different individuals in a single species (whether attached in a colony or not) is known as *polymorphism* (Gr. "many forms").

Scyphozoa (Jellyfishes). Scyphozoa (Gr. "cup animals") includes the larger jellyfishes (Fig. 75). They are almost transparent, usually have a disk-like or dome-like form, and may attain a diameter of seven feet. The stings of large specimens are capable of inflicting painful injury on one

Fig. 76. Sea anemones, several species. (From Jordan, Kellogg and Heath, *Animal Forms;* copyright, D. Appleton-Century.)

who touches the organism. In this group, as in some of the Hydrozoa, there is an alternation of attached and free-swimming stages, but in Scyphozoa the latter is the more prominent stage. Between cell layers is a thick, jelly-like mesoglea. The body of a large jellyfish may be about 96 percent water.

Anthozoa (Sea Anemones and Corals). Anthozoa (Gr. "flower animals") resemble hydras but are usually very thick and have radial partitions or *mesenteries* (Gr. "mid-intestine") which increase the amount of the gastrodermis and hence the secreting and absorbing surface of the gastrovascular cavity. A sea anemone (Fig. 76) usually has the form of a simple cylinder and adheres by the basal disk, by means of which it also glides from place to place; it is provided with many tentacles around the mouth. Its form and bright coloration give it a striking, flower-like appearance. Corals are ANTHOZOA usually grouped in colonies of several or many individuals attached to a common base of calcium carbonate which they have secreted. (The term "coral" has also been applied to certain of the HYDROZOA, red algae, and other marine organisms that accumulate calcium carbonate.) Each individual is known as a polyp and rests on a cup of the mineral secretion which is divided into chambers by radial par-

FIG. 77. Great Barrier Reef, a coral formation off the northeast coast of Australia. Several kinds of coral are included in the detail here shown. (Photo from American Museum of Natural History, New York.)

titions. Coral is an important agent in the formation of land, for it grows in shallow water and accumulates large amounts of calcium carbonate that is torn loose by the waves and heaped up above the water level. Much of Florida, many of the South Sea islands, and also reefs or land ridges running parallel to Australian and other tropical shores are of coral origin (Fig. 77). To the ANTHOZOA belong the *sea fans*, which have a horny skeleton, and the *precious* or *red coral* which occurs in the Mediterranean region and is widely used in the manufacture of jewelry.

CTENOPHORA

The CTENOPHORA (Gr. "comb bearers"), popularly known as *comb jellies* or *sea walnuts*, is a group of nearly transparent, free-swimming marine animals formerly regarded as coelenterates but now placed in a phylum of their own (Fig. 66). They differ from jellyfishes in lacking nematocysts, but they have eight bands of *ciliary combs* extending as meridians from pole to pole of the spherical or elongated body. Their symmetry is said to be *biradial* because the comb bands and certain other structures are radially arranged whereas the two opposite tentacles of many forms suggest bilateral symmetry. As in the jellyfish and sea anemone, the gelatinous mesoglea contains scattered cells and approaches a mesoderm.

EXERCISES

1. Compare the mechanisms by which response to a stimulus is made in *Hydra* and in *Amoeba*.
2. How far back in geological history did coelenterates exist?
3. In what respects are the coelenterates more highly organized than the sponges?
4. Define fringing reef, barrier reef, coral atoll. How might these be explained?

REFERENCES

Brown, F. A., Jr. (ed.), *Selected Invertebrate Types,* John Wiley & Sons, Inc., 1950.
Hyman, L. H., *The Invertebrates: Vol. I, Protozoa Through Ctenophora,* McGraw-Hill Book Company, 1940.
See also general zoology texts and (for coral formations) books on geology.

Chapter X

THE SIMPLER WORM PHYLA

The simplest multicellular animals with bilateral symmetry include a miscellaneous assemblage of elongated creeping or swimming forms which were once grouped together as "worms" but are now separated into a number of phyla, some of which are small and unimportant. Of these organisms we shall consider mainly the flatworm and roundworm phyla, but give brief reference to some of the others.

FLATWORMS (PLATYHELMINTHES)

Planaria, General Characteristics. Among the most primitive of the worm groups is the Phylum PLATYHELMINTHES (Gr. "flatworms"). A typical representative is the planarian (Fig. 78), a flattened, ovoid, or linear, often dark-colored worm which may attain half an inch in length. It may be found under logs or stones along lake borders or in shallow streams. At the anterior end are the sense organs—a pair of *eyes* and a pair of *tactile lobes*. It ordinarily glides along by means of cilia borne by the epidermal cells, but it uses its muscles also, not only for changing form and withdrawing from offending stimuli, but for moving forward rapidly. The muscles are not part of the epithelium, as in the hydra, but cells specialized solely for movement. The greater part of the body thickness is derived from a third germ layer, the *mesoderm* (Gr. "middle skin"). Because of the presence of this layer the flatworms and all groups above them are called *triploblastic* (Gr. "triple bud") animals. The tissue is solid from the outer surface to the digestive cavity, there being no *coelom* or body cavity such as is found in more advanced groups.

Digestive System. As in the hydra, the digestive cavity has but one opening, the mouth; it is not at the anterior end, as might be expected, but at the end of a flexible proboscis, the pharynx, which can be protruded through an opening near the center of the ventral body surface. The pharynx leads to the *gastrovascular cavity*, so called because it serves the twofold function of digestion and circulation. The latter function is facilitated by the division of this cavity into three large lobes with many branches that reach nearly all parts of the body. The food consists of small living organisms and tissues of dead animals. Most of the smaller ingested particles are taken immediately into the endoderm cells that line the cavity and are digested intracellularly in food vacuoles. Some extracellular digestion, however, takes place within the cavity. Enough food is stored after one meal to keep the animal alive for months.

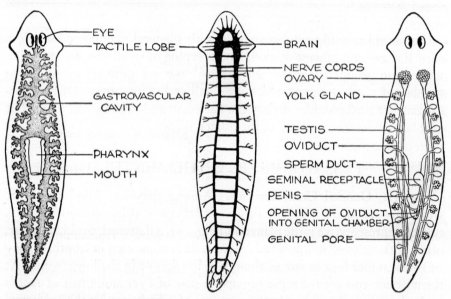

FIG. 78. The flatworm *Planaria*. Left, a specimen that has been injected with a dye to reveal the outline of the gastrovascular cavity; center, detail of nervous system; right, detail of reproductive system, showing that organs of both sexes are in one individual.

Excretory System. An advance over the hydra in specialization is the presence of special excretory organs. They consist of a network of fine tubes running lengthwise of the body on either side and opening to the exterior by several small pores on the dorsal surface. Branches of these tubes end in the mesoderm in small enlargements known as *flame cells* (Fig. 79). The central cavity of a flame cell contains a tuft of cilia, the beat of which resembles the flickering of a flame and supplies the power that drives the excreted fluid along the tube system to the external pores.

Cephalization. Another advance over the hydra is that, instead of a net-like system, the planarian has a centralized nervous system. Since the head end must be most responsive to the environment, it is fitting that the head-quarters of the nervous system should be located here in the form of a fairly large two-lobed *ganglion* (Gr. "swelling"), a group of nerve cell bodies. From this ganglion, or *brain*, two *nerve cords* extend posteriorly. These in turn send branches to all parts of the body. Each eye consists of several light-sensitive nerve cells partially enclosed in a cup of pigment which shuts out all light except that entering the open part of the cup. The eye does not form an image but registers light direction and intensity; it thereby enables the worm to get away from strong light, hence into places of relative safety. The tactile lobes are organs of touch, and perhaps react also to food and other chemical stimuli. If a piece of raw meat is placed in a vessel containing flatworms, they detect it by a chemical sense (taste) and move toward it. Concentration of nervous structures and functions at the head end is known as *cephalization* (Gr. "making of the head").

Metabolic Gradient. When the worm has grown sufficiently in length, it often divides transversely into two individuals. Experimentation has shown that a young worm has a *metabolic gradient* from front to rear; i.e., the most rapid metabolism, as determined by the most rapid intake of oxygen and the most rapid outgo of carbon dioxide, is at the head end, the rate gradu-

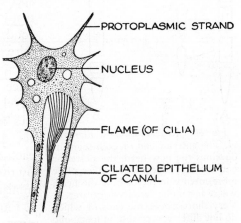

PROTOPLASMIC STRAND

NUCLEUS

FLAME (OF CILIA)

CILIATED EPITHELIUM OF CANAL

Fig. 79. Flame cell of a planarian. The wastes of metabolism are excreted into the canal, along which they are driven by the vibration of the flame-like tuft of cilia. The individual canals from many such cells unite into large anastomosing canals which carry the wastes to excretory pores opening on the body surface. (Redrawn from Aron et Grassé, *Biologie Animale*.)

ally diminishing toward the posterior end. Such a gradient is rather general among both animals and plants. The dominance of the head end over the rest of the body is correlated with a greater rate of metabolism at this end. As the individual increases in length and bulk, a point develops well toward the posterior end, where the dominance of the head disappears. Fission may take place at this point, a new region of dominance being established at the front end of the rear segment, which now becomes a separate worm. Like the hydra, the flatworm has remarkable powers of regeneration, for a relatively small piece will develop the missing portions and become a complete worm. The gradient of such a piece determines where the new head and tail will appear. If there is no marked gradient, a head or a tail may appear at both ends (Fig. 80).

Reproduction. In addition to asexual reproduction by fission, the planarian reproduces sexually. Both testes and ovaries are in the same individual. Such an organism is called *monoecious* (Gr. "one house"), as distinguished from the *dioecious* (Gr. "two house") type, in which separate individuals (males and females) produce sperms and eggs respectively. The sperms do not fertilize the eggs of the same worm, however; it is necessary for two worms to copulate and exchange sperms. Cross-fertilization is thereby assured, and variation of the species made more certain. The eggs of many animals contain yolk, or stored food, within the cytoplasm; but in the flatworms, along the course of the oviduct, there are *yolk glands* which produce yolk cells containing food for the developing embryos. The oviduct carries both fertilized eggs and yolk cells to the genital chamber, where several of each are enclosed in a capsule secreted by the chamber walls. From this capsule miniature worms emerge.

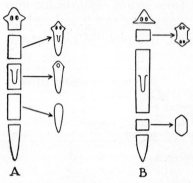

Fig. 80. Regeneration in *Planaria*. *A*, The anterior end of each segment develops the new head, the posterior end the tail; regeneration takes place more rapidly in pieces near the head, where metabolic activity is greater. *B*, Very short pieces, the ends of which do not differ appreciably in metabolic activity, may form heads at both ends. (Redrawn from Buchsbaum, *Animals Without Backbones;* after Child.)

Flukes. The flukes are parasitic flatworms, the liver fluke of sheep (*Fasciola hepatica*) being one of the better known. The life history of this organism involves two hosts—a sheep or related mammal which serves as the final host for the adult fluke, and a snail which serves as intermediate host for the larval stage (Fig. 81). The adult, a flat leaf-like worm an inch long and half an inch wide, lives in the bile ducts or in the substance of the liver. Like the planarian, it is monoecious; its eggs pass by way of the bile duct and the intestinal tract of the host to the exterior with the feces; if they chance to fall in water or a damp place they undergo development and each hatches into a ciliated larva known as a *miracidium*. If this larva does not encounter a snail of the proper genus within eight hours after hatching, it dies; if it does meet such a snail it drills its way into the soft part of the body of the latter by the application of its pointed end and the vibration of its cilia. In the snail it becomes a *sporocyst* and produces egg-like cells which develop without fertilization into another type of larva called a *redia* (named for the Italian biologist Redi, page 349). Since this is reproduction by a sexually immature form, it is an example of *paedogenesis*

(Gr. "birth by child"). The redia, in the same way, produces one or more additional generations of rediae. Eventually, also without fertilization, one of these generations produces a third type of larva known as a *cercaria* (Gr. "tail"). This larva leaves the snail and swims about until it comes in contact with a grass blade or similar object, to which it adheres just beneath the surface of the water; it loses its tail, encysts, and as a *metacercaria* remains inactive until the grass on which it rests chances to be eaten by a sheep. The acid of the sheep's stomach dissolves the cyst,

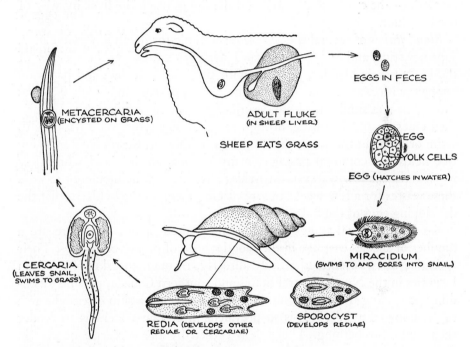

Fig. 81. Diagram of life history of the liver fluke of sheep. The adult fluke is nearly an inch long; the larval stages are all microscopic.

thus liberating the young fluke, which burrows through the intestinal wall into the body cavity, enters the liver, and reaches the bile duct. "Liver rot," the disease caused by the parasite, is often fatal to the host; it causes a vast amount of damage to the livestock industry, particularly in England and South America. It may be prevented by removing stock from pastures in which there are swamps or water courses that harbor snails, or by treating the water to kill the snails.

Flukes as Human Parasites.   Millions of people, mainly in Africa and the Orient, are victims of parasitic flukes, various sorts of which affect the liver, the lungs, the intestines, and the blood. *Clonorchis*, a liver fluke, has two intermediate hosts—a snail and a fish. When egg-containing human feces come in contact with water, the eggs are swallowed by snails, in whose digestive tracts they hatch into miracidia. These larvae bore their way into the tissues of the snail, where they become sporocysts that produce rediae, which in turn produce cercariae. The latter escape from the snail, burrow through the skin of a fish, lose their tails, and encyst. When an infected fish is eaten raw—a widespread custom in oriental countries—the cysts are digested and the flukes reach the liver by way of the bile duct.

Blood flukes of several species are responsible for much illness in China, Japan, Africa, and South America. Their eggs are laid in the vicinity of the intestines or bladder, pass out with the feces or urine, and hatch on contact with water. The young fluke enters a snail, in which it passes through stages similar to those described for the liver fluke. The cercaria then emerges and burrows through the skin of anyone who happens to swim or wade in the water. Since the use of human wastes for fertilizing rice fields is a common practice, many farmers are infected while they work in the shallow water of the fields. They are now being taught to store these wastes for a few weeks before placing them on the fields, so that the developing eggs of the fluke will die.

No human blood flukes occur in the United States, but there are a number of species that live in the blood stream of other vertebrates. Their cercariae likewise enter the body directly, through the skin. In certain localities in the North Central States and southern Canada, persons swimming or wading during the summer season develop a skin disease known as "swimmer's itch." This is so prevalent in certain waters as to render them unfit for bathing. The itch is caused by the cercariae of certain flukes, which have emerged from snails, boring into the skin of the bathers. The snails are presumably infected by larvae hatched from eggs dropped by ducks during the fall migration. Since man is the wrong host, these cercariae merely penetrate the skin and die, but in the process they set up a local irritation that is sometimes severe, particularly to susceptible individuals.

In many parts of the world a serious disease is caused by a human *lung fluke*. The adult burrows into the lung, from which it liberates eggs; the latter escape from the body with the sputum or in the feces. The miracidium attacks a snail as usual; on escaping from the snail, the cercaria burrows into a crayfish or fresh-water crab. When the crustacean is eaten uncooked, man becomes a victim.

Significance of Parasitism. Parasitism is often thought of as an unusual mode of life, but it is of surprisingly widespread occurrence. There may be as great a number of parasitic individuals in the animal kingdom as of free-living ones, for it is usual for one of the higher animals to harbor several or many parasites. There is evidence that the first step toward parasitism is the loose association known as *commensalism* (Lat. "being with at the table"). An example of this relationship is the attachment of a certain flatworm to the book gills of the king crab, where it receives shelter, free transportation, and the benefit of fragments of the food on which the king crab feeds. An organism that begins to take advantage of another in this fashion might ultimately come to feed upon the latter's tissues and become a parasite. A few species of flukes have only a molluscan host. The fact that in those that have two or more hosts the larva begins life in a mollusk suggests that mollusks were probably the hosts of the ancestors of the flukes, and that the adult stages, with their various final hosts, represent a later development. Through evolution, means have developed for the transfer of the parasite from host to host. Perhaps the simplest means is the eating of the snail by the final host, the mode still used by many of the fluke parasites of snail-eating animals. In other flukes, however, as we have seen, the cercaria leaves the snail and encysts on vegetation if the host is herbivorous, and in fishes, crabs, insect larvae, or tadpoles if it is carnivorous; or the cercaria may, as in the blood flukes, seek out its final host for direct attack.

Flukes, like most parasites, are notoriously prolific. The many hazards attending their successful transfer from one host to the next are offset by a complicated reproductive system which produces an enormous number of eggs and by repeated multiplication in the various larval stages.

Parasites are ordinarily less free to move about and less amply provided with sense organs, nervous mechanisms, and locomotor structures than are the corresponding free-living animals, and they often show simplification in other respects.

Tapeworms. Although the flukes, which live in various parts of the body, have digestive systems comparable to those of the planarians, the tapeworms, which live in the intestinal tract where there is free access to the digested food of the host, are entirely without such systems and are structurally little more than highly elaborate systems of reproductive organs. Many species of tapeworm inhabit the alimentary tracts of different kinds of vertebrates. A tapeworm usually consists of a long ribbon-like series of similar flat parts known as *proglottids* attached at one end to the intestinal wall by a rounded *scolex*, which is provided with suckers and often with hooks. Each proglottid may be regarded as an individual produced asexually by a budding process which takes place in the region just back of the scolex; hence the whole worm may be regarded as a colony of individuals. The mature proglottid, some distance back from the scolex, contains many testes and an ovary and is capable of producing thousands of eggs. These are retained in the uterus, in which they begin their development and which expands with the growing embryos until it nearly fills the proglottid. The ripe proglottid now breaks loose, is discharged with the feces, and disintegrates. In the beef tapeworm (*Taenia saginata*, Fig. 82) a cow becomes infected when its food is contaminated with these embryo-containing eggs. Six-hooked spherical larvae, which hatch in the intestine, bore through the intestinal wall, are carried by the blood or lymph to voluntary muscles, and encyst. Within the cyst develops another larval stage, the *bladder worm*, an inpushing of the wall of which represents the beginning of a scolex. When beef containing bladder worms is eaten raw, or not thoroughly cooked, the scolex becomes everted and attached to the wall of the human intestine. The bladder is then thrown off, proglottids begin to form, and growth may continue until the worm attains a length of up to forty feet.

Another common tapeworm parasite of man usually spends its encysted period in the muscles of the pig and is contracted through eating undercooked pork. This parasite is particularly dangerous to man because accidentally ingested eggs are capable of developing in the human body, resulting in cysts which, if lodged in some vital part—heart, spinal cord, brain, etc.—may cause serious and even fatal consequences. Still another tapeworm has two intermediate hosts, a small fresh-water crustacean and a fresh-water fish. The fish becomes infected by eating the crustacean, and man is infected by eating the fish raw or insufficiently cooked. This parasite has been introduced by European immigrants into a number of localities in the region of the Great Lakes. Thorough cooking of any meat likely to contain tapeworm cysts is the most effectual means of preventing infection.

ROUNDWORMS (NEMATHELMINTHES)

The Phylum NEMATHELMINTHES (Gr. "threadworms") consists for the most part of elongated, more or less cylindrical organisms. They differ widely in structural complexity, but are alike in the fact that the *alimentary canal* is a straight tube through the body, from *mouth* to *anus*, separated from the *body wall* by a space, the *body cavity*. Since this cavity is not entirely lined by cells derived from the mesoderm, it is not regarded as a true *coelom*. Circulation is effected by the movement of fluids in this cavity, aided by writhing movements of the worm.

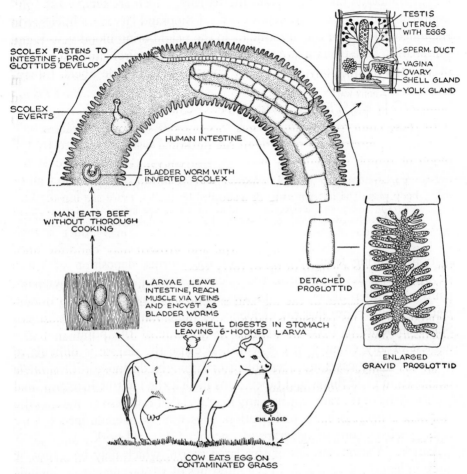

FIG. 82. Life history of the beef tapeworm (*Taenia saginata*). (Adapted from various sources.)

Roundworms are numerous in both species and individuals and are widely distributed. Free-living species are abundant in the soil and in both fresh and salt water. The vinegar eel, which lives in vinegar, is a familiar form (Fig. 83). Parasitic species infect both animals and plants and are responsible for a number of serious diseases in both kingdoms.

Trichinella. *Trichinella* is a parasitic roundworm which causes the disease trichinosis in man and some other mammals; its human victims become infected by eating insufficiently cooked lean pork containing encysted larval worms (Fig. 84). In the intestine, about forty hours after ingestion, the larvae mature into male and female worms about 1 mm. long. Copulation takes place, and the females, which are *viviparous* (giving birth to living young), deposit several thousand larvae each, either in the mucous lining of the intestine or in the neighboring blood vessels and lymphatics. These larvae are transported along the circulatory system to other parts of the body where they encyst in the muscle fibers. Inflam-

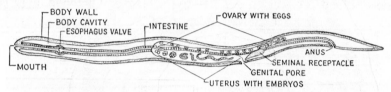

FIG. 83. Vinegar eel (*Turbatrix aceti*, female, × 50), showing general body plan. The intestine is partly concealed by the left ovary and uterus. Stages in embryonic development within the uterus are indicated diagrammatically. (Based on Wodsedalek, General Zoology Laboratory Guide, John S. Swift Co.)

mation resulting from movements of the worms, deposition of waste products, and development of the calcareous cyst give rise to rheumatic pains and other discomfort. Heavy infections may terminate fatally. Recent studies show that the incidence of human infection in the United States amounts to between 16 and 18 percent of the population, the highest of any country in the world. Because the disease is difficult to diagnose, many cases are overlooked or wrongly diagnosed. *Trichinella* differs from most flukes and tapeworms in that the intermediate and final hosts may be of the same species; any mammal that eats flesh containing the encysted worms is liable to infection. Pigs usually become infected by eating garbage containing scraps of uncooked diseased pork.

Ascaris. Various species of this large worm, which may be a foot or more in length, are parasitic in the intestines of various mammals, including man. The eggs leave the host with the feces and in about two weeks develop embryos capable of infection if they are accidentally swallowed in contaminated water or food, such as green vegetables that have been fertilized with sewage and are eaten without thorough cleansing or cooking. Upon reaching the intestine they hatch into young worms which burrow through the intestinal wall into the lymph vessels, reach the veins, are carried to the heart and thence to the lungs, bore their way out of the capillaries into the air sacs, then go to the intestine by way of the trachea, larynx, esophagus, and stomach. This tour of the body requires about ten days. Upon their return to the intestine, they grow to maturity, live on the digested food of the host, and cause intestinal pains and weakness.

Hookworm. Hookworm disease is responsible for much of the anemia and lack of vigor found in most moist tropical and subtropical regions. It is estimated that two million people in the southern United States are infected. The hookworm, which is about half an inch long, attaches itself to the intestinal wall. By means of a secretion it stops the coagulation of blood and when present in large numbers causes the host to be weakened by loss of blood. The eggs pass out with the feces and hatch in moist earth.

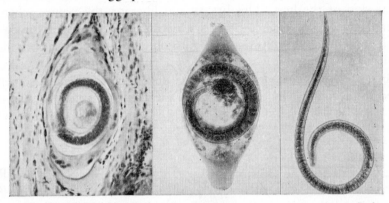

Fig. 84. *Trichinella spiralis,* the roundworm that causes trichinosis. Left, cyst in striated muscle of the pig; center, cyst removed from muscle; right, larva after escape from cyst. (× 150; photos, copyright, General Biological Supply House, Inc., Chicago.)

When the young worms come in contact with bare feet or other bare skin, they burrow through to the capillaries; then, much as in *Ascaris,* they travel by way of the veins to the heart, follow the pulmonary arteries to the lungs, and, by way of air sacs, trachea, larynx, esophagus, and stomach, finally reach the intestine. Proper sewage disposal and the wearing of footgear are means of prevention. Diseased persons are freed from the parasites by the administration of carbon tetrachloride or some other drug to loosen the hold of the worms; this is followed by a cathartic to remove them from the intestine.

Filaria. This roundworm, which is very troublesome in many tropical countries, has two hosts in its life cycle, a mosquito and man. The adults live in human lymph glands, where the slender, thread-like female gives birth to thousands of larvae. At night, when these larvae leave the large blood vessels and enter small ones near the body surface, they are swallowed by certain nocturnal species of mosquitoes. They migrate from the stomach of the mosquito through its body and take a position near its mouth parts, from which they can easily crawl out upon and penetrate the skin of a later victim of the insect. In some cases, probably after prolonged and multiple exposure, filaria infection may lead to the disease *elephantiasis*, in which the blocking of the lymph ducts may result in enormous growth of the limbs or other parts of the body and wrinkling of the skin suggesting that of an elephant.

Guinea Worm. This worm is a troublesome parasite in parts of Africa and Asia. The adult female is two to four feet long and lies as a ridge just beneath the skin. Living young are deposited in a blister which develops on the skin of the host. This breaks and liberates the young when the infected person comes in contact with water, as do washerwomen and people who go down steps into wells to obtain water for household use. The larva swims until it is swallowed by *Cyclops* (a small one-eyed crustacean), in which it undergoes further development. Man becomes infected by accidental ingestion of these infected crustaceans, usually by drinking the water in which they live.

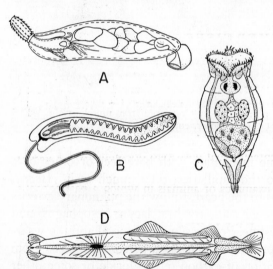

FIG. 85. *A*, A spiny-headed worm, *Acanthocephalus ranae* (from Van Cleave). *B*, Diagram of a proboscis worm (after Hubrecht). *C*, A rotifer, *Hydatina senta*. *D*, an arrowworm, *Sagitta hexaptera* (after Hertwig). (*A*, *B*, and *D* redrawn from Guyer, *Animal Biology*, 3rd ed., copyright, 1941, Harper & Brothers.)

ADDITIONAL WORMS AND WORM-LIKE ANIMALS (Fig. 85)

Sometimes parasitic in the intestines of vertebrate animals (especially fish and birds, rarely man) are the spiny-headed worms (Phylum ACANTHOCEPHALA, Gr. "thorny-headed"). Though there is a body cavity, as in the roundworms, a digestive system is entirely lacking. These worms were once included in the NEMATHELMINTHES, but study of the details of their structure has made it seem best to put them in a separate phylum. Living in the sea are found the proboscis worms (Phylum NEMERTEA, Gr. "unerring ones," because of the apparent accuracy with which they capture prey). These are flattened worms which, on account of their shape, were once considered to belong to the PLATYHELMINTHES; however, they differ from the members of that phylum in having a body cavity and an alimentary canal. The rotifers (Phylum ROTIFERA, Gr. "wheel-bearers") are a group of microscopic multicellular animals often found in the water of ponds and in infusions containing PROTOZOA. Though no larger than some of the latter creatures (Fig. 56), their bodies are made of from 500 to 1000 cells and are highly differentiated. The cilia surrounding the mouth often vibrate in a manner suggesting revolving wheels, hence the name. These animals have both body cavity and alimentary canal. In the open sea may be found the slender, transparent arrowworms (Phylum CHAETOGNATHA, Gr. "bristle-jawed," because of curved bristles beside the mouth). Though this is a very small phylum, it is quite distinct from the rest. These creatures are different from all the animals thus far studied in having a body cavity which is lined with cells of mesodermal origin and hence is a true *coelom* (Gr. "hollow"). Such a body cavity is characteristic of the higher animals. The arrowworms also have an alimentary canal.

EXERCISES

1. List the ways in which a flatworm represents an advance over a coelenterate.
2. Explain how parasitism may have originated among the flatworms.
3. Knowing what you do of their life histories, what steps would you take to avoid infection by the blood fluke? By the lung fluke? By the beef tapeworm? By the hookworm? By the guinea worm?
4. Name a protozoan with two alternating hosts; a plant parasite with two.
5. What advantage has an alimentary canal with two openings over a gastrovascular cavity with only one?
6. What is a pseudocoel? Give examples of animals in which a pseudocoel is found.

REFERENCES

Buchsbaum, R., *Animals Without Backbones*, Univ. of Chicago Press, rev. ed., 1948.

Chandler, A. C., *Introduction to Parasitology*, John Wiley & Sons, 8th ed., 1949.

Craig, C. F., and Faust, E. C., *Clinical Parasitology*, Lea and Febiger, 5th ed., 1951.

Culbertson, J. T., *Medical Parasitology*, Columbia Univ. Press, 1942.

Faust, E. C., *Human Helminthology*, Lea & Febiger, 1952.

Hyman, L. H., *The Invertebrates: Vol. II, Platyhelminthes and Rhyncocoela; Vol. III, Acanthocephala, Aschelminthes, and Entoprocta*, McGraw-Hill Book Company, Inc., 1951.

Wardle, R. A., and McLeod, J. A., *The Zoology of Tapeworms*, University of Minnesota Press, 1952.

Chapter XI

THE EARTHWORM AND OTHER ANNELIDS

The Phylum ANNELIDA (Lat. "little ring") is structurally far advanced over the phyla already studied. Its members are triploblastic, bilaterally symmetrical, provided with a large *coelom*, and made up of a series of repeated body portions called *segments* or *somites* (Gr. "little bodies"), which appear externally as rings. Annelids occur in the sea, in fresh water, and as burrowers in the soil. The annelids in the last-named habitat are the earthworms, of which there are many species. Most of the following discussion refers to *Lumbricus terrestris*, the large earthworm most widely studied.

Habits. Earthworms live in underground burrows which they construct partly by eating the soil, from which they derive much of their nourishment, and partly by packing it by means of the pointed *prostomium* (Gr. "before the mouth"). These burrows run in every direction through rich garden soil. When the soil is damp the worms stay near the surface, but in dry weather they burrow until they reach a damp layer. In dry regions, burrows have been traced more than eighteen feet below ground. In the late fall worms burrow to a level below the frost line and enlarge the end of the burrow into a cavity in which they coil up and hibernate during the winter. During summer they come to the surface on damp nights, whereby they gain at least three physiological advantages. (1) They obtain food. With the posterior portion of the body still clinging to the burrow, the worm reaches about, searching for juicy vegetable matter such as leaves, petals of flowers, and tender parts of seeds. When such material is found, the worm grasps it by the prostomium and draws it into the burrow for future use. Leaves or other objects which are too large to be pulled into the burrow may sometimes be seen piled above it the next morning. (2) They egest castings, which consist of the undigested part of the soil or other food. These are conspicuous in places where worms are numerous. (3) They exchange sperms in copulation, a part of the reproductive process which will be studied later. Correlated with their subterranean habit is their negative response to light, for when placed in strong light they quickly move away from it. They seldom come to the soil surface except at night, when they probably make a positive response to weak light. If a strong light is then brought near them, they dart back into their burrows.

External Features. On account of their adaptations for subterranean life, earthworms show little external differentiation. They have no eyes, almost no mouth parts, and only very rudimentary appendages. As in roundworms, the alimentary canal has both an anterior opening, the *mouth*, and a posterior opening, the *anus* (Fig. 86). The body is cylindrical in form but is somewhat flattened on its ventral surface, which is also recognizable by its lighter color. The ring-like segments which make up the body are separated by circular grooves. The number of these segments varies somewhat; it is close to 150 in *L. terrestris*. The posterior segments are somewhat flattened dorsoventrally. Attached to each segment, except a few of the anterior and posterior ones, are four pairs of spine-like appendages called *setae* (pl. of *seta*, Lat. "bristle"). Relatively

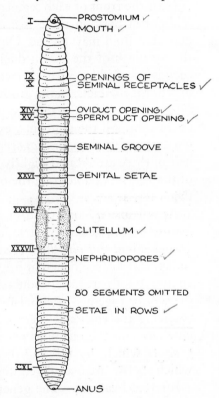

FIG. 86. Ventral surface of an earthworm, about natural size.

large in sexually mature worms are the *genital setae* of segment XXVI. The setae are not jointed and are capable of free movement because of special muscles connecting them with the body wall. When employed in forward locomotion, either in the burrow or on the surface, their points are directed backward. They thus enable the worm to be carried constantly forward by the wave-like elongations and contractions of the body, brought about by the alternate contraction of the circular and the longitudinal muscles. The whole outer surface of the body is covered with a thin noncellular layer called the *cuticle*. This contains many small pores and is crossed in two directions by microscopic grooves which give the surface an iridescent appearance. The pores provide an outlet for the mucus secreted by gland cells in the epidermal layer just below. This mucus lubricates the surface and helps to keep it moist; it thus facilitates respiration, since in order to enter the cells oxygen must be dissolved in water.

Near the front of each segment (except a few of the foremost) and in a mid-dorsal position there is a *dorsal pore*, through which an excess of coelomic fluid may escape. On the ventral surface of segment XV are the openings of the sperm ducts through which sperms are discharged; each is guarded by a pair of swollen lips. On segment XIV are the openings of the oviducts. In the grooves between IX and X and between X and XI are the openings to the two pairs of seminal receptacles. These are not easily seen. All the segments, except a few of the anterior and posterior ones, bear paired *nephridiopores*, or openings to the kidney tubes. About half of these are located slightly laterally and anteriorly to the outer setae of the ventral double row; the others are high on the body, mostly above the lateral setae.

Approximately one-third of the distance from the anterior end of a mature worm, generally including segments XXXI to XXXVII, there is a thickening, the *clitellum* (Lat. "packsaddle"), somewhat flattened on the ventral surface, where it has two longitudinal ridges. This organ plays an important part in reproduction by secreting a slime band which holds the worms together in copulation, and later by developing a capsule for receiving the eggs and sperms at the time of fertilization. Between the clitellum and the openings of the sperm ducts are two pairs of *seminal grooves* which, by meeting the grooves of the mate, form tubes along which sperms are exchanged during copulation.

Internal Features. The general plan of organization of an earthworm is a tube within a tube (Fig. 87). The body wall, consisting of epithelium and muscles, forms the outer tube; the alimentary canal, the inner. Be-

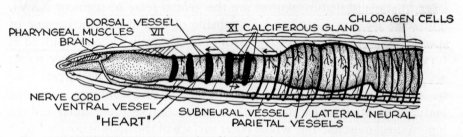

FIG. 87. Earthworm (front end), with left body wall removed, showing alimentary canal, circulatory system, and nervous system. The arrows indicate the direction of blood flow. The reproductive organs, which occupy most of the space about the esophagus, are omitted. Roman numerals indicate segments. For parts of the alimentary canal, see Fig. 89.

tween the tubes is the *coelom* or *body cavity*, which is lined on both surfaces by a thin membrane called the *peritoneum* (Gr. "stretched around") and derived from the mesoderm layer. This cavity is divided into compartments by partitions, or *septa*, which extend from the grooves between segments inward to the alimentary canal. Within the coelom is the coelomic fluid, of a composition similar to blood except that it lacks the red pigment. This fluid moves back and forth with the movements of the worm, passing through pores in the septa. It probably supplements the circulatory system.

Movement and the Muscular System. A well-developed muscular system is present in the earthworm. Its main parts are as follows:

I. Muscles of the body wall.
   A. Circular; outer layer, which by contracting lengthen the body.
   B. Longitudinal; inner layer, which by contracting shorten and thicken the body.
II. Muscles of intestinal wall, thin layers between lining epithelium and chloragen cells.
   A. Circular, within, which constrict the intestine.
   B. Longitudinal, without, which shorten the intestine.
III. Muscles of setae.
   A. Protractors, which protrude the setae from their sheaths.
   B. Retractors, which draw the setae into their sheaths.

As is always true of muscles, the earthworm's muscles contract or shorten, producing changes in the shape of the worm or in the position of parts to which they are connected. Rhythmic or *peristaltic* (Gr. "clasping and compressing") contractions of the muscles of the body wall cause a wavelike constriction that passes along the body. Similar contractions of the intestinal muscles help to force the food along the intestine and to expel the wastes. The protractors of the setae contract to push the setae outward; the retractors, which connect the two pairs of setae on the same side of the segment, contract to draw the setae back into their sacs. (Fig. 88 shows muscles and other organs in cross section.)

Digestion. The highly developed *alimentary canal* (Fig. 89) is a nearly straight tube which runs the entire length of the body. This tube is differentiated into the following parts:

1. A *mouth cavity*, which extends back to segment III.

2. A somewhat spindle-shaped *pharynx*, with a thick muscular wall and connected with the body wall by muscle fibers. It extends from the mouth to the sixth segment.

3. A narrow straight tube, the *esophagus*, which extends back to seg-

ment XIV, and to whose sides are attached a pair of three-lobed glands called *calciferous glands*.

4. A thin-walled pouch-like sac, the *crop*, in segments XV and XVI, which serves as a temporary storage chamber for food.

5. A thick-walled muscular *gizzard*, in segments XVII and XVIII, which is adapted for grinding the food.

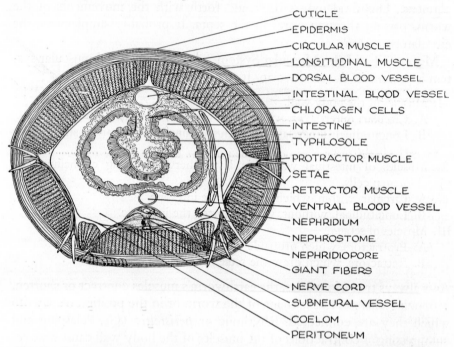

CUTICLE
EPIDERMIS
CIRCULAR MUSCLE
LONGITUDINAL MUSCLE
DORSAL BLOOD VESSEL
INTESTINAL BLOOD VESSEL
CHLORAGEN CELLS
INTESTINE
TYPHLOSOLE
PROTRACTOR MUSCLE
SETAE
RETRACTOR MUSCLE
VENTRAL BLOOD VESSEL
NEPHRIDIUM
NEPHROSTOME
NEPHRIDIOPORE
GIANT FIBERS
NERVE CORD
SUBNEURAL VESSEL
COELOM
PERITONEUM

Fig. 88. Cross section of an earthworm in the intestinal region. Somewhat diagrammatic, especially the nephridium, which would not be entirely visible in any single section.

6. A tubular *intestine* which leads back through the remaining part of the body to the anus. A ridge projecting downward from the midline of the dorsal wall of this tube is known as the *typhlosole* (Gr. "blind channel"); this increases considerably the absorptive surface of the interior lining. This surface is still further increased by transverse foldings along part of the length.

Physiology of Digestion. The use of the prostomium for grasping food and directing it to the mouth opening has already been mentioned. Muscles about the mouth cavity help to push this food back, but the muscles that connect the pharynx with the body wall play a more important part in the process. When these muscles contract, the body wall becomes tense and the wall of the pharynx is pulled outward. This enlarges the pharynx cavity and thus reduces the pressure within, causing the atmospheric pressure outside to push the food into the pharynx.

After the food passes into the esophagus, it is forced along by peristaltic movement, a wave-like progression of constrictions in the wall of the alimentary canal brought about by the cooperation of the circular and longitudinal muscles. This action continues throughout the length of the intestine. In the esophagus the food receives the secretion of the calcif-

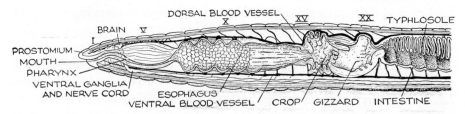

Fig. 89. Sagittal (median vertical) section through the fore part of the body of *Lumbricus*. Roman numerals indicate segments.

erous glands. This secretion, which is alkaline in nature, is thought to neutralize the acid from the vegetable foods, preparing it for enzyme action.

Because of its thin elastic walls, the crop is fitted for storing the food until it can pass into the gizzard and intestine. The gizzard has thick muscular walls which are well fitted for breaking up the food into fine particles readily acted on in the intestine. Sand grains ingested by the earthworm help in this process, the action being similar to that which takes place in the gizzard of a bird.

Digestion in all organisms is essentially a chemical process—the conversion, by means of enzymes, of insoluble foods into soluble equivalents, or the change of larger soluble molecules into smaller. It is aided by the mechanical process already described. The inner layer of the intestine of the earthworm is made up of glandular cells which secrete the necessary enzymes—*trypsin*, one of the proteases, which changes proteins into peptones or amino acids; *amylase*, which changes carbohydrates into simple sugars; and *lipase*, which changes fats into glycerin and fatty acids. After digestion, the nutritive part of the food is absorbed into the blood and the coelomic fluid. Both digestion and absorption are facilitated by the increased surface provided by the typhlosole. Such an increase of surface suggests the increase brought about by folds and villi in the human intestine (Fig. 31). After absorption of the digested food, the indigestible portions are egested through the anus.

Respiration. There are no special structures for respiration, the interchange of oxygen and carbon dioxide taking place by diffusion through the moist outer membrane which covers the body wall. The many capillaries that lie near the outer surface of this wall facilitate the exchange of these gases. The comparatively small size of the animal makes this possible; larger animals require specialized organs that provide an increase of surface for this purpose.

Circulation. The process of *circulation* or transportation is more complex than in the forms already considered. It results in carrying food and oxygen to the tissues and in collecting and carrying wastes from the tissues to the body surface or to the organs of excretion. In most of the animals already considered, circulation is achieved by the movement of fluids in the alimentary cavity or in the body cavity (the proboscis worms have a primitive circulatory system). In the earthworm these fluids are supplemented by *blood,* which flows in a closed system of tubes known as *blood vessels* (Fig. 87). The blood is composed of a liquid part called *plasma,* and of numerous ameboid cells called *white corpuscles* which are suspended in the plasma. No red corpuscles are present. The red color of the blood is due to a red pigment, a kind of *hemoglobin* similar to that of human blood, but dissolved in the plasma instead of being held in the red corpuscles. Hemoglobin unites chemically with oxygen to form the unstable *oxyhemoglobin,* which in the capillaries breaks down again into hemoglobin and oxygen, thus liberating oxygen to the tissues. In addition to the hemoglobin, the plasma contains water, dissolved foods, wastes, and certain necessary mineral constituents.

Vascular System. This system is based on the same general plan as that of the higher animals. It consists of a central pumping station, vessels or tubes leading out to the tissues, and a capillary network connecting these vessels with others which lead back to the pumping station, the whole constituting a continuous system of tubes. The pumping station consists of the muscular *dorsal* blood vessel and five pairs of so-called *hearts* in segments VII to XI. These are tubes which connect the dorsal with the *ventral* blood vessel just underneath the intestine. Their walls are thick and muscular, and they are provided with pocket-like valves which prevent the backward flow of blood. There are similar valves along the dorsal vessel. Besides the dorsal and the ventral there are three other longitudinal vessels, a *subneural* and two *lateral neural* vessels, enclosed in the sheath surrounding the nerve cord. A pair of *parietal* vessels in each segment posterior to the hearts connects the subneural with the dorsal vessel. Distributing vessels extend from the ventral vessel to the body wall, the nephridia, and the alimentary canal, where they break up into networks of capillaries. These capillaries converge into collecting vessels which extend to the subneural, the lateral neural, the parietal, and the dorsal vessels.

The general course of the circulation is forward in the dorsal vessel; downward in the "hearts"; backward in the ventral vessel for distribution to body wall, nephridia, and intestine; and directly or indirectly (by way of parietals, or of lateral neurals, or subneural, and parietals) to the dorsal vessel again. Three parts of this circuit are of special significance: (1) that to the surface of the body, where carbon dioxide is given up by, and oxygen received into, the blood; (2) that to the alimentary canal, where a supply of nutriment is obtained; (3) that to the nephridia, where the blood discards nitrogenous wastes collected from the body.

Excretion. Excretion in the large sense involves the removal of four kinds of wastes—*carbon dioxide* derived from the carbon of foods; *water* derived from the hydrogen of foods; nitrogen compounds, such as *urea*, $(NH_2)_2CO$, derived from nitrogenous, or protein foods; and *inorganic salts*, which are always present in the food. These wastes may result from the direct oxidation of the foods or from the destructive metabolism of protoplasm built up by the assimilation of foods.

It has already been shown how the carbon dioxide and much of the water are removed through the process of respiration. The nitrogen compounds, with considerable water and some mineral salts, are excreted by special organs called *nephridia* (from Gr. "kidney"), which correspond to the kidneys of the higher animals. A pair of nephridia are located close to the ventral wall on each side of the nerve cord in all segments of the body except the first two and last (Fig. 90). Each occupies parts of two successive segments. In one segment is a small, funnel-like structure called the *nephrostome* (Gr. "kidney mouth"); this is narrowed into a tube which leads through the septum to the segment behind, where it covers a considerable part of the body wall, lying in several loops and becoming enlarged at successive stages. The nephrostome and upper part of the tube are lined with cilia.

Physiology of Excretion. There are three successive steps in the process of excretion as carried on by the nephridia: (1) the nephrostome, by the action of its cilia, brings into the tube a current of coelomic fluid, which is carried along by the vibration of the cilia in the upper part of the tube; (2) the middle part of the tube, which has glandular walls and is supplied with a network of capillaries, secretes wastes from the blood into the central canal and returns water and useful minerals to the blood from the fluid of the canal; (3) the last loop (bladder), which has a large cavity and thick muscular walls, serves as a storage place for the waste liquid, and at intervals expels it from the body through the nephridiopore.

Chloragen (from Gr. "yellow") **Cells.** The *chloragen* (or *chloragogen*) *cells*, which constitute the outer layer of the intestine, are said to aid in excretion. They first absorb certain wastes from the blood, then disintegrate in the coelomic fluid, whereupon the wastes are largely removed by the nephridia.

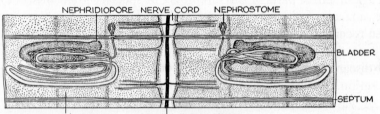

NEPHRIDIOPORE NERVE CORD NEPHROSTOME
BLADDER
SEPTUM
MUSCLES OF BODY WALL VENTRAL BLOOD VESSEL

Fig. 90. Nephridia of earthworm, showing position in segment, also segmental ganglion and nerves. The body wall has been slit along the middorsal line and spread out. (Adapted from Sedgwick and Wilson.)

Nervous System. The student will recall the nerve net of *Hydra*, and the two-lobed ganglion of nerve cells in *Planaria*. A ganglion is a group of nerve cell bodies which serves as a center for the coordination of the activities of the body, much as a telephone switchboard serves for the coordination of the activities of a community. The earthworm, more highly differentiated than the above-mentioned animals, has a chain of double ganglia, one for each segment, extending the entire length of the body and connected to form a *nerve cord*. Most of this cord lies along the midventral line against the body wall (contrasting with the dorsal position of the vertebrate nerve cord), but the front end divides into two *circumpharyngeal connectives* which pass around the pharynx on either side and join the pair of united *cerebral ganglia* on the dorsal side of this organ. These ganglia are sometimes called the *brain*, but they are scarcely enough more prominent than the other ganglia to deserve this distinction. *Cephalization* has not proceeded far in the earthworm. From each of the ventral ganglia proceed three pairs of lateral nerves, the branches of which reach all parts of the segment in which the ganglion lies. The cord consists of nerve cells and fibers. Embedded in its connective tissue sheath are the subneural and the two lateral neural blood vessels, and extending along its upper side are three large hollow nerve fibers known as *giant fibers*.

Neurons, or Nerve Cells. The units of the nervous system, like those of any other system of the body, are cells. The *nerve cell*, or *neuron*, has a body somewhat similar in size to most of the other cells of the organism, but prolonged into slender processes (Fig. 64). It has, to a higher degree than other cells, the power to transmit an *impulse*, a physico-chemical change resulting from a *stimulus*. The processes are usually one or more somewhat branched *dendrites* (Gr. "pertaining to a tree"), which conduct the impulse toward the cell body, and a usually elongated *axon* or *nerve fiber*, which conducts it away from the cell body. The remote end of the axon may be branched several times, coming in contact with similar branches of another neuron at a point called a *synapse* (Gr. "union"), or with a gland or muscle cell. There are three types of neurons: the *sensory* or *afferent*, which extend from the body surface toward a ganglion; the *association* or *intermediate*, with fibers extending along the nerve cord from one ganglion to another, and the *motor* or *efferent*, which extend from the nerve cord and end in muscles or glands.

Sensory Neurons. A sensory neuron is sometimes known as a *receptor*, since its function is to receive stimuli. The sense organs of the earthworm are merely the enlarged and nucleated cell bodies of sensory neurons lying among other cells of the epidermal layer. Senses in the earthworm are not highly specialized, for there are no eyes, ears, or organs of smell. But it can be shown experimentally that the animal perceives and avoids intense light, that it is disturbed by sound vibrations, and that it can distinguish between edible and obnoxious substances. At the head end of the body the sensory neurons are most numerous and also most varied, being specialized for the reception of light, chemical, and other stimuli. Hence the cerebral ganglia toward which these neurons lead may be thought of as representing functionally the beginning of a brain.

Association and Motor Neurons; the Reflex Arc. The neuron or series of neurons that intervene between the receptor and the muscle or gland constitute the *adjustor*; the muscle or gland cell which responds to the impulse by contracting or secreting is known as the *effector*. A reflex arc (Fig. 91) in its simplest form consists of a sensory neuron or *receptor*, a motor neuron or *adjustor*, and an *effector*. A stimulus acting upon the body surface gives rise to an impulse which, carried to the ganglion and then out to the effector, causes the proper response by the effector. Actually most reflexes are more complex, since several receptors are usually stimulated at the same time, several adjustors may be linked with a single receptor, and several effectors may take part in the response. Not only does this spreading occur over several neurons within the same ganglion, but it may pass from one ganglion to another by means of one or more of the association neurons mentioned above. Investigation has shown that the three giant fibers consist of association neurons and that their function is the longitudinal conduction of those impulses which extend over much or all of the length of the body. If a single ganglion resembles a telephone switchboard, a chain of ganglia, such as those of the earthworm, corresponds to a series of connected switchboards whereby information received by the sensory neurons may lead to action of the organism as a whole.

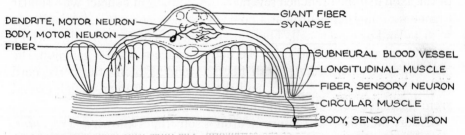

DENDRITE, MOTOR NEURON
BODY, MOTOR NEURON
FIBER
GIANT FIBER
SYNAPSE
SUBNEURAL BLOOD VESSEL
LONGITUDINAL MUSCLE
FIBER, SENSORY NEURON
CIRCULAR MUSCLE
BODY, SENSORY NEURON

Fig. 91. Cross section of ventral nerve cord and lower body wall of earthworm, showing diagrammatically the two nerve cells or neurons involved in the simplest reflexes. The light spots in the neuron bodies are the cell nuclei. (Based on Retzius.)

Reproduction. The earthworm reproduces only by a sexual process. Like *Planaria*, it is *monoecious*, both sexes being in the same individual. Such an organism is also called *hermaphroditic* (from a mythological character in which male and female are said to have been joined in one body). The male organs are the *testes*, or *spermaries*, in which sperms develop; the *seminal vesicles*, in which sperms are matured and stored; and the *sperm ducts*, which carry the sperms to the outside (Fig. 92). The female organs are the *ovaries*, where the eggs develop; the *egg sacs*, for storing them; the *oviducts*, for carrying them to the exterior; the *seminal receptacles*, for receiving and storing sperms; and the *clitellum*, for secreting a capsule to receive the eggs and sperms.

Two pairs of glove-shaped testes are situated on each side of the nerve cord, attached to the anterior septa of segments X and XI. The seminal vesicles at first are three pairs of whitish sacs on each side of the esophagus in segments IX to XIII. As the worm matures, they come to be connected by two central reservoirs that enclose the testes. Immature sperms are passed out of the testes and into the lobes of the seminal vesicles, where they complete their development and are stored. Here is also secreted the seminal fluid in which the sperms are carried. Back of each testis is a somewhat folded ciliated funnel which receives the mature sperms swept into it by the cilia. The sperms pass on into the sperm ducts, which coil as they enter the segment behind and then unite to form on each side a single straight tube opening to the outside through the ventral body wall of segment XV.

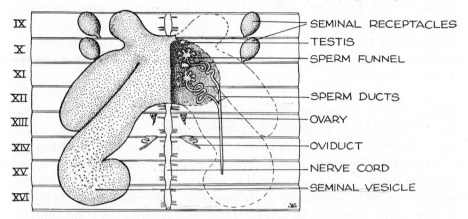

IX
X
XI
XII
XIII
XIV
XV
XVI

SEMINAL RECEPTACLES
TESTIS
SPERM FUNNEL
SPERM DUCTS
OVARY
OVIDUCT
NERVE CORD
SEMINAL VESICLE

FIG. 92. Reproductive organs of the earthworm. The three pairs of seminal vesicles are at first separate, but later merge together. They are cut away on the right to show the testes and sperm ducts.

A single pair of *ovaries* is attached to the anterior septum of segment XIII, one on each side of the nerve cord. They are somewhat elongated triangular organs (Fig. 93), the base of which is filled with immature eggs.

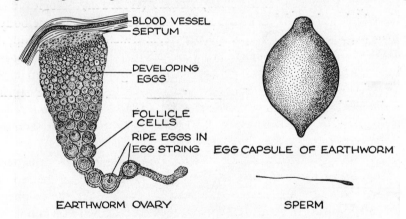

BLOOD VESSEL
SEPTUM

DEVELOPING EGGS

FOLLICLE CELLS
RIPE EGGS IN EGG STRING

EGG CAPSULE OF EARTHWORM

EARTHWORM OVARY

SPERM

FIG. 93. Ovary of earthworm (× 40); egg capsule (× 6); sperm (very highly magnified.)

These mature as they move outward toward the tapering end of the organ. At this end the mature eggs are strung out in a single row, forming the *egg string*, each egg being surrounded by small nutrient cells known as *follicle cells*. Back of each ovary is a ciliated funnel which leads into the oviduct. Just after this duct passes through the septum into segment XIV, it enlarges into an egg sac in which the eggs may be temporarily stored. Beyond the sac the two ducts diverge and open to the outside in the same segment. Each egg is spherical in form and has a somewhat thickened pellicle, a highly granular food-containing cytoplasm, and a distinct nucleus and nucleolus. The sperm has a cylindrical *head*, a shorter and narrower *middle piece*, and a long *tail*, which by its vibrations drives the sperm along.

Two pairs of small whitish *seminal receptacles* are attached to the ventral body wall in segments IX and X. These are globular sacs which open to the outside in the grooves at the posterior ends of these segments. These sacs receive and store sperms from another individual during copulation.

Physiology of Reproduction. When the sperms are mature, the worms come to the surface of the ground at night to exchange them. While still clinging to their burrows by their posterior ends, two worms come together with ventral surfaces in contact and anterior ends in opposite directions, and are held together by slime bands which are secreted by the epidermal gland cells, particularly those of the clitellum. The position of the worms is such that segments IX to XI of each worm are opposite

Fig. 94. Two earthworms exchanging sperms. The posterior ends of both are in the burrows and the anterior ends overlap along the ventral surfaces, the clitellum of each being opposite the genital openings of the other. Sperms pass along the seminal grooves from the sperm duct openings of each worm to the seminal receptacle openings of the other. (Photo, copyright, General Biological Supply House, Inc., Chicago.)

the clitellum of the other (Fig. 94). In this position both worms become completely surrounded by a common slime tube extending from clitellum to clitellum. Sperms are now passed out from the sperm openings of each worm and moved backward by muscular contractions until they reach and enter the seminal receptacles of the other worm. This passage is facilitated by the two pairs of seminal grooves already mentioned. The grooves come together in such a way as to form two complete tubes on each side, making passageways for the sperms in both directions. When the exchange is completed the worms separate, ready for egg laying at a later time. When eggs are ready to be laid, the clitellum secretes another complete girdle which hardens and slips forward. As it passes the openings of the oviducts, the girdle receives the eggs; it then passes on to the seminal receptacles, where it receives the sperms from the other individual. It will be noted that by the plan just described self-fertilization—that is, the uniting of sperms and eggs from the same individual—is prevented and cross-fertilization secured, as nearly always occurs among METAZOA. After sperms and eggs have been received, fertilization takes place within the girdle, which receives also an albuminous secretion from certain skin glands for the nourishment of the developing embryos. As the girdle slips off over the anterior end of the body, its ends close together to form the egg capsule. This is placed just beneath the surface of the ground, where the embryos develop (only one in a capsule in *Lumbricus terrestris*). Several capsules may form in succession after copulation. The worm which after a time emerges from the capsule is very much like the adult in structure (Fig. 95).

FIG. 95. Young earthworm emerging from egg capsule (× 6). Note similarity of young to the adult worm. (Photo, copyright, General Biological Supply House, Inc., Chicago.)

Regeneration and Grafting. The higher the group in the animal kingdom the less in general is the ability to regenerate lost parts. This ability is less pronounced in the earthworm than in the flatworms. If the former is severed between segments XII and XVIII, it will regenerate a new tail on the head piece and a new head on the tail piece. When cut back of this, however, the head regenerates a tail, but the tail develops another tail, producing a worm that will not long survive. Curious combinations, such as two-headed or forked worms, can be produced by grafting together parts of two or more worms.

Economic Importance. Aside from their use to the fisherman, earthworms are beneficial to the soil. Darwin carried on over a period of forty years a significant study of this subject. He found that in a field of average fertility worms bring to the surface a layer of soil an inch thick every seven years. At this rate, in a period of forty years the tillable soil has been entirely renewed by worm castings. This soil is improved in several ways. Organic matter is added to it; minerals from below are brought into the zone of tillage; the texture of the soil is improved by the lumps being broken into finer particles, thereby giving a greater surface for absorption by the roots; rain water and oxygen from the air are admitted by way of the burrows, supplying plants with these needed substances as well as promoting chemical action which assists in making the soil minerals available and in decomposing and nitrifying the organic matter. On the debit side, the burrowing of the worms may start leaks in irrigation canals and the finely divided material of their castings encourages soil erosion.

Other Annelids (Fig. 96). Aside from the small primitive marine group of ARCHIANNELIDA, the annelids consist of OLIGOCHAETA (Gr. "few bristles"), POLYCHAETA (Gr. "many bristles"), and HIRUDINEA, or leeches. The earthworm and its relatives, including several microscopic genera found in fresh water, are placed with the OLIGOCHAETA. *Nereis*, the clamworm, is a representative of the POLYCHAETA. Since the earthworm, somewhat like the mole among mammals, has undergone degeneration of sense organs and other external features in keeping with the requirements of a subterranean life, *Nereis* may be regarded as a more typical annelid. At its anterior end it has a pair of horny, toothed jaws, five pairs of slender tentacles, two thickened palps, and four eyespots. On each segment is a pair of paddle-like appendages (*parapods*) each bearing several setae; they serve as organs for both locomotion and respiration. These worms are very abundant along the seacoast, where they burrow in the sand or swim about in the water with graceful waving movements. They remain during the day in burrows, which may be two feet in depth, and emerge at night to seek food. The internal structure of *Nereis* resembles that of the earthworm, although the former is dioecious, i.e., the male and female organs are in separate individuals.

The leech, which represents the HIRUDINEA, has a flattened body with a number of transverse ridges corresponding to each true segment. It has no setae but is provided with an adhesive sucker at each end, the anterior one surrounding the mouth. There are several eyespots at the anterior end. Like the earthworm, it is monoecious but cross-fertilized. The most striking internal adaptation is an enormously elongated and branched crop which has the function of receiving and storing the blood of its victim. It

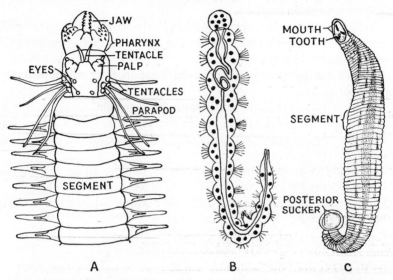

Fig. 96.   Representative annelids. *A, Nereis,* the clamworm, with pharynx everted. Only the nine anterior segments of about 150 are included. *B, Aeolosoma,* a small worm (2 mm. long) common in fresh water. Conspicuous yellowish or salmon-colored pigment globules are scattered through the body. *C, Hirudo medicinalis,* the leech used by early physicians. Each segment is represented by five external rings.

is said to take nine months to digest all the blood in a filled crop; therefore few meals are necessary. The blood is secured by the action of chitinous teeth which open the victim's blood vessels; it is sucked in by the pumping action of the muscular pharynx. Its clotting is largely prevented by a secretion from glands located near the jaws. Leeches were used extensively by physicians a few centuries ago when it was believed that many diseases could be cured by the removal of bad blood from the patient.

EXERCISES

1. What has led to the popular idea that earthworms rain down?
2. Explain why so many earthworms are to be seen crawling over the sidewalk and on the surface of the ground after a rain.

3. Does it cause pain to an earthworm when it is put on a fishhook? What evidence on this question can you find in your study of this chapter?
4. Compare the movements of an earthworm over a horizontal surface with those of a snake; with those of a "measuring worm" (caterpillar).
5. What other animals besides the earthworm possess gizzards? Correlate the character of the mouth parts of an animal with the presence or absence of a gizzard.
6. Compare the enzyme action in digestion in the earthworm with that in the same process in man.
7. Trace a complete reflex nerve reaction in the earthworm, naming all the structures in this path and showing the action of each. Compare with a similar reaction in man.
8. What are the advantages of cross-fertilization over self-fertilization in animals or plants?
9. Describe adaptations in the earthworm for ingestion.
10. Cite as many examples as you can in the animal kingdom where folding or coiling of a structure brings about an advantageous increase in the surface area.
11. How would contraction of the protractor muscles affect the position of the seta? Contraction of the retractor muscles? (See Fig. 88).
12. What is the origin of the word "leech"? How did it come to have its present meaning?

REFERENCES

Barrett, T. J., *Harnessing the Earthworm*, Bruce Humphries, Inc., 1947.

Beddard, F. E., *Earthworms and Their Allies*, The Macmillan Company, 1912.

Darwin, C., *The Formation of Vegetable Mold Through the Action of Worms*, Appleton-Century-Crofts, Inc., 1907.

Stephenson, J., *The Oligochaeta*, Clarendon Press, 1930.

See also texts in zoology listed in the Appendix.

Chapter XII

MOLLUSKS

MOLLUSCA (from Lat. "soft") is a large phylum of soft-bodied and usually hard-shelled animals, most of which inhabit either salt or fresh water; a few live on land. They are unsegmented and generally bilaterally symmetrical, though in most members of the class GASTROPODA the symmetry is distorted by the spiraling of the shell. Mollusks vary widely in their external features; nevertheless, a close examination reveals a number of common structures: (1) a thin tissue, the *mantle*, just within the shell (if this is present) and partially separated from the main body by a *mantle cavity*; (2) usually a *shell* secreted by and surrounding the mantle; (3) a ventral muscular organ of locomotion, the *foot*. A *radula*, a horny band covered with many rows of hard rasping teeth, is possessed by many mollusks but by no other group of the animal kingdom. A ciliated larval stage, the *trochophore*, through which some of the mollusks pass, suggests close relationship of mollusks to annelids, some of which have such a larva, and to some of the minor phyla.

Classification. The classes of mollusks are:

1. AMPHINEURA (Gr. "nerves on both sides"): primitive mollusks usually with a shell of eight transverse plates; foot covering the ventral surface; chitons (Fig. 97).
2. GASTROPODA (Gr. "belly foot"): asymmetrical mollusks with ventral foot and spirally twisted shell; snails, whelks, slugs, etc.
3. SCAPHOPODA (Gr. "boat foot"): marine forms with tubular shells open at both ends; tooth-shells.
4. PELECYPODA (Gr. "hatchet foot"): headless forms with two-valved shell and hatchet-like foot; clams, oysters, scallops.
5. CEPHALOPODA (Gr. "head foot"): marine forms with shell often reduced or absent; squids, octopuses, nautiluses.

General Biology

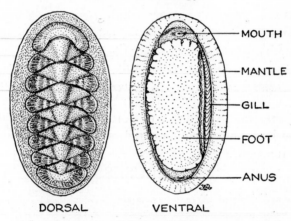

DORSAL VENTRAL

Fig. 97. A chiton (*Chiton apiculata*), member of the least specialized class of mollusks. The skeleton consists of eight overlapping dorsal plates; the foot extends over the greater part of the ventral surface.

THE CLAM AND ITS RELATIVES (PELECYPODA)

Since various species of clams are widely available in both fresh and salt water and are large enough for satisfactory dissection, the clam is often studied as a representative mollusk. Its shell consists of two similar halves which are hinged along the dorsal edge by an elastic ligament (Fig. 98). Near the anterior end of this hinge each shell bears a hump, the *umbo*, which is the center of its growth. Surrounding this are eccentric ridges, the lines of growth, which mark the intervals of rest between growth in successive seasons. Between these are less conspicuous lines,

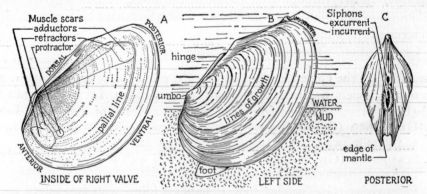

Fig. 98. Fresh-water clam (*Anodonta*), showing external aspects and internal surface of shell. Lines radiating from the umbo show the paths of muscle attachments as the shell increases in size. (From Storer, *General Zoology*, McGraw-Hill Book Company; courtesy of the author and the publisher.)

showing successive periods of growth during the same season. Two large transverse muscles (*adductors*) are attached to the inner surfaces of the valves; by their contraction they bring the edges of the valves firmly together. When the muscles relax, the valves separate because of the elasticity of the ligament, and a large muscular foot may be protruded anteriorly. The foot extends into the sand or mud, the tip swells and serves as an anchor, then the foot contracts, drawing the body of the clam forward. It often leaves a conspicuous trail as it moves along.

When the animal is undisturbed, it usually rests obliquely with the foot extended downward and the posterior end upward. At this end may be seen two openings, the large ventral or *incurrent siphon*, through which water enters the mantle chamber, and the smaller dorsal or *excurrent siphon*, through which water leaves the chamber. In some genera the former is bordered by a fringe of finger-like projections which probably function as a filter. The action of cilia within the body keeps a current of water moving through the mantle chamber, and by this means food particles and oxygen are brought into the body and waste matter is discarded.

Shell Structure. On the inside of the shell may be seen the two large scars of attachment of the adductor muscles, the smaller scars of the protractor and retractor muscles which operate the foot, and, parallel to the ventral margin of the shell, the groove-like scar marking the line of attachment of the muscular layer of the mantle. A cross section of the shell (Fig. 99) shows it to be made up of three layers: (1) a brown horny outer covering, the *periostracum* (Gr. "around the shell"), which is secreted by the edge of the mantle and is thickest at the ventral margin of the shell. Its chitinous substance, *conchiolin*, protects the inner layers from the action of carbonic acid in the water. (2) A *prismatic layer*, consisting of prisms of calcium carbonate at right angles to the surface; this is also secreted by the edge of the mantle. (3) The inner, *mother-of-pearl layer* secreted by the epidermal cells of the entire mantle; it is made up of alternating sheets of calcium carbonate and conchiolin. The interference of the light waves reflected from the opposite surfaces of these thin sheets gives the iridescence characteristic of the inner surface of many shells.

Internal Features. Within the two valves are the mantle lobes; next, on either side, are two flat, leaf-like gills; in the middle is the soft, practically headless body containing organs for digestion, circulation, excretion, and reproduction (Fig. 100).

Respiration. The gills are the respiratory organs. They are flat plates, consisting mainly of bars enclosing parallel vertical water tubes, in the walls of which are pores, or *ostia*, through which the water enters. As the water moves along these tubes, its dissolved oxygen is taken up by the blood which flows through capillaries in the walls of the gills running parallel to the water tubes; at the same time, the carbon dioxide which is in the blood diffuses out into the water of the tubes. The water flows from the tubes into a horizontal channel at the upper or dorsal edge of the gill (*suprabranchial chamber*), whence it leaves by way of the excurrent siphon.

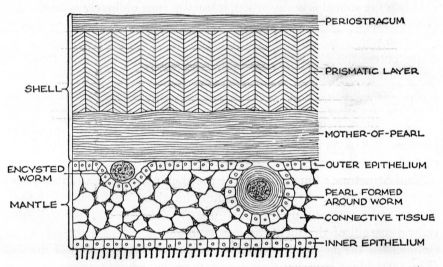

Fig. 99. Structure of mantle and shell of clam in section (× 20). The outer epithelium of the mantle secretes along its edge all three layers of the shell and adds to the mother-of-pearl layer on the entire surface of contact. An encysted parasitic worm or other foreign body that lodges between mantle and shell may be surrounded by pearly layers, as indicated, which form the pearl of commerce.

Circulation. The blood is a colorless fluid. The organs of circulation consist of the dorsal *heart*, which is located in the *pericardial sinus* and has one central ventricle and two lateral auricles; *arteries*, which carry blood to the tissues; irregular spaces, or *sinuses*, unlined by epithelium, which provide a means of interchange of oxygen and carbon dioxide between blood and tissues; and *veins*, which return the blood to the heart. The course of the blood is from pericardium to auricles, then to ventricle, then over the body by way of the arteries, then through the sinuses, then by way of the kidneys and gills back to the pericardium.

Digestion. The alimentary canal consists of a *mouth*, located just above the foot at the anterior end, a short *esophagus*, a pouch-like *stomach*, a somewhat coiled *intestine*, and a *rectum*, which opens into the excurrent siphon by way of the anus. The food consists of minute organic particles carried into the mantle cavity by the water and strained out as the water enters the pores of the gills. On each side of the mouth are two triangular flaps called *labial palps,* covered with cilia which help carry the food into the mouth. Studies of marine clams indicate that most of the digestion is intracellular, the minute food particles entering the *digestive gland,* whose cells engulf and digest them.

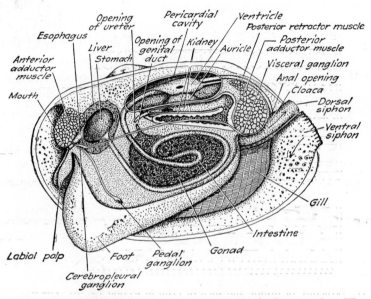

Fig. 100. Diagram of the internal anatomy of a fresh-water clam. The mantle and gills on the near side are not shown, and the body is indicated as having had part of the wall cut away. The stomach, liver, gonad, pericardium, and kidney are shown in section. (From Wolcott, *Animal Biology,* McGraw-Hill Book Company; courtesy of the author and publisher.)

Excretion. Nitrogenous wastes are excreted by two U-shaped *kidneys* lying just below the pericardial cavity, one on each side. Each kidney consists of a ventral *glandular part* and a dorsal thin-walled *bladder.* The former opens anteriorly into the pericardial cavity, and the latter narrows into a *ureter,* which opens into a dorsal gill passage and discharges the wastes secreted by the glandular portion into the suprabranchial chamber, whence they are carried out through the excurrent siphon.

Coordination. As we might expect in so sluggish an animal, the nervous system is not highly developed. It consists of three pairs of *ganglia* with their *connectives,* and branches leading to different parts of the body. The *cerebral ganglia* lie on either side of the mouth and are joined by a connective that runs above the esophagus. From each of these a connective nerve runs downward to a *pedal ganglion* in the foot, and another backward to a *visceral ganglion* on the same side.

Sense organs are little developed, for an animal enclosed in a shell need not be particularly active. An organ of equilibrium lies near the pedal ganglia. This consists of a cavity called the *statocyst*, within which is a concretion of lime whose movement stimulates certain sensory cells. The *osphradium* (Gr. "strong scent"), a mass of epithelial cells on the surface of the visceral ganglia, is believed to test the purity of the water in the mantle cavity. *Tactile cells* along the edges of the siphons and along the margin of the mantle are sensitive to contact and to light.

Reproduction. Clams reproduce sexually and are dioecious. The eggs of the female leave the ovary and pass to the suprabranchial chamber. Here they are fertilized by sperms which have been discharged from the male and have entered the female by way of the incurrent siphon. The gills, or parts of them, become enlarged into brood chambers. The eggs hatch into two-valved larvae known as *glochidia* (Gr. "like an arrowpoint," Fig. 101), some species of which have hooks on the edges of the

Fig. 101. Left, glochidium larva of clam; right, head of fish showing glochidia as small white spots embedded in the gill filaments.

shells. On leaving the mother, the young clam snaps its valves together on the fins or the gills of a fish, becomes embedded in the tissue of the fish, and lives parasitically for a time, after which it drops off and grows into an adult. As is true with many parasites, glochidia of a particular species of clam live upon only one or a few closely related species of hosts. This parasitic stage upon a fish enables the species to become far more widely distributed than would be possible if dispersal were left to the slow movement of the mother. Extensive fishing operations in the Mississippi valley over a period of years have resulted in a marked reduction in the number of clams.

Oysters.   Oysters are marine bivalves which differ from clams in several important respects (Fig. 102). (1) The oyster is *sessile* in the adult stage, being fastened to a submerged object by the left valve of the shell. As a result, the valves lack symmetry. The left one is convex and contains the body; the right one is flattened, or even concave. (2) There is a single *adductor muscle* instead of two. (3) The *foot* is lacking in the adult. It is a significant fact, however, that the larva has symmetrical valves, two adductor muscles, and a foot. (4) The life history of the oyster lacks the

Fig. 102. Young oysters showing attachment to rocks by the convex valve of the shell. The one at the extreme left has been turned over. (Photo by L. W. Brownell.)

parasitic stage found in the clam. Oysters are extraordinarily prolific. It has been estimated that a single female may contain a half billion eggs. The fertilized egg soon hatches into a small larva which swims about by means of a ciliated velum. In about two weeks it is ready to settle upon and become attached to some object in the water. The food consists of protozoans, algae (largely diatoms), and the eggs and swimming larvae of various animals.

Economic Aspects.   Fresh-water clams are found in lakes and streams all over this country, being especially abundant in the Mississippi valley, where they are collected on a large scale for the manufacture of buttons and other objects of pearl. On our Atlantic coast the soft-shell or long-neck clam is generally used locally for clambakes and chowders; the hard-shell or quahog is the one used extensively for shipping and canning.

Oysters are especially valuable as a source of food. The oyster industry has become of great importance especially in three regions: (1) the waters about Japan, (2) the west coast of Europe, from England into the Mediterranean, (3) the Atlantic seaboard, where the value of the crop is some ten million dollars annually; the Chesapeake Bay region is particularly favorable. The yield is increased by the use of cultural techniques. The shipworm, *Teredo navalis*, is a bivalve that burrows into wood, making

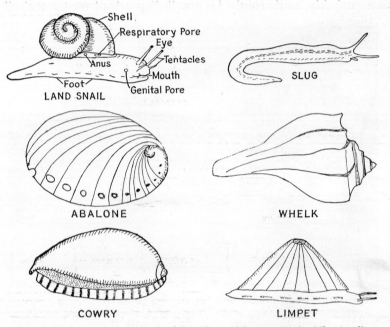

Fig. 103. Gastropods. A land snail in the position assumed while crawling; a slug, similar to a snail but lacking the shell; and four common marine forms. The shell only is shown in the first three of the latter.

round tunnels sometimes two feet in length. It does great damage to wooden ships and piers. Fresh-water clams and snails are often used to keep pools and aquariums free of organic debris.

Pearls. If a parasitic worm burrows into the mantle of a clam or oyster or a foreign object such as a grain of sand lodges in or against it, and if a pocket of epithelial cells derived from the mantle surrounds the intruding particle, a deposit known as a pearl is formed (Fig. 99). Long ago in China the formation of pearls was artificially stimulated by the introduction of foreign objects between mantle and shell, and the practice is now carried on scientifically in Japan, preferably with small bits of mother-of-pearl from clam shells.

OTHER MOLLUSKS

Gastropods. The GASTROPODA, or snail-like mollusks, are very numerous and are found under a wide range of conditions (Fig. 103). Most of them have a twisted shell, like that in the snails, and in accommodating themselves to such a shell they have lost their former bilateral symmetry. There are two pairs of tentacles, one of which bears a pair of eyes; the other is probably used mainly for smell. Some fresh-water and all land snails breathe air, which is taken through a respiratory pore into the mantle cavity (lung); marine and many fresh-water snails are provided with gills. The slug, which often causes injury to vegetation, is a land snail with a rudimentary internal shell.

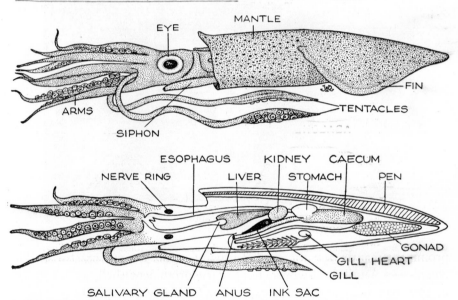

FIG. 104. The squid. Above, side view in swimming position; below, sagittal section, showing principal anatomical features. The circle of arms constitutes the ventral surface, corresponding to the foot of a snail or chiton, and has suggested the group name CEPHALOPODA (Gr., "head-foot"). The pen, of chitinous composition, corresponds to the shell of the other mollusks. The water of respiration, the intestinal and kidney wastes, and the reproductive cells are discharged through the funnel-like siphon. The force of the ejected stream serves also to propel the animal; ink from the ink sac produces a "smoke screen" which helps the squid to elude its pursuers.

Cephalopods. The CEPHALOPODA, including the squid (Fig. 104), cuttlefish, octopus, and nautilus, have a well-developed head, the distal end of which bears a circle of tentacles, the "foot." On the head is located a pair of eyes that are capable of serving in a camera-like fashion to form images of objects before them. The eyes are strikingly similar to those of the vertebrates. However, while the greater part of the eyeball of the vertebrate develops as an outpushing from the brain, that of the cephalopod comes entirely from the superficial ectoderm. This is an example of *convergent evolution*, the development of structures originating independently but similar in structure and function. On the tentacles are suckers which help the animal in seizing and holding its prey. There is a

FIG. 105. Giant octopus or devilfish captured at Friday Harbor, Puget Sound. (Photo by Charles J. Chamberlain).

prominent mantle, but the shell is usually inconspicuous or absent. The chambered nautilus, however, has a very prominent shell, as did its ancestors, which are abundantly represented in early geological deposits.

The giant squid of the north Atlantic is the largest known living invertebrate; it may become fifty feet or more in length. The octopus (Gr. "eight feet") or devilfish has eight sucker-bearing arms (Fig. 105). It feeds chiefly on crabs, but the larger species are dangerous to man.

NONMOLLUSKS WITH SHELLS

Though the majority of shells found along the seashore and around other bodies of water are derived from members of the Phylum MOLLUSCA, there are some which belong to animals of other groups. Superficially rather similar to the mollusks are the lamp shells (Phylum

BRACHIOPODA, Gr. "arm-footed," based on the erroneous idea that the arm-like structures of these animals correspond to the foot of the clam). These creatures, like the clams and oysters, have two valves (Fig. 106), but the valves are dorsal and ventral rather than lateral as in the bivalve mollusks. This is a very ancient group, and fossils obtained from rocks of considerable age show that some members have changed only little during many millions of years (Fig. 397). Somewhat similar to the lamp shells, but less like the mollusks, are members of the Phylum BRYOZOA (Gr. "moss animals"). These are small creatures that live in the water and form plant-like colonies sometimes mistaken for seaweeds (Fig. 106). Bryozoans resemble certain mollusks (and annelids) in possessing a similar early larval stage, known as the *trochophore*. Both brachiopods and bryozoans have an alimentary canal and a coelom, thus showing their development be-

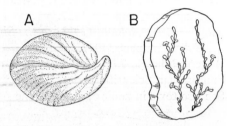

Fig. 106. *A*, A brachiopod, *Magellania flavescens* (after Davidson); the upper valve is dorsal, the lower ventral. *B*, A colony of the bryozoan *Plumatella repens* on the surface of a stone. (Redrawn from Guyer, *Animal Biology*, 3rd ed., copyright, 1941, Harper & Brothers.)

yond the level of the simplest metazoans. Certain members of the Class CRUSTACEA (Phylum ARTHROPODA), to be considered in the next chapter, particularly the barnacles, are sometimes confused with the mollusks; however, though they may have shells, their body structure clearly shows them to be different.

EXERCISES

1. How were pearl images of Buddha made by the Chinese? (See *Encyclopædia Britannica*.)
2. What is the principal region for oyster culture in the United States? Describe the methods employed.
3. What is sepia? How does it get its name? How is it used by the animal secreting it? How by man?
4. From what peculiarity in the growth of the animal does Holmes derive a lesson in his poem, "The Chambered Nautilus"?
5. Describe the ancient relatives of the nautilus. What types existed, and what were they called?
6. Construct a table for the comparison of the main characteristics (symmetry, coelom, segmentation, skeleton, digestion, circulation, respiration, excretion, nervous system, reproduction) of the animal phyla that you have studied.

7. How does the eye of a cephalopod differ in its development from that of a vertebrate?
8. Account for the fact that the larval oyster has symmetrical valves, two abductor muscles, and a foot, whereas the adult lacks these characteristics.

REFERENCES

Goodrich, C., *The Mollusca of Michigan*, Univ. of Michigan Press, 1932.

Johnson, M. E., and Snook, H. J., *Seashore Animals of the Pacific Coast*, The Macmillan Company, 1927.

Morris, P. A., *A Field Guide to the Shells of Our Atlantic Coast*, Houghton Mifflin Company, 1947.

Rogers, Julia E., *The Shell Book*, rev. ed., Branford Press, 1951.

Smithsonian Scientific Series, Vol. X, Part III, 1931.

See also texts in zoology listed in the Appendix.

Chapter XIII

THE CRAYFISH AND OTHER CRUSTACEANS

Phylum Arthropoda. The largest phylum of animals is ARTHROPODA (Gr. "jointed feet"), a group characterized chiefly, as the name implies, by jointed appendages. These give a much greater flexibility and range of movement than is found among annelids, which the arthropods resemble in having a body with externally visible segmentation. The classes of arthropods are outlined here, with certain significant characters.

Class	Body Regions	Antennae	Legs	Respire by
CRUSTACEA Crustaceans	Cephalothorax and abdomen (usually)	2 prs.	Varying	Gills
INSECTA Insects	Head, thorax, abdomen (usually with 2 prs. wings)	1 pr.	3 prs.	Tracheae
ONYCHOPHORA *Peripatus*	Head and long body	1 pr.	Many	Tracheae
CHILOPODA Centipedes	Head and long body	1 pr.	1 pr. per segment	Tracheae
DIPLOPODA Millipedes	Head, short thorax, long abdomen	1 pr.	2 prs. (abdominal segments)	Tracheae
ARACHNOIDEA Spiders, etc.	Cephalothorax and abdomen	None	4 prs.	Tracheae, book lungs

The Crayfish, a Crustacean. Since it is the largest inland arthropod, the crayfish (Fig. 107) is both available and suitable for laboratory study. Most of its morphological characters are similar to those of the closely related lobster, the largest of all arthropods. The crayfish and lobster represent the class CRUSTACEA (from Lat. "shell"), which is characterized by a *crust-like exoskeleton* composed of a horny organic substance, *chitin* (Gr. "coat of mail"), often impregnated with calcium carbonate and affording an efficient protective armor. This covering is noncellular and has no power of growth; therefore the growth of the crustacean requires frequent *molting*. In this process the old skeleton is cast off and replaced by a new one secreted by the epithelial cells of the body wall. Instead of

Fig. 107. Crayfish (*Cambarus clarkii*) on the alert at the bottom of the pond. (Photo, copyright, John G. Shedd Aquarium, Chicago.)

being joined to the outer surface of the bones, as in vertebrates, the muscles are attached to the inside surfaces of the tubular segments of the chitinous skeleton (Fig. 108). The softer and thinner chitin at the joints permits movement.

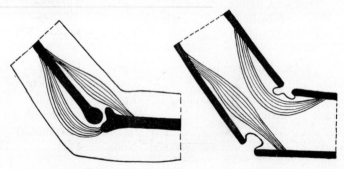

Fig. 108. A vertebrate limb (left), contrasted with an arthropod limb (right) as regards skeletal and muscular arrangement. In the former, the bony skeleton (heavy shading) is internal and muscles are joined to its outer surface, while in the latter the chitinous skeleton is external and muscles are joined to its inner surface. Note that the muscles shown are antagonistic pairs. (Redrawn from Buchsbaum, *Animals Without Backbones*, Univ. of Chicago Press.)

Occurrence and Habits. Many species of the crayfish are found in streams, lakes, and ponds, where they rest in crevices or other hiding places watching for the small animals they use as food. They seize their prey with their muscular pincers and tear it with their strong mandibles. When disturbed they dart back by powerful strokes of the tail (abdomen). Other species live in swamps, burrowing down to a point below water level and making chimneys of the excavated material. These types use vegetable as well as animal food.

External Features. Not only is the crayfish more highly developed than the earthworm, but its segments are differentiated into three well-defined regions: *head, thorax,* and *abdomen.* The first two are fused, forming the *cephalothorax* (Gr. "head-thorax"), and their segments are indistinct, especially on the dorsal surface. The dorsal shield, called the *carapace,* extends forward into a tapering pointed beak, the *rostrum* (Lat. "prow of a ship"). The separation of head and thorax is indicated by a shallow groove called the *cervical* ("neck") *groove.* In the abdominal region the segments are distinct, giving flexibility of movement to this part. The side pieces of the carapace, called *gill covers,* are marked by shallow grooves along the dorsal surface and cover the gills, which lie in the chamber beneath.

Appendages. On the ventral side are nineteen pairs of appendages, each pair attached to a body segment (Fig. 109). A typical appendage is two-

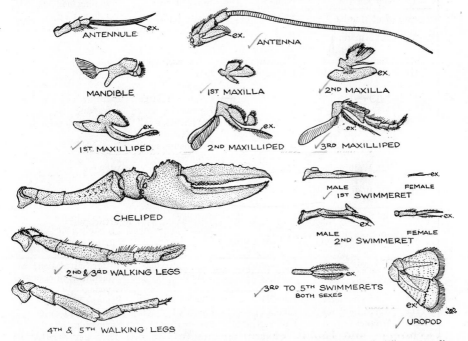

FIG. 109. Appendages on the left side of a crayfish, as seen from beneath. The exopodite is indicated (*ex.*) wherever present; the other branch is the endopodite; the basal portion is the protopodite. See Table of Appendages for uses of the appendages.

branched. It consists of the base or *protopodite* (Gr. "first foot"), and two terminal branches, an outer, the *exopodite* (Gr. "outer foot"), and an inner, the *endopodite* (Gr. "inner foot"). Each of these parts consists usually of several or many joints. In primitive crustaceans, and even in the young crayfish, the appendages of an individual are all very similar; in the adult crayfish profound modifications adapt them to a variety of functions. The abdominal appendages do not depart widely from the primitive type, but those of the cephalothorax are highly specialized, having undergone profound modification or loss of certain parts. For example, each walking leg in early life has an outer branch which it loses before the adult stage is reached. The accompanying table outlines the structure and function of the appendages.

TABLE OF APPENDAGES

	No.	Name	Exopodite	Endopodite	Function
HEAD	I	Antennule	Many-jointed filament	Like exopodite	Touch, taste, equilibrium
	II	Antenna	Flat squame	Many-jointed filament	Touch, taste, excretory pore at base
	III	Mandible	None	Jointed palp	Crushing food
	IV	1st Maxilla	None	Small blade	Handling food
	V	2nd Maxilla	Flat	Small, pointed	{ Handling food { Drawing water over gills
THORAX	VI	1st Maxilliped	Filamentous	Flat	Touch, taste, holding food
	VII	2nd Maxilliped	Filamentous	5 short segments	Same as VI
	VIII	3rd Maxilliped	Filamentous	Like VII but larger	Same as VI
	IX	Cheliped (1st Walking leg)	None	5 segments, large pincer	Fighting, seizing food, walking
	X	2nd Walking leg	None	5 segments, small pincer	Walking, cleaning body
	XI	3rd Walking leg	None	5 segments, small pincer	Walking
	XII	4th Walking leg	None	5 segments, no pincer	Walking
	XIII	5th Walking leg	None	5 segments, no pincer	Walking
ABDOMEN	XIV	1st Swimmeret	{ ♂ None { ♀ Small	Tubular Small	Sperm transfer Probably none
	XV	2nd Swimmeret	{ ♂ Filamentous { ♀ Like XVI	Conical Like XVI	Sperm transfer Same as XVI
	XVI	3rd Swimmeret	Flat jointed filament	Flat jointed filament	Water circulation; attachment of eggs and young
	XVII	4th Swimmeret	Like XVI	Like XVI	Same as XVI
	XVIII	5th Swimmeret	Like XVI	Like XVI	Same as XVI
	XIX	Uropod	Flat oval plate, 2 segments	Flat oval plate	Swimming

NOTE: ♂ is symbol for male, ♀ for female.

The structure of a segment of the abdomen, including the appendages, is shown in Fig. 110. The arched dorsal part of the exoskeleton is known as the *tergum;* the ventral portion, between the appendages, is the *sternum;* and each lateral extension is a *pleuron.*

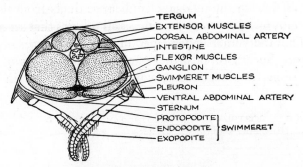

TERGUM
EXTENSOR MUSCLES
DORSAL ABDOMINAL ARTERY
INTESTINE
FLEXOR MUSCLES
GANGLION
SWIMMERET MUSCLES
PLEURON
VENTRAL ABDOMINAL ARTERY
STERNUM
PROTOPODITE]
ENDOPODITE } SWIMMERET
EXOPODITE]

Fig. 110. Cross section of the abdomen of a crayfish. (Slightly enlarged.)

Body Cavities. The coelom of the embryo becomes greatly reduced in the adult crustacean. The main spaces in the body are of a different origin and consist of *sinuses* or blood spaces distributed through the tissue and making up the *hemocoel* (Gr. "blood hollow").

Digestion. The digestive system consists of an alimentary canal and a pair of large digestive glands ("livers," Fig. 111). The alimentary canal

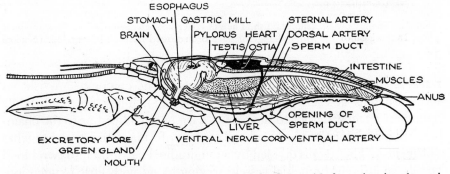

ESOPHAGUS
STOMACH | GASTRIC MILL | STERNAL ARTERY
BRAIN | PYLORUS HEART / DORSAL ARTERY
TESTIS/OSTIA / SPERM DUCT
INTESTINE
MUSCLES
ANUS
OPENING OF
LIVER SPERM DUCT
EXCRETORY PORE / VENTRAL NERVE CORD VENTRAL ARTERY
GREEN GLAND
MOUTH

Fig. 111. Section of crayfish, made just to the left of the mid-plane, showing the position of the internal organs. (Natural size.)

is differentiated into the *mouth,* the *esophagus,* the *stomach,* and the straight, tubular *intestine,* which opens at the *anus* on the ventral surface of the *telson.* The stomach consists of two chambers, a large anterior *cardiac chamber* and a smaller posterior *pyloric chamber.* Near the rear end of the cardiac chamber is the *gastric mill,* which consists of one median and two lateral sets of chitinized teeth operated by muscles outside the stomach. These teeth complete the grinding process initiated by the mouth parts. At the entrance to the pyloric chamber is a fringe of hairs which serves as a strainer, permitting only the finer particles to pass to the intestine. Entering the pyloric chamber are ducts from the two large *digestive glands*, which consist of many small tubules that secrete enzymes which act upon the various types of food.

Respiration. In arthropods, there are two main types of respiratory systems—*gills* in the crustaceans, which generally live in water, and

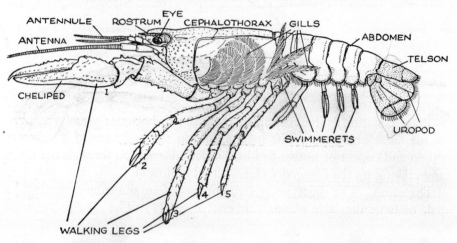

Fig. 112. Side view of male crayfish. The gill cover has been removed to show the gills. Those at the base of the 4th walking leg have been turned back and separated. (Natural size.)

tracheae in most of the air-breathing classes. The common crayfish has seventeen gills in each gill chamber (Fig. 112). They are feather-like structures attached either to the base of a leg or maxilliped or to the chamber wall just above the base. Each gill consists of a main stem with branches (filaments). The stem is divided by a longitudinal partition into two blood vessels, an afferent branchial vessel carrying blood with little oxygen into the gill from the sternal sinus, and an efferent branchial vessel, conveying the oxygenated blood from the gill on its way back to the heart. The partition is continued into each of the filaments, so that the blood flows out along one side of the filament, around the tip, and back along the other side. Through the walls of the filament oxygen diffuses from the water of the gill chamber into the blood, and carbon dioxide diffuses from the blood to the water. The water of the chamber is renewed by the vibration of certain appendages, particularly the gill bailer at the base of the second maxilla.

Circulation. The blood resembles that of most invertebrates in consisting of *plasma* and *white corpuscles*. The oxygen-carrying chemical is the almost colorless copper-containing compound, *hemocyanin*, which is dissolved in the plasma. It becomes *oxyhemocyanin* as the blood passes through the gill vessels. The vascular system (Fig. 113) consists of the *heart*, *arteries* leading out from the heart, and irregular spaces called *sinuses* which distribute the blood through the body tissues. These sinuses take the place of the definite tubes (capillaries and veins) found in annelids

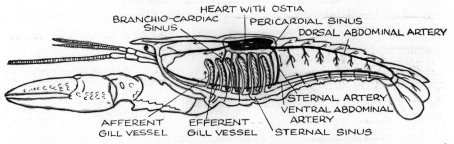

HEART WITH OSTIA
BRANCHIO-CARDIAC   PERICARDIAL SINUS
SINUS   DORSAL ABDOMINAL ARTERY

STERNAL ARTERY
VENTRAL ABDOMINAL
ARTERY
AFFERENT   EFFERENT
GILL VESSEL   GILL VESSEL   STERNAL SINUS

Fig. 113. Diagram of the circulation of a crayfish, side view. From the branches of the arteries the blood goes into sinuses or open spaces between the body cells, represented by the clear area in the diagram thence to the sternal sinus. Oxygenated blood is carried in all vessels shown in black. (Natural size.)

and vertebrates. A system with sinuses is called an *open system;* one with capillaries is a *closed system*. The heart is a hollow muscular organ lying in an ovoid cavity, the *pericardial sinus*, in the dorsal portion of the thorax. In its walls are three pairs of slit-like openings, the *ostia*, which are valvular and prevent the backward flow of the blood. The heart contracts, forcing blood into the arteries. From their branches it enters the sinuses, supplying food and oxygen to, and removing wastes from, the body cells. The sinuses all lead to the *sternal sinus;* from here the blood enters the gills by way of the *afferent vessel* in each, exchanges wastes for oxygen, leaves by way of the *efferent vessel*, and thence goes upward along the side of the body through the *branchio-cardiac sinus*, reaching the *pericardial sinus* and entering the heart through the ostia. (See also Plate I.)

Excretion. Nitrogenous wastes are removed by the *kidneys* or "*green glands*" (Fig. 114), small, paired organs located near the base of the antennae. Each consists of a greenish *secreting portion*, a sac-like *bladder* situated dorsally, and a short *duct* opening to the exterior in the basal joint of the antenna.

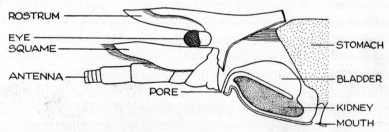

ROSTRUM

EYE
SQUAME

ANTENNA

PORE

STOMACH

BLADDER

KIDNEY
MOUTH

FIG. 114. Excretory organs of crayfish in relation to head and thorax (left body wall dissected away.)

Nervous System. The well-developed nervous system (Fig. 115) consists of a dorsal bilobed ganglion, the *brain;* a *nerve ring* around the esophagus; a double, ventral *nerve cord,* connecting a ventral *chain of ganglia;* and *nerves* from brain and ganglia to the various organs. The whole system functions much as does that of the earthworm. Advances over the earthworm are the tendency toward fusion of the ganglia, a somewhat higher development of the brain, and a much higher development of the sense organs. The large subesophageal ganglion at the base of the nerve ring represents a fusion of three pairs belonging to the head and three to the thorax. The sense organs include *antennules, antennae,*

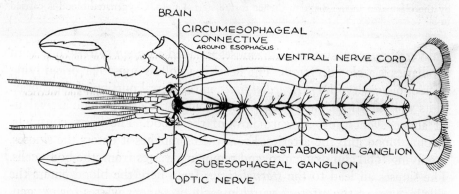

BRAIN

CIRCUMESOPHAGEAL
CONNECTIVE
AROUND ESOPHAGUS

VENTRAL NERVE CORD

FIRST ABDOMINAL GANGLION
SUBESOPHAGEAL GANGLION
OPTIC NERVE

FIG. 115. Diagram of the nervous system of a crayfish as seen from above, dorsal body wall and viscera having been removed. (Natural size.)

palps of mouth parts, and two *compound eyes.* Sensitive hairs on the appendages mentioned respond to smell or taste; other hairs widely distributed over the body are the organs of touch.

Eyes. The eyes are elevated on movable stalks, one on each side of the head. Each consists of about 2500 divisions called *ommatidia* (Fig. 116). The surface of the eye is covered with a transparent chitinous cuticle, the *cornea*, divided into square lenses known as *facets*, one of which covers the front of each ommatidium. A complete ommatidium has the form of a square pyramid, with the facet forming the base, a *crystalline cone* just back of it, and a group of *retinal cells* (optic nerve endings corresponding to the rods and cones of the vertebrate eye) at the apex or inner end. A considerable portion of the interior of the ommatidium is lined with *pigment cells* containing a black pigment. This absorbs the oblique rays of light which, if reflected, would reach the retinal cells and blur the image.

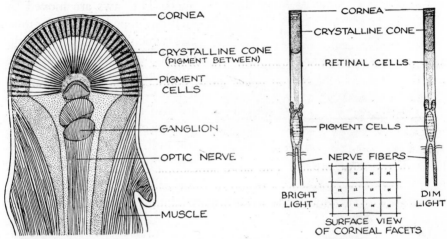

Fig. 116. Compound eye of crayfish. Left, diagrammatic longitudinal section of entire eye. Right, above. two ommatidia. In bright light the pigment in the pigment cells forms a continuous sheath around the ommatidium, restricting the light reaching the optic nerve to a small point in the center. In dim light the pigment retreats to the outermost and innermost parts of the sheath, allowing more light to reach the nerve ends but making the image less distinct. Right, below, surface of the eye. (Ommatidia based on Bennitt and Merrick.)

Shifting of the position of the pigment adjusts the eyes to bright or dim light. Compound eyes, which occur also in insects, are believed to give *mosaic vision*. In this there is an overlapping of images formed by the individual eyes, but all of these partial images combine to form the complete image. Such vision fails to give definite outlines but is particularly well adapted for the detection of movement of objects.

Statocysts. Opening on the dorsal surface of the basal segment of each antennule is a cavity lined with sensory hairs and containing grains of sand, which are placed there by the animal following molting. The cavity is the *statocyst* (Gr. "sac for standing"), and the sand grains are called *statoliths*. If the body is tilted from its upright position, the grains of sand stimulate the sensory hairs, bringing about such muscular adjustments as will enable the animal to regain its equilibrium. In an experiment in which shrimps that had just molted were placed in water free from sand but supplied with small particles of iron, the animals assumed an inverted position when a magnet was brought above them closely enough to influence the particles of iron they had taken into their statocysts.

Muscular System. The largest muscles of the body are the ventral and dorsal abdominal muscles (*flexors* and *extensors*, respectively, Fig. 110),

which bring about the movements of the abdomen in swimming. The jaws are moved by well-developed mandibular muscles which are attached to the dorsal body wall and connect with the jaws by strong tendons. Within the body proper are also the heart muscles, gastric muscles that operate the gastric mill, and intestinal muscles. The appendages are all supplied with muscles; the large ones that operate the pincers are in the base of the larger pincer claw. The crayfish shows a great advance over the earthworm in variety and range of movement.

Reproduction. The crayfish is dioecious, the sexes occurring in separate individuals. The female organs include an *ovary*, a pair of *oviducts*, and a *seminal receptacle* for receiving sperms during copulation. The ovary consists of one posterior and

FIG. 117. Female crayfish, ventral view, showing eggs attached to the swimmerets. Note the seminal receptacle along the midline between the legs of the last pair. (Photo by Cornelia Clarke.)

two anterior lobes situated just below the pericardial sinus; it represents a pair which have fused at the posterior end. An oviduct extends from each side of the ovary to an opening on the basal segment of the third walking leg. The seminal receptacle is a pit on the ventral surface between the fourth and fifth pairs of walking legs. The male organs are the *testis* and *sperm ducts* (*vasa deferentia*). The testis is similar in form and position to the ovary but is somewhat smaller; the sperm ducts are coiled tubes that open in the basal segments of the fifth pair of walking legs. In copulation, sperms pass from the male to the seminal receptacle of the female, where they remain until the time of egg-laying.

When ready to lay eggs, the female cleans her ventral surface thoroughly, then lies on her back and flexes her abdomen. Slime from the cement glands at their bases now flows over the swimmerets. As the eggs pass from the oviducts they are fertilized by sperms from the seminal receptacle, and are attached by means of the slime to the stiff hairs of the swimmerets (Fig. 117). They are kept clean and well oxygenated by movements of the swimmerets in the water. Several weeks are required for hatching. When the eggs hatch, the young crayfish is prevented from dropping from the mother by a cement thread which extends from the egg shell to the tail of the larva. In a short time, however, the larva is able to grasp and cling to a swimmeret by means of its pincers. A little later it drops off to begin an independent life.

FIG 118. Fiddler crab (*Uca wordax*), dorsal view of male. The large cheliped, the "fiddle," is waved, apparently as a means of attracting the female. Both chelipeds of the female are similar to the small one of the male. (Photo by American Museum of Natural History, New York.)

Regeneration and Autotomy. The crayfish though highly organized still has some power to *regenerate* lost parts such as eyes and appendages; this power is greater in young animals. It sometimes happens, however, that the part regenerated is not the same as the part lost; for example, an antenna is sometimes developed in place of a lost eye.

If an appendage is crushed or broken, it is automatically separated from the body at a definite breaking point not far from its base. Just back of this is a small diaphragm which prevents loss of blood. At the next molt appears a small replacement of the missing appendage. This becomes larger with each succeeding molt. This ability to sever an organ is called *autotomy* (Gr. "self-cutting") and is also found in other groups of animals (pages 217, 239).

Relatives of the Crayfish. Of the 16,000 living species of crustaceans, those of the same subclass as the crayfish are of greatest economic importance; most of them are residents of the sea. The largest is the *lobster*, which is common along our Atlantic coast; one that was caught weighed 34 pounds. The lobster of the north Atlantic is strikingly like the crayfish in its external and internal anatomy. One cheliped, however, is massive and useful for crushing, whereas the other is more delicately formed and is used for picking up smaller food particles. As is true of many of the marine crustaceans, the lobster undergoes metamorphosis after hatching, the larval stage being quite different from the adult. *Crabs* differ from the

FIG. 119. Hermit crab (*Petrochirus baha-mensis*) in the discarded shell of a marine gas-tropod mollusk. The abdomen, which is not chitinized, is constantly within the shell. In times of danger the head and legs can be drawn inside. (Photo, copyright, John G. Shedd Aquarium, Chicago.)

crayfish in that the abdomen is much reduced and is normally folded into a ventral groove in the broad cephalothorax. The *blue crab* of the Atlantic is the common edible crab. The male *fiddler crab* (Fig. 118) has one large pincer, the shape and position of which suggests a fiddle; it is waved when in the presence of the female and is supposed to be an organ of sexual attraction. The *hermit crab* (Fig. 119) has a soft coiled abdomen which it protects by backing into a discarded snail shell; it grasps the shell by means of a specially modified pair of abdominal appendages, carries it about while walking, and withdraws completely into it when disturbed. When it outgrows one shell, it changes to a larger one. The *sow bug* (Fig. 120) is a terrestrial form found abundantly under boards, stones, or old rubbish. Its body is dorsoventrally com-pressed and nearly uniform in segmentation; there is almost no differentiation of appendages.

The large crustaceans, including lobsters, crabs, shrimps, and prawns, are extensively caught for food. In a single year $9,000,000 worth of these crustaceans were caught by commercial fishermen in the United States. It has been necessary to en-force strict regulations to prevent the threatened extermination of the lobster.

Smaller Fresh-Water Crustacea. Small to micro-scopic crustaceans are exceedingly abundant in lakes and streams. It has been estimated that, on the average, 40,000 exist in every cubic meter of water in the small lakes of Wisconsin. They are indirectly of economic importance in furnishing food to many of the valuable commercial fishes.

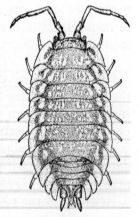

FIG. 120. Sow bug, a land-dwelling crustacean found in damp places ($\times$ 4). From Pratt, *Manual of Invertebrate Animals*; copyright, Blakiston.)

Among the many genera are *Daphnia* (the water flea), *Eubranchipus* (the fairy shrimp), *Cyclops*, and *Cypris*.

Daphnia (Fig. 121) is about a millimeter in length and is especially abundant in fresh water. A contaminated water reservoir in the city of Antwerp was found to contain ten tons of water fleas. Since the body is nearly transparent, the beating of the heart is easily seen through the body wall with low magnification. The organism is of special interest because of the fact that many of the eggs develop in the brood pouch of the female without fertilization. Development of unfertilized eggs is called *parthenogenesis* (Gr. "virgin birth") and is found in various invertebrates. In the fall, males appear and fertilize the large winter eggs. *Eubranchipus* is common among water plants

FIG. 121. *Daphnia* or water flea (× 50). Note right eye and forked antenna. Above the alimentary canal (dark curved streak) is the heart (rounded anterior structure) and the brood sac. (Photomicrograph, copyright by General Biological Supply House, Inc., Chicago.)

in the shallow water of lakes and ponds. It has an elongated body with ten or more pairs of similar swimming appendages. *Cyclops* (Fig. 122) is frequently found in stagnant water and lives well in the laboratory. Because of its single median eye, it was named after the fabulous race of giants. In summer the female is rendered conspicuous by two egg-filled brood pouches attached to the anterior end of her abdomen. As has been noted, the Guinea worm, a parasitic roundworm, reaches its human victim by way of drinking water that contains infected *Cyclops*. *Cypris* has a two-valved shell, suggesting that of a clam.

Sedentary Forms. Barnacles (Fig. 123) are marine crustaceans which attach themselves to rocks, piles, ships, or other animals. They were once regarded as mollusks because of their heavy calcareous shells, but their chitinous, jointed, two-branched appendages re-

FIG. 122. *Cyclops*, dorsal view of female (× 50). Note the median compound eye, the long antennules and shorter antennae, and the pair of egg sacs filled with eggs. (Photomicrograph, copyright by General Biological Supply House, Inc., Chicago.)

veal their true classification. The larvae are free-swimming and closely resemble larvae of some of the more active crustaceans, a fact illustrating the general principle of recapitulation (page 100). The appendages of the adult serve to produce water currents which bring food to the mouth and oxygen to the gills. Rock or acorn barnacles, which have no stalk, often become so numerous on the hulls of ships that it is necessary to take the

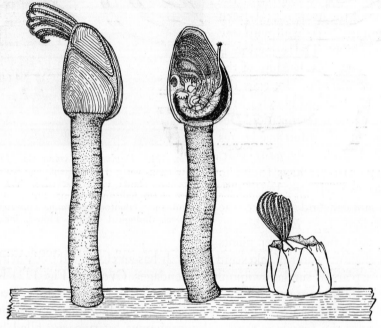

Fig. 123. Barnacles attached to a plank. Left, goose barnacle, external view; center, same with half of shell removed; right, acorn barnacle.

ship into dry dock and remove them. Goose barnacles have stalks and usually live in deeper water.

Parasitic Forms. A number of crustaceans are parasitic on other animals. As is often true of parasites, many of these have undergone much structural simplification. Probably the extreme is illustrated by *Sacculina* (Fig. 124), a species of barnacle. When young, this is an active larva, provided with well-developed sensory and motor organs and closely resembling larval stages of many of the related crustaceans. It soon burrows into a crab, becomes an undifferentiated mass of cells, passes through the blood stream of the host, becomes attached to its intestine, and lives as an internal parasite. Soon a sac-like ovary appears at the base of the abdomen of the crab; the remainder of the parasite's body becomes an extensively

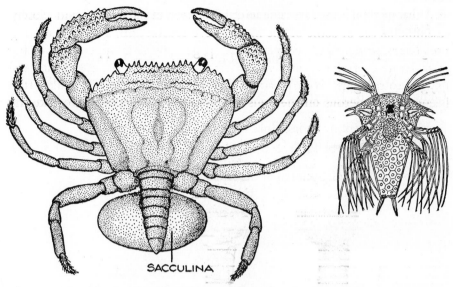

SACCULINA

Fig. 124. *Sacculina*, a typical larval crustacean in its early stage (right), but becoming parasitic and undergoing profound modification on attaining adulthood (left). The adult consists of root-like processes ramifying all parts of the body of the crab, and an external sac, shown beneath the abdomen of the crab, containing reproductive organs and a nerve ganglion. (Larva redrawn from Leuckart.)

branched, root-like structure that penetrates and absorbs food from all parts of the crab's body. The latter continues to live, although its reproductive glands are destroyed.

EXERCISES

1. Why does a current of fresh water need to be kept moving through the gill chamber in gill-breathers? How is such a current maintained in crayfishes? In clams? In fishes?
2. Compare the method of interchange of carbon dioxide and oxygen in the crayfish and the clam.
3. Make a list of the wastes of metabolism in the animal body; show from what foods each is derived, and explain how each is excreted in the crayfish and in the earthworm.
4. List a number of respects in which the crayfish shows higher differentiation than the earthworm.
5. What structure in the earthworm corresponds in function to the gastric mill in the crayfish, and how does it work?
6. Classify as *diploblastic* and *triploblastic* the phyla studied thus far.
7. Why is molting necessary in the ARTHROPODA? How is the new exoskeleton formed?

8. What method is used by commercial fishermen in catching lobsters? Crabs? Shrimps?

REFERENCES

Calman, W. T., *The Life of Crustacea*, The Macmillan Company, 1911.

Comstock, A. B., *Handbook of Nature Study*, Comstock Pub. Co., Inc., 24th ed., 1939.

Smithsonian Scientific Series, Vol. X, Part II, 1931.

Ward, H. B., and Whipple, G. C., *Fresh-Water Biology*, John Wiley & Sons, Inc., 1918.

See also texts in zoology listed in the Appendix.

Chapter XIV

AIR-BREATHING ARTHROPODS

INSECTS

INSECTA (Lat. "cut into") is by far the largest class in the Phylum ARTHROPODA, and in many other respects the most remarkable. It includes at least 700,000 described species, which is more than three-fourths the number of such species for the entire animal kingdom; probably several times this number are still to be described; 270,000 species are contained in the United States National Museum, and it is estimated that 6500 new species are discovered and named each year. Insects are adapted to a wide range of environmental conditions. They live in air, in soil, in fresh or sea water (though they are relatively little represented in the sea), in trunks of trees or in dry wood, in the heat of hot springs or in the cold of the severest winter, and as parasites on animals or plants; one species even lives in crude oil. They can utilize a great variety of foods and many can live practically without water except what they get through their own destructive metabolism. Their food includes almost every form of plant or animal material—rugs, clothing, wooden structures, paper, feathers, dried insect specimens, face powder, mustard, stored grains, cigarettes. Insects have wonderful powers of multiplication, for they lay great numbers of eggs and mature in a short period. A single female fly is estimated to be potentially capable of having five million million descendants in one season; 9.5 million million plant lice might develop from one mother in a single year. A queen bee may lay a thousand eggs a day.

Beneficial Insects. While we ordinarily think of insects as pests, we must give many of them credit for real benefits to man. They produce articles of great commercial importance, such as honey, beeswax, silk, shellac, cochineal, and tannic acid; they carry on or aid in the pollination of our fruits and other useful plants; they serve as food for many of our domestic and game birds and mammals, as well as most of our prized songbirds; they help keep injurious insects and weeds in check; they have aesthetic, scientific, and medicinal values. As examples of these, jewelry is made from colored butterfly wings; the fruit fly (*Drosophila*) has contributed greatly to research in genetics; and the maggots of certain flies, aseptically grown, are valuable in the treatment of certain wounds and bone diseases.

Harmful Insects. On the debit side of the ledger, the damage done by injurious forms is immense. An estimate places this damage for the United States alone at $1\frac{1}{3}$ billion dollars annually. The annual cost of spraying materials to hold injurious insects in check has been placed at 23 million dollars. Ten million dollars was appropriated by the government at one time to fight the European corn borer, and much more has been spent to keep down the cotton boll weevil.

Not only do insects eat all kinds of cultivated plants, but many of them spread the microorganisms or viruses of disease among such plants. Others annoy or attack our domestic animals, often spreading diseases among them. We must be ever alert to save our houses, furnishings, clothing, stored products, and other possessions from destruction by insects. Finally, they cause annoyance and pain to man himself, to say nothing of their propensity for transmitting various human diseases.

General Features. Like the crustaceans, the insects have distinct *segmentation*, a *chitinous exoskeleton*, and *jointed appendages*. The body is divided into three distinct regions: *head, thorax*, and *abdomen* (Fig. 125). The number of appendages is reduced from that usual among the crustaceans to one pair of *antennae*, one pair of *mandibles*, two pairs of *maxillae*, and three pairs of *thoracic legs*. In the embryo all the abdominal segments bear appendages. Some of these remain as abdominal legs in certain insect larvae; but in the adult stage, except for rudiments such as the cerci of a grasshopper, they have disappeared. As in the crayfish, the abdomen has the most evident segmentation. The legs are highly specialized for a great variety of functions, such as walking, swimming, capturing prey, or carrying pollen, or as the seat of the organ of hearing. On the dorsal surface of the thorax there are generally two pairs of *wings*. The anterior (outer) is often mainly protective; the posterior, light and membranous, is fitted for swift and powerful flight. Both sets of wings are stiffened by definite systems of *veins*, which are merely portions of the wing membrane thickened and crimped around tracheae into trough-like or tubular structures. In many insect groups the pattern of these veins is of great value in the identification of species. The posterior end of the abdomen is often modified for copulation or egg-laying.

No adult abdom. append. except cerci of grasshopper

Insects as a rule have compound eyes, which, like those of the crayfish, form a mosaic image, and simple eyes (*ocelli*). The former are especially sensitive to nearby moving objects, and their sensitivity seems to be increased by stimuli received by the ocelli. Many insects have highly sensitive ears, located in such unusual places as the first abdominal segment (grasshopper) or the tibia of the foreleg (cricket and katydid). In others, as in the male mosquito, the antennae have an auditory function.

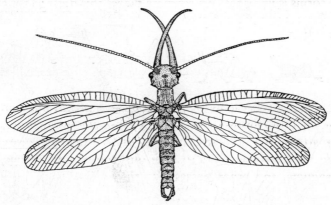

Fig. 125. Dobson fly (*Corydalis*, Order Neuroptera), male, seen from above, with wings in flight position, natural size. The head bears elongated mandibles, antennae, two compound and three simple eyes. The thorax is composed of three segments, each with a pair of legs; each of the posterior two bears a pair of wings. The abdomen consists of nine segments, with short copulatory appendages from the posterior ones. The larva, known as the hellgramite, is used for fish bait.

Internal Structure. Insects have a respiratory system which fits them well for land life, though it is often modified for water-breathing. This system consists of air tubes (*tracheae*) which connect with openings called *spiracles* and ramify through the body, thus reaching nearly all the tissues with a supply of oxygen. The oxygen dissolves in fluid retained in the fine terminal branches of the tracheae, and from here diffuses to the body tissues. The digestive system of insects is highly differentiated and fitted to care for the varied foods already mentioned. In the alimentary canals of termites and wood-eating cockroaches are flagellate protozoans which devour and digest particles of wood or cellulose eaten by their hosts, and in this way nourish the hosts. The latter would die without their protozoan guests. This is an example of mutualism (page 559).

Unlike many animals, insects have blood that carries but little oxygen. The *circulatory system* of a grasshopper consists of (1) an elongated, dorsal, tubular *heart*, located in the pericardial sinus and provided with valves to admit the blood; (2) the *aorta*, extending anteriorly from the heart; and (3) a system of *sinuses*, similar to those of the crayfish, that enable the blood to reach all the organs of the body and return to the heart.

The *muscles* of the insect are exceedingly numerous in comparison with those of vertebrate animals, a caterpillar having some 2000 of the striated,

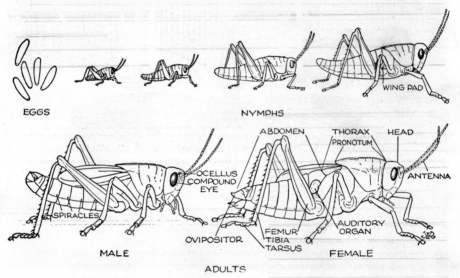

FIG. 126. Metamorphosis and external structure of the lubber grasshopper (*Romalea*, a short-horned grasshopper of the Order ORTHOPTERA; natural size). The chitinous exoskeleton is molted between the successive nymph stages (instars), also between the final nymph stage (with wing pads) and the adult (with mature though, in this species, short wings). The right wings of the female are removed to show the auditory organ. The ocelli are simple eyes.

voluntary type, as compared with about 600 in man. The muscles of flight are especially delicate and capable of producing swift movement. The wings of a honeybee make 400 strokes per second.

Metamorphosis. *Metamorphosis* (Gr. "change of form") is the change in structure undergone by an animal between an immature but active stage and a mature stage. With regard to the extent of this change, insects may be classified as follows:

1. *Gradual*, or *simple*, *metamorphosis*. Egg, nymph, adult. The nymph passes through several *instars* (stages between successive molts), and finally becomes an adult, which is commonly winged. Nymphs have compound eyes and develop their wings externally. Grasshoppers (Fig. 126), bugs. Some

FIG. 127. Metamorphosis of dragonfly (*Aeschna grandis*), an example of incomplete metamorphosis. The nymph (or naiad) climbs a water plant and makes a dorsal slit in the exoskeleton, pulls out its head and thorax, then takes hold with its legs and removes the abdomen. The abdomen and wings expand and stiffen until finally the beautiful iridescent-winged creature is ready to fly away. (Photographs by Ernst Krause, courtesy of *Nature Magazine*, Washington, D.C.)

forms, such as the silverfish and springtail, never develop wings, and are sometimes said to be without metamorphosis. Others, such as the dragonfly (Fig. 127), undergo a somewhat striking change in form as the aquatic nymphs become aerial adults, but still lack the quiescent, or pupal, stage. Their metamorphosis is sometimes referred to as *incomplete*.

2. *Complete*, or *complex, metamorphosis*. Egg, larva, pupa, adult. The larva (e.g., caterpillar, maggot) lacks compound eyes, and often differs from the adult with respect to legs and mouth parts. It goes into a relatively inactive stage, the pupa, which develops wings internally. Butterflies, beetles, flies, bees (Figs. 140–147).

Role of Hormones in Metamorphosis. In some insects, metamorphosis has been found to depend on hormones. During the early life of the caterpillar of the Cecropia moth, the *corpora allata*, a pair of small glands behind the brain, secrete a hormone which serves to prevent premature pupation; but as the time for pupation approaches, this function is discontinued. Certain cells of the brain then secrete another hormone, which stimulates the secretion of a third hormone by the prothoracic glands. When enough of this last hormone has accumulated, the caterpillar is transformed into a pupa, which develops into an adult moth.

Grasshopper Anatomy. The grasshopper (Fig. 126) belongs to the Order ORTHOPTERA (Gr. "straight wings"). The following description applies to any of the numerous species of short-horned grasshopper. The exoskeleton is divided into segments which are grouped, as in all insects, into *head, thorax*, and *abdomen*.

The Head. The head, the controlling region of the body, is made up of a number of firmly joined chitinous plates, the *sclerites*, to which are attached a single pair of *antennae*, two *compound eyes*, three *ocelli*, and the *chewing mouth parts*. The antennae are filiform in shape and consist of many segments to which are attached sensory hairs. The compound eyes are similar to those of the crayfish but are without stalks, and the facets, of which there are a large number, are hexagonal rather than square.

The ocelli are located, one near the middle of the forehead and the others near the bases of the antennae. The *mouth parts* (Fig. 128) consist of (1) a *labrum*, or upper lip; (2) a pair of horny *mandibles* provided with teeth on the inner surface; (3) a pair of maxillae, each consisting of two basal segments and three branches—a toothed *lacinia*, a rounded *galea*, and a jointed *palp* or feeler; (4) a *labium* or lower lip, which represents a fused second pair of maxillae and bears a pair of *palps*; and (5) a central, somewhat club-shaped tongue called the *hypopharynx*. These structures are well adapted for biting and chewing food. The mandibles are moved sideways by strong muscles, thus cutting the food as they come together; the toothed laciniae also aid to some extent in cutting. The other mouth parts aid in grasping the food.

The Thorax. The thorax of a grasshopper (or any insect) consists of three fixed segments, the *prothorax* (Gr. pro, "forward"), the *mesothorax* (Gr. meso, "middle"), and the *metathorax* (Gr. meta, "beyond"). To each of these segments a pair of legs is attached. The wings are attached on the upper side of the two posterior segments. Covering the prothorax dorsally and laterally is a broad collar, the *pronotum*.

The divisions of the legs, starting at the base, are *coxa, trochanter, femur, tibia,* and *tarsus.* The coxa and trochanter are short. There are three segments in the tarsus (four or five in some insects). At the end of the terminal segment are two curved *claws* between which is a glandular pad, the *pulvillus*. The claws aid the insect in sticking to rough surfaces; the pad, to smooth surfaces. The metathoracic leg of the grasshopper has a greatly enlarged femur which contains powerful jumping muscles. The tibia is equipped with many spines along the posterior edge and a sharp spur at the end, enabling the animal to gain a firm foothold as it starts to jump. Two

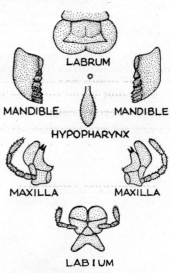

Fig. 128. Mouth parts of the grasshopper, the chewing type.

pairs of breathing pores (*spiracles*) are located in the thoracic region. The anterior wings, which are narrow and leathery, are a help in gliding, and also protect the posterior wings, which are folded like fans beneath the anterior and are of special value in flight.

The Abdomen. The abdomen is made up of eleven segments, which are more clearly defined than those of the head and thorax; each has a *tergum* and a *sternum,* as do the abdominal segments of the crayfish. *Pleura* are present on the thorax but lacking on the abdomen. The foremost abdominal segment is incomplete, having only the tergum, on either side of which is a *tympanic membrane* (covering the organ of hearing). Each complete abdominal segment bears a spiracle on each side. The abdomen of the female terminates in four horny points which constitute the egg-laying apparatus (*ovipositor*); that of the male is blunt and curves upward. Near the tip in both sexes is a pair of rudimentary appendages, small chitinous projections (*cerci*).

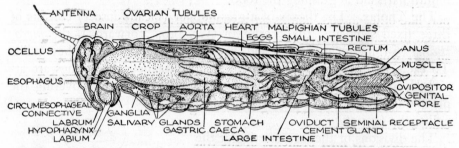

FIG. 129. Internal anatomy of a short-horned grasshopper, as revealed by dissecting away the left side. (Redrawn from Hegner, *College Zoology*, copyright Macmillan.)

Digestive System. All the systems of organs usually present in higher animals are represented in the grasshopper (Fig. 129). They lie within a cavity which, like that of the crayfish, is regarded as a hemocoel instead

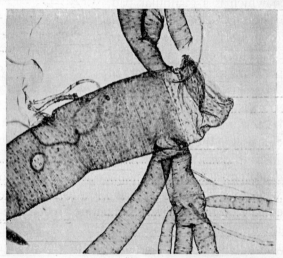

FIG. 130. Respiratory organs of an insect. Portion of a large trachea of a grasshopper (× 120), showing the branching, the reinforcing chitinous rings (dark lines), and the nuclei of the epithelial covering (dark spots). (Photomicrograph, copyright by General Biological Supply House, Inc., Chicago.)

of a coelom. The alimentary canal consists of *mouth, esophagus, crop, gizzard, stomach, large intestine, small intestine,* and *rectum.* Located below the crop on each side is a pair of branched *salivary glands* which run forward and open into the mouth at the base of the hypopharynx. Saliva lubricates the food and contains digestive enzymes. At the junction of gizzard and stomach is a ring of hollow digestive glands, the *gastric caeca*.

Respiratory and Circulatory Systems. The grasshopper, like other insects, admits air through *spiracles* into much-branched *tracheae* (Fig. 130). It has several large *air sacs* which serve as reservoirs for air. The tracheae are reinforced by spiral chitinous threads which prevent their collapse from the pressure of surrounding structures. These threads, suggesting the cartilaginous thickenings of the vertebrate trachea, give the structures their name. The finer branches of the tracheae contain fluid which dissolves oxygen and allows it to diffuse to the cells in its vicinity (Fig. 131). The change of air in the tracheae is accomplished, in part, by the rhythmic contraction of muscles in the abdominal walls accompanied by alternate opening and closing of groups of spiracles. There are no arteries or veins in the circulatory system, the blood passing from the *heart* anteriorly through the *aorta*, thence into the *sinuses* forming the hemocoel, thence into the pericardial sinus, from which it again enters the heart through lateral *ostia*. The blood, like that of the crayfish, contains plasma and white corpuscles. It does not, however, contain a respiratory pigment and has little to do with respiration.

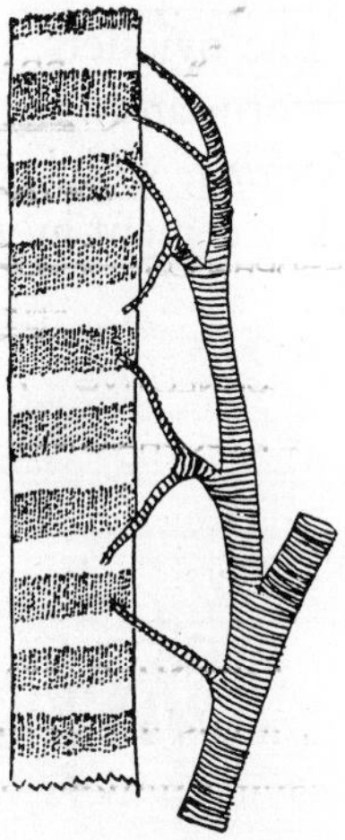

Fig. 131. Striated muscle fiber of a grasshopper (left) and fine tracheal branches which come in contact with it, supplying oxygen and removing carbon dioxide. This direct connection of the cells with the supply lines relieves the circulatory system from participation in the respiratory process.

Excretion. To the constriction between the stomach and intestine are attached many *Malpighian tubules* (named for the Italian biologist Malpighi, 1628–1694, founder of microscopic anatomy); they are wavy and unbranched. They take from the blood the nitrogenous waste as uric acid (instead of urea) and empty it in a solid form into the anterior end of the intestine, whence it passes out through the rectum.

Coordination. As in the earthworm and crayfish, the nervous system of an insect consists of a dorsal *brain*, a *nerve ring* around the esophagus, and a *double, ventral nerve cord* which is enlarged at intervals into two-lobed *ganglia*. The brain, as one would expect from the elaborate sense organs, is rather highly developed and consists of three fused double ganglia. More or less fusion has occurred, also, among the ganglia of the ventral chain. As compared with a vertebrate, an insect has a more fixed type of behavior, based mainly on reflexes and instincts and with less capacity for adjustment to changes in the environment.

Reproduction. Grasshoppers, like all other insects, are *dioecious*. *Ovaries*, *oviducts*, and a single *seminal receptacle* are present in the female. The oviducts, however, instead of having separate exits as in the earthworm and crayfish, unite within the body to form a common tube, the *vagina*, which opens at the genital pore. Cement glands furnish a jelly-like cement in which the eggs are embedded. In the male are paired *testes*,

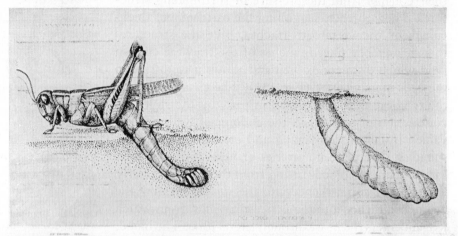

Fig. 132. Left, female two-striped grasshopper (*Melanoplus bivittatus*) laying eggs in the soil; right, complete egg capsule. (From U.S. Dept. Agri., *Farmer's Bulletin 1828*, courtesy of C. M. Packard.)

sperm ducts, and *seminal vesicles*, in the latter of which sperms are stored. Certain accessory glands are also present; these probably furnish a seminal fluid in which sperms are carried. The sperm ducts unite to form an *ejaculatory duct*, at the end of which is a copulating organ, the *penis*. This is used to introduce the sperms into the seminal receptacle, where they remain till the time of egg-laying. When she is ready to lay her eggs, the female drills a hole into the ground almost the length of her abdomen, by successively opening and closing the tips of the ovipositor, and deposits in this hole a mass of eggs (Fig. 132).

As has been indicated (Fig. 126), the grasshopper on hatching looks like the adult, except for the proportionally large head and the absence of wings. Through about five successive molts it undergoes gradual metamorphosis as it grows to adulthood.

Secondary Sex Characters. In addition to differences between the sexes in reproductive organs, many insects exhibit *secondary sex characters;*

these are differences in color, size, antennae, and presence or absence of horns or other structures. Females are generally larger than males, except in some species in which the males fight for a mate, as in the stag beetles. When any difference occurs, the antennae of the males are usually larger, as in mosquitoes and moths. Striking differences in the colors of the sexes are found in many moths and butterflies.

Modifications in Mouth Parts. In a class as widely varied in food habits as are the insects, we find, as we might expect, a wide variety of mouth parts. No matter how extensively modified, they consist fundamentally of

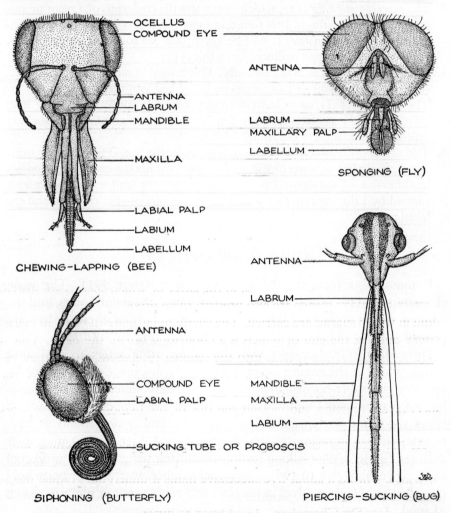

OCELLUS
COMPOUND EYE

ANTENNA

ANTENNA
LABRUM
MANDIBLE

LABRUM
MAXILLARY PALP
LABELLUM

MAXILLA

SPONGING (FLY)

LABIAL PALP
LABIUM
LABELLUM

ANTENNA

CHEWING-LAPPING (BEE)

LABRUM

ANTENNA

COMPOUND EYE
LABIAL PALP

MANDIBLE
MAXILLA

LABIUM

SUCKING TUBE OR PROBOSCIS

SIPHONING (BUTTERFLY)

PIERCING-SUCKING (BUG)

Fig. 133. Four modifications of insect mouth parts. The butterfly head is seen from the right, the others from the front.

the same appendages, although some may be rudimentary or absent and others greatly changed in form and function. They may be classified under the following headings (Figs. 128, 133):

1. The *chewing type*, just described for the grasshopper. This is the most primitive type and is also found in dragonflies, beetles, and several other groups. It is significant that some insects, such as butterflies, which possess this type in the larval stage have a very different type in the adult stage.
2. The *rasping-sucking type*, adapted to lacerating the plant epidermis and sucking the sap. This is found in thrips, a small plant-feeding insect.
3. The *piercing-sucking type*, which penetrates the epidermis of a plant or animal and sucks the fluids. It is found in bugs (HEMIPTERA), in HOMOPTERA, in biting flies, and in lice. It will be noted that the so-called biting insects, such as mosquitoes and bedbugs, have this type.
4. The *sponging type*, as in the housefly. This is used in moistening solid foods and rubbing them into a paste that can be sucked into the mouth.
5. The *siphoning type*, as in butterflies and moths. It consists of a very long tube, coiled like a watch spring when not in use, and employed in sucking exposed liquids such as the nectar of flowers.
6. The *chewing-lapping combination type*, as in the bee. The chewing mandibles are similar to those of the grasshopper, the nectar-lapping tongue is a modification of the central portion of the labium, and a sucking tube is formed by bringing together four trough-like pieces—the maxillae and the labial palps.

ORDERS OF INSECTS

Entomologists recognize 22 or more orders (page 591). The main characters used in separating them are the wings, the mouth parts, and the type of metamorphosis. Only the more important of these orders are presented here.

Orthoptera (Gr. "straight wings"). The name refers to the outer wings, which in the resting insect cover the folded inner ones. The order includes the short-horned grasshoppers (already described); the long-horned grasshoppers (including katydids, Fig. 134); the crickets, of which types are found in houses, fields, and trees, and underground as burrowers; the praying mantises, which grasp food (other insects) with their enlarged forelegs; the walking sticks, which lack wings and are protected by their resemblance to twigs; and cockroaches, world-wide household pests that secrete themselves in crevices and venture out at night in search of food.

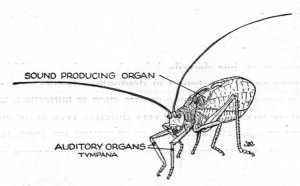

SOUND PRODUCING ORGAN

AUDITORY ORGANS
TYMPANA

Fig. 134. Katydid, a long-horned grasshopper (Order ORTHOPTERA). Note the sound-producing organ, consisting of the overlapping dorsal portions of the forewing bases, and the auditory organs (eardrums) on the front tibiae.

Isoptera (Gr. "equal wings"). The termites ("white ants") are so numerous and destructive of organic materials in tropical countries that in many such places it is impracticable to build houses of wood. They come up from their underground homes, eat away the timbers of buildings, and destroy furniture, clothing, and books. A few species cause damage over much of the United States (Fig. 135). They are somewhat like ants and bees (though of a very different order) in their social organization. The colony consists of a male and a female, which drop their wings after swarming and before burrowing into the ground to form a new colony, which consists of many wingless workers and many wingless soldiers of two or three different ranks. They have chewing mouth parts and undergo gradual metamorphosis.

Odonata (Gr. "toothed"). This order includes the dragonflies (Fig. 127) and the damsel flies so commonly seen about the water where they lay their eggs. They have membranous wings and chewing mouth parts, and undergo incomplete metamorphosis. Dragonflies are known as mosquito hawks because they capture great numbers of mosquitoes from the air. The popular name "devil's darning needle" is based on an unwarranted fear of these harmless and useful insects.

Anoplura (Gr. "unarmed tail"). These insects, the true lice, are wingless, have piercing-sucking mouth parts, and live as parasites on man and other mammals. The metamorphosis is slight. Most common on man are the head louse, the pubic louse, and the body louse, the last-named being especially notorious as the carrier of typhus fever (Fig. 136).

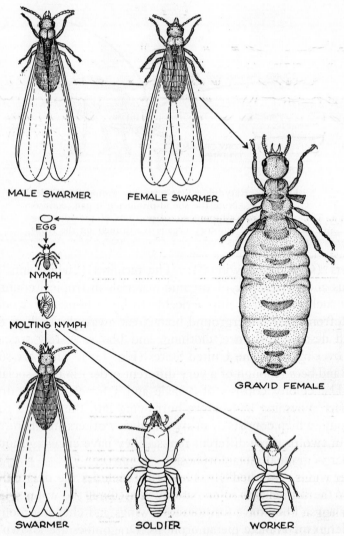

MALE SWARMER   FEMALE SWARMER

EGG

NYMPH

MOLTING NYMPH

GRAVID FEMALE

SWARMER   SOLDIER   WORKER

FIG. 135. Termites or "white ants" (Order ISOPTERA). Stages in the life history of *Reticulitermes flavipes*, a species destructive to wooden structures throughout most of the United States. The abdomen of the gravid female (queen) is distended by many thousands of eggs. Aside from the swarmers (which lose their wings after mating), there are two other castes of males and females—one with wing pads and one with no wings. These substitute for the regular king or queen in case anything happens to one of them. (After Snyder; × 5.)

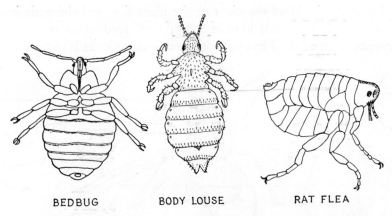

BEDBUG BODY LOUSE RAT FLEA

Fig. 136. Insects attacking or externally parasitic upon man. The bedbug (5 mm. long, Order HEMIPTERA) is shown in ventral view to include the piercing sucking beak; the body louse (2 mm. long, Order ANOPLURA) is in dorsal view; and the flea (2.5 mm. long, Order SIPHONAPTERA) in side view, with appendages on far side omitted. All are wingless but are descendants of winged forms. The louse is instrumental in carrying typhus fever; the flea is the carrier of plague.

Hemiptera (Gr. "half-wings"). HEMIPTERA are the true bugs, many of which are among the most destructive enemies of crops—for example, the chinch bug and the squash bug. The stink bug, the giant water bug (Fig. 137), the water strider, and the back swimmer are other members of the group. They all have piercing-sucking mouth parts and undergo gradual metamorphosis. The order is so named because of the division of the outer wings into a thickened basal half and a thin membranous distal half. When at rest, the membranous parts of the two overlap, giving a pattern suggesting the letter X. In some forms, as in the bedbug, wings are rudimentary or absent (Fig. 136.)

Homoptera (Gr. "similar wings"). Like the preceding order, HOMOPTERA are characterized by piercing-sucking mouth parts and gradual metamorphosis, but the wings, when present, are membranous through-

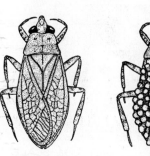

Fig. 137. Water bug (*Belostoma*, Order HEMIPTERA), showing the overlapping of the forewings, the distal parts of which are much thinner than the bases (hence the order name, meaning "half-winged"). Note modification of the front legs into grasping organs and of the others into oars. The male shown on the right is carrying on his back the eggs which have been placed there by the female. His piercing-sucking beak is shown extended. (Natural size.)

out. The order includes the cicadas, the plant lice, and the scale insects. The nymph of the cicada lives in the ground, feeding on roots until its emergence as an adult. The cycle of the dog-day cicada is two years, that

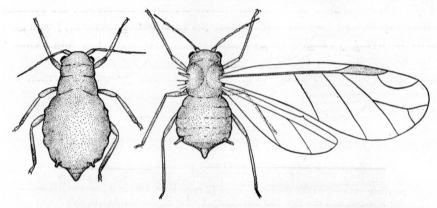

Fig. 138. Aphids or plant lice (Order HOMOPTERA), pests on garden vegetation. Left, wingless parthenogenetic female; right, winged sexual individual showing right wings only. (× 16.)

of the periodic cicada (often called a locust) is 13 years for one strain, 17 for another. As adults, cicadas produce the long, shrill, stridulating sound so commonly heard in the treetops. Plant lice (aphids) and scale insects

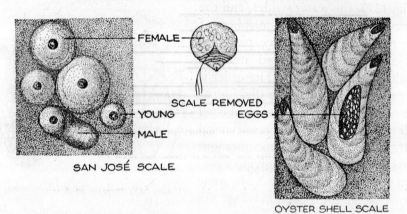

FIG. 139. Armored scale insects (Order HOMOPTERA). These insects, common pests of fruit and shade trees, are stationary on the bark of branches and twigs; each is protected by a waxy scale which it secretes. The male scale insect undergoes complete metamorphosis, emerges from the pupa with a pair of wings but no mouth, then flies to and fertilizes the blind, legless and wingless female. The young are born alive underneath the scale. Note the form of the body of the oyster shell scale (*Lepidosaphes ulmi*) at the small end of the scale. A portion of one of the scales is removed to show the eggs. The San Jose scale is *Aspidiotus perniciosus*. (All × 12.)

are the most destructive Homoptera. Plant lice of various species are exceedingly common on many kinds of plants. They can as a rule be recognized by two wax-secreting tubes on the upper side of the abdomen (Fig. 138). Wingless individuals, which are most numerous, are females which reproduce without fertilization (i.e., parthenogenetically) and give birth to living young. Winged individuals include males and females which mate; the latter then lay eggs. Scale insects are so named from the scale that covers the body (Fig. 139). The San Jose scale which has spread over the country from the West has caused fruit growers millions of dollars of loss annually.

Coleoptera (Gr. "sheath wings"). The largest order of insects, the Coleoptera, includes the beetles. They are characterized by hard, shield-

Fig. 140. Stages in the life history of the Mexican bean beetle (*Epilachna varivestis*, Order Coleoptera) on the lower surface of a bean leaf. Note that the soft leaf tissue has been chewed away, exposing the veins. Upper row, two early larval stages, and adult, with spotted wing sheaths. Lower row, eggs, mature larva, and pupa with remnant of larval skin. (From U.S. Bureau of Entomology, courtesy of N. F. Howard.)

like outer wings under which are neatly folded the broad, membranous inner wings. All have complete metamorphosis and chewing mouth parts in both the larval and the adult stages. Many of them are exceedingly destructive to plants and plant products. One of the best known is the potato beetle, which causes great loss to potato growers every year. The May beetle, also called the June bug, often defoliates trees; its larva, the white grub, is destructive to grass sod, the roots of garden crops and sometimes potato tubers. The Japanese beetle and the Mexican bean beetle (Fig. 140) are crop destroyers that spread over the country in the 1920's. There are many aquatic beetles, and may wood-boring species. In one large group known as snout beetles, the head is prolonged into a long beak at the end of which are the mouth parts; the various species bore into the wood of trees, destroy stored grains, or produce the larvae found in wormy plums and peaches. The carpet beetle is a destructive household pest because of its attacks on carpets and upholstered furniture.

Lepidoptera (Gr. "scale wings"). This large order includes butterflies, moths, and skippers. The wings are covered with colored scales which are so arranged as to produce beautiful and much admired color patterns. Metamorphosis is complete. Chewing mouth parts in the larva, known as a caterpillar, give place to a long, coiled siphoning tube in the adult. Butterflies are diurnal and have clubbed antennae; moths are generally nocturnal and have antennae of other shapes. A caterpillar has three pairs of true legs on the thoracic segments and usually five pairs of temporary unsegmented legs on the abdominal segments. Many species are among the worst enemies of fruit, garden, and field crops, upon which they feed while in the larval stage. The codling moth injures the apple

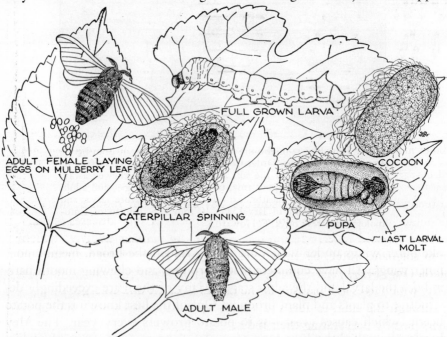

ADULT FEMALE LAYING EGGS ON MULBERRY LEAF

FULL GROWN LARVA

CATERPILLAR SPINNING

COCOON

PUPA

LAST LARVAL MOLT

ADULT MALE

Fig. 141. Life history of the silkworm moth (*Bombyx mori*, Order Lepidoptera), illustrating complete metamorphosis. (Natural size.)

crop; cutworms cut off young stalks of corn and garden vegetables; cabbage worms ruin the cabbage and cauliflower crop; canker worms and tent caterpillars defoliate trees; and the corn ear worm attacks ears of corn and bolls of cotton. The silkworm moth (Fig. 141) is a species highly beneficial to man.

Diptera (Gr. "two wings"). DIPTERA include flies, mosquitoes, midges, and gnats. The order is characterized by complete metamorphosis, either piercing-sucking or sponging mouth parts in the adult, and only one pair of functional wings. In place of a second pair of wings are the *halteres*, stalked knobs that serve as balancers. Larvae of flies are called *maggots;* most of them are headless and footless and have a rasp-like feeding organ. Biting flies suck blood from horses, cattle, and man, and sometimes carry disease organisms on their mouth parts. Houseflies (Fig. 142) breed in

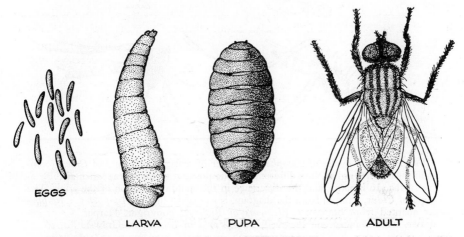

EGGS   LARVA   PUPA   ADULT

FIG. 142. Life history of the housefly (*Musca domestica*). Eggs are laid in manure piles or other filth. Under favorable conditions the fly spends one day in the egg stage, five days as larva, five days as pupa; then an adult emerges which about fourteen days later produces eggs or sperms.

and feed upon filth; from such sources they carry to our foods or our lips, by contact with their hairy bodies, the organisms of such diseases as diarrhea and typhoid fever. Mosquito larvae are the familiar *wigglers* which live in stagnant water; by their bites the adults transmit such diseases as malaria (Fig. 143), yellow fever, and filariasis. The larva of the ox-warble botfly, which lives as a parasite in the tissues of cattle and emerges by boring through the skin, lowers the vitality of cattle and causes millions of dollars' loss by perforating their hides.

Siphonaptera (Gr. from "siphon" and "wingless"). This is the order of fleas, which are similar to flies in their metamorphosis and mouth parts

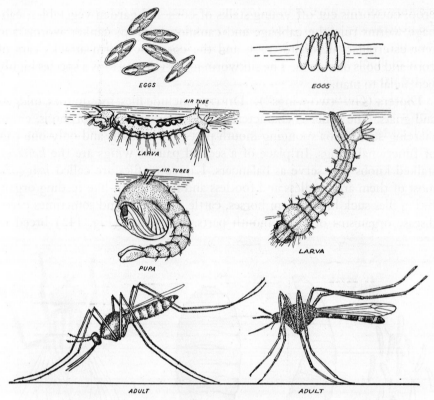

FIG. 143. Life cycles of *Anopheles* (carrier of malaria), left, and of *Culex* (common mosquito), right. Note difference in the position of the larvae when at the water surface to breathe, and the difference in the standing position of the adult. The pupa of *Culex*, omitted from the diagram, is similar to that of *Anopheles*. (*Anopheles* adapted from Buchanan, *Elements of Biology*; copyright, Harper. *Culex* redrawn from Duncan and Pickwell, *The World of Insects*; McGraw-Hill.)

but lack wings. They are blood-sucking parasites on birds and mammals. Aside from annoying the host, they may carry the organisms of disease. The rat flea of India is the principal agent in transmitting the bacillus of bubonic plague (Fig. 136).

Hymenoptera (Gr. "membrane-winged"). HYMENOPTERA are regarded as the most highly developed among insects, in both morphology and behavior. The order includes bees, wasps, ants, sawflies, horntails, ichneumon wasps, and gall wasps. They have membranous wings and chewing-lapping mouth parts and undergo complete metamorphosis; wings are sometimes lacking, as in the workers of the ant colony. Highly developed social organizations are found among the bees, ants, and wasps. The HYMENOPTERA are the only insects provided with stings. The sting is a form of modified ovipositor and is found only in females, including the neutral workers in such forms as the honeybee. The sawflies, such as the currant worm, and the rose slug are injurious to gardens; the pigeon horntail bores in trees. The ichneumons and braconids (Fig. 148) are useful parasites that feed on injurious forms.

Social Organization of Bees. Honeybees have a complex social life in which there is division of labor among individuals. This has apparently evolved from a simpler type of relationship of individuals such as that of

Fig. 144. Adult honeybees (*Apis mellifica*), dorsal view (× 2). Left to right, worker, queen and drone. (Courtesy of Bureau of Entomology and Plant Quarantine, U.S. Dept. Agr.)

bumblebees, which, in turn, has developed from the solitary mode of life still found in many species of wild bees. The hive or colony of the honeybees contains one *queen* or fertile female, several hundred *drones* or males, and approximately sixty thousand *workers* or infertile (nonreproducing) females (Fig. 144). Queens and workers develop from eggs which have been fertilized; drones develop from unfertilized eggs, that is, by a kind of parthenogenesis. Metamorphosis is complete, each legless larva developing in a brood cell of the comb (Figs. 145, 146). The difference between the queen and the worker is determined by the kind of food used in the larval stage, the young workers being fed upon pollen, the so-called beebread, and the queens upon "royal jelly," a secretion from the bodies of the nurse bees. When more than one queen develops, a new colony may be formed by swarming (if the original colony is large enough), or there may be a struggle between the queens until one is victorious and the others are killed.

Structures. The worker honeybee exhibits many adaptations for its various activities. Soon after achieving adulthood the worker serves as a nurse for the young bees (Fig. 146). Later it takes on such duties as the construction and repair of the comb; cleaning, aeration, and defense of the hive; and the gathering of pollen and nectar from flowers. The mouth parts of the worker (Figs. 133, 147) include *mandibles*, which are useful in biting and shaping wax, and a long *proboscis*, consisting of other mouth parts and including a lapping *tongue* with which nectar is obtained. The

Fig. 145. Metamorphosis of honeybee. Egg, young larva, full-grown larva, and pupa, all considerably enlarged. (Courtesy of Bureau of Entomology and Plant Quarantine, U.S. Dept. Agr.)

three pairs of legs bear modifications for handling and carrying pollen. Outstanding among these are the *pollen baskets* on the outer surfaces of the hind tibiae. On the ventral side of the abdomen are the glands that secrete the wax with which the comb is constructed, and at the posterior end of the abdomen is the *sting* which enables the worker to defend the colony against its enemies (though using this weapon generally costs the life of the individual bee, because the worker's sting, unlike that of the queen, is barbed and cannot easily be withdrawn). Nectar is brought back to the hive in the *crop* or *honey stomach;* it is then regurgitated into cells of the comb. Through the action of an enzyme that transforms sucrose into glucose and fructose, with the evaporation of water, the nectar is changed into honey.

Communication. Experiments with honeybees have revealed some interesting facts concerning their ability to perceive their surroundings, to find their way about, and to communicate certain kinds of information

FIG. 146. Nurse bees attending the nearly grown larvae which can be seen in the open cells of the comb. The capped cells contain pupae. (Courtesy of *Nature Magazine*, Washington, D.C.)

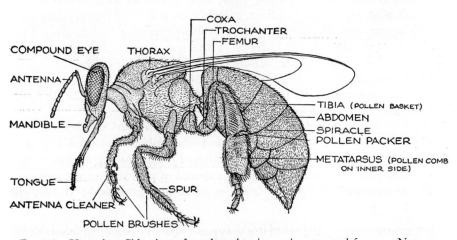

FIG. 147. Honeybee. Side view of worker, showing main structural features. Note especially the modifications of mouth parts and legs that adapt the bee for securing nectar and pollen from flowers. The mandible is the biting jaw.

from one individual to another. Especially interesting are the discoveries of the German investigator von Frisch concerning the ways in which a worker honeybee informs other individuals of the whereabouts of a source of food. Such information is conveyed by dancing. If the source of food is close to the hive (less than about 300 feet), the bee dances in a circular path; but if the food is far, the bee dances in a straight line, wagging the abdomen at a rate approximately inversely proportional to the distance of the food. The direction of the distant food source is disclosed by the direction of the "tail-wagging" dance; this dance is straight up if the food source is in the same direction from the hive as the sun, but otherwise it deviates from the vertical by an angle corresponding to the angle between the direction of the food and that of the sun.

Control of Insects. Since so many insects are detrimental to man's crops, his property, his comfort, and his health, he has devised various means of combating them. These means may be grouped under four general headings:

1. *Mechanical methods* include fly swatters, sticky bands on trees to capture crawling insects, trenches to stop grasshopper migrations, and the like.
2. *Chemical methods* vary with type of insect. For insects with chewing mouth parts, like grasshoppers, beetles, and caterpillars, *stomach poisons* such as lead arsenate may be used. *Contact poisons*, which are employed to kill many types of insects, include oils, soap solutions, nicotine sulfate, and DDT, a highly effective nerve paralyzer which was first put into use during World War II, particularly for killing the body louse which transmits the typhus fever organism. *Poison gases,* such as carbon disulfid and hydrocyanic acid, are used in buildings, greenhouses, and other places where gases can be confined. *Repellents,* such as naphthalene, keep insects away from clothing and other objects likely to be attacked. A promising new development is the use of *systemic insecticides,* which are substances (e.g., phosphorus organic compounds) which may be taken up by a plant through its roots or leaves and which, though harmless to the plant, make the plant poisonous to insects that feed on it.
3. *Cultural methods* include crop rotation, destruction of weeds, and early disposal or plowing under of stubble and other rubbish from fields.
4. *Biological methods* include the destruction of organisms that aid insect pests (such as poisoning ants to prevent the spread of aphids) and the introduction or encouragement of predatory or parasitic organisms that destroy the pests.

Important among the predatory types used in biological control are lady beetles and lacewing flies, which feed upon aphids and scale insects. Some years ago the cottony cushion scale threatened destruction of the citrus fruit trees in California. When it was learned that this insect had come with nursery stock from Australia, entomologists from California studied the situation in Australia and found that the scale is not troublesome there because it is held in check by a certain lady beetle. The consequent introduction of this beetle into California saved the orchards from the pest. A common parasitic insect is a small braconid wasp belonging to the Order HYMENOPTERA. The eggs are laid on a tomato caterpillar or other moth larva. The larva of the parasite burrows through and feeds upon the tissues of its host, but with uncanny skill avoids vital organs. After a time the parasite larvae come to the surface of the host, where they form cocoons which protrude in all directions (Fig. 148). Again,

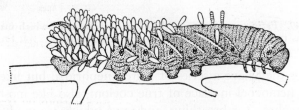

FIG. 148. Larva of the tomato sphinx moth ("tomato worm"), parasitized by braconid wasps which have spun cocoons after emerging from the host. Near the head of the host are two braconid larvae which have just emerged and have not yet formed cocoons.

on aphid-covered leaves one frequently sees the brown empty skin of the aphid, with a trap door at the top through which a similar parasitic wasp has emerged after destroying the aphid. The Kansas wheat crop was saved one year from the grain aphid by the introduction of this parasite. Still other wasps, some of them minute, are parasitic on the eggs of chinch bugs, moths, and other insects. They have proved of great value, for with their aid the cotton "worm" of the South, a pest that has caused losses of as much as fifteen million dollars in one year, was eventually held in complete check. Fungi are sometimes used to produce epidemics among destructive insects. Birds, snakes, and toads are helpful in keeping insects in check.

OTHER CLASSES OF ARTHROPODS

Onychophora. The Class ONYCHOPHORA (Gr. "claw bearer") includes a few species of shy, worm-like animals found in several tropical areas but little known except to biologists (Fig. 149). They are of interest because they are thought to represent a possible transitional evolutionary stage between the annelids and the air-breathing arthropods. The segments of the body are not marked externally. A rather indistinct segmentation of the appendages indicates the transitional position of the animal.

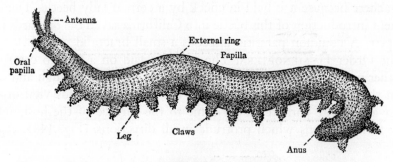

FIG. 149. *Peripatus*, member of the Class ONYCHOPHORA which may be regarded as transitional between annelids and arthropods (× 2½). From Hegner, *College Zoology;* copyright, Macmillan.)

Like annelids they have a series of paired nephridia, but like arthropods they have a hemocoel in place of true coelom; also like most arthropods they have tracheae for breathing, and jaws which are modified appendages.

Chilopoda and Diplopoda. The CHILOPODA (Gr. "lip-footed," Fig. 150) are the centipedes, and the DIPLOPODA (Gr. "double-footed," Fig. 151) are the millipedes. These are elongated animals with all segments

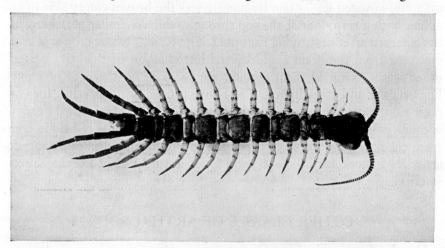

FIG. 150. A centipede (Class CHILOPODA), about natural size. The body segments, which vary somewhat in length, each have a pair of appendages. Centipedes prey on small animals which they benumb or kill with their poison claws (partly concealed by the head in the figure). (Photo, copyright by General Biological Supply House, Inc., Chicago.)

similar, except those of the head, and with all appendages walking legs, except the antennae and mouth parts. Centipedes have one pair of legs to each body segment. All but the first few segments of a millipede's body are abdominal, and each of these bears two pairs of legs. Members of both

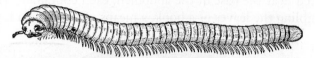

Fig. 151. A millipede (*Spirobolus*) representing the Class DIPLOPODA. Each of the four thoracic segments bears a pair of legs; each of the numerous abdominal segments, two pairs. Millipedes feed on plants and dead organic matter. (From Storer, *General Zoology*, McGraw-Hill Book Company; courtesy of the author and the publisher.)

groups have one pair of antennae and, like insects, breathe by means of tracheae. Centipedes live on small animals which they capture by means of a pair of poison claws, the appendages of the first segment back of the head. Large tropical species may inflict painful bites in self-defense. Millipedes live wholly on vegetable food.

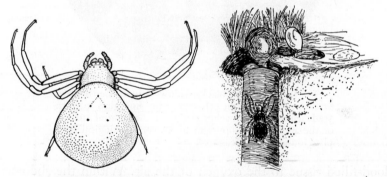

Fig. 152. Spiders. Left, crab spider, a yellow species common on vegetation (dorsal view, × 3). Antennae and compound eyes are wanting. Note the eight simple eyes (ocelli), the division of the body into cephalothorax and abdomen, and the chelicerae and pedipalpi in front of the four pairs of walking legs. Right, trap door spider in its tunnel. An open and a closed tunnel are also indicated. (Right figure redrawn from Jordan and Heath.)

Arachnoidea. The Class ARACHNOIDEA (Gr. "spider-like") includes spiders, harvestmen, mites, ticks, scorpions, and king crabs. They lack antennae, their head and thorax are in one piece, and they usually have four pairs of walking legs. A spider (Fig. 152) has as its first pair of appendages modified mandibles, or *chelicerae*, connected with which are poison glands. With the sharp claws of these mandibles, aided by the poison, it kills its prey, whereupon it sucks the body juices. The second pair of appendages are *pedipalpi* (Gr. "foot feelers"); then come the four pairs of legs. Respiration is carried on by *tracheae* (of limited extent compared with those of insects), and by a pair of *book lungs*. The latter are sacs ventrally situated near the base of the abdomen, each containing 15 to 20 flat plates resembling the leaves of a book, a means of exposing a large surface

Fig. 153. Female black widow spider, *Latrodectus mactans*, showing the characteristic hourglass pattern (red against black background) on the ventral surface of the abdomen. (Copyright by General Biological Supply House, Inc., Chicago.)

of blood-filled tissue to the oxygen of the air. Within the abdomen are large *silk glands* which connect with three pairs of *spinnerets* on the ventral surface. These are blunt projections, each perforated with many fine holes through which the secretion of the glands is squeezed in the form of delicate threads, often several hundred in number. These threads harden on exposure to the air, remaining in a tangled mass or becoming united into a single firm thread. The silk is used in spinning webs or snares for catching the prey, in making cocoons in which the eggs are placed, or in lining burrows. A remarkable example of the latter use is seen in the trap-door spider, which digs a perpendicular tunnel in the ground and over the top fits a neat hinged door made of earth and strengthened with a lining of web (Fig. 152). When pursued by an enemy, the owner darts

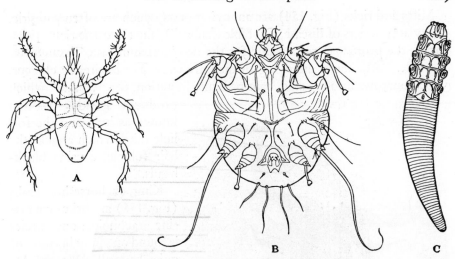

FIG. 154. Some mites parasitic upon and annoying to man. *A*, Chigger or harvest mite, the six-legged larval stage which burrows in the skin, causing inflammation; *B*, itch mite; *C*, follicle mite, the organism that causes blackheads. (*A* redrawn from Osborn; *B* and *C*, from Hirst.)

FIG. 155. King or horseshoe crab (*Limulus poly-phemus*), which inhabits the quiet shallow waters of the Atlantic coast and represents one of the oldest groups of the ARACHNOIDEA. At left, in natural walking position; at right, inverted. (Photos by L. W. Brownell.)

into the burrow and closes the door, which is seldom broken open. The orb weavers spin accurately constructed webs in which they lie in wait for their prey. The black widow spider (Fig. 153), which is distributed throughout the United States, frequently lives in houses and other places of human construction; it is our most poisonous spider, its bite being accompanied by very painful, sometimes fatal, results.

Mites and ticks (Fig. 154) are annoying pests which are often parasitic. Many are carriers of disease, a notable example being the cattle tick, which carries the protozoan responsible for the destructive disease, Texas fever, in cattle. Particularly annoying to man are the harvest mite, or chigger, which burrows into the skin, causing acute irritation; the itch mite, which produces a skin eruption known as itch; and the follicle mite, which attacks the hair follicle, causing blackheads.

King or horseshoe crabs (Fig. 155) are primitive marine arachnoids; one species is found on sandy bottoms of quiet bays all along the Atlantic coast. The large head and thorax are united into a horseshoe-shaped piece, behind which lies the triangular abdomen with a long spine-like tail. Similar forms called trilobites (Fig. 398) lived in the Paleozoic Era several hundred million years ago and were the probable ancestors of modern ARACHNOIDEA. The young king crab bears a striking resemblance to a trilobite.

FIG. 156. Scorpion. The five pairs of legs are attached to the cephalothorax. The abdomen consists of a broad portion and a slender, tail-like portion terminating in a sting with its poison sac. (Photo by Cornelia Clark.)

The scorpion (Fig. 156) is a nocturnal animal with a poisonous sting at the tip of the long jointed abdomen. This sting is used in stunning the larger prey, and as a weapon of defense. It is painful to man, but rarely dangerous.

EXERCISES

1. What mode of control would you employ for aphids? For Mexican bean beetles? Give reasons for difference.
2. State the habits of the digger wasp, *Sphex* (or *Ammophila*), in connection with provisioning the nest for the young.
3. To which order does the spittle insect belong, and what gives it its name?

4. Describe the structural device for sound-making in the cricket; the katydid; the cicada. Of what benefit to these insects are the sounds produced?
5. To what group do yellow jackets belong, what kinds of nests do they build, and where do they obtain their building material?
6. What is a hellgramite and for what is it used?
7. What differences distinguish the workers, the queens, and the drones of the honeybee? What kind of egg develops into each, and what food does the larva of each receive?
8. What is a plant gall? What kind of insects and arachnoids are responsible for the various galls?
9. List ten kinds of insects that are destructive to crops in your locality; name the food of each and an effective means for the control of each.
10. Describe the mutual relationship between aphids and ants, stating its advantage to each.
11. What are the locusts mentioned in Exodus 10:12–19? When and where did a similar visitation occur in American history?
12. To what part of the spectrum of sunlight is a honeybee sensitive? How has this been determined?

REFERENCES

Brues, C. T., *Insects and Human Welfare*, Harvard Univ. Press, 1947.

Chu, H. F., *How to Know the Immature Insects*, William C. Brown Company, 1949.

Comstock, J. H., *Introduction to Entomology*, Comstock Publishing Co., Inc., 9th ed., 1940.

Crompton, J., *The Life of the Spider*, Houghton Mifflin Company, 1951.

Duncan, C. D., and Pickwell, G., *The World of Insects*, McGraw-Hill Book Company, Inc., 1939.

Essig, E. O., *College Entomology*, The Macmillan Company, 1942.

Fabre, H., *Book of Insects*, Dodd, Mead & Co., Inc., 1921. Also various other works.

Haskins, C. P., *Of Ants and Men*, Prentice-Hall, Inc., 1939.

Imms, A. D., *Outlines of Entomology*, E. P. Dutton & Co., Inc., 1942.

Jaques, H. E., *How to Know the Insects*, William C. Brown Company, 2nd ed., 1947.

Jaques, H. E., *How to Know the Beetles*, William C. Brown Company, 1951.

Matheson, R., *Entomology for Introductory Courses*, Comstock Publishing Co., Inc., 2nd ed., 1951.

Metcalf, C. L., Flint, W. P., and Metcalf, R. L., *Destructive and Useful Insects*, McGraw-Hill Book Company, Inc., 3rd ed., 1951.

Snodgrass, R. E., *Anatomy and Physiology of the Honeybee*, McGraw-Hill Book Company, Inc., 1925.

Snodgrass, R. E., *Principles of Insect Morphology*, McGraw-Hill Book Company, Inc., 1925.

Thorp, R. W., and Woodson, W. D., *Black Widow, America's Most Poisonous Spider*, Univ. of North Carolina Press, 1945.

Von Frisch, K., *Bees—Their Vision, Chemical Senses, and Language*, Cornell Univ. Press, 1950.

West, L. S., *The Housefly*, Comstock Publishing Co., Inc., 1951.

Wigglesworth, V. B., *The Principles of Insect Physiology*, Methuen & Co., Ltd., 4th ed., 1950.

Yearbook of Agriculture, *Insects*, United States Department of Agriculture, 1952.

See also zoology texts listed in the Appendix, and the many pamphlets and bulletins issued by the U.S. Department of Agriculture and by state experiment stations.

Chapter XV

ECHINODERMS

Distribution and General Features. The ECHINODERMATA (Gr. "spiny-skinned") are found only in sea water. A few are attached, but the majority are free to move about. Most of the group possess radial symmetry, the type that is most often associated with stationary or slow-moving habits. Apparently they have evolved from bilaterally symmetrical ancestors, for young echinoderms are bilateral, and even the adults often show traces of bilateral symmetry. Hence they are said to have *secondary radial symmetry*. The skeleton, generally present, is composed of calcareous plates just beneath the ectoderm. The alimentary canal usually extends through the body near the axis of symmetry, and is surrounded by a spacious coelom. This is the only phylum that has a *water-vascular system*, a water-pressure mechanism serving mainly for locomotion but aiding in touch and food getting.

Relationships and Classification. The echinoderms are here considered just before the chordates because, although superficially very unlike the latter, there is a growing conviction that similarities in the early embryological development imply relationship between the two groups; furthermore, their larvae resemble that of *Balanoglossus*, a simple chordate. The phylum is divided into five classes, as follows:

1. ASTEROIDEA (Gr. "starlike"): starfishes, or sea stars.
2. OPHIUROIDEA (Gr. "like a serpent's tail"): brittle stars, basket stars.
3. ECHINOIDEA (Gr. "hedgehog-like"): sea urchins, sand dollars.
4. HOLOTHUROIDEA (Gr. "like a water polyp"): sea cucumbers.
5. CRINOIDEA (Gr. "lily-like"): sea lilies.

Starfishes. The starfish has a star-like body with radiating arms, usually five but somewhat variable in number (Fig. 157). Its surfaces may be designated as the *oral* (mouth) and the *aboral* (opposite mouth), the latter being normally uppermost. The *mouth* opens upward into the *stomach*, which has distinct compartments known as the *cardiac* and the *pyloric*;

from the latter a small, short *intestine* leads to the little-used *anus* in the center of the aboral surface. A pair of *digestive glands* in each arm connects by a duct with the pyloric stomach. The calcareous plates of the skeleton form a network and are united by flexible joints which permit considerable freedom of movement. Locomotion is carried on by means of hundreds of *tube feet* located in the grooves on the oral side of the arms (Figs. 157, 158). At the base of each tube foot, just inside the skeletal framework, is a bladder-like sac called the *ampulla* (Lat. "flask"). Tube feet and ampullae constitute part of the water-vascular system, which communicates with the outside sea water by means of a sieve-like plate (*madreporite*) located on the aboral surface between two of the arms. When the circular muscles of the ampulla contract, they force water into the tube foot, causing its distension. The disk at its tip adheres to the surface over which the animal is moving; then the longitudinal muscles of the foot contract and pull the animal forward. The pull of the tube feet is supplemented by movements of the flexible arms. The starfish feeds on various marine animals, chiefly mollusks (Fig. 157). It opens a clam by exerting a steady pull on the valves of the shell until the two large muscles that hold the valves together yield. It is probable that a substance secreted by the starfish aids in the relaxation of these muscles. Then the stomach of the starfish is everted from the mouth and wrapped about the soft body of the clam, which is digested by means of enzymes secreted by the digestive glands; it is then absorbed by the stomach. As in *Hydra*, the indigestible parts of the food are egested through the mouth.

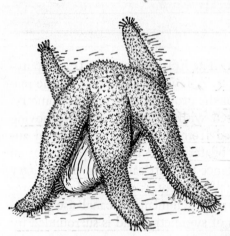

Fig. 157. Starfish feeding on a clam. Note the sieve plate (light spot just off the aboral center), and the tube feet shown near the tips of the arms. For the feeding process, see the text. (From Wieman, *General Zoology*; copyright, McGraw-Hill.)

The *coelom* of a starfish is very large and contains a lymph-like circulating fluid; the true circulatory system is rudimentary. There are numerous small outpushings of the body wall known as *skin gills* (*dermal branchiae*), through which oxygen enters the coelomic fluid and carbon dioxide is given off from it. The body surface is also roughened with blunt calcareous *spines*. Around the bases of these spines are numerous microscopic pincers (*pedicellariae*), the function of which seems to be the removal of any debris that might accumulate over the gills. The nervous system consists of a *nerve ring* around the mouth and radial nerves along each arm. The sense organs are (1) *touch endings*, which are especially developed in the tube feet; (2) a pigmented *eyespot*, sensitive to light, at the end of each arm; (3) a short *tentacle* thought to be an organ of taste, also at the end of each arm. The sexes are separate; a pair of *testes* or *ovaries* is located at each interval between the bases of the arms. The sperms and eggs discharge through ducts leading to the aboral surface into the sea water, where fertilization occurs.

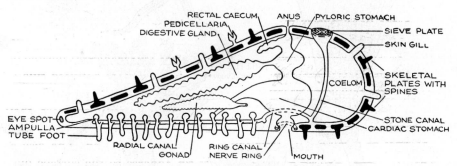

Fig. 158. Median section of body center and one arm of a starfish, showing the principal organs diagrammatically.

Brittle Stars. Brittle stars have arms more flexible and slender than those of the starfish. These serve as the only means of locomotion, the tube feet being merely organs of touch. In the basket stars the arms are repeatedly branched and have tendril-like tips. For illustrations of this and the following classes, see Fig. 159, page 216.

Sea Urchins. Sea urchins are usually hemispherical, and like the starfish have the oral surface below. The intestine makes a turn about the coelom, then reverses for another turn. Projecting from the mouth are five white teeth which connect with a complicated muscular structure known as *Aristotle's lantern*. The body is covered with conspicuous long spines which supplement the thread-like tube feet in locomotion. The skeletal plates unite to form a continuous firm shell. Sand dollars are similar to sea urchins in structure, but are flat on the oral and slightly convex on the aboral side, and have much smaller spines.

Sea Cucumbers. The body of a sea cucumber is elongated along the axis of symmetry and has a muscular wall almost without skeletal plates. The animals often bury themselves in the mud or sand, with only the tentacles projecting. These are modified tube feet surrounding the mouth.

Sea cucumbers do not move sidewise, as do starfishes and sea urchins, but stretch the body along the sea floor. Many species have differentiated dorsal and ventral surfaces, thus showing a tendency toward bilateral symmetry.

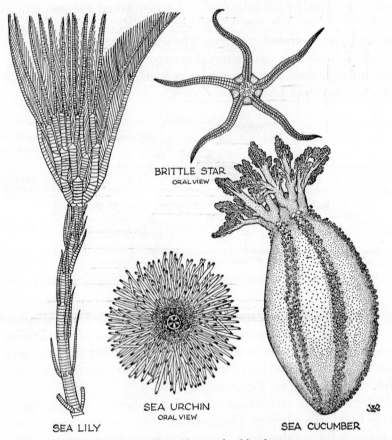

BRITTLE STAR
ORAL VIEW

SEA URCHIN
ORAL VIEW

SEA LILY

SEA CUCUMBER

Fig. 159. Four classes of echinoderms.

Sea Lilies. These organisms are generally attached by the aboral end, the five much-branched arms being somewhat suggestive of the petals of a flower. Some species break from the stalk and swim about at maturity. They are among the oldest of the echinoderms, and are often found as fossils in limestone beds.

Regeneration. All echinoderms have remarkable powers of regeneration. Not only does the starfish restore lost arms (Fig. 160), but a single arm with part of the disk attached will grow into a new individual. The starfish and brittle star have the power to cast off an injured arm near its base, as a preliminary to growing a sound one.

This cutting-off process, called *autonomy* (Gr. "self-cutting"), has already been mentioned in connection with crustaceans. When the sea cucumber is disturbed, it sometimes casts out its digestive and respiratory organs. Slimy threads secreted by the latter may entangle and incapacitate an enemy, and the missing organs are soon regenerated.

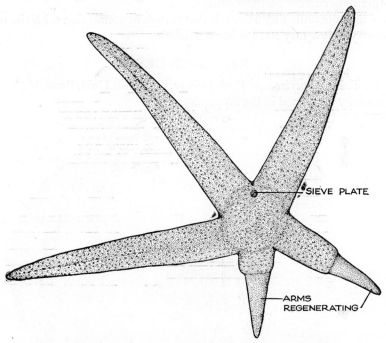

Fig. 160. Aboral view of a starfish, showing the partial regeneration of two arms that have been severed.

Experimental Embryology. Because of the ease with which they can be fertilized and developed in the laboratory, echinoderm eggs have been much used in embryological experiments. Jacques Loeb (1859–1924) and others reared normal larvae from unfertilized eggs by stimulating the eggs with salts, fatty acids, or other chemicals, by increasing the concentration of the sea water, or by using mechanical or electrical stimulation. This is known as *artificial parthenogenesis*. In other experiments, the eggs of one species of sea urchin were stimulated to develop by the application of sperms of another species; also, fragments of egg from which the nucleus had been removed were induced to grow after the introduction of a sperm nucleus. These experiments illustrate the importance of the nucleus as a controller of growth, and the approximate equality in value of sperm and egg nuclei.

EXERCISES

1. Find out what you can about the use of sea cucumbers ("trepang") as food.
2. What is the literal meaning of "parthenogenesis"? Give two examples of naturally occurring parthenogenesis.
3. Of what economic importance is the starfish in connection with the oyster industry? How may starfish be controlled?

REFERENCES

Morgan, T. H., *Experimental Embryology*, Columbia Univ. Press, 1927.
Any zoology text listed in the Appendix.

Chapter XVI

CHORDATES

Invertebrates and Vertebrates. Zoologists of a century ago divided the animal kingdom into *invertebrates*, those without backbones, and *vertebrates*, those with backbones. It was later realized that the invertebrates are too diverse to be included in a single phylum; hence the phyla we have already discussed were established. There are a few forms which, although they have no true backbone, have at some stage in their development a rod of turgid cells, the *notochord* (Gr. "back cord"). Such a structure is also present in the embryo vertebrate before the backbone appears. The forms just mentioned are called *prevertebrates*, and they, with the true vertebrates, constitute the Phylum CHORDATA (Gr. "with cord"). All chordates agree in having at some time in their life history:

1. A dorsal skeletal axis, known as the *notochord*, which in most cases is later replaced by a backbone.

2. Paired *gill slits* through the side walls of the pharynx, leading directly or indirectly to the exterior of the body. In the higher, air-breathing classes, these are normally functionless grooves that do not break through and that disappear or become modified during the later development of the embryo.

3. A dorsal, tubular *nerve cord*, just above the notochord.

There are four subphyla of chordates. The first three—HEMICHORDATA, UROCHORDATA, and CEPHALOCHORDATA—constitute the prevertebrates; VERTEBRATA, including the true vertebrates, is by far the largest. We shall first notice briefly the prevertebrate subphyla.

PREVERTEBRATES

Hemichordata (Gr. "half cord"). These little-known marine forms look much like worms but resemble other chordates in having a suggestion of a notochord, gill slits along the sides of the body, and a poorly de-

veloped dorsal nerve axis. The notochord is suggested by a stiffened tube
of cells extending from the dorsal wall of the mouth forward into the
proboscis. The form usually studied is the acorn worm, or balanoglossid
(Gr. "acorn tongue," because the proboscis protrudes like an acorn from
its cup), which burrows in sand or mud along the seashore (Fig. 161).
The ancestors of the present vertebrates were lacking in bony tissue and
hence have not persisted as fossils. But we can easily speculate that they
may have borne some resemblance to the HEMICHORDATA. Similarities in

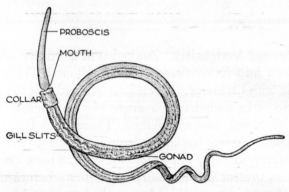

FIG. 161. The acorn or balanoglossid worm (*Saccoglossus kowalevskii*), one of the lowest of organisms
that have chordate affinities. The notochord is restricted
to the collar region. (Slightly enlarged.)

the early embryological development of the chordates and the echinoderms, however, are strongly suggestive of a common origin for these two
phyla, which seems remarkable when we consider the wide difference between them in the adult stage. The suggestion of common origin is given
added support by the striking resemblance between the larva of the acorn
worm and that of an echinoderm. These two phyla, then, seem to represent one great branch of the evolutionary tree; the flatworms, mollusks,
annelids, and arthropods, which agree among themselves in certain embryological details, represent another (Fig. 41).

In a typical invertebrate the main nerve axis is on the ventral side and
the heart is on the dorsal, whereas in the typical chordate these organs are
reversed. This leads many to believe that an inversion of the body may
somehow have taken place in the course of chordate evolution. Body
segmentation, which occurs to some extent in the chordate, seems to have
arisen independently of that in the annelid-arthropod line.

Urochordata (Gr. "tail cord"). The typical representatives of URO-
CHORDATA are the sea squirts or tunicates, which in their adult stage have

little in common with vertebrates, for they appear as sac-like or irregular lumps attached to rocks or piles near the sea margin. Only by observing them in an early stage are we able to classify them. The larval tunicate is somewhat like a small tadpole in shape and structure, having gill slits, a distinct notochord, and a dorsal nerve cord. It soon becomes attached to some suitable support by its anterior end and then undergoes a remarkable metamorphosis in the course of which tail and notochord are eliminated (Fig. 162).

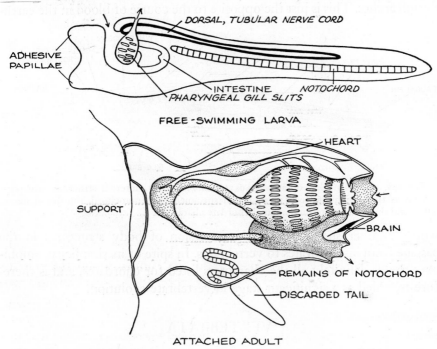

Fig. 162. A tunicate or sea squirt, larval and adult stages shown diagrammatically and not to the same scale. Arrows show the course of the water that brings in the food and oxygen. It will be noted that the larva possesses all three chordate characters (italicized in figure). These characters are less obvious in the adult, for the notochord degenerates and the nerve ganglion (labeled brain) becomes insignificant.

Cephalochordata (Gr. "head cord," because the notochord extends into the head). The lancelet, commonly called amphioxus (Gr. "sharp at both ends"), is a spindle-shaped animal about two inches long; it looks somewhat like a fish but is much simpler in structure (Fig. 163). Hundreds of tons taken from the mouths of Chinese rivers are used as food each year. It has no true brain or limbs. The body wall contains prominent V-shaped muscles. The notochord is a dorsally placed rod extending the whole length of the body and composed of vacuolated cells which by reason of their turgor afford some rigidity to the body. Water from the pharynx passes through the gill slits into a chamber called the *atrium*, whence it reaches the exterior. Its passage through the slits enables it to furnish dissolved oxygen to the blood as the latter flows through the gill arches which bound the slits. There is no heart, but the blood vessels have muscular walls. The blood flows backward in the dorsal vessel, downward in the intestinal laterals, forward in the ventral vessel, and upward through the gill arches. This is just the opposite to the course of blood in the earth-

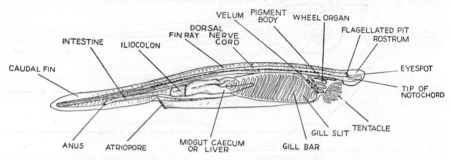

FIG. 163.   The lancelet, or amphioxus (*Branchiostoma*). Internal structures are portrayed as they might be seen in a cleared specimen. The notochord, the dorsal nerve cord, and the gill slits are fundamental chordate characters.

worm, another suggestion of the inversion of body structures in the passage from invertebrates to vertebrates. In spite of its simplicity, amphioxus shows definitely all the characters listed for chordates, and is therefore regarded as a significant stage in vertebrate evolution.

VERTEBRATA

General Characteristics.   The vertebrates have, in addition to the characters already noted for chordates in general, the following:

1. Around the notochord is developed a sheath of cartilage or bone divided into segments, or *vertebrae*, and constituting the *vertebral* (*spinal*) *column* or *backbone*. Each vertebra (Fig. 164) has a *centrum*, and a *neural arch* which surrounds the nerve cord. The notochord itself may persist (as in fishes), or it may disappear. In addition to the vertebrae, other elements of cartilage or bone, constituting an *endoskeleton*, support the body.

2. The anterior end of the nerve tube is enlarged into a *brain*, which is enclosed in a cartilaginous or bony case called the *cranium*.

3. There are two pairs of *appendages*, except in the primitive class

CYCLOSTOMATA and in some other forms which have undergone loss of these organs. The appendages, or *limbs*, generally contain internal skeletal elements, and these are associated with basal supporting structures, the

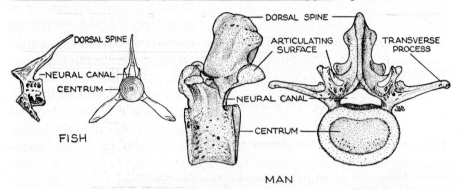

FIG. 164. Vertebrae of fish and man, showing left side view and anterior view. Remains of the notochord occupy the small opening in the centrum of the fish vertebra.

limb girdles. The anterior limbs and their girdles are called *pectoral*, and the posterior ones are called *pelvic*.

4. The *heart* is ventrally placed, with two to four chambers, and the *blood*, which contains red corpuscles, flows through a closed system of vessels.

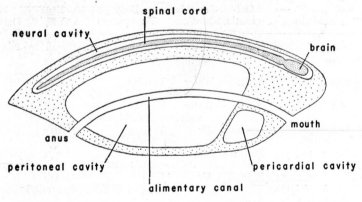

FIG. 165. Body plan of a vertebrate in longitudinal section. Highly diagrammatic.

5. The body has two important longitudinal cavities: (1) the dorsally situated *cranium* and *neural canal*, containing the brain and spinal (nerve) cord respectively; (2) the *coelom*, or body cavity (Figs. 165, 166). The latter is subdivided; its smaller anterior portion, the *pericardial cavity*, contains the heart, and the visceral organs lie in its larger posterior portion,

the *peritoneal cavity*. In mammals the peritoneal cavity is further divided into the *pleural cavities*, which contain the lungs, and the *abdominal cavity*, posterior to the *diaphragm*, which contains the stomach, intestines, pancreas, and spleen. The mesoderm of the vertebrate splits, as does that of the earthworm, into an external portion, which makes up most of the body wall, and an internal portion, which forms most of the wall of the alimentary canal. Also as in the earthworm, the coelom is completely lined with a layer of cells known as the *peritoneum*.

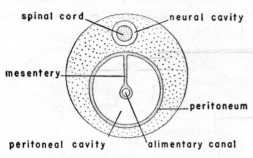

Fig. 166. Body plan of a vertebrate in cross section through the neural and peritoneal cavities. Highly diagrammatic.

In the vertebrate this is doubled upon itself to form *mesenteries* (Fig. 166) that connect the alimentary canal and the reproductive glands with the body wall, and is continued as an outside covering for these organs.

Classification. The distinctive characters of the six classes of vertebrates are outlined in brief in the accompanying table.

Class	Limbs	Skin Outgrowths	Breathing Medium	Body Temperature	Egg Yolk	Place of Development
CYCLO-STOMATA	None	None	Water	Varying (cold-blooded)	Small	In water
PISCES	Fins	Scales	Water	Varying (cold-blooded)	Small[a]	In water
AMPHIBIA	Legs	None	Water and air	Varying (cold-blooded)	Small	In water
REPTILIA	Legs (sometimes wanting)	Scales or plates	Air	Varying (cold-blooded)	Large	Buried in earth
AVES	Legs and wings	Feathers	Air	Uniform (105°–108° F.)	Large	Nests above ground
MAMMALIA	Legs (sometimes wings, flippers, or hands)	Hair	Air	Uniform (98°–103° F.)	Small (generally)	In uterus (generally)

[a] Eggs of cartilaginous fish have much yolk and generally develop inside the mother.

CYCLOSTOMATA

Cyclostomes (Gr. "round mouth") live in both salt and fresh water. They bear considerable resemblance to fishes, except that they have a *circular mouth* without jaws, a *single median nostril, cartilaginous skele-*

ton, and *no paired fins* (Fig. 167). The group includes the lampreys and the hagfishes. On each side of the poorly defined head of the lamprey are an eye and seven circular gill slits. The notochord persists through life, but in the adult stage, vertebrae which consist of definite segments of carti-

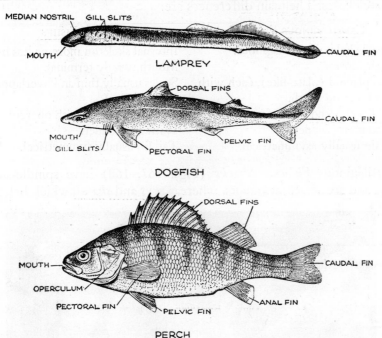

FIG. 167. Comparative study of a lamprey, a cartilaginous fish (dogfish), and a bony fish (perch), the significant external structures. (Modified from Buchanan, *Elements of Biology;* copyright, Harper.)

lage have developed around it. The front end of the nerve tube is enlarged into a primitive brain, resembling that of the embryos of the higher vertebrates. Many lampreys live parasitically on fishes. Attaching itself to the victim with its mouth, which serves as a suction disk, the lamprey bores into the flesh by means of a tongue covered with horny teeth. In recent years sea lampreys have invaded the upper Great Lakes and have caused considerable economic loss by their depredations on commercially important fishes.

PISCES (FISHES)

The Class PISCES (fishes) is one of the largest classes of vertebrates. Fishes differ from cyclostomes in having (1) two pairs of limbs--the paired fins; (2) elongated instead of circular gill slits; (3) upper and lower jaws instead of a circular mouth. There are two subclasses—CHON-DRICHTHYES (Gr. "cartilaginous fishes") and OSTEICHTHYES (Gr. "bony fishes"). They differ in so many ways that some authorities consider them separate classes. The main differences are:

CARTILAGINOUS FISHES	BONY FISHES
Internal skeleton cartilaginous.	Internal skeleton more or less bony.
Mouth ventral.	Mouth usually terminal.
Scales placoid (plate-like), each with a projecting tooth.	Scales usually thin and overlapping.
Gill slits exposed on surface.	Gill slits covered with operculum.
Without air bladder.	With air bladder.
Tail fin usually asymmetrical.	Tail fin usually symmetrical.

Cartilaginous Fishes. *Sharks* (Figs. 167, 168) have spindle-shaped bodies and are active swimmers, whereas *rays* and *skates*, which belong to

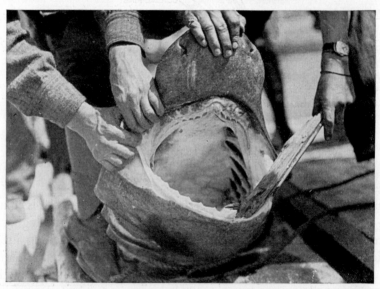

FIG. 168. Shark captured at Friday Harbor, Puget Sound. Note the ventral position of the mouth, the pointed teeth, the gill slits which extend from the pharynx through the body wall, and the nostrils which lead to the olfactory capsules and are used only for smelling. (Photo by C. J. Chamberlain.)

the same subclass, are dorsoventrally flattened and live mainly on the bottom of the sea. Sharks are great pests, inasmuch as they destroy large quantities of lobsters and game fishes; some of the larger ones attack people swimming. However, sharks have recently proved useful as a food source, the liver oil being particularly rich in vitamins A and D. Of special interest is the torpedo ray, which is armed with a pair of electric "storage batteries" capable of administering a severe shock as a means of offense or defense.

Bony Fishes, External Features. A bony fish is usually spindle-shaped, and is thus "streamlined" for life in the water. The *scales* vary in different types, but are usually flattened to cover the body somewhat as shingles cover a roof (Fig. 167). On each side are four *gill arches* separated from each other by *gill slits*, the whole covered by a bony *operculum*, or gill cover.

Like sharks, bony fishes have paired fins, the *pectoral* fins being fore limbs and the *pelvic* fins hind limbs. There is no pelvic girdle, such as vertebrates of the higher classes have, to connect the hind limbs with the spinal column. The unpaired fins consist of one or two *dorsal*, one *caudal* (tail), and one *anal* (near the anus). The caudal fin is generally fan-shaped and externally symmetrical; its lashing propels the fish in rapid swimming. In slow swimming the paired fins act much as do the oars of a boat. The paired fins and the tail cooperate in steering; the former also seem to help in maintaining equilibrium, for if they are removed the heavier dorsal surface of the body turns downward.

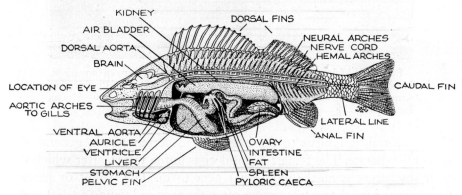

Fig. 169. Diagram of a bony fish (perch), showing the fins (except pectoral) and the more important internal organs. (Modified after Woodruff.)

Internal Features (Fig. 169). The centrum of a fish vertebra is concave at both ends; between the vertebrae are the remnants of the notochord. The *mouth*, a widely opening food trap, leads into a large *pharynx*, which is bounded laterally by the *gill arches* with their fringing, filamentous gills. A short *esophagus* opens into the *stomach*, which is followed by a relatively short *intestine*. From the dorsal side of the esophagus is a large outpushing called the *air bladder;* this acts as a hydrostatic organ, for by secreting into it gases derived from the blood or by absorbing gases from it the fish changes its specific gravity and thereby adjusts itself to different depths of water.

A fish has a two-chambered heart (Plate I). The blood goes forward from the heart, then upward through the gill arches; thence, as oxygenated blood, it is distributed to capillaries in all parts of the body; from there,

Fig. 170. African lungfish (*Protopterus aethiopicus*) in an aquarium. Note the slender paired fins. The lungs suggest some ancestral connection with the amphibians. (Photo, copyright, General Biological Supply House, Inc., Chicago.)

deoxygenated, it returns to the heart. As in vertebrates in general, the sexes are separate. The female deposits eggs in the water, after which the male discharges seminal fluid (*milt*) over them. The parent or parents sometimes guard the nest, but more often the eggs and young are left without attention. A few species are *ovoviviparous;* i.e., the eggs hatch before leaving the body of the female.

Sense Organs. The *eyes* of a fish have nearly spherical lenses which cannot be focused. The *ears* are not visible on the surface; they consist only of the equivalent of the inner ear in higher vertebrates, and are more important in equilibrium than in hearing. Extending lengthwise of the body on either side is the *lateral line*. This is a sense organ by means of which low-frequency water vibrations are perceived. The *olfactory sacs*

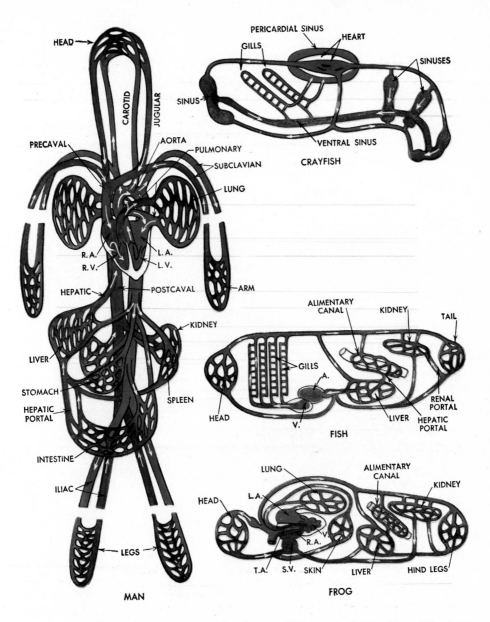

PLATE I. Diagrams of the Circulatory Systems of the Crayfish (an Arthropod) and of the Fish, the Frog, and Man (Vertebrates). Deoxygenated blood is indicated in blue, oxygenated in red. Only the major vessels are shown and only a few of the gills and sinuses. The aortic arches on the right side of the frog are cut off. R.A., L.A., R.V., L.V. indicate, respectively, right auricle, left auricle, right ventricle, left ventricle; T.A., truncus arteriosus; S.V., sinus venosus. Forked arrows indicate an artery and a vein of the same name.

at the anterior end are organs of chemical sense ("smell"); touch is especially developed on the lips, and a chemical sense ("taste") in the mucous membrane of the mouth.

Lungfishes. Lungfishes are a small archaic group with only three living genera—one each in Africa (Fig. 170), South America, and Australia. The air bladder or bladders (two in the African and South American types) are attached to the ventral side of the pharynx and are used as lungs in breathing. Lungfishes live either in stagnant water that is poor in oxygen, or in water bodies that dry up periodically; in the latter they burrow into the mud as the dry season approaches and breathe air until the water reappears. Their air-breathing habit and the fact that they were numerous and widespread before the amphibians appeared suggest a possible connection with the ancestors of the land vertebrates.

Lobe-Finned Fishes. The members of this ancient group, like lungfishes but unlike most fishes, had both external and internal nostril openings, adapting the nostrils for breathing as well as for smell. The bony framework of their paired fins, somewhat like that of the limb of an amphibian, suggests these fishes as possible ancestors of the land vertebrates. They were thought to have become extinct some sixty million years ago, but in 1939 a commercial fisherman of South Africa hauled up in his net a five-foot fish with large bluish scales. This fish, which was named *Latimeria*, proved to be a living member of this ancient group.

Fig. 171. Common pike (*Esox lucius*), a widespread and important freshwater game fish. It is one of the true or bony fishes. Note the paired pectoral and pelvic fins, the terminal mouth, the gill cover, and the symmetrical tail. (Photo, copyright, courtesy of John G. Shedd Aquarium, Chicago.)

Ray-Finned Fishes. The vast majority of the fishes of the world belong to this group, in which the thin, paired fins are stiffened by slender cartilaginous rays. Their olfactory sacs open only to the exterior. The food value of this group to man is enormous, to say nothing of the great popularity of fishing as a means of recreation (Fig. 171).

Adaptation Among Fishes. Diverse and curious adaptations to environment are found in many fishes. The pectoral fins of the "flying fishes" are modified into wing-like organs that permit them, in their leaps from the water, to glide through the air for considerable distances. In the sea robin (Fig. 172), the three lowest rays of each pectoral fin are modified into finger-like structures for crawling on the bottom or digging into the sand in search of food. The dorsal fin of the shark sucker (Fig. 428) is modified into an adhesive disk which it uses in holding fast to a shark or other fish, thus securing a free ride. Unlike skates and rays, bony fishes when flat for bottom dwelling are flattened laterally, as is the flounder (Fig. 427), which

Fig. 172. Red-winged sea robin (*Prionotus strigatus*). This is a marine fish which attains a length of eighteen inches. Three of the rays of its pectoral fin are finger-like feelers by means of which it pulls itself along on the bottom or stirs the sand in search of food. (Photo, copyright, courtesy of John G. Shedd Aquarium, Chicago.)

is curiously adapted to life on the sea bottom. During development, one eye socket becomes twisted about in such a way that both eyes are on the same side of the flattened body—the side that is uppermost as the fish lies on the sand. In the depths of the ocean are found odd-shaped fishes that are capable of sustaining tremendous external pressure (Fig. 173). Some of them are wholly blind, while others possess large eyes and brilliant luminous organs. Their food must consist largely of organisms that have fallen from near the surface, or of organisms that themselves live upon such food, for light is not available for photosynthesis.

AMPHIBIA

The Class Amphibia (Gr. "double life") includes, for the most part, animals that live both in water and on land. In most members of this group the early larval stage is fitted only for life in the water, breathing being carried on entirely by means of gills. The adult develops lungs for air-breathing, but is able to stay under water for long periods because the skin also functions as a respiratory organ. The paired fins of their fish-like ancestors have been modified into limbs for walking or hopping on land. Their nostrils are not, as in the fishes, used merely for smelling, for they open into the mouth cavity and serve for the intake of air. Lungs develop and either supplement or supplant the gills as organs of respiration. Amphibians usually hatch from small gelatin-coated eggs laid in the water, undergo development or *metamorphosis* in water, and, as adults, spend a part or all of their time on land. They are sometimes confused with rep-

FIG. 173. A deep-sea angler. This species lives at ocean depths to which sunlight does not penetrate. The dorsal fin has a luminous bulb at its tip and seems to serve as a lure to attract the smaller denizens of the deep for food. This is a female; the much smaller male adheres by his mouth to the skin of the female and becomes a permanently attached parasite upon her. (Photograph by William Beebe.)

tiles, but can be distinguished by the fact that they lack the covering of scales or plates which the reptiles have. Amphibians are divided into three orders, as follows:

1. APODA (Gr. "without feet"): worm-like forms without legs; tail short or absent; blindworms.
2. URODELA (Gr. "evident tail"): tail present in adult; salamanders, mud puppies.
3. ANURA (Gr. "without tail"): tail absent in adult; frogs, toads.

Apoda and Urodela. The APODA are small, burrowing, worm-like animals found only in the tropics and commonly known as blindworms. The URODELA belong mainly to north temperate regions. The retention of the

Fig. 174. Giant salamander (*Megalobatrachus japonicus*), a native of Japan, where it is prized as food. It is the largest of existing amphibians. (Copyright, courtesy of John G. Shedd Aquarium, Chicago.)

Fig. 175. Tiger salamander (*Ambystoma tigrinum*). Above, the usual terrestrial adult form; below, the permanent larval form (axolotl) found in cool lakes in the Rockies and on the Mexican plateau. The latter lives in water, retains the external gills, and breeds. It can be changed into the normal adult by certain stimuli, such as the feeding of thyroid extract. (Courtesy of General Biological Supply House, Inc., Chicago, and the New York Zoological Society.)

tail, and sometimes of the external gills, both of which characters are found in the frog only during the larval stage, suggests that the order is less advanced than the ANURA. Largest of the URODELA is the giant sala-mander of Japan (Fig. 174), which attains a length of five feet; its relative, the hellbender, found in streams of the eastern United States, may grow to twenty inches in length. The common tiger salamander (*Ambystoma tigrinum*, Fig. 175) is dark, with scattered, pale yellow spots. The axolotl,

FIG. 176. Mud puppy (*Necturus maculosus*), a salamander common through the eastern United States. It is strictly aquatic and retains its external gills throughout life. (Copyright, courtesy of John G. Shedd Aquarium, Chicago.)

formerly thought to be a different species, has been found to be a perma-nent larval stage of the same species. Environmental conditions determine whether the animal goes through its transformation or retains the larval form through the breeding portion of its life. The mud puppy (*Necturus maculosus*, Fig. 176) is a well-known species that lives in water and retains its external gills through life. On the other hand, the red-back salamander (*Plethodon*)

FIG. 177. Tree toad. (New York Zoological Society Photo.)

spends its entire life on land. The eggs are laid in damp places, under logs or stones; the larvae lose their gills soon after or even before emerging from the egg.

Anura. The most numerous of the amphibians are the tailless ones. The more familiar families in the United States include (1) frogs, which are generally found in and about water, and dive under it for protection; (2) toads, which migrate for some distance from water as adults and return to the ponds to breed; and (3) tree frogs (tree toads, Fig. 177), generally characterized by pads on the tips of the toes, the habit of sitting in

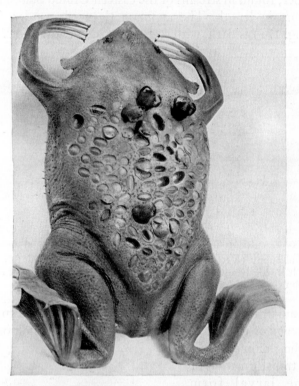

Fig. 178. The Surinam toad (*Pipa americana*), a large, ungainly, tongueless toad from South America. The eggs are deposited and fertilized on the back of the mother, to which they are glued by a sticky secretion. The skin then grows over them, leaving each in a pit covered by a flap. Here they undergo complete development and, omitting the usual tadpole stage, emerge as miniature forms of the adult. (Photograph from a model by the American Museum of Natural History, New York.)

shrubs and trees, and the ability to change color through a considerable range to match their surroundings. The Surinam toad (*Pipa*) of the Guianas (Fig. 178) has a peculiar method of incubating its eggs, in that the female, probably with the aid of the male, distributes them over her back where they are held by a sticky secretion. Then the skin grows in such a way that each egg is sunk in a little pocket, over which a gelatinous lid forms. Here the embryos develop until they are liberated as miniature adults. The male obstetrical toad (*Alytes*) of Europe wraps the egg strings around his hind limbs until they are ready to hatch, then jumps into the water and allows the tadpoles to escape.

In temperate climates, frogs bury themselves during winter in the bottom of ponds. Life processes are reduced to a minimum and the animal remains inactive until spring. The eggs continue to develop within the ovary during this time and are ready to be laid as soon as the frogs appear in the ponds in the spring. Toads hibernate by burrowing into the ground in gardens and similar places.

Frog morphology and physiology will be treated more extensively in the next chapter. The life history of the frog is discussed in Chapter XVIII.

REPTILIA

General Characteristics. Reptiles (Lat. "creepers") are characterized by a body covering of scales or plates; by the presence, except in snakes and some lizards, of four short, stout limbs; by vertebrated tails; by being restricted to air-breathing; by the relatively large, yolk-containing egg, covered with a leathery or calcareous shell; and by the fact that they hatch from the egg in the adult form, a larval stage being omitted. Like fishes and amphibians they are cold-blooded, their body temperature varying with that of the surrounding medium. With the exception of a few snakes and lizards, which are *ovoviviparous*, reptiles are *oviparous*, the eggs generally being buried in the earth. Extreme variation occurs in the habitats of these animals—from the sea, in which sea turtles live, to the desert regions, the home of many snakes and lizards.

This was the dominant group of vertebrates in the Mesozoic era of geological time, approximately 100,000,000 years ago. During this time giant dinosaurs, some of them more than a hundred feet in length and weighing forty or fifty tons, stalked over the land, struggling with each other for food and dominating the landscape. Others were huge sea forms, and still others had wings and dominated the air. Of about sixteen orders that existed then, only the following four have living representatives today:

1. RHYNCHOCEPHALIA (Gr. "snout head"): a single living representative, the tuatara, found only on small islands of New Zealand.
2. CROCODILIA (Gr. "crocodile"): crocodiles, alligators, gavials, caimans.

3. TESTUDINATA (Lat. "like a tortoise"): turtles, tortoises.
4. SQUAMATA (Lat. "scaly"): lizards, snakes.

Rhynchocephalia. This group contains only the New Zealand reptile, *Sphenodon*, the tuatara (Fig. 179), which is regarded as the lone survivor of a primitive group. Immature individuals possess a vestigial median eye-like structure which is connected with the small *pineal body* just above the brain. Although the pineal body is found in all vertebrates, its function is in doubt. It has been regarded by some as an endocrine gland, but its

FIG. 179. The tuatara (*Sphenodon punctatus*) on a small island off New Zealand. This is the only living species of the RHYNCHO-CEPHALIA. (Photo by F. N. Blanchard; courtesy of National Geographic Society.)

connection with an "eye" in *Sphenodon* suggests that it may be merely a useless vestige.

Crocodilia. The CROCODILIA are well-known forms which inhabit the warmer regions of the earth, especially along the great rivers. They have nostril openings at the tip of the nose, permitting them to lie almost entirely immersed in the water, with only the tip of the nose projecting for breathing. The nostrils and ears have valves which keep out the water, and the tongue closes the throat while under water.

Some members of the group endanger human life, the Nile crocodile being probably the greatest menace. The American alligator (Fig. 180) is of importance because of its valuable leather; alligator farms have been established in some parts of the United States to raise the animals for this product, and the larger wild forms have been largely killed off for the

Fig. 180. The American alligator (*Alligator mississippiensis*).

same purpose. Their food consists almost wholly of animals which they capture by means of their powerful toothed jaws. From twenty to forty hard-shelled eggs are deposited in a mound-like nest constructed of earth and decaying vegetation.

Fig. 181. Western painted turtle (*Chrysemys belli*), a land turtle of a genus that is widely distributed. (Copyright, courtesy of John G. Shedd Aquarium, Chicago.)

Testudinata. Turtles (Fig. 181) are characterized mainly by a shell which is a modified exoskeleton attached firmly to the endoskeletal *ribs* and spinal column. The dorsal, convex part of the shell is called the *carapace;* the ventral, flat part is the *plastron.* The outer part of this shell is made up of a number of horny plates. Beneath them, but not corresponding in shape, are thick bony plates. Lateral bridges unite the carapace and plastron in most of the species. The four short legs, the long neck and head, and the tail can all be withdrawn into the shell. The neck can be stretched out to capture food; and the legs, which are very poorly fitted for walking or running, are so placed as to adapt them for rapid and graceful swimming. As in the crocodiles, nasal openings are at the tip of the snout, so that the animal remains almost invisible on coming to the surface for air. Turtles have no teeth; but their food, mostly flesh, can be grasped and torn by the sharp edges of the horny covering of the jaws and, in some forms, by the hooked beak. Eggs are laid in depressions scooped out in the sand along the shores of lakes and streams.

Fig. 182. Loggerhead turtle (*Caretta caretta*), a large marine turtle which attains a weight of more than 500 pounds. Its limbs are modified into paddles for swimming. (Copyright, courtesy of John G. Shedd Aquarium, Chicago.)

The snapping turtle is a common fresh-water species which attains a large size and is sometimes powerful enough to snap off a human finger with its hooked jaws. The soft-shell turtle is very flat and has a spotted, leathery carapace and a narrow, pointed snout. Musk turtles are noted for their musk-like odor and for the high carapace and very narrow plastron. The box turtle has a hinged plastron, the ends of which may fit against the carapace, completely enclosing the body. The limbs of sea turtles (Fig. 182) are modified as paddles, with finger bones and one or two claws. These turtles leave the water only to deposit their eggs. They reach giant size, sometimes weighing from 500 to 1000 pounds; they are of value for food and furnish the tortoise shell of commerce.

Squamata. This order, which includes snakes and lizards, is characterized by a scaly covering that is cast off periodically. That of snakes is shed completely at one time (Fig. 187), whereas that of lizards is sloughed off in shreds over a period of several days. Snakes and some lizards are without limbs. Legless lizards may be distinguished from snakes by the possession of movable eyelids, tympanic membranes, and small ventral scales instead of the broad *scutes* found on the ventral surface of the snake.

The true chameleon (Fig. 183) is found only in the eastern hemisphere. It is a quaint arboreal animal with a long, prehensile tail used in climbing, peculiar squinting eyes, a large head, and a long club-shaped tongue for

FIG. 183. A three-horned chameleon (*Chameleo jacksoni*) from Africa. Chameleons are characterized by a prehensile tail, a tongue capable of great extension for insects, eyes with independent motion, and considerable power to change color. (Copyright, Chicago Natural History Museum.)

capturing its insect food. The tongue can be thrown out with great speed three to five inches from the mouth.

Some other kinds of lizards have the power of changing their color for protection. One of these, *Anolis* of our southern states, is often erroneously called a chameleon. The tail of a lizard is generally not prehensile. The tail can be snapped off to escape an enemy and then be regenerated in a short time, though new vertebrae do not develop. The horned lizard ("horned toad," Fig. 184) is a lizard shaped somewhat like a toad but readily recognized by the horny scales that cover the body. The only poisonous lizards in the world are the Gila monster (Fig. 185), a conspicuous black-and-yellow lizard of the deserts of southwestern United States, and the Mexican beaded lizard, both members of the genus *Heloderma.* Their poison fangs, unlike those of poisonous snakes, are in

FIG. 184. Horned lizard, popularly called "horned toad," a rather sluggish lizard with defensive horns on the head and along the edges of the body (natural size). (Copyright, General Biological Supply House, Inc., Chicago.)

FIG. 185. Gila monster (*Heloderma suspectum*), a member of the only genus of poisonous lizards. Its beaded coat is an interesting pattern of black and pink. (× ⅓.) (Photo from Arizona; courtesy of Larry Tetzlaff.)

the lower jaw. The largest lizard in the world is the giant monitor lizard (Fig. 186) that inhabits the small island of Komodo in Indonesia.

Snakes. With the exception of the tropical pythons and boas, which have short, claw-like hind limbs, snakes are without limbs and limb girdles. The free edge of the broad ventral scales, or *scutes*, is at the rear, and each is connected with a pair of movable ribs. As the ribs move backward, the edge of the scute catches on slight irregularities in the ground and pushes

FIG. 186. Giant monitor lizard (*Varanus komodoensis*), the largest of living lizards, a carnivorous form native to Komodo Island in the East Indies. Its tongue is forked like that of snakes. It attains a length of 9½ feet. (Copyright, Chicago Natural History Museum.)

the snake forward. Strong longitudinal muscles, by alternating contractions on opposite sides, make the movement wave-like.

The eyelids of a snake are fused over the eyes but are transparent enough to permit the snake to see. There is no eardrum; the sense of hearing is probably absent. The soft, slender tongue is forked at the end and can be thrust out, even when the mouth is closed, through an opening between the jaws. It is used as an auxiliary olfactory organ and, contrary to popular notion, is entirely harmless. Snakes use animal food such as frogs, toads, and small mammals. The front ends of the two lower jawbones are joined only by an elastic ligament, and the rear end of each forms a loose joint with a slender *quadrate bone*, which in turn forms a loose joint with the skull. Hence the mouth can be stretched to a remarkable extent, enabling the snake to swallow large prey whole. Swallowing is aided by short, sharp teeth which project backward along the jaws. These teeth can inflict a shallow scratch on a person's skin, causing slight bleeding, but they are not poisonous in most species.

Among the common harmless snakes, the garter snakes are most abundant and best known, being widely distributed over the United States. They are characterized by three longitudinal yellowish stripes and by the ovoviviparous method of reproduction. Other harmless forms are the black snake (Fig. 187), the blue racer, the water snake, the milk snakes, and the hog-nosed snake, also called the puff adder or blow snake. This last has a habit of raising its body, puffing out its neck, and emitting a hissing noise which makes it seem vicious. It is, however, entirely harmless, though a great bluffer.

Fig. 187. Black snake (*Coluber constrictor*) a nonvenomous species, showing the recently shed skin. (Photo by L. W. Brownell.)

Poisonous Snakes. Most poisonous snakes have a pair of specialized upper teeth, the poison fangs, which are much elongated and are each provided with a tube or groove leading from a poison sac (Fig. 188). When the mouth is closed, the fangs are folded inward against its upper surface. They are used both for securing prey and for defense. When the snake strikes, the mouth is opened wide and the fangs are raised nearly at right angles to the jaw. With the fangs in this position, the snake by a quick thrust of the head can make a deep wound into which the poison is injected. When the fangs are injured or lost, they can be replaced by new ones which lie concealed behind the original ones.

The poisonous snakes of the United States include twenty species of rattlesnakes, the water moccasin, the copperhead, and two coral snakes. All these, except the coral snakes, belong to a group known as *pit vipers*, because of a distinct pit between the eye and the nostril. The pit acts as a temperature detector, enabling the snake to recognize the presence of a warm-blooded animal at a distance of several feet. Poisonous snakes have very long, tubular fangs and vertically elongated eye pupils. In all of them, the eggs hatch while still within the body of the mother. Rattlesnakes are spread over most of the nation but are most abundant in the southwestern desert area. The characteristic buzzing, heard when the tail is shaken, is produced by a series of shell-like epidermal buttons on the end of the tail. Each button represents a portion of the old skin which is not sloughed off at the time of molting. The common idea that the number of these buttons indicates the age of the snake is erroneous, for the skin may be shed several times a year; furthermore, buttons are frequently lost. The rattle may give warning to animals that would disturb the snake, or it may be a lure which attracts animals that serve as prey. Coral snakes lack pits, have round eye pupils, and are

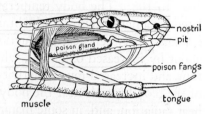

FIG. 188. Head of rattlesnake partly dissected to show location of poison gland and fangs, side view. (From Smallwood, *New Biology*; copyright, Allyn and Bacon.)

marked with broad circular bands of red and black separated by narrow bands of yellow. The two species found in the United States are confined to the south.

Antivenin ("against poison") is the best remedy for snake bite. Numerous laboratories have been established for the manufacture of this serum, which is made on the same principle as are the antitoxins used for the treatment of tetanus and other diseases (see Chapter XX). A horse is given several injections of snake poison, and after it becomes thoroughly immune its blood is drawn and the serum used as antivenin. Since the different poisonous snakes produce different venoms, antivenin made from the poison of the kind of snake which bit the victim must be administered.

AVES (BIRDS)

AVES (Lat. "birds") constitute one of the most fascinating of the animal groups. The brilliant beauty of their plumage, the joyousness and rich melody of their songs, and the grace, swiftness, and long range of their flight have always aroused unusual human interest.

Warm-Blooded Animals. The organisms that we have studied up to this point have internal temperatures varying in almost as great degree as does the temperature of their environment. They are commonly called *cold-blooded*, but a more expressive term is *varying-temperatured*. Flies and frogs practically cease their metabolic activities at freezing temperatures. The body temperatures of birds and mammals remain fairly constant, no matter what the temperature of the surrounding medium, and these animals are called *warm-blooded* or *uniform-temperatured*. The normal body temperature of most mammals ranges between 98° and 103° F., according to the species; that of some of the primitive mammals is somewhat lower and somewhat more variable. In birds it ranges from 105° to 108°. The body temperature of a warm-blooded animal is regulated by a nerve center in the brain. Messages sent from this center effect a balance between heat production and heat loss. The former is brought about by increased oxidation, which may be caused by increased muscle tone and increased muscle activity, as in shivering; the latter, by dilation of the blood vessels near the body surface, increasing the opportunity for heat radiation, and, in some mammals, by increase in the rate of perspiration which, by evaporation from the skin, takes heat from the body.

Adaptation for Flight. The most striking general feature of birds is their adaptation for flight. The spindle-shaped body with its tapering ends cuts the air in rapid movement. *Feathers* are the epidermal outgrowths of a bird, corresponding to the scales of a reptile and the hairs of a mammal. A typical feather has a stalk, or *quill*, an axis, or *shaft*, and a spreading portion, or *vane*. The latter consists of *barbs*, which are still further divided into *barbules*. In the large *flight feathers* the barbules are hooked together to form an air-resisting surface capable of keeping the bird in the air. In the *contour feathers* the distal barbules, at least, are hooked together, enabling them to give form to the body and, to a large extent, to shed water. The *down feathers*, with soft, hookless barbs, lie close to the body and protect it against loss of heat. The modification of the fore limbs of birds for flight constitutes the most apparent adaptation. Only three digits remain of the five possessed by the reptilian ancestor, and there has been considerable fusion and reduction of bones. The hind limbs are modified to aid the bird in standing, walking, or running, especially in rising from the ground and alighting from the air.

Other skeletal modifications are seen in the keel-like *sternum*, or *breastbone*, fitted for the attachment of the powerful muscles of flight and contributing to the spindle-like form. Further, the long bones are hollow, reducing weight; many other bones are very thin and are fused together to give added firmness. The ribs, which are extremely thin, are reinforced by *uncinate processes* that project out from the edge of one rib and rest firmly on the rib behind. Another striking internal adaptation is the possession of large *air sacs* which extend from the lungs between the organs of the body and into the cavities of the larger bones. These increase the buoyancy of the body and aid respiration; they also aid in regulating body temperature through evaporation of water from their surfaces. An important necessity in any "flying machine" is abundant and sustained power, which the bird is well fitted to impart. The large breast muscles supply the power, and this is effectively applied to the wings by a pulley-like arrangement of the tendon through the ring-like junction of the bones of the pectoral girdle. The large *crop* provides storage for an abundant supply of food, and the *gizzard* grinds it, thus relieving the bird of the need of mastication. Primitive birds had teeth, which are completely lacking in our modern birds, although vestiges may appear in the embryo. A four-chambered heart and a highly developed circulatory system provide for the most efficient distribution of food and oxygen to the tissues for oxidation, the source of the energy needed. The long wing and tail feathers greatly increase the surface of the body, and the tail acts as an excellent steering mechanism. The leading features of bird anatomy are shown in Fig. 189.

Colors. The attractive colors of feathers are due to two different causes. Some result from colored pigments produced by metabolic processes within the body. These colors are always brightest, especially in the males, during the breeding season. The reds, the yellows, and the browns are usually due to pigments; black is an intensifying of the brown. Other colors have been shown to be produced by microscopic ridges and furrows, or by an exceedingly thin transparent outer layer which causes interference of light waves and breaks up the light into prismatic colors. Blue and all the metallic colors are of this sort. A combination of these two types of color is frequent.

Songs and Calls. A special charm of the birds is their songs. These are produced by means of a structure called a *syrinx* (Gr. "pipe") which is located not at the upper end of the windpipe (*trachea*) as is the *larynx* of mammals, but at the lower end, at the point where the bronchi branch off. The syrinx contains a fold on each side which, when stretched, vibrates with the flow of exhaled air as do the vocal cords of a mammal. It is most highly developed in the Order PASSERIFORMES, or perching birds, which are therefore often spoken of as "songbirds." The songs should not be confused with the call notes of the birds, which are undoubtedly their language or means of communication. The calls and songs of birds are distinctive and assist in the identification of species. Song, like bright plumage, is biologically a secondary sex character of birds. The breeding season is almost exclusively the time of song and the singing is confined largely to the male. Its purpose is primarily to announce to the female the presence of the male, and to warn other males to keep off the territory that he is guarding as a source of food for his young. There are a few species in which the female can equal or excel the male in her song; this is true of the cardinal and the rose-breasted grosbeak.

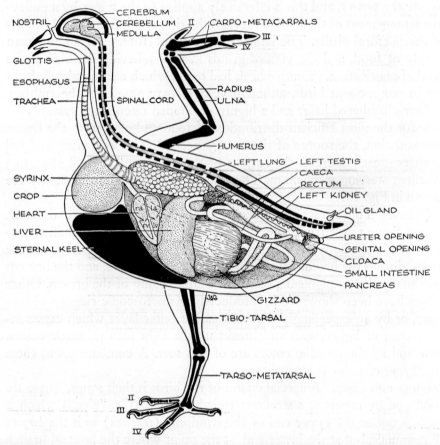

FIG. 189. Diagram of a bird (pigeon), showing the principal parts of the skeleton (in black) and the more important internal organs. (Based on Buchanan.)

Nest Building. The activity of birds is at its height during the nesting season—the time of mating, nest building, laying and incubation of eggs, and rearing young (Fig. 190). Nest building and care of eggs and young are found in some invertebrates and lower vertebrates. However, the birds constitute the first animal group in which this care of the eggs and young has become general. Usually, as we advance toward the more highly organized groups, this care seems correlated with a longer period of incubation and with greater helplessness of the young.

The greatest variation occurs among different birds as to the location and structure of the nest. With some birds, like the killdeer and the night-hawk, the nest is scarcely more than a simple depression in the ground—the eggs of the nighthawk may even be placed on the flat roof of a build-ing. Again, the nest may be like that of the mourning dove—a few sticks put together in slovenly fashion, with scarcely enough depression to prevent the eggs from rolling off. Other nests show a high degree of architectural skill as to both materials and construction. Striking examples are the nest of the hummingbird, skillfully constructed of delicate lichens

FIG. 190. Altricial or helpless young of the bronzed grackle in the nest awaiting food. (Photo, courtesy of M. D. Pirnie, Michigan State College.)

and lined with softest down, and the hanging nest of the Baltimore oriole, which is compactly woven together in the form of a deep pouch, spoken of by Lowell as "a cup of felt." In general, the location of nests depends largely upon the habitat of the bird; thus they may be built on the ground, in low trees or shrubs, in tall trees, in holes of trees, in posts or banks of earth, under bridges or roofs of buildings, on marshy hummocks or mounds, or along sandy shores of isolated islands. The coloring of the eggs, like that of the birds themselves, is frequently protective, i.e., caus-ing them to blend with their surroundings. The eggs are often completely covered by the mother bird when she leaves the nest. This is especially true of nests on the ground, such as those of ducks and geese. The eider duck furnishes a striking example—the mother lines the nest and covers the eggs with down feathers pulled from her own breast.

Birds are of two general types as regards the condition of the young when hatched. In the *precocial* type (Fig. 195), the young are covered with down when hatched, and are able to follow the mother in search of food in a few hours. In the *altricial* type (Fig. 190), the young are helpless and almost featherless when hatched and must be fed by the parents for a week or more until they are able to fly. Grouse, quail, and ducks are precocial; songbirds are altricial. The time of incubation is from ten days for the cowbird to fifty or sixty for the ostrich. For most birds the average time is from two to three weeks.

Migration. Migration occurs in various groups of animals, the seal and the salmon being well-known examples; but among the birds, on account of their remarkable powers of flight, it is more prevalent and hence has been more fully studied. Recent work in birdbanding directed by the federal government has brought to light a great body of facts relating to this habit. No one cause or set of causes has been found to account completely for it, though many of the factors involved are known. Chief among them are the instinct for seclusion in rearing young, overcrowding in winter homes, the large feeding area afforded by the north, the opportunity which the long summer days of the north give for procuring the large amount of food needed by the young, and the influence of changing seasons on sex hormones. The oncoming and recession of continental glaciers may have encouraged the northward-southward movement at the time the habit was developing. This is a promising field for further research.

Migration habits are extremely varied. In general, certain very definite routes are followed by each species of birds (Fig. 191). Sometimes the spring route and the fall route differ widely. Changing temperatures and abundance of food influence many birds, though others seem to disregard these entirely. Many birds, such as the robins and bluebirds, fly entirely in the daytime, moving along in a desultory fashion and feeding as they go; but a larger number of species fly wholly at night, feeding during the day. Still others, such as ducks, geese, and shore birds, make continuous flights, stopping neither day nor night. The males often precede the females, especially in the spring migration, as is true of red-winged blackbirds. There are many dangers to birds on these flights. On cloudy nights they fly low and often become confused by lights; hundreds are killed by flying into lighthouses, monuments, and other tall structures. Many others are killed by storms, especially as they cross large bodies of water.

Remarkable instances of migration are afforded by the golden plover and the arctic tern. The golden plover nests in the extreme northern part of North America. In the fall, when the young are old enough, the birds fly eastward to Labrador, feeding as they go. From here they fly to Nova

Scotia and then strike out over the Atlantic in a direct line to the coast of South America. In favorable weather they make this entire distance of approximately 2400 miles in a continuous flight, often flying 200 miles from land. They do not return by the same route, but instead follow the Mississippi valley to the nesting grounds.

The arctic tern, the champion long-distance migrant, nests in the summer within the Arctic Circle as far north as it can find land for a nest.

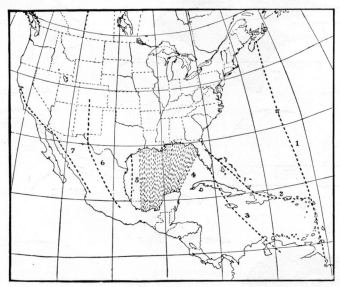

Fig. 191. Principal bird migration routes of North America. No. 1 is used by certain water birds, such as the golden plover; No. 2 is followed in part or whole by some 25 species; No. 3 is used by the bobolink and others; No. 4, directly across the Gulf of Mexico, is taken by most migratory birds of the eastern states; No. 5 is used by a few species of warblers; Nos. 6 and 7 are the main routes of the western birds. (Photo, courtesy of the Fish and Wildlife Service, U.S. Dept. Int.)

Its winters are spent 11,000 miles away within the Antarctic Circle on the opposite side of the earth, which means that this bird travels 22,000 miles each year. A striking fact is that it sees little darkness for eight months of the year, since the sun does not set during its stay in either its winter or its summer home. Its exact route is not known, though banding evidence shows that some of the birds cross the Atlantic from Labrador and go south with their Scottish cousins.

Classification. Conspicuous among the characters used in classifying birds are the shape of the bills, the feet, and the wings (Figs. 192, 193). It is obvious that these characters not only affect the fundamental structure and form of the bird, but also largely determine its distribution and habits. Color is useful in distinguishing different birds of the same family, but is of little value in distinguishing families. For instance, the common robin and the bluebird, though differing widely in color, are both placed in the Thrush family because of their structural characters.

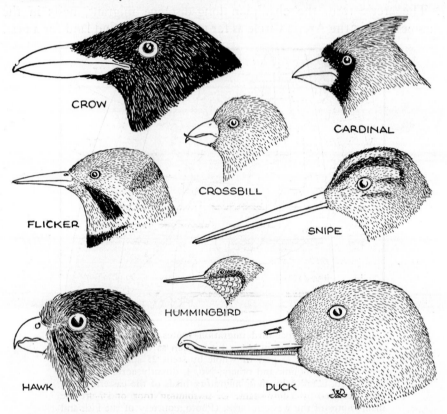

Fig. 192.   Modifications in bird beaks. The crow has a rather generalized beak, adapted to securing a wide variety of foods; the cardinal cracks seed capsules; the crossbill pries apart the scales of the cones of conifers and extracts the seeds; the flicker, a woodpecker, uses its beak and barbed tongue for boring into trees and extracting insects; the snipe probes into the mud for food; the hummingbird sucks nectar from long-tubed flowers; the hawk grasps prey with its beak, and the duck scoops and strains its food from the mud.

Birds were represented in the Mesozoic era of geological time, about a hundred million years ago, by *Archaeornis* (Gr. "ancient bird," Fig. 194), a fairly complete fossil specimen of which was found in Bavaria. Its teeth, its long, vertebrated tail, and its separate clawed fingers on the wing are characters which ally it to the reptiles and help establish the reptilian ancestry of birds. It is a significant fact, in this connection, that the nestling of the hoatzin, a living South American bird, has on the wing free clawed digits which are used for scrambling about among the thorny shrubs in which the nest is built.

Modern birds consist of about twenty orders which may be grouped into two subdivisions: RATITAE and CARINATAE. The RATITAE are running

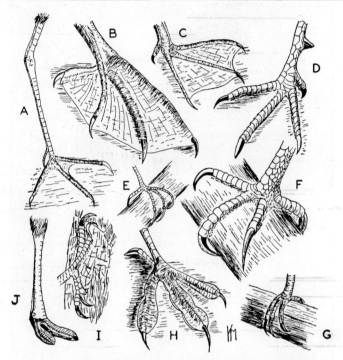

FIG. 193. Bird feet. *A*, Wading foot of greater yellowlegs. *B*, Webbed foot of cormorant. *C*, Swimming foot of duck. *D*, Scratching foot of pheasant. *E*, Perching foot of yellowthroat. *F*, Seizing foot of hawk. *G*, Foot of kingfisher. *H*, Wading foot of coot. *I*, Clinging foot of flicker. *J*, Two-toed running and defensive foot of ostrich. (Redrawn from Wolcott.)

birds, often of giant size, in which the wings are vestigial or entirely lacking and the sternum possesses no keel. Among them are the ostrich (Fig. 195), the emu, the cassowary, and the wingless kiwi of New Zealand. The CARINATAE have wings, though in the penguin they are reduced to swimming paddles; the sternum has a keel to which are attached the powerful muscles of flight. The largest order in this group is PASSERIFORMES, to which belong our common songbirds such as thrushes, flycatchers, crows, jays, tanagers, and nuthatches, including altogether some twenty-five families in North America. More than half of the 30,000 known species of birds belong to this order.

Value of Birds. Birds would arouse unusual human interest if only because of their beautiful coloring, their joyous songs, and their vivacious

Fig. 194. *Archaeornis*, a bird that lived in Europe in the Mesozoic era. It had teeth in the jaws, fingers on the wings, and a long, jointed tail—characteristics which suggest reptilian ancestry for the birds. It is mounted on a cycad, one of the prevailing plants of Mesozoic days. (Photo of a restoration; copyright, Chicago Natural History Museum.)

habits. But they also have considerable economic importance. A now classical example of their usefulness to agriculture is the story of the gulls which saved from the crickets the crops of the early settlers about Salt Lake City in 1848. In the heart of that city today is a tall monument of granite commemorating this deliverance, which the settlers considered a direct answer to their prayers.

In addition to the food obtained from birds as meat and eggs, and the use of their feathers for ornaments, pillows, quilts, and the like, four benefits are usually recognized:

1. Destroying insects harmful to man. Nuthatches, chickadees, flycatchers.
2. Destroying small mammal pests. Hawks, owls, shrikes.
3. Eating weed seeds. Sparrow family, true larks, doves.
4. Clearing up animal and plant waste, as scavengers. Turkey vultures, crows, gulls.

By far the most important of these is the destruction of insects; for even with the help of the birds, man has to wage a constant fight to hold injurious insects in check. New enemies have been appearing in recent years, and, as we have seen, the federal government has been spending many millions of dollars yearly in waging the campaign against them. Without the birds the struggle would be hopeless. Everyone knows that birds eat insects, but few people realize the extent to which this is true. As a result of scientific studies which have been made by the United States Department of Agriculture

FIG. 195. Male ostrich and his hatching brood. The ostrich, native of African and Arabian deserts, is the largest living bird. The male attends to most of the incubation. The young are precocial, running about immediately after hatching. (Photo from Los Angeles Ostrich Farm.)

and a number of the states, many facts are now available on this question. For example, in a single chickadee's stomach were found 454 plant lice. A warbler, the northern yellowthroat, ate 3500 of the same insects in forty minutes. It has been estimated that the birds of Massachusetts destroy 21,000 bushels, or 160 carloads, of insects daily from May to September. While many adult birds eat some vegetable food, most young birds eat only insects—and in surprising quantity.

MAMMALIA

Mammals, like birds, maintain a uniform body temperature. Many of them exceed birds in mental development, the culmination being found in man, the dominant member of the animal kingdom. For the most part, mammals have become modified for land life. A few forms, such as the whale and the seal, have undergone a retrogression to water life. The most striking characteristic of the group is the development by the female of *mammary* (Lat. "breast") *glands*, whereby milk is secreted for the nourishment of the young; from this characteristic is derived the group name *mammal*.

External Features. The mammal possesses external ears, movable upper eyelids fringed with eyelashes, and a snout or nose. Four legs for walking are typical, though in water forms one or both pairs are modified for swimming; in the PRIMATES one or both pairs are used as hands; and in the bats the front pair is modified for flying. Mammals are distinguished from reptiles and birds by having hair, instead of scales or feathers, as the prevailing body covering. Other epidermal outgrowths in mammals are hoofs, horns, claws, and nails. It is significant that, just as scales remained on the legs of certain kinds of birds, so in mammals scales are still found covering the body of the pangolin (Fig. 209), and on the tails of certain rodents such as the beaver (Fig. 203) and the rat. In the armadillo (Fig. 422) these scales have taken the form of heavy bony plates, among which are scattered hairs.

Internal Features. Unlike birds, mammals are characterized by well-developed teeth which are specialized for various purposes. In general, these may be grouped into *incisors,* or cutting teeth; *canines,* or tearing teeth; and *premolars* and *molars,* or grinding and crushing teeth. Mammals differ among themselves with regard to the presence or absence and relative prominence of these various kinds of teeth. A *diaphragm,* or muscular partition, separates the *thoracic* and *abdominal* portions of the coelomic cavity. The *pleural* cavities, containing the lungs, and the *pericardial* cavity, containing the heart, are included in the thoracic cavity. As in birds, there is a four-chambered heart. The *larynx,* or voice box, is at the anterior end of the trachea.

Classification. There are three subclasses of mammals, as follows:

1. PROTOTHERIA (Gr. "first beasts"): laying eggs with large yolk.
2. METATHERIA (Gr. "after beasts"): without placenta; young born prematurely in a helpless condition and undergo further development in the brood pouch of the mother.

3. EUTHERIA (Gr. "true beasts"): with placenta, whereby the young are nourished before birth.

In the EUTHERIA, the embryo becomes joined to the uterus of the mother by a connection called the *placenta* (Lat. "flat cake"); these mammals are therefore known as placental mammals. This group is believed to represent an evolutionary advance over the transitional groups noted—the PROTOTHERIA, in which eggs are laid and developed as in birds and reptiles, and the METATHERIA, in which the young are developed in the uterus, but without a placental connection, and then enter a pouch on the mother's abdomen to undergo further development.

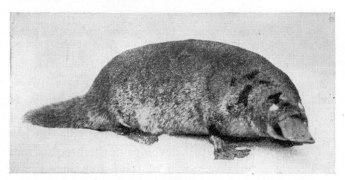

FIG. 196. The duckbill, or platypus (*Ornithorhynchus anatinus*), a protothere or egg-laying mammal of eastern Australia and Tasmania. It is about 18 inches long. (Photo, copyright, Chicago Natural History Museum.)

Prototheria. These animals, called the monotremes (Gr. "one opening" i.e., for intestine and urogenital system), include two genera which are restricted to Australia and the neighboring islands—the duckbill (Fig. 196) and the spiny anteater (Fig. 197). They have horny beaks; their oviducts open separately into a cloaca as do those of reptiles and birds; they lay eggs with large yolks; and their body temperature is considerably lower than in most mammals. These characters all suggest a transitional position between reptiles and mammals. True mammalian characters are the body covering of hair and the presence of mammary glands. No teats are present, however; the young suck or lick the milk secreted by scattered groups of glands among the hairs of the mother's abdomen. The eggs of the duckbill, one to three in number, are deposited in a nest made above water level at the end of a burrow in the bank of a stream; the single egg of the spiny anteater is placed by the mother in a fold of skin on the abdomen, where it remains until it is hatched.

Fig. 197. The spiny anteater (*Tachyglossus aculeatus*), a proto-there or egg-laying mammal of Australia. It is about 17 inches long. (Photo, copyright, Chicago Natural History Museum.)

Metatheria. These animals are known as marsupials (from Lat. "pouch"). They include the opossums of America and the kangaroos, koalas, wombats, and other types of Australia and adjacent islands (Figs. 198, 407). The egg of a marsupial develops in the uterus, from the walls of which it absorbs a certain amount of food. But since there is no placenta, the young are born in a very early stage of development and crawl into the mother's pouch, which serves as an incubator. Each seizes a nipple, the tip of which enlarges until it cannot be released. Muscles in the mammary gland then force milk into the mouths of the offspring. A young kangaroo weighs only about one three-thousandth as much as the mother.

Eutheria. The placental mammals are subdivided into about sixteen orders (see Appendix). The more important ones will be briefly characterized here.

INSECTIVORA (Lat. "insect eaters") include shrews, hedgehogs, and moles. Shrews resemble mice in external appearance, and probably are similar to the early ancestral placental mammals. The pigmy shrew, one and one-half inches long and weighing one-seventh of an ounce, is the smallest existing mammal. Moles are highly specialized for underground life, having small eyes, long pointed noses, powerful neck muscles, and spade-like feet (Fig. 199).

CHIROPTERA (Gr. "hand-winged") are the bats, adapted for flying by the enormous lengthening of four fingers and the development of a skin membrane which connects these fingers and extends along the fore limb and trunk back to the hind limbs and tail (Fig. 200). Bats are mostly in-

Fig. 198. Female wallaby (*Macropus*), an Australian kangaroo-like marsupial, with its young in a pouch. (New York Zoological Society photo.)

Fig. 199. The common mole (*Scalopus aquaticus*), an insectivorous mammal with special adaptations for underground life—pointed snout, spade-like feet, and poorly developed eyes. (From Hegner, *Parade of the Animal Kingdom;* copyright, Macmillan.)

sectivorous and nocturnal. Vampire bats which feed on the blood of other vertebrates, including man, are found in tropical America.

Fig. 200. Big brown bat (*Eptesicus fuscus*) of the Order CHIROP-TERA. One wing is extended, showing thumb and fingers. (Photo, courtesy of Ernest P. Walker.)

Fig. 201. Tiger (*Felis tigris*), a large cat of India, representing the Order CARNIVORA. Male (left) and female.

CARNIVORA (Lat. "flesh eaters") include cats (Fig. 201), dogs, foxes, bears, raccoons, minks, and skunks. Clawed digits help in the capture of the prey. The incisors are small and largely useless, the canines enlarged and adapted for seizing, the molars pointed and useful in cutting their food. PINNIPEDIA (Lat. "feather foot"), a suborder of the CARNIVORA, includes aquatic forms, such as seals, walruses, and sea lions (Fig. 202).

Their limbs are modified into paddles and their body shape is adapted to swimming. The tail of their land ancestors was apparently too much reduced to take up the function of a rudder, so the hind limbs are turned back and function as does the tail of a fish or whale. In the walrus, the upper canine teeth are powerful tusks. Many of these animals are valuable for fur.

Fig. 202. Stellar's sea lion (*Eumetopias jubatus*), Order Carniv-ora, Suborder Pinnipedia. The fish-like form of the body and the paddle-like feet adapt this group to an aquatic life. (From National Zoological Park, courtesy of Ernest P. Walker.)

Rodentia (Lat. "gnawers") include the gnawing animals, such as rats, mice, squirrels, chipmunks, beavers (Fig. 203), muskrats, and porcupines. They are characterized by the absence of canine teeth, and by long chisel-shaped incisors which continue to grow throughout life. The in-cisors are kept sharp by a difference in the rate of wear between the hard *enamel* in front and the soft *dentine* behind. Rats are very serious pests, destroying foods and other commodities and transmitting disease germs, particularly the bacillus of bubonic plague (carried by fleas harbored by the rats). Beavers, muskrats, and squirrels are valuable fur animals; squir-rels are hunted for food.

Lagomorpha (Gr. "hare form") includes the hares, rabbits (Fig. 204), and pikas. These animals were once considered to be rodents. However, they differ from the members of that group in having an extra pair of small incisors in the upper jaw just behind the large gnawing pair. Rab-bits are very useful as a source of fur and as food.

Artiodactyla (Gr. "even-toed") are the even-toed hoofed mammals or ungulates (Fig. 205). The group includes pigs, deer, antelopes, sheep, goats, cattle, hippopotamuses, giraffes, and camels. They have lost the first digit of the original five, in most of them the second and fifth have become much reduced, and in some (e.g., camels) only two digits remain. Many of the large and important game animals are included in this order.

Fig. 203. Above, American beaver (*Castor canadensis*), a well-known aquatic rodent; below, beaver dam impounding a pool in which may be seen two of their homes, at the right center. (Upper figure, from New York Zoological Park; lower figure, courtesy of Fish and Wildlife Service.)

PERISSODACTYLA (Gr. "odd-toed") are the odd-toed ungulates. The order includes the tapirs and rhinoceroses with three toes, and the horse and its relatives (Figs. 206, 403, 411) with only one functional toe (the third) and vestigial splint bones representing the second and fourth.

PROBOSCIDEA (Gr. "with proboscis") include the highly specialized elephants. The trunk is a greatly elongated and flexible nose used in bringing food to the mouth. The two upper incisors are greatly enlarged as tusks. The five digits each bear a nail-like hoof. The group has a remarkable history, but only two genera, including the Indian and African elephants (Fig. 207), are living today.

Fig. 204. Cottontail rabbit (*Sylvilagus transitionalis*) of the Order LAGOMORPHA. (New York Zoological Society photo.)

Fig. 205. African buffalo (*Syncerus caffer*), an even-toed ungulate (ARTIODACTYLA). (Photo, courtesy of Ernest P. Walker.)

Fig. 206. Grant's zebra (*Equus burchelli granti*), an ungulate of the Order PERISSODACTYLA. The zebras are African relatives of the horse. (From the National Zoological Park, courtesy of Ernest P. Walker.)

Fig. 207. African elephant (*Loxodonta africana*) of the Order PROBOSCHIDEA. (From the National Zoological Park, courtesy of Ernest P. Walker.)

Fig. 208. Great anteater (*Myrmecophaga jubata*), a South American edentate. It feeds on ants and termites which it captures by means of its sticky tongue, protruded through a very small mouth opening.

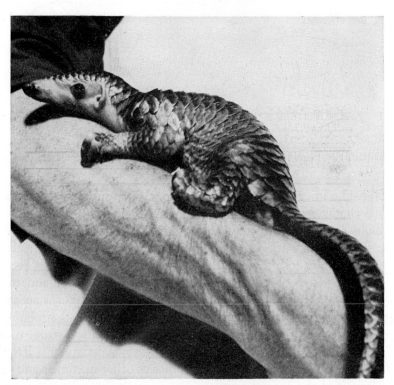

Fig. 209. Young Sumatran pangolin or scaly anteater (*Paramanis javanica*), a mammal of the Order PHOLIDOTA. Instead of hair these mammals have scales resembling those of a lizard. (Photo, courtesy of Ernest P. Walker.)

EDENTATA (Lat. "toothless") are the anteaters (Fig. 208), the armadillos (Fig. 422), and sloths. Not all of them are toothless but all lack incisors, and the teeth are without enamel. The pangolin or scaly anteater, with a scale-covered body suggestive of reptiles, represents the related order, PHOLIDOTA (Gr. "with scales," Fig. 209).

SIRENIA and CETACEA are aquatic orders. The former are the sea cows, which feed upon aquatic vegetation in tropical or subtropical seas and rivers; the latter are the whales, dolphins, and porpoises, which feed largely on marine animals. Although members of these orders have be-

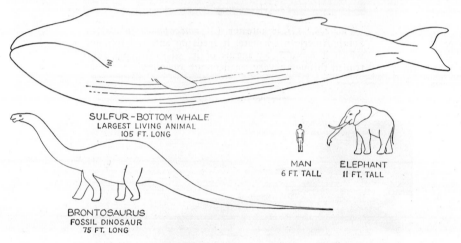

SULFUR-BOTTOM WHALE
LARGEST LIVING ANIMAL
105 FT. LONG

MAN
6 FT. TALL

ELEPHANT
11 FT. TALL

BRONTOSAURUS
FOSSIL DINOSAUR
75 FT. LONG

FIG. 210. Comparative sizes of certain mammals and one of the largest extinct reptiles. The smallest living mammal, the pigmy shrew, is only 1½ inches long, shorter than a man's nose.

come fish-like in certain aquatic adaptations, they show the fundamental mammal characters. Their fore limbs are modified into paddles, and their hind limbs are either reduced to a few vestigial bones wholly concealed within the flesh, or entirely wanting. *Toothed whales* possess teeth. The *whalebone whales* lose their teeth early in life. Their mouths are filled with parallel plates of whalebone hanging from the roof and used in straining the water to secure food, which consists of tiny crustaceans and other small organisms. The largest existing mammal, and probably the largest animal of any kind that ever existed, is the sulfur-bottom whale, a kind of whalebone whale, which has been known to attain a length of 105 feet. Fig. 210 compares its size with that of other mammals and of one of the largest of the extinct reptiles.

PRIMATES (Lat. "chief") are in important respects the most highly developed mammals, particularly in the large brain and the accompanying superior mental powers, and in the development of the hand as an organ for grasping. They have, however, some primitive characters; their limbs, for example, having the original number of digits (5), show far less specialization in structure than is found in some groups. In the order

Fig. 211. Spectral tarsier (*Tarsius carbonarius*) from the Philippines. This arboreal primate, about the size of a large rat, has toe pads and jumps from limb to limb like a tree frog. Similar forms with prominent eyes and reduced nose are among the earliest primate fossils and suggest a possible ancestry to the higher primates. (Photo, courtesy of Ernest P. Walker.)

of increasing brain development the group includes the lemurs, the tarsiers (Fig. 211), the monkeys, the apes, and man. Apes have attracted special attention, for they most nearly resemble man. Like man, but unlike the lemurs and monkeys, they are without tails. Their skeletal structure is similar to that of man, but with the following differences: (1) The arms of an ape are very long and serve for aid in walking as well as in climbing; (2) the legs are relatively much shorter than in man; (3) the brain case is

Fig. 212. A chimpanzee family, consisting of father, mother, and infant son of two weeks. The mother is grooming the father. (From Robert M. Yerkes, *Chimpanzees*, p. 51, by courtesy of the Yale University Press.)

much smaller and the forehead is low and receding; (4) prominent brow ridges project above the eyes, the nose is depressed, the jaws protrude and the chin recedes; (5) both the thumb and the great toe are opposable

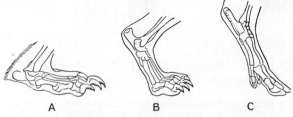

Fig. 213. Three representative foot postures of mammals. *A*, Plantigrade foot of bear; *B*, digitigrade foot of dog; *C*, unguligrade foot of cow. (After Pander and D'Alton.)

to the other digits; (6) the canine teeth interlock. The apes are the gibbon, the orangutan, the gorilla, and the chimpanzee (Fig. 212).

Foot Posture. An interesting variation exhibited in mammals is in the type of foot posture. The most primitive type, found in bears, rabbits, and man, is the *plantigrade* (Lat. "sole of foot step"), in which the entire sole is placed on the ground. In the cat and dog is found the *digitigrade* (Lat. "finger step") type, in which the fingers are brought against the ground. Hoofed mammals are of the *unguligrade* (Lat. "hoof step") type, in which only the enlarged nail, or hoof, touches the ground (Fig. 213).

EXERCISES

1. Discuss the economic importance of fishes, and tell where fishing as an industry has attained its greatest development.
2. Name the geological period in which fishes dominated. How long ago was it? According to geological evidence, what group or groups of fishes came first?
3. What is the axolotl, and what does it illustrate as to the influence of environment upon the characteristics of an organism?
4. Where are the Apoda found? Describe one of them.
5. When did the Amphibia appear in geological history? Did the earlier ones resemble frogs or salamanders? Significance? Describe one of them.
6. Mention some Amphibia that have unusual methods of providing for eggs and young, and describe these methods.
7. State several reasons for believing that the ancestors of Amphibia were water-breathing animals.
8. In what ways does a toad differ from a frog in structure and life habits?
9. Discuss the economic importance of Amphibia.
10. How may a lizard and a salamander be distinguished, and to what class does each belong? What is the difference between a common toad and a horned toad?
11. How is snake antivenin made, and how does it prevent poisoning from the bite of a venomous snake? What specific effects does the venom of the different types of snakes have upon the body?
12. How are crocodiles, alligators, and gavials distinguished? What parts of the world does each inhabit?
13. What snakes are ovoviviparous? Where are the eggs of the oviparous forms laid?
14. What are the leading theories of bird migration? Which do you favor? Explain why.
15. Name some birds in which the colors of male and female are markedly unlike. The female phalarope is more brightly colored than the male. Explain on the basis of breeding habits.
16. Make a list of birds that build their nests on the ground; that build in holes; that build in tall trees; that build in low bushes.
17. Distinguish between precocial and altricial birds, and list ten species under each.

18. Show how and why protective coloration occurs in birds; give illustrations.
19. Sketch and name the bones in the pectoral and pelvic girdles and the attached appendages in a mammal.
20. Compare the bones in the arm of a man, the wing of a bird, the foreleg of a horse, and the foreleg of a dog. What is meant by the term homologous, and how does it apply to the above animals?
21. What is meant by convergent evolution? Show how this is illustrated in aquatic mammals as compared with other aquatic forms.
22. Compare the time of the appearance of the mammals on the earth with that of the appearance of other groups. What are some of the early mammals that are now extinct?
23. What anatomical structure is represented by each of the following: (1) the trunk of an elephant, (2) the hump of a camel, (3) the splint bones of a horse, (4) the paddle of a whale, (5) the quills of a porcupine?

REFERENCES

Bishop, S. C., *Handbook of the Salamanders of the United States, Canada, and Lower California*, Cornell Univ. Press, 1947.

Breland, O. P., *Animal Facts and Fallacies*, Harper & Brothers, 1948.

Cahalane, V. H., *Mammals of North America*, The Macmillan Company, 1947.

Ditmars, R. L., *Reptiles of the World*, The Macmillan Company, 1933.

Jordan, D. S., *Fishes*, Appleton-Century-Crofts, Inc., 1925.

Ley, W., *The Lungfish, the Dodo, and the Unicorn*, Viking Press, Inc., 1948.

Lincoln, F. C., *Migration of Birds*, Government Printing Office, 1950.

Peterson, R. T., *A Field Guide to the Birds*, Houghton Mifflin Company, 2nd rev. ed., 1947.

Rand, H. W., *The Chordates*, Blakiston Company, 1950.

Romer, A. S., *Man and the Vertebrates*, Univ. of Chicago Press, 3rd ed., 1941.

Romer, A. S., *The Vertebrate Body*, W. B. Saunders Company, 1949.

Roule, L., *Fishes and Their Ways of Life*, W. W. Norton & Company, Inc., 1935.

Storer, J. H., *The Flight of Birds: Analyzed Through Slow-Motion Photography*, Cranbrook Institute of Science, Bulletin No. 28, 1948.

Thomson, J. A., *The Biology of Birds*, The Macmillan Company, 1923.

Wright, A. and A. H., *Handbook of Frogs and Toads*, Comstock Publishing Company, 1933.

Writer's Program of the Works Project Administration of the City of New York, *American Wild Life Illustrated*, William H. Wise & Co., 1946.

See also zoology texts listed in the Appendix.

Chapter XVII

VERTEBRATE MORPHOLOGY AND PHYSIOLOGY

Since our best-known animals are vertebrates and since man belongs to this group, a detailed consideration of vertebrate structures and functions is desirable. The frog, belonging to the class AMPHIBIA, serves as a convenient form for study; but because of our natural interest in man, a member of the class MAMMALIA, frequent comparisons will be made.

FIG. 214. Bullfrog (*Rana catesbeiana*), the largest of our common frogs. (Photo, copyright, courtesy of John G. Shedd Aquarium, Chicago.)

General Features of the Frog (Fig. 214). Like other vertebrates, the frog has a head, a trunk, and two pairs of limbs, the hind pair of which function as powerful jumping and swimming organs; the absence of a neck is an adaptation favorable for swimming. The *eyes* protrude from the head and permit vision in all directions, but may be drawn into the sockets for protection when the lids are closed. Between and in front of the eyes is the *brow spot*, thought to be the vestige of a median eye that may have functioned in some vertebrate ancestor. The *eardrum membrane* is on a level with the skin, there being no external ear. Near the end of the snout are two openings known as *external nares* or *nostrils*, from which extend tubes that enlarge into *olfactory* chambers and end as *internal nares* on the roof of the mouth cavity.

INTEGUMENTARY SYSTEM

Skin.   The skin is smooth and moist, and also somewhat slimy because of secretions of the mucous glands. Between it and the underlying muscles are large lymph spaces and scattered strands of connective tissue. Its func-

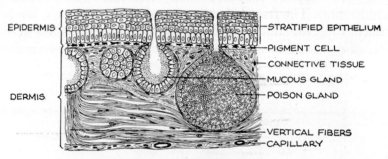

Fig. 215.   Cross section of the skin of a frog ($\times$ 50).

tion is protection, color, secretion, absorption of water, and respiration. As in other vertebrates, the skin consists of two layers: the *epidermis*, made up of stratified epithelial cells, and the *dermis*, connective tissue with glands, blood vessels, and nerves (Fig. 215). The glands are of two types, *mucous* and *poison* glands. Both epidermis and dermis contain several kinds of *pigment cells* or *chromatophores*, black and golden being the most prominent. In many amphibians, such as tree toads, the dark pigment granules of the black cells may either mi-

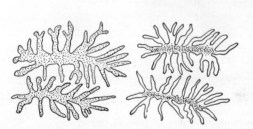

FIG. 216.   Chromatophores from the skin of an amphibian, showing mode of color change. Left, pigment extended into the pseudopods, giving the skin a dark color. Right, pigment withdrawn into the body of the cell, making the color lighter.

grate into pseudopods which extend from these cells, or be withdrawn into the cell body (Fig. 216). In the former condition they cover more area, absorb more light, and give the skin a darker color. Hence these animals have the power of changing color, usually making an approach to the color of the background and thereby securing protection against enemies. The change to dark coloration is brought about primarily through the action of the *pituitary*, an endocrine gland situated underneath the brain. A secretion of still other endocrine glands, the *adrenals*, has an opposite effect, making the skin pale. It is possible that nerve impulses to the chromatophores also influence their coloration. Amphibians probably have no blue or green pigment. Whenever these colors appear, they may be attributed to a cell arrangement that absorbs the other colors of the spectrum, allowing only these to be reflected.

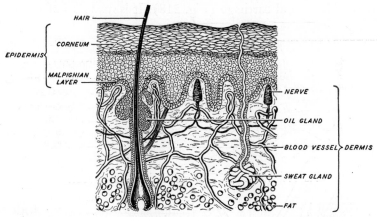

Fig. 217. Section of human skin, magnified. Note that although the hair root, oil gland, and sweat gland are deeply embedded in the dermis, the Malpighian layer around them indicates that they belong to the epidermis. The hair follicle extends to the lower edge of the figure. Its lower margin is elevated as the papilla. (From Buchanan, *Elements of Biology*, copyright, Harper.)

In amphibians there are no skin outgrowths, such as are rather common among vertebrates. Most fishes and reptiles are covered with *scales* or *plates*, birds with *feathers*, and mammals with *hairs*. The scales and plates of fishes are of dermal origin, as are bony plates found elsewhere among vertebrates. However, the scales of reptiles, the feathers of birds, and the hairs of mammals are outgrowths of the epidermis. The hair is a cylinder of epidermal cells projecting from a pit in the skin, the *hair follicle*. At the base of this follicle is an elevation, the *hair papilla*, by means of which the developing hair is supplied with blood. The hair is formed by a profuse multiplication of the epidermal cells just above the papilla, followed by the gradual death and hardening of the outer cells (Fig. 217). Mammals have *oil glands* and *sweat glands;* the former produce an oily secretion for the hair, and the latter serve to keep the skin moist, thereby helping to regulate the temperature of the body through the cooling effect of evaporation. Incidentally they are accessory organs of excretion. The sweat gland has a much-coiled secreting portion embedded in the dermis, and a spiral duct which reaches the surface of the epidermis. The nerve endings of the senses of touch, temperature, and pressure are in the dermis; those of pain, in the epidermis.

SKELETAL SYSTEM

Skeleton. The skeleton of a frog, as of other vertebrates, is internal, consisting of bone and cartilage (Fig. 218). It is made up of an *axial* and

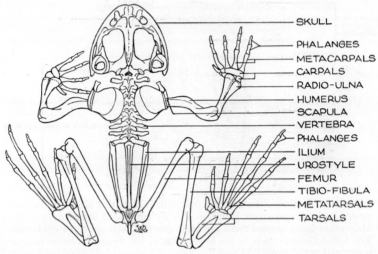

SKULL

PHALANGES

METACARPALS

CARPALS

RADIO-ULNA

HUMERUS

SCAPULA

VERTEBRA

PHALANGES

ILIUM

UROSTYLE

FEMUR

TIBIO-FIBULA

METATARSALS

TARSALS

Fig. 218. Skeleton of the frog, dorsal view. The limbs on the left are in the normal sitting position.

an *appendicular* portion. The former includes the *skull,* the *vertebral column* of nine *vertebrae,* and a posterior extension called the *urostyle.* The ends of the long transverse processes of the vertebrae originate independently of the bodies of the vertebrae, and are said to represent rudimentary *ribs.* The skull furnishes support and protection for the brain, eyes, ears, and nasal capsules, and forms the framework of the jaws. Some of its bones develop from the cartilaginous cranium of the tadpole, others from the overlying membrane.

The appendicular skeleton consists of the *pectoral girdle* with attached *fore limb* bones, and the *pelvic girdle* with attached *hind limb* bones. The pectoral girdle includes the *sternum* (breastbone) along the midventral

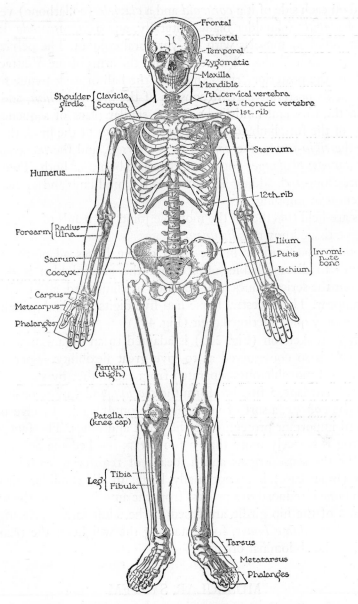

Frontal
Parietal
Temporal
Zygomatic
Maxilla
Mandible
7th cervical vertebra
1st thoracic vertebra
1st rib

Shoulder girdle { Clavicle
Scapula

Sternum

Humerus

12th rib

Forearm { Radius
Ulna

Ilium
Pubis } Innominate bone
Ischium

Sacrum
Coccyx

Carpus
Metacarpus
Phalanges

Femur (thigh)

Patella (knee cap)

Leg { Tibia
Fibula

Tarsus
Metatarsus
Phalanges

FIG. 219. Human skeleton, indicating position with reference to the body contour. (From Millard and King, *Human Anatomy and Physiology*, W. B. Saunders Co.; courtesy of the authors and the publisher.)

line, and on each side of it a *coracoid* and a *clavicle* (collarbone) ventrally placed, a *scapula* (shoulder blade) laterally, and a *suprascapula* dorsally. It is connected by muscles with the vertebral column. The pelvic girdle consists of a stout V-shaped structure with the arms of the V attached to the ends of the posterior "ribs" and with the ball of each femur fitted to a socket at its posterior part. It consists of the *ilium, ischium,* and *pubis.* Bones in the fore and hind limbs follow similar plans of sequence. The *humerus* of the fore limb corresponds to the *femur* of the hind, the *radio-ulna* to the *tibio-fibula,* the *carpals* to the *tarsals,* and the *metacarpals* to the *metatarsals; phalanges* constitute the digit bones of both. Two of the tarsals are elongated, adding a segment to the hind limb and increasing its effectiveness in jumping.

Bones are held together at the movable joints by bands of tough elastic connective tissue known as *ligaments.*

Profound modifications in the form of the bones adapt the various vertebrates to diverse habits of life, but the general plan is the same throughout the series. Bones may be fused or eliminated, and entire digits may disappear. The ancestral horse had five digits to a limb, the modern animal has only one functional digit (Fig. 403).

The human skeleton (Fig. 219) is adapted to an organism with erect posture and is so constructed as to give great flexibility. There are 33 vertebrae—24 movable ones separated from each other by shock-absorbing pads of cartilage, 5 fused to form the *sacrum,* and 4 more or less fused to form the *coccyx,* a sort of vestigial skeleton of a tail. Twelve pairs of *ribs* afford important protection to the heart and lungs. The face, which in the frog is scarcely more than a food trap, has become an important setting for the sense organs and a means of registering emotions. The *cranium* (brain case) is exceptionally large. In the shoulder girdle the coracoid bone is reduced to a process from the anterior edge of the scapula. The bones of the hip girdle are fused in the adult into a pair of structures, the *innominate bones,* for sustaining the weight of the trunk and supporting the abdominal organs.

MUSCULAR SYSTEM

Voluntary Muscle. All movements of the skeleton are brought about by *skeletal* or *voluntary muscles.* Each end of such a muscle is usually attached to a bone by means of a *tendon,* the two ends being on opposite sides of a joint. The fixed end nearest the center of the body is the *origin;* the movable or distal end, the *insertion.* A muscle brings about movement only by contracting, thus shortening the distance between the origin and the insertion. Muscles are generally arranged in antagonistic pairs which bring about opposite movements (Fig. 220). A *flexor*, for example, bends a joint, whereas the opposing *extensor* straightens it. The *biceps* ("two-headed") is the flexor in the upper arm of man, bending the elbow joint; the *triceps* ("three-headed") is the extensor.

Involuntary Muscle. *Involuntary muscle* is responsible for the movements of the internal organs. *Smooth muscle* is present in the alimentary canal, blood vessels, urinary bladder, and iris of the eye. *Cardiac muscle* is present in the heart.

DIGESTIVE SYSTEM

Organs. The adult frog takes as food only moving objects such as insects and worms. Its mouth consists of two large hinged jaws (Fig. 221). For aid in holding the prey, the upper jaw is fitted along the edge with a fringe of pointed *maxillary teeth*, and has on the roof two slight elevations bearing the *vomerine teeth*. The *tongue* is attached in front and is free at

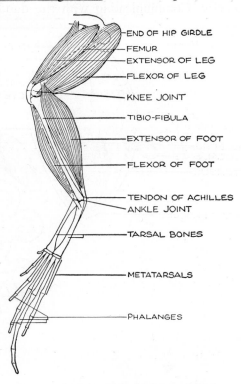

END OF HIP GIRDLE
FEMUR
EXTENSOR OF LEG
FLEXOR OF LEG
KNEE JOINT
TIBIO-FIBULA
EXTENSOR OF FOOT
FLEXOR OF FOOT
TENDON OF ACHILLES
ANKLE JOINT
TARSAL BONES
METATARSALS
PHALANGES

Fig. 220. Muscles of the hind leg of the frog. Two antagonistic pairs are shown, concerned with the bending and straightening of the knee and the ankle. The extensor of the leg is also called triceps because of its three heads. There are other leg muscles not shown here.

its forked posterior end. The filling of the lymph space beneath it flips it forward out of the mouth, whereupon the prey adheres to its sticky surface. As in most vertebrates, the alimentary canal is considerably lengthened, increasing the effective surface for the secretion of enzymes and the absorption of digested food. From the funnel-shaped *pharynx* a short *esophagus* leads to the elongated muscular *stomach*. Food from the lower end of the stomach enters the *small intestine* through a muscular constriction known as the *pylorus* (Gr. "gate keeper"). The first portion of the small intestine is the *duodenum* (Lat. "twelve each," because the corresponding structure in the human body has a length of about twelve fingerbreadths); the remaining, coiled portion is the *ileum*. The small intestine is held in position by means of a *mesentery* (Gr. "mid intestine"), which is an infolded membrane from the peritoneum lining the body cavity. Communicating with the duodenum through the *common bile*

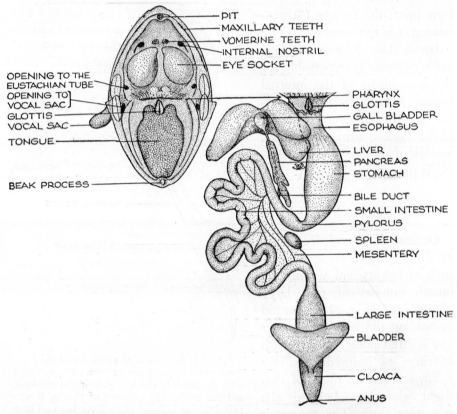

PIT
MAXILLARY TEETH
VOMERINE TEETH
INTERNAL NOSTRIL
EYE SOCKET

OPENING TO THE EUSTACHIAN TUBE
OPENING TO VOCAL SAC
GLOTTIS
VOCAL SAC
TONGUE

BEAK PROCESS

PHARYNX
GLOTTIS
GALL BLADDER
ESOPHAGUS

LIVER
PANCREAS
STOMACH

BILE DUCT
SMALL INTESTINE
PYLORUS

SPLEEN
MESENTERY

LARGE INTESTINE
BLADDER

CLOACA
ANUS

Fig. 221. Digestive system of a frog. The mouth (of male) is spread open after cutting the hinge of the jaws, and is moved to the left to avoid concealing other organs.

duct are the *pancreas* (Gr. "all flesh"), an irregular elongated gland lying in the mesentery between stomach and duodenum, and the *liver*, three-lobed and reddish, which is the largest organ of the body. The latter serves as a storehouse for glycogen and secretes bile which accumulates in the *gall bladder* until it is conveyed through the bile duct to the duodenum. Bile is a waste product that consists largely of the pigments of broken-down red corpuscles, but it aids digestion by creating conditions favorable for the activity of the fat-digesting enzyme of the pancreas.

Digestive enzymes are contained in the *gastric juice*, secreted by the gastric glands in the stomach lining, in the *pancreatic juice*, secreted by the pancreas, and in the *intestinal juice*, secreted by the glands in the intestinal lining. Along the ileum most of the digested food is absorbed. The undigested food accumulates in the short *rectum* (Lat. "straight"), or large intestine, and is then discharged into the *cloaca* (Lat. "sewer"),

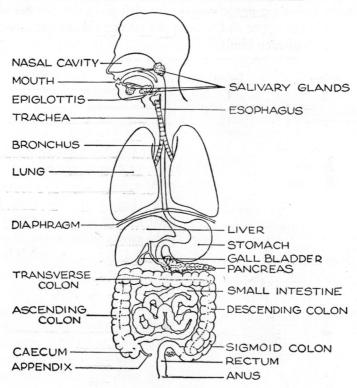

NASAL CAVITY
MOUTH
EPIGLOTTIS
TRACHEA
SALIVARY GLANDS
ESOPHAGUS
BRONCHUS
LUNG
DIAPHRAGM
LIVER
STOMACH
GALL BLADDER
PANCREAS
TRANSVERSE COLON
SMALL INTESTINE
ASCENDING COLON
DESCENDING COLON
CAECUM
SIGMOID COLON
RECTUM
APPENDIX
ANUS

FIG. 222. Digestive and respiratory systems in man.

from which it is egested through the *anus*. The cloaca also serves as a passageway for urine and sperms or eggs, products of the excretory and reproductive systems.

The alimentary canal in mammals is similar to but somewhat more complex than that in the frog (Fig. 222). In addition to the digestive glands already mentioned, mammals have *salivary glands* (three pairs in man), which open into the mouth. Also, the teeth are usually more highly developed than in the frog, being adapted for biting and chewing. The length of the intestine is somewhat correlated with the type of food used. In man the small intestine is about 25 feet long, the large about 5 feet.

Teeth. The *teeth* of different vertebrates vary greatly in number and form, throwing interesting light on food habits and revealing much of the evolutionary story of the various types. Two sets of teeth usually occur in mammals, the milk or temporary teeth and the permanent set. In man, a permanent set generally consists of 32 teeth—8 incisors (in front), 4 canines, 8 premolars, and 12 molars; these are distributed as shown in the following *dental formula*, which gives the number of teeth of each kind in the upper and lower jaws on one side of the mouth (i.e., half of the teeth of each kind).

Incisors	Canines	Premolars	Molars
2	1	2	3
2	1	2	3

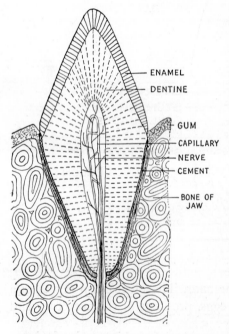

ENAMEL
DENTINE
GUM
CAPILLARY
NERVE
CEMENT
BONE OF JAW

Fig. 223. Diagram of a tooth, showing parts and relation to jawbone.

The parts of a tooth are the exposed part, or *crown;* the embedded part, or *root;* and the *neck* connecting the two (Fig. 223). The neck is covered by the gum. The center is a pulp cavity into which blood vessels and nerves enter. The main body of the tooth enclosing the pulp cavity is bony material called *dentine*. The outer surface of the tooth is covered on the crown with *enamel*—the hardest substance in the body—and on the neck and root with *cement*, which anchors the tooth to the jaw.

Digestive Process. The digestion of food in the human alimentary tract involves certain steps. In the mouth, food is ground by the teeth and mixed with *saliva*, the secretion of the salivary glands. The saliva moistens and lubricates the food, making it more easily swallowed, and by means of the enzyme *ptyalin* (salivary diastase) begins the digestion of starch. In the stomach two additional enzymes are present in the gastric juice: *rennin*, which denatures (curdles) milk proteins, and *pepsin*, which digests proteins to peptides. The action of pepsin is aided by the presence of hydrochloric acid, also secreted by the gastric glands. In the small intestine, in which the contents are alkaline rather than acid, two additional groups of digestive enzymes continue the process. The pancreatic juice contains *lipase*, which digests fats to fatty acids and glycerol; *trypsin*, which continues the breaking down of proteins to peptides; and *amylopsin* (or diastase), which, like ptyalin, digests starches to double sugars. From glands in the lining of the small intestine is derived the intestinal juice, containing *erepsin*, which digests peptides to amino acids, and a number of sugar-splitting enzymes (*maltase, sucrase, lactase*), which digest double sugars to simple sugars. Bile from the liver, though containing no digestive enzyme, facilitates the action of lipase in fat digestion. In both the stomach and small intestine, digestion is aided by rhythmical churning movements of the wall of the digestive tract which cause thorough mixing of the food substances with the digestive enzymes, and by peristaltic movements which propel the intestinal contents onward. A summary of the important digestive enzymes of man is given in the following:

Enzyme	Present in	Transforms
Ptyalin	Saliva	Starches to double sugars
Rennin	Gastric juice	Milk proteins (coagulated) *Curdles*
Pepsin	Gastric juice	Proteins to peptides (in acid medium)
Lipase	Pancreatic juice	Fats to fatty acids and glycerol
Trypsin	Pancreatic juice	Proteins to peptides (in basic medium)
Amylopsin	Pancreatic juice	Starches to double sugars
Erepsin	Intestinal juice	Peptides to amino acids
Maltase	Intestinal juice	Maltose to glucose
Sucrase	Intestinal juice	Sucrose to glucose and fructose
Lactase	Intestinal juice	Lactose to glucose and galactose

RESPIRATORY SYSTEM

The gill-breathing system which the tadpole inherits from its fish ancestry disappears before the adult stage is reached; meanwhile a pair of lungs has formed. A simple lung is merely an outpushing of the floor of the alimentary canal into the body cavity, thus increasing the surface over which gases are exchanged. Such a structure suits the needs of a land animal better than does the gill, for since it is inside the body it is in less danger of drying by exposure to the air. The lungs of the frog are relatively simple, being merely sacs with infoldings of the wall which divide its cavity into numerous pockets called *alveoli*, or *air sacs*. The alveoli are lined with epithelium and are well provided with capillaries. The *glottis*, a slit in the floor of the mouth, opens into the *larynx*, which leads to the lungs by very short *bronchi*, without an intervening trachea. In the breathing process the floor of the mouth is lowered. This decreases the internal air pressure, causing air to flow through the external nares, the olfactory chamber, and the internal nares into the mouth. The external nares are then closed, whereupon a muscular contraction of the floor of the mouth decreases the capacity of the mouth cavity and forces air

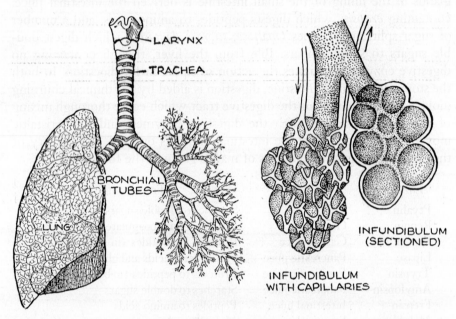

LARYNX

TRACHEA

BRONCHIAL TUBES

LUNG

INFUNDIBULUM (SECTIONED)

INFUNDIBULUM WITH CAPILLARIES

FIG. 224. Human respiratory structures. Left, system from larynx to lungs with tissue removed from left lung to show bronchi and bronchioles; right, two bronchioles with infundibula (alveolar sacs) on which are air sacs (alveoli) grouped like grapes in a cluster. Arrows show the course of circulation from a small pulmonary artery through a network of capillaries to a small pulmonary vein. (Left diagram from Ritchie, *Sanitation and Physiology*, World Book Co.)

through the glottis into the lungs. Here its oxygen diffuses from the air sacs into the pulmonary capillaries, enters into temporary combination with the hemoglobin of the red cells, and is distributed by the circulation of these cells to all parts of the body. The carbon dioxide diffuses from the blood into the air sacs, to be exhaled by the contraction of muscles in the body wall.

In addition to its primary function, the respiratory system produces sound. Cartilages and muscles in the larynx stretch or relax two *vocal cords*, which are elastic folds of the wall of the larynx. When they are stretched, the vibration of the edges causes the familiar croaking notes. In the male this sound is intensified by means of a pair of *vocal sacs* which open into the mouth cavity near the hinges of the jaw and act as resonators when filled with air.

In mammals, the glottis is covered with a cartilaginous lid known as the *epiglottis,* which prevents entry into the larynx of food as it is being swallowed. The *larynx* (Fig. 224) is an enlarged cartilaginous box that provides room for the highly developed vocal cords. The *trachea,* which has cartilaginous rings to prevent its collapse, extends downward from the larynx and branches into two *bronchi,* one of which leads to each lung. Here they branch repeatedly, the terminal branches, or *bronchioles,* ending in *infundibula (alveolar sacs),* which are clusters of small globular *air sacs (alveoli).* It is estimated that the pair of lungs in man is composed of about 750 million of these tiny sacs, which have a total surface area equal to approximately one hundred times the external body surface. This extensive area is necessary to provide for an adequate exchange of gases between the air and the blood.

The frog also carries on considerable exchange of oxygen and carbon dioxide through its skin. In animals that are wholly terrestrial, the skin is dry and of little value in such exchange.

CIRCULATORY SYSTEM

The circulatory system consists of (1) a circulating fluid, the *blood;* (2) the *heart,* a pump for propelling the blood; (3) *arteries,* which carry the blood from the heart, (4) *veins,* which return the blood to the heart, and (5) *capillaries,* minute tubes connecting the arteries with the veins.

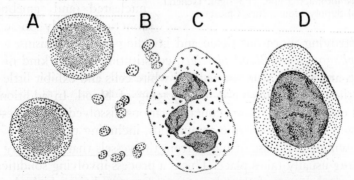

Fig. 225. Human blood cells (greatly enlarged). *A,* Erythrocytes, or red cells. *B,* Platelets. *C* and *D,* White cells: granular leucocyte and lymphocyte respectively.

Blood. The blood of a vertebrate consists of a liquid called *plasma* in which are suspended numerous small bodies (*formed elements,* Fig. 225).

By far the most numerous of these are the *red cells*, which give the red coloration to the blood. *Hemoglobin*, the pigment of the red cells, has a strong affinity for oxygen; temporarily it becomes oxyhemoglobin. This affinity gives the blood a carrying power for oxygen about fifty times as great as that of an equal volume of water. The red cells of the frog are oval, biconvex, nucleated cells (Fig. 226); in mammals these cells lose their nuclei before passing from their place of formation into the blood stream and become biconcave disks. Human red corpuscles are said to have an average life span of about 130 days. Since they have lost their nuclei, they cannot reproduce themselves but must constantly be replaced by new cells produced in the red marrow of the bones. Instrumental in their removal at the end of their usefulness are the *liver* and *spleen*, the latter being a reddish organ attached to the mesentery near the stomach. The spleen also serves as a reservoir for blood to be thrown into the circulation in emergencies. The *white cells* of the blood are nucleated and ameboid and function mainly in engulfing and destroying worn-out tissue and invading microorganisms, a process called *phagocytosis*. *Blood platelets*, constituting a third kind of formed element, are smaller than the red and white cells and exhibit little cellular detail; they are important in the clotting of blood. In addition to the formed elements the plasma contains various dissolved substances—gases, salts, sugar and other organic compounds, including proteins.

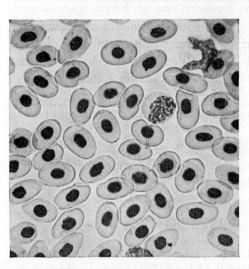

Fig. 226. Blood of frog (× 485). The red cells are elliptical and provided with nuclei. Two white cells, with irregular nuclei, are shown. (Photomicrograph, copyright, General Biological Supply House, Inc., Chicago.)

Following the release of blood from the vessels that ordinarily contain it, *clotting* usually takes place. This is a process involving solidification of a protein substance of the plasma into a network in which the formed elements are held and from which liquid (*serum*) exudes. An important contributing factor is the disintegration of the platelets, which releases a substance that initiates clotting. Also important is the element calcium, normally present as an ion in blood plasma. Blood may be prevented from clotting by adding to it a calcium-removing substance such as sodium citrate. Blood which has been treated in this manner may be stored temporarily and used for experimental purposes and in transfusions.

Blood Groups. When blood from one person is mixed with blood from another, there sometimes takes place an *agglutination*, or clumping of the red cells of one or both of the individuals (a process quite different from clotting). On the basis of this reaction, all human beings may be classed in four main blood groups: O, A, B, and AB. The phenomenon of agglutination depends on the reaction of red cell substances called *antigens* (agglutinogens) with plasma substances called *antibodies* (agglutinins). Two kinds of antigens, A and B, and two kinds of antibodies, a and b, are sufficient to explain the four main types. The distribution of these antigens and antibodies in the blood of individuals of the four groups is shown in the following table:

Blood Group	Antigen(s)	Antibody(ies)
O	None	a and b
A	A	b
B	B	a
AB	A and B	None

Agglutination takes place whenever an antigen is present with the corresponding antibody (i.e., the one designated by the corresponding small letter). It may be seen that any mixture of blood of persons in different groups will contain either one or both of the A-a and B-b antigen-antibody pairs. Under such circumstances agglutination will take place. Since agglutination of red cells in an individual's body may have serious results because it blocks the tiny blood vessels with clumps of cells, it is desirable that blood transfusions be made between members of the same blood group. However, successful intergroup transfusions have been made with blood that has no antigens corresponding to antibodies of the recipient (the donor's antibodies appear to be diluted quickly without causing much agglutination); blood from Group O people (they are called "universal donors") has been used most often, since it contains neither antigen.

Individuals may also be classified according to blood group systems other than the A-B-O series. These other systems likewise involve antigens carried by the red cells. But since antibodies corresponding to these antigens are usually lacking, these other groups are of less importance in transfusions. However, the Rh blood groups may be important. People are either Rh-positive, having one or more red cell antigens of a cer-

tain kind, or Rh-negative, lacking these antigens. Antibodies corresponding to these antigens are normally absent. But if an Rh-negative person
is exposed to Rh-positive blood (as in a transfusion), such antibodies may
develop, and subsequent exposure to the Rh antigen(s) may have serious
results; i.e., another infusion of Rh-positive blood would bring on the
antigen-antibody reaction resulting in destruction of red blood cells in the

patient. It has also been observed
that an Rh-negative mother
may sometimes, while carrying
an Rh-positive child (who inherits the trait from an Rh-positive father), receive in her system some of the child's blood.
This may develop antibodies in
her which might react with the
blood cells of a subsequent Rh-
positive child, causing in the latter a sort of anemia called *erythroblastosis*.

The hereditary basis of the
human blood groups has been
studied extensively. Some aspects of blood group inheritance
will be discussed in Chapter
XXVIII.

FIG. 227. William Harvey, Renaissance scientist and discoverer of the circulation of the
blood.

Heart and Blood Vessels. The circulatory system of a vertebrate, like
that of the earthworm, is a closed system of tubes in which the blood
makes a complete circuit and in the course of which it delivers certain
substances to and collects other substances from the *tissue fluid* that fills
the intercellular spaces. A most important achievement in the history of
biology was the demonstration of the circulation of vertebrate blood by
the Englishman William Harvey (1578–1657; Fig. 227); it had formerly
been believed that the blood simply ebbed and flowed within the blood
vessels. The *heart*, the muscular pump which drives the blood along
through the arteries, capillaries, and veins, is in the anterior ventral part of
the coelom. Valves in the heart and in the veins cause the blood to flow
in one direction only. We shall here designate as *oxygenated*, the blood
that has a relatively high oxygen content, and as *deoxygenated*, that
which has given up most of its oxygen and received carbon dioxide. Blood
in these two conditions is often called *arterial* and *venous* respectively,

but this designation is not entirely correct because the pulmonary artery carries deoxygenated blood and the pulmonary veins carry oxygenated blood. The terms *pure* and *impure* are also inexact, since blood leaving the lungs still contains nitrogenous wastes.

Evolution of Circulatory Systems. No part of the anatomy of vertebrates reveals the stamp of evolution more clearly than does the circulatory system. Comparison of the hearts of the different classes (Fig. 228) reveals the following significant differences:

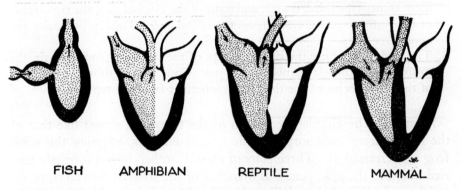

FISH AMPHIBIAN REPTILE MAMMAL

Fig. 228. Comparison of hearts of four classes of vertebrates. That of the fish has two main chambers and carries only deoxygenated blood (indicated by stippling). That of the amphibian has two auricles but permits some mixing of the blood in the ventricle. That of the reptile has an incomplete partition, permitting slight mixing. That of the mammal has two separate ventricles enforcing complete separation. Arrows indicate direction of flow.

1. The fish, a gill breather, has but one auricle and one ventricle. The blood leaving the ventricle goes first to the gills, then to all parts of the body before returning to the heart. This is designated as a *single circulation* (Plate I).
2. The amphibian, a pioneer in lung breathing, has two auricles and one ventricle. Oxygenated and deoxygenated blood, though separate in the auricles, are mixed in the ventricle. Some of the blood, however, must go through the heart twice in a complete circuit. This is *incomplete double circulation*.
3. The reptile has two auricles and an incompletely divided ventricle, permitting slight mixing of the blood. (In Crocodilia the ventricle is completely partitioned, but the union of the two arterial arches still permits some mixing.)
4. The bird or mammal has a four-chambered heart with completely separate ventricles. All the blood in its tour of the body passes through the heart twice. The complete separation of oxygenated and deoxygenated blood allows more effective oxidation, compatible with the needs of a warm-blooded animal. This may be designated *complete double circulation*.

There are also interesting modifications of the *arterial arches*, the branches into which the main artery soon divides after leaving the heart.

1. In some primitive fishes and in the embryos of most vertebrates there are six pairs of these arches, the primary function of which is to carry blood through the gill arches.
2. Sharks retain five of these pairs of arches; most of the fishes have four (Plate I).
3. The frog, as we shall note under the next heading, retains three pairs of these arches (the third, fourth, and sixth of the original six); the two arches of the systemic pair unite to form the dorsal aorta. The reptile retains the same three pairs.
4. The bird retains only the right member of the systemic (fourth) pair, the mammal only the left member of this pair. There is some shifting and fusion of the other arches of the three pairs inherited from the reptiles.

Arteries.   The circulatory system of the tadpole is almost like that of the fish. During metamorphosis the system changes, adapting the adult frog to terrestrial life. Three pairs of *arterial arches*, which formerly carried blood to the gills, persist as branches of the *truncus arteriosus*, or arterial trunk (Fig. 229 and Plate I). They are the *carotid* (Gr. "heavy sleep," because the Greeks believed that these arteries caused drowsiness), each of which divides into two branches supplying the head; the *systemic*, which, after supplying the forelegs, unite back of the heart into a single trunk, the *aorta*, from which branches lead to the visceral organs and hind legs; and the *pulmocutaneous* (Lat. "lungs, skin"), which carry blood to the lungs and skin for the renewal of oxygen.

Veins.   The terminal branches of the arteries break up into capillaries, which reunite as veins. By means of three large veins, two *precaval* and one *postcaval* (Fig. 230), blood from the general circulation enters the *sinus venosus* of the heart, from which it flows into the right auricle; the *pulmonary* veins carry blood from the lungs into the left auricle. As the frog has but one ventricle, there must be some mixing of oxygenated and deoxygenated blood.

Action of Heart.   On the simultaneous contraction of the two auricles of the frog's heart, the oxygenated blood from the left auricle goes into the left side of the ventricle, and the deoxygenated blood from the right auricle goes into the right side of the ventricle. The contraction of the ventricle follows, driving the blood into the truncus arteriosus and thence into the pulmocutaneous, systemic, and carotid arteries. It has been suggested that the contraction of the ventricle takes place so soon after the entry of blood into this part of the heart that there is little chance for mixing of deoxygenated and oxygenated bloods, which are distributed so as to cause largely deoxygenated blood (entering the truncus arteriosus first) to flow through the pulmocutaneous arteries, largely oxygenated blood through the systemic and carotid arteries. However, recent study

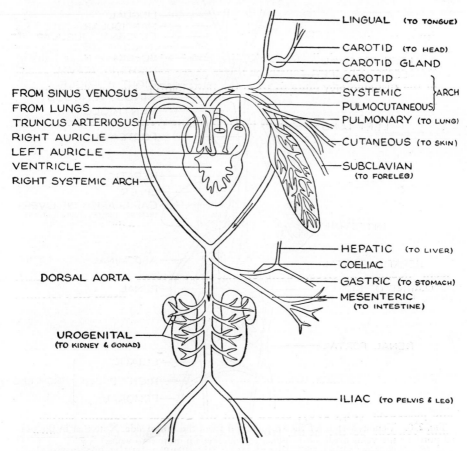

Fig. 229. Arterial system of the frog as seen from the ventral side. The heart, truncus arteriosus, and right common arch are sectioned, showing the spiral valve which directs the blood when it first leaves the ventricle, into the pulmocutaneous arches.

of the action of the frog heart, employing x-rays and x-ray opaque substances injected into the blood, has shown that considerable mixing of blood takes place in the ventricle. While this system seems less efficient than that of the birds and mammals, it must be adequate for the needs of a "cold-blooded" type of organism in which the oxygen requirement is relatively low.

Portal Circulations. Part of the blood finds its way back to the heart by way of one or the other of two *portal* (Lat. "gate") systems, in which a vein, after receiving the blood from a set of capillaries, breaks up into a second set of capillaries. The *renal* (Lat. "kidney") *portal* veins receive a portion of the blood returning from the hind limbs and carry it through

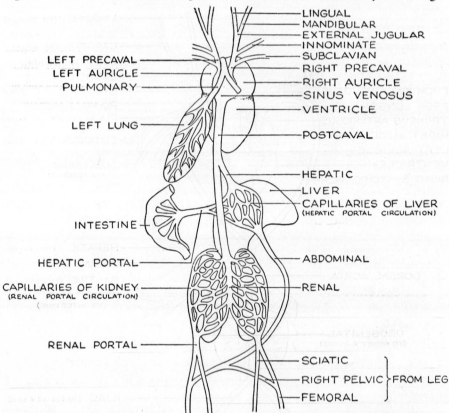

Fig. 230. Venous system of the frog viewed from the dorsal side. Note that in the portal portions the veins break into capillaries which again unite into veins.

the capillaries of the kidneys, where its nitrogenous waste is removed. The *hepatic* (Gr. "liver") *portal* vein receives blood from the stomach and intestines and carries it through the liver, where sugar absorbed from the alimentary tract is stored as *glycogen*, and where certain wastes that result from the breaking down of hemoglobin are removed from the blood and secreted as bile. Although the hepatic portal system persists in reptiles, birds, and mammals, the renal portal system is much reduced in birds and entirely lacking in mammals, the kidneys of the latter being supplied with blood by the arterial system only.

Lymphatic System. The cells of the body are bathed by *tissue fluid* which acts as a middleman, transporting food and oxygen from capillaries to cells, and wastes from cells to capillaries. It consists of blood plasma minus some of its protein constituents, and enters the body spaces by seepage from the capillaries. This fluid has no red cells, but many of the white cells work their way through the capillary walls and appear in it. Starting from the tissue spaces are thin-walled, capillary-like *lymphatic vessels*, which the tissue fluid enters; it is now known as *lymph*. These vessels merge into larger ones and finally, by way of two major ducts, convey the lymph into the blood stream in the right and left subclavian veins. The duct on the left drains the lymph from about three-fourths of the body and delivers to the blood the digested fats absorbed in the villi of the intestine by lymph vessels known as *lacteals* (Fig. 31). The frog has small, muscular lymph hearts to propel the lymph, but in mammals it is propelled mainly by respiratory and other body movements, and is kept moving in the right direction by valves in the vessels. *Lymph nodes* along the course of the vessels filter the lymph, removing bacteria and other solid particles that have found their way into the tissue fluid.

EXCRETORY SYSTEM

The excretory system of a vertebrate consists of a pair of *kidneys* attached to the dorsal wall of the coelom and covered by the peritoneum; two *ureters*, which convey the secretion, *urine*, to the *urinary bladder*, and (in mammals) a *urethra*, or outlet from the bladder. Each kidney has a rather dense outer *cortex* and an inner *medulla*, the former consisting of many *urinary tubules* (about a million in man). Each tubule (Fig. 231) starts from a double-walled cup, *Bowman's capsule*, in the depression of which is a *glomerulus*, a mass of capillaries arising from branches of the renal artery. Capsule and glomerulus constitute a *renal corpuscle*. Another network of capillaries lies along the course of the tubule. Both sets of capillaries play a part in execretion.

Process of Excretion. Water and substances dissolved in the plasma (with the exception of proteins) filter by pressure through the thin walls of the glomerulus capillaries and the capsule, and enter the tubule. As this solution passes along the tubule, certain substances, including the sugar and most of the water, are reabsorbed from the tubule into the blood and retained by the body. By this selective reabsorption of water and salts, the salt concentration of the body fluids is maintained at a fairly constant level, and while useful substances are in general retained by the

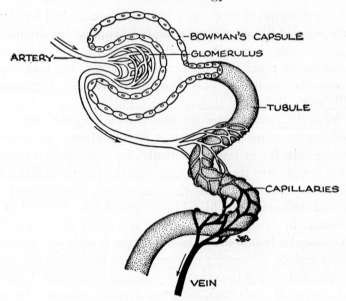

Fig. 231. A renal corpuscle (the glomerulus plus Bowman's capsule) and a small part of the urinary tubule proceeding from it. Note the blood supply via one set of capillaries in the glomerulus and another along the tubule.

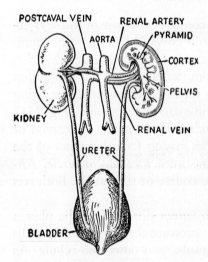

Fig. 232. Human excretory system. The base of the urethra is shown at the lower end of the bladder.

blood, wastes go into the urine. The uriniferous tubules of the frog enter a set of larger collecting tubules, which in turn enter a *ureter* extending along the outer border of each kidney and leading to the *cloaca* (Figs. 233, 234). The urine may be stored temporarily in the bladder, which branches off from the cloaca opposite the ureters, but it is sooner or later passed out through the anus. In mammals, the ureters extend from the inner margin of the kidneys to the bladder; the urethra, from the bladder to the exterior (Fig. 232).

In most vertebrates, *urea* ($NH_2)_2CO$, an end product in the catabolism of protoplasm and the proteins, is the principal solute in urine. In birds and reptiles, however, *uric acid*, a more complex substance, predominates.

REPRODUCTIVE SYSTEMS

Male. Male and female frogs are much alike externally, except that the thumb of the male is thicker than that of the female. The *testes* of the male are two ovoid yellow bodies lying near the inner edge of and ventrally to the kidney (Fig. 233). By the division of epithelial cells forming

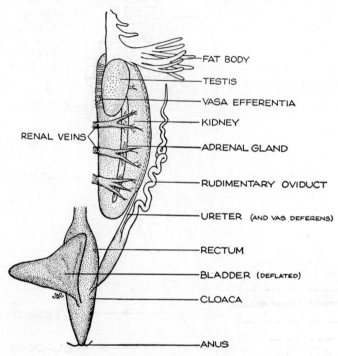

FAT BODY

TESTIS

VASA EFFERENTIA

KIDNEY

RENAL VEINS

ADRENAL GLAND

RUDIMENTARY OVIDUCT

URETER (AND VAS DEFERENS)

RECTUM

BLADDER (DEFLATED)

CLOACA

ANUS

FIG. 233. Urogenital system of male frog and associated fat body (ventral view, paired organs on the right omitted). The sperms pass from testis through vasa efferentia to the kidney, then through the collecting tubules, they reach the cloaca by way of the larger duct, which serves jointly as ureter and vas deferens.

the walls of their many fine, convoluted tubules, *sperms* are produced. These, the male reproductive cells, are carried by several small sperm ducts (*vasa efferentia*) to the kidney, where they enter the collecting tubules, then pass by way of the ureter (functioning as a *vas deferens*) to the cloaca. The tubules and ureter serve a double function, since they also convey urine from the kidney to the cloaca. The male, especially when young, has a pair of rudimentary and functionless oviducts; these are persistent in some species, such as the leopard frog.

Female. An *ovary* lies ventral to each kidney (Fig. 234) and during the breeding season extends forward almost to the front end of the body cavity. Hundreds of eggs in various stages of development give it a granu-

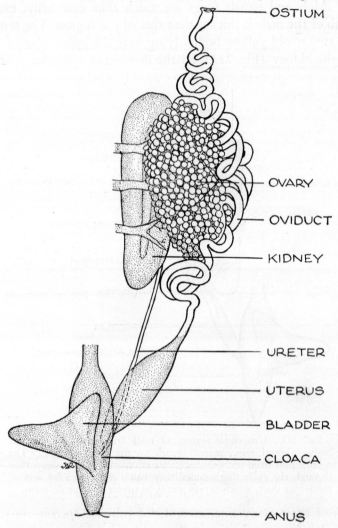

OSTIUM

OVARY

OVIDUCT

KIDNEY

URETER

UTERUS

BLADDER

CLOACA

ANUS

Fig. 234. Urogenital system of female frog, ventral view, paired organs on right side omitted. Note that the eggs and the urine reach the cloaca by separate ducts.

lar texture. The *oviduct* is a much-convoluted tube not connected with the ovary but having a funnel-shaped free end, the *ostium*, immediately behind the lung. When mature, the eggs break out into the coelom, are received by the funnel, and pass down the oviduct. This movement is aided by the vibration of cilia that cover the peritoneum and the inner lining of the oviduct. Glandular cells of the oviduct deposit gelatinous coats over the eggs. Each oviduct is enlarged near the cloaca to form a *uterus* (Lat. "womb"). This serves for the temporary storage of eggs during the breeding season but not, as in mammals, as a place for their further development. It is therefore not necessary for the egg to be fertilized until after it leaves the body.

Fertilization is preceded by *"copulation."* The male holds himself to the back of the female for a day or two, with his thumbs pressed just behind her arms. As the eggs of the female pass from the uterus and cloaca, *semen*, the fluid containing the sperms, is discharged over them by the male. Each sperm has a tail, the active vibration of which helps to carry it to the egg. A single sperm unites with each egg. The gelatin swells until the mass of about 500 floating eggs becomes considerably larger than the frog that laid them. Their development will be followed in the next chapter.

Modifications in Reproductive Systems. The essential parts of the reproductive system are the same in all vertebrates—a pair of testes to produce sperms and a pair of ovaries (only one functional in birds) to produce eggs. The ducts which in the frog carry both sperms and urine, in reptiles, birds, and mammals carry sperms alone, for the kidneys have their own ducts. Since most reptile and bird eggs are protected by thick shells which the sperms cannot penetrate, and since in the mammal the young usually develop in the body of the mother, most of these forms have accessory structures that provide for internal fertilization. In mammals (and a few reptiles and birds), the male has a *penis* (Fig. 235), by means of which sperms are introduced into the *vagina* (Fig. 236) of the female. The latter is the fused terminal portion of the two oviducts. The *uterus*, the more or less fused and expanded middle portion of the oviducts, encloses and nourishes the young mammal during its development. In a few mammals (e.g., marsupials, some rodents, and bats) there are two distinct uteri; in many members of the class the uterus is distinctly two-horned; in man there is complete fusion of the two into a single pear-shaped body (Fig. 236). In most mammals the testes are contained in a pouch of skin, the *scrotum* (Fig. 235), located just behind the penis. The testes develop inside the body of the animal but descend into the scrotum. There is evidence that the proper functioning of the testes of these animals requires the relatively low temperatures afforded by their external position (e.g., artificially keeping the scrotum warm, as by wrapping in cloth, renders these animals sterile).

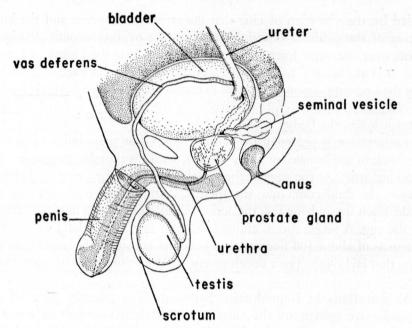

FIG. 235. Human reproductive organs, male. (Redrawn from Young and Stebbins, *The Human Organism and the World of Life*, rev. ed., copyright, 1951, Harper & Brothers.)

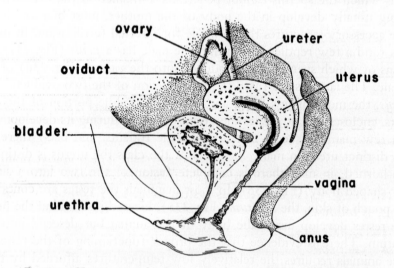

FIG. 236. Human reproductive organs, female. (Redrawn from Young and Stebbins, *The Human Organism and the World of Life*, rev. ed., copyright, 1951, Harper & Brothers.)

Oviparous and Viviparous Forms. Most fishes, amphibians, and reptiles, all birds, and the egg-laying mammals lay eggs which hatch outside the body of the mother; these forms are known as *oviparous* (Gr. "egg-bearing"). However, in some sharks, bony fishes, amphibians, and reptiles, the eggs develop by means of food in the yolk and hatch while still in the oviducts of the mother; these forms are called *ovoviviparous.* Most mammals are *viviparous* (Gr. "live-bearing"). Their embryos are supplied before birth with food and oxygen which diffuses into them from the blood stream of the mother by way of the placenta.

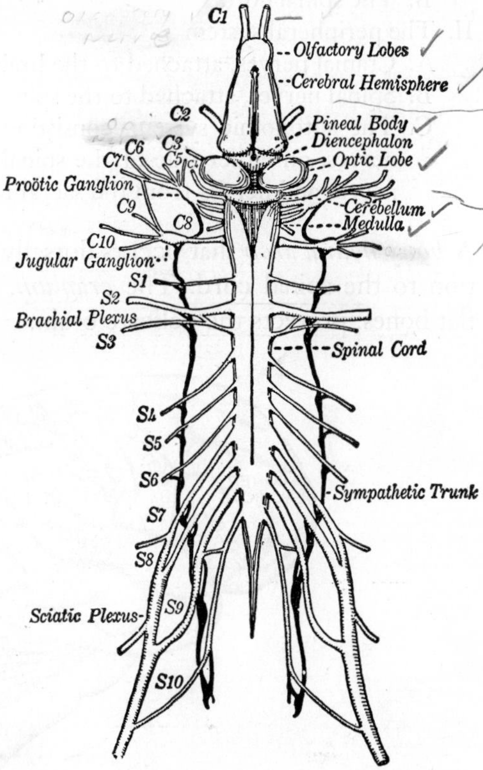

FIG. 237. Nervous system of the frog. The roots of the cranial nerves, *C*, and the spinal nerves, *S*, are numbered in order from the anterior end. Note the two sympathetic trunks of the autonomic system. (From Wellhouse and Hendrickson, *Brief Course in Biology;* copyright, Macmillan.)

NERVOUS SYSTEM

The chordates, as we have seen, differ from the invertebrates in the *dorsal* position of the nerve cord. This cord begins in the embryo as an inpushing of the ectoderm along the mid-dorsal line; it develops into a hollow, tubular structure. The enlargement of this nerve tube at the anterior end is the *brain,* the headquarters of the nervous system. The primitive brain soon comes to consist of three divisions: the *forebrain, midbrain,* and *hindbrain.*

The fully developed nervous system (Fig. 237) consists of two portions, as follows:

I. The central system
 A. The brain
  1. Olfactory lobes
  2. Cerebrum
  3. Diencephalon, bearing pituitary and pineal bodies

} from forebrain of embryo

Fore-Brain
Mid-Brain
Hind-Brain

C1 - olfactory nerve
C3 - optic "
C4 - trigeminal "

Medulla (Oblongata)

    4. Optic lobes, from midbrain of embryo
    5. Cerebellum ⎫
    6. Medulla   ⎬ from hindbrain of embryo
  B. The spinal cord
II. The peripheral system
  A. Cranial nerves, attached to the brain
  B. Spinal nerves, attached to the spinal cord
  C. The autonomic system, consisting of nerve trunks, with ganglia and nerves, on either side of the spinal cord, and including certain cranial nerves and nerves from the sacral region

A *bony neural arch* that occurs dorsally to each vertebra serves as protection to the spinal cord. The *cranium*, a box-like cavity surrounded by flat bones, protects the delicate brain.

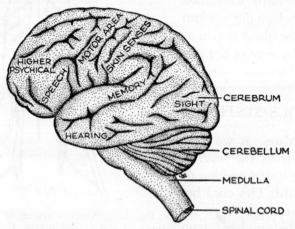

Fig. 238. Human brain, viewed from the left. The different regions of the cerebrum seem to be associated with the mental faculties indicated in the diagram.

Brain. The *olfactory lobes*, the seat of the sense of smell, are well developed in the frog, but are small and hidden under the cerebrum in man. The *cerebrum* corresponds to the two hemispheres of the human brain. It is functionally insignificant in the frog because its removal does not greatly alter the behavior of the animal; but in the more advanced vertebrates it is the largest part of the brain and serves as the seat of sense perception, voluntary motion, and the higher mental faculties, such as association, memory, and thought. The *diencephalon* serves as a bridge connecting the cerebrum with the optic lobes. It seems to be the chief seat of spontaneous movement in the frog, and it bears the pituitary and pineal bodies, the former an important endocrine gland. The *optic lobes* are the seat of the sense of sight and are also inhibitors in toning down excessive reflex activity of the spinal cord. The *cerebellum* (Lat. "little brain") is regarded, in general, as a center for coordinating muscular activity. However, it is very small, and is probably of relatively little importance in the frog. The *medulla* (Lat. "marrow") not only is the pathway between the brain and the spinal cord, but contains the roots of most of the *cranial nerves* and is an important reflex center for the regulation of the respiratory movements, heartbeat, and the size of the arteries.

In the more intelligent mammals, not only is the cerebrum greatly enlarged, but its surface is much furrowed (Fig. 238). The gray matter, which in the frog is centrally located in the brain as well as in the spinal cord, forms a surface layer on the mammalian brain. The increase in size and in furrowing increases the amount of gray matter, and therefore the number of nerve cells or neurons that can be accommodated. It is estimated that the human brain has about ten trillion of these neurons. Intelligence, however, must be governed not merely by the number of neurons, but by the extent of the development of dendrites and nerve fibers that connect neurons with one another and thus make possible a high degree of association of nerve responses.

Cranial Nerves. Connected with the brain are nerves through which sensory impulses are conducted from the sense organs to the brain, and motor impulses from the brain to muscles and glands.

The cranial nerves of man and other mammals in order from the anterior end are as follows, the frog having the first ten:

1. Olfactory—from smell receptors
2. Optic—from sight receptors
3. Oculomotor—to and from eye muscles
4. Trochlear—to superior oblique muscle of eye
5. Trigeminal—from sensory receptors in face, lips, and tongue; to jaw muscles
6. Abducens—to and from external straight muscle of eye
7. Facial—from sensory endings in tongue; motivates facial expression
8. Auditory—from hearing and equilibrium receptors in the ear
9. Glossopharyngeal—to muscles and from sensory endings in tongue and pharynx
10. Vagus—from sensory and to motor endings in lungs, heart, stomach, and intestine; also called pneumogastric
11. Spinal accessory—mainly to motor endings in thoracic region
12. Hypoglossal—to muscles of tongue

Spinal Cord and Spinal Nerves. The spinal cord of the vertebrate is the axis of the nervous system, and is made up of *gray matter* (principally cell bodies of neurons) completely surrounded by *white matter* composed of nerve fibers (axons and dendrites) which are the processes of neurons (Fig. 239). Each nerve fiber of the cord and the peripheral (but not the autonomic) nerves has a sheath of fatty material, the function of which is probably similar to that of the rubber used in telephone cables—the insu-

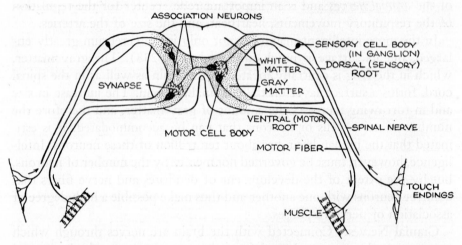

FIG. 239. Diagram of the spinal cord (cross section) of a vertebrate and a pair of spinal nerves, indicating the paths along which an impulse travels in reflex action. Note by the arrows that an impulse, as from a touch stimulus, reaches the cord by way of the dorsal root of the spinal nerve, passes through a synapse directly into a motor neuron by way of its dendrites, or reaches the motor neuron by way of one or more intervening association neurons.

lation of each fiber from the others to prevent any intermingling of the impulses traveling over them.

The neurons constituting the brain, cord, and connected nerves are of three general kinds: (1) *Sensory neurons*, which bring sensory impulses from the sense receptors in various parts of the body to the brain or cord. The sense receptors may be parts of these neurons or closely associated with them. (2) *Association neurons*, which transmit impulses from one point to another in the cord or brain. (3) *Motor neurons*, which carry impulses from the sensory or association neurons to the reacting structures, such as muscle fibers or gland cells. Curiously enough, before they reach their destination most of the ascending and descending nerve fibers in the cord cross over to the side of the cord opposite that at which they entered. It thus happens that the left hemisphere of the brain receives sensory impulses from, and transmits motor impulses to, the right side of the body.

There are ten pairs of *spinal nerves* in the frog, one from each junction between the vertebrae. The tadpole has about twice as many, but the posterior ones disappear when the tail degenerates. In man there are thirty-one pairs. Each spinal nerve is attached to the cord by two roots: the *dorsal*, made up of *sensory* axons, and the *ventral*, made up of *motor* axons. The cell bodies of the sensory neurons are in the spinal ganglion on the dorsal root; those of the motor neurons are in the gray matter of the cord.

Reflex Action. Aside from being the highway for nerve communication to and from the brain, the spinal cord is a center for *reflex action.* A reflex action is one that regularly follows a particular kind of stimulus without involving any volition. If a piece of blotting paper moistened with dilute acetic acid is placed on the side of the body of a frog whose brain has been destroyed, the frog will bring forward the hind leg on that side and wipe the paper away. The vigor of the wiping movement varies with the intensity of the stimulus, but the response invariably follows the stimulus. The mechanism by which this reflex response is carried out is shown in Fig. 239. The impulse reaches the cord by way of the sensory neuron, which in the cord forms a synapse (contact) either directly with the motor neuron or through one or two intermediate association neurons. The axon of the motor neuron comes in contact with muscle fibers and transmits the impulse which causes their contraction. Usually the sensory neuron also makes contact with neurons whose axons are extended lengthwise in the white matter of the cord. Impulses may thereby be carried to the brain and thus register in consciousness.

Autonomic System. The *autonomic* (Gr. "self-governing") portion of the peripheral system is that which governs movements of involuntary muscles and secretions of glands. Each organ receives two sets of fibers belonging to this system—the *sympathetic*, which arise from ganglia forming a sympathetic trunk on each side of the spinal cord (Fig. 237), and the *parasympathetic*, which arise with certain cranial nerves from the brain and with certain spinal nerves from the sacral region of the cord. These sets of fibers are antagonistic, in that one stimulates the muscle or gland to greater activity, whereas the other retards its activity. The autonomic neurons are closely connected with the cerebrospinal system and are influenced by stimuli received through the sense organs. For example, stimuli received by the sensory endings for cold (in mammals) cause the contraction of the skin capillaries; this exposes less blood to loss of heat by radiation and brings about an increase in oxidation, liberating more heat. By these processes the body is enabled to maintain a uniform temperature.

SENSES AND SENSE ORGANS

Smell. Most vertebrates have nasal cavities or passages on the surface of which the brush-like tips of *olfactory cells* are exposed (Fig. 240). These cells are the smell receptors. Particles of gases or volatile substances

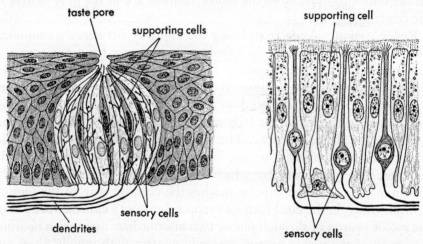

Fig. 240. Diagram of the receptors for the chemical senses, as seen with the microscope. Left, section of a taste bud from the tongue, showing the pore through which the dissolved substance enters, the sensory cells that receive the stimulus, and the nerve endings that carry the impulse to the brain. Right, olfactory epithelium lining the nasal cavity. Vapors entering the nostril dissolve in the mucus and come in contact with the sensory cells, giving rise to smell sensations. (From Young and Stebbins, *The Human Organism and the World of Life*, rev. ed., copyright 1951, Harper & Brothers.)

dissolve in the mucus in contact with these exposed tips and give rise to impulses which are carried by the olfactory nerve to the olfactory lobe of the brain and produce sensations of smell. The sense is much more highly developed in many of the lower mammals than in man.

Taste. In the lining of the mouth, and particularly on the tongue, are groups of sensory cells known as *taste buds* (Fig. 240). With them are associated fine nerve branches which, when the cells are stimulated by substances in solution, carry to the brain impulses which give rise to taste sensations.

Sight. The eye of a vertebrate (Fig. 241) consists essentially of (1) a system of lenses and humors (liquids) properly arranged for forming an inverted image of the object toward which the eye is directed. These are, from front to rear, the *cornea*, the *aqueous humor*, the *crystalline lens*, and the *vitreous humor*. (2) A diaphragm, the *iris*, which regulates the

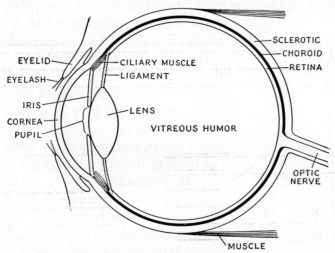

Fig. 241. Median longitudinal section of the human eye. The pupil is the aperture of the iris.

amount of light entering; (3) an inner coat, the *retina*, an expansion of the distal end of the optic nerve; it is made up of sensory neurons, of which highly specialized dendrites, known as *rods* and *cones*, are very sensitive to light (Fig. 242). (4) A middle or *choroid coat*, which is black and thus keeps light from entering except through the cornea; (5) an outer or *sclerotic* coat which forms a firm protective covering; (6) four *straight* (rectus) and two *oblique muscles* for directing the eye; (7) *lids* for protection, and (8) a *lachrymal gland* for keeping the anterior surface moistened.

An interesting adaptation in the higher vertebrates is the presence of *ciliary muscles*, which by their contraction relax the ligament that stretches the crystalline lens and thereby allow the latter to become more convex. Light rays are thus focused so that sharp images are formed, regardless of the distance of the object. The lens in the frog is nearly spherical and cannot be focused; hence the animal is near-sighted in air and far-sighted in water, the motion of objects being probably more evident than their form. Near-sightedness and far-sightedness in man are due to variations from normal either in the length of the eyeball or in the shape or elasticity of the lens. Near-sightedness may be corrected by means of concave glasses; far-sightedness, by convex glasses.

In vertebrates there may be as many as three eyelids; the upper and lower, which move vertically over the eyeball, and the lateral (*nictitating membrane*), which moves outwardly from the inner angle of the eye. The last-named is important in many of the lower vertebrates (in the frog it is fused with the lower lid, which is movable); in man it is reduced to a functionless vestige.

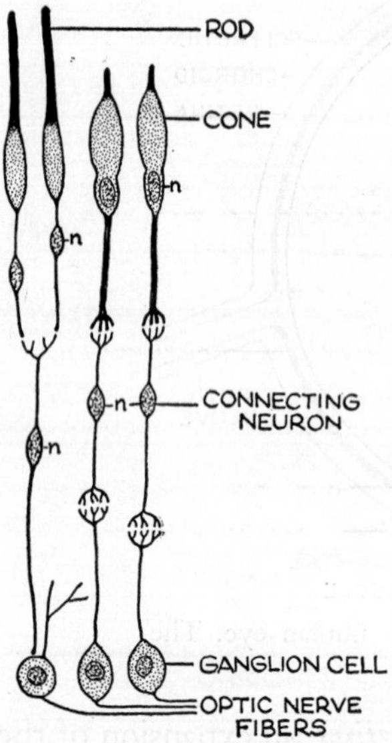

FIG. 242. Diagram of the neuron layers constituting the retina of the eye, highly magnified. The diagram represents the thickness of the retina, the inner surface being the nerve fiber layer below. The light rays which form the image on the retina penetrate to the sensory layer, made up of rods and cones. The impulses originated by the stimulus then travel back over the connecting neurons to the optic nerve fiber. The rods function in dim light; the cones, which have the power to distinguish color, in bright light. *n*, nuclei.

Hearing. The frog has only the *middle* and the *inner ear*. The *tympanic* or *drum membrane* is level with the skin of the head. Man and other mammals have in addition an *outer ear*, consisting of a *pinna* that catches the sound waves, and an auditory *canal* that carries them to the drum membrane (Fig. 243). The air pressure within the middle ear, or drum, is adjusted by means of the *Eustachian tube*, which connects the middle ear with the pharynx. This tube is formed from the anterior gill slit as the organism develops. The air-filled chamber of the drum is crossed in the frog by a cartilaginous rod; in man and other mammals, by a chain of three small bones. The function of these structures is to convey vibrations caused by sound waves from the drum membrane to the inner ear.

The inner ear consists of a very complex sac, the *membranous labyrinth*, that occupies an irregular cavity in the temporal bone, the *bony labyrinth*. It consists of three parts—the *vestibule*, and the *cochlea* and three *semicircular canals* which are attached to the vestibule. The cochlea is a coiled structure in which are sensory cells that receive the sound stimuli and transmit to the brain impulses arising from them. One of the semicircular canals is in a horizontal plane; the other two lie in vertical planes at right angles to each other. Each has an expanded end called the *ampulla*. In the ampullae and the vestibule are sensory cells which respond to changes in the position of the body, giving rise to the sense of equilibrium.

Other Senses. Generally distributed over the skin, but more numerous in certain areas such as the finger tips, are nerve endings for *touch*. Other endings in the skin are sensitive to stimuli which give rise to sensations of *heat, cold, pressure,* and *pain.* Still other sensory endings lie within the body; for example, in the muscles are *muscle spindles* which respond to muscular position and movement, giving rise to a *muscle sense* that enables

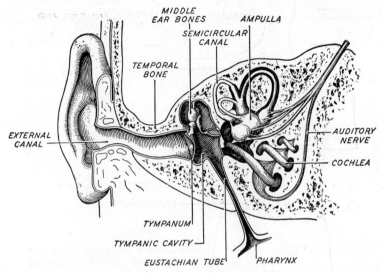

MIDDLE
EAR BONES   AMPULLA

SEMICIRCULAR
CANAL

TEMPORAL
BONE

EXTERNAL
CANAL

AUDITORY
NERVE

COCHLEA

TYMPANUM

TYMPANIC CAVITY

EUSTACHIAN TUBE   PHARYNX

FIG. 243. Longitudinal section of the human ear, represented diagrammatically. (From Haggard, *Science of Health and Disease;* copyright Harper; original by Tschermak.)

us to know the position of the parts of the body. Also within the body are nerve endings which, when stimulated, give rise to various sensations such as *pain, nausea, hunger, thirst,* and *fatigue.*

ENDOCRINE SYSTEM

In coordinating the activities of the various parts of the body, the nervous system is supplemented by the endocrine system. The name (Gr. "secreting internally") refers to the fact that the secretions are not carried away by ducts but are poured directly into the blood that passes through the gland. The secretions are called *hormones* (Gr. "exciters"), or *endocrines.* They are carried in the blood stream and affect parts of the body more or less remote from the gland that produces them.

While the nervous system serves in the rapid adjustment of the organism to changes in its environment, the endocrine system serves in the slow internal adjustments involving the rate of metabolism, the functioning of the various organs, and the growth of the organism and its parts. Hormones are usually effective in very minute quantities.

The endocrine glands of man (Fig. 244), the hormones secreted, and their functions are summarized in the table on page 305.

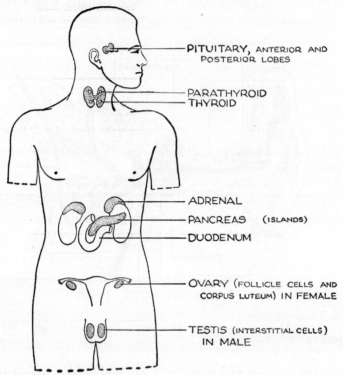

PITUITARY, ANTERIOR AND POSTERIOR LOBES

PARATHYROID
THYROID

ADRENAL

PANCREAS (ISLANDS)

DUODENUM

OVARY (FOLLICLE CELLS AND CORPUS LUTEUM) IN FEMALE

TESTIS (INTERSTITIAL CELLS) IN MALE

FIG. 244. Endocrine glands shown diagrammatically. Glands peculiar to each sex are included in this figure. The parathyroids are dorsal to the thyroid.

Thyroid. The *thyroid* (Gr. "shield-shaped") glands in the frog consist of two small ovoid bodies, one on each side of the larynx. In man the two are merged into one two-lobed gland. They secrete an endocrine, *thyroxin*, which has been chemically analyzed and produced artificially. It exerts two primary effects. (1) It controls the rate of *basal metabolism*, that part of the metabolism which is concerned with the maintenance of the vital activities of the body. If too much thyroxin is produced, there is a speeding up of the rate of heartbeat, accompanied by increased restlessness and irritability, and often a protrusion of the eyeballs; the condition is called *exophthalmic* (Gr. "out eyes") *goiter*. If too little is produced in the adult, the result is often a retarding of the activities and mental faculties, together with a deposit of excess fat beneath the skin. (2) Thyroxin exercises some control over growth and development. Tadpoles

Gland	Hormone	Function
Thyroid	Thyroxin	Regulates basal metabolism and normal development of the body.
Parathyroids	Parathormone	Regulates calcium metabolism and calcium content of the blood.
Pituitary (anterior lobe)	Growth hormone	Stimulates growth, particularly of the bones.
	Follicle-stimulating hormone	Stimulates follicle formation in ovary of female; stimulates growth of sperm-bearing tubules in male.
	Luteinizing hormone	Stimulates formation of corpus luteum in female; stimulates interstitial cells in male.
	Prolactin	Stimulates secretion of milk by mammary glands in female.
	Thyrotropic hormone	Stimulates thyroid secretion.
	Parathyrotropic hormone	Stimulates parathyroid secretion.
	Adrenotropic hormone	Stimulates adrenal cortex secretion.
	Blood-sugar-raising principle	Regulates activity of insulin.
Pituitary (posterior lobe)	Pituitrin (perhaps resolvable into more than one hormone)	Increases blood pressure; decreases water secretion in urine; causes contraction of smooth muscle.
Adrenal cortex *outer*	Cortin	Regulates salt and water metabolism.
Adrenal medulla	Epinephrine (adrenin)	Regulates blood pressure; gives greater capacity for meeting emergencies.
Pancreas (islands of Langerhans)	Insulin	Storage, release and oxidation of sugar.
Mucous membrane of duodenum	Secretin	Activates secretion of enzymes by pancreas.
Testis (interstitial cells)	Testosterone	Develops secondary sex characters of male; contributes to sex behavior.
Ovary (follicle cells)	Estrogen	Prepares wall of uterus to receive fertilized egg.
Ovary (corpus luteum)	Progesterone	Directs the various changes associated with pregnancy and childbirth.
Chorion (of embryo)	Gonadotropin	Similar in function to luteinizing hormone.

fed upon thyroid tissue undergo rapid differentiation and change prematurely into frogs which may be no larger than houseflies. If the human thyroid atrophies in infancy, the result is a condition known as *cretinism*, in which growth, both physical and mental, is arrested. Cretins may be benefited by administration of the powdered thyroid glands of animals or manufactured thyroxin, but the improvement is apparent only so long as the treatment is continued (Fig. 245).

Iodine is a constituent of thyroxin, hence is essential for its formation. Failure to receive this element in sufficient quantity results in a compensatory enlargement of the thyroid, *simple goiter*, often visible as a more or less pronounced swelling of the neck. Since iodine is present in sea water, those who live near the sea usually do not fail to obtain, in water or food, the minute quantities that are essential. In other areas, such as the Great Lakes, the Rockies, and the Alps, the shortage of iodine is such that goiter has at times been very prevalent. Its incidence has been reduced greatly in recent years by the use of table salt to which a small amount of potassium iodide has been added. The incidence of goiter among school children in Detroit was reduced, during a seven-year period immediately following the introduction of iodized salt, from 36 to 1.2 percent.

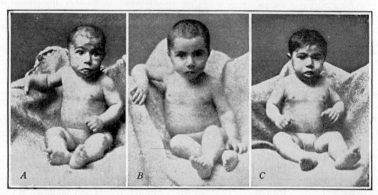

Fig. 245. Cretinism, a disease caused by a deficiency of the hormone thyroxin. *A*, Patient before treatment; *B*, after three weeks' treatment with thyroxin; *C*, six months after discontinuance of the treatment. (From Fasten, *Genetics and Eugenics*, Ginn and Company; copyright, *Journal of Heredity*.)

Parathyroids. The *parathyroids* are apparently restricted to the higher classes of vertebrates. There are two on each side of the dorsal surface of the thyroid in man. Their partial removal leads to a number of disturbances which seem to be due primarily to a reduction in the calcium content of the blood and bone. Complete removal leads quickly to death. A lessening of their activity in early childhood results in defective bone formation resembling rickets, caused by an insufficiency of available calcium.

Pituitary. The *pituitary* gland, attached to the ventral side of the diencephalon or bridge of the brain, is in reality two glands in one—the *anterior lobe*, which develops as a pouch from the roof of the mouth, and the *posterior lobe*, which develops as a projection from the brain. It will be seen from the above table that the anterior lobe secretes a wide variety of hormones. It has been called "the director of the endocrine orchestra," inasmuch as it exercises control over most of the other endocrine glands. An excess of *growth hormone* tends to make one a giant; a deficiency, a dwarf. If its secretion is excessively stimulated after the bones have attained normal development, some of the bones may enlarge, giving rise to disproportion, particularly in facial features, a condition known as *acromegaly*.

Adrenals. The *adrenal* glands may be observed in the frog extending along the ventral surface of the kidneys; in man, they resemble caps that rest on the tips of the kidneys. The *cortex* (Fig. 246), or outer portion

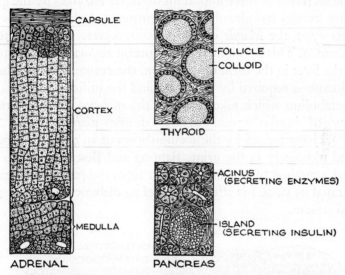

Fig. 246. Adrenal gland, thyroid, and pancreas; sections as seen with the microscope. The adrenal is a combination of two glands, the cortex and medulla, which secrete different hormones. The pancreas is a dual-functioning gland; it secretes digestive enzymes in the acini and the hormone insulin in the islands of Langerhans.

of the gland, secretes the endocrine complex *cortin*, which influences carbohydrate and salt metabolism. *Cortisone*, a component of cortin, has been reported as producing striking improvement when used in the treatment of arthritis. Damage to the adrenal cortex may bring on *Addison's disease*, characterized by reduced heart rate, low blood pressure, and darkening of the skin. The *medulla* secretes *epinephrine*, an endocrine that regulates blood pressure and various other activities that are controlled by the autonomic nervous system. In times of emotional stress its secretion rate is accelerated, resulting in increased blood pressure; increased discharge of glucose from the liver into the blood, making possible vigorous action of the muscles; increase in the rate of heartbeat; dilation of the pupil of the eye; and erection of the hair, which is particularly noticeable in such mammals as the cat. The effect of most of these changes is to prepare the animal for the successful meeting of emergencies. Epinephrine can be obtained from the adrenal glands of mammals, or it can be made synthetically. Injections have been used to restore heart action which has been stopped by surgical shock. It is often employed to stop local hemorrhage and to relieve acute attacks of asthma.

Pancreas. The *pancreas* is both a digestive and an endocrine gland (Fig. 246). The secretion of three important digestive enzymes by the glandular cells lining its sacs has already been mentioned. Isolated groups of cells of another type, the *islands of Langerhans,* secrete the hormone *insulin* (Lat. "island"). This hormone is an important regulator of the storage of sugar in the liver in the form of glycogen, the reconversion of the glycogen to glucose as required by the body, and the utilization of this glucose in the metabolism which takes place in the muscles and other tissues. A deficiency of insulin results in the disease *diabetes* (Gr. "passing through"), characterized by the accumulation of an excess of sugar in the blood and ultimately in the urine. Banting and Best at Toronto in 1922 developed a method of obtaining insulin from the pancreas of cattle and demonstrated its value for affording relief to diabetics when injected into the blood stream.

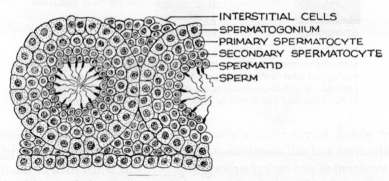

FIG. 247. Section of a mammalian testis, showing a complete tubule and part of another. The spermatogonia give rise to primary spermatocytes. Each of these divides into two secondary spermatocytes which divide again into spermatids. These each differentiate into a sperm with head and tail. The interstitial cells secrete the hormone testosterone. (Diagrammatic.)

Duodenum. When the acidified food from the stomach enters the duodenum, the epithelial cells of the latter secrete a hormone, *secretin,* which is carried by the blood stream to the pancreas and incites it to secrete pancreatic juice.

Testes. The testes (Fig. 247) are made up of *tubules,* which produce sperms, and of groups of *interstitial* (Lat. "standing between") *cells,* which secrete the male hormone, *testosterone.* The function of this substance is primarily to bring about the bodily changes that accompany adolescence or puberty, i.e., the development of secondary sexual characters, such as the growth of hair on the face and the deepening of the voice in man. It contributes to the development of antlers in the deer, mane in the lion, and corresponding male characters in other mammals.

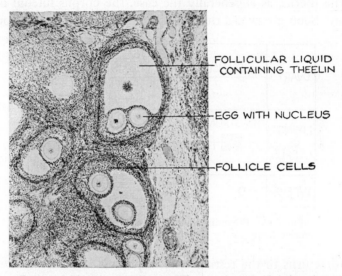

FOLLICULAR LIQUID CONTAINING THEELIN

EGG WITH NUCLEUS

FOLLICLE CELLS

Fig. 248. Portion of the ovary of a cat (× 70), showing three advanced follicles, two of which contain two eggs each. The follicle cells secrete the hormone estrogen. (Photomicrograph, copyright, General Biological Supply House, Inc., Chicago.)

Ovaries. The *ovaries* give rise to two important hormones. An ovary contains many eggs in various stages of development. As each egg increases in size, it comes to be surrounded by a mass of small cells known as follicle cells, the whole structure being called a *follicle* (Fig. 248). These cells secrete the hormone *estrogen* (Gr. "estrus producing," *estrus* being the mating season of lower mammals). At intervals during the reproductive period of life, from about the twelfth to about the forty-fifth year in the human female, a follicle comes to the surface of the ovary and bursts, discharging the egg and a small quantity of estrogen into the body cavity. The egg is caught by the ostium of the oviduct and moves down the duct toward the uterus; this takes several days. The hormone, which is distributed by the blood, causes the wall of the uterus to thicken so that it may receive the egg in case the latter has been fertilized in the oviduct by a sperm. Soon after the discharge of the egg and follicular fluid, the space they formerly occupied is filled, by the proliferation of some of the follicle cells, with a yellowish mass of cells known as the *corpus luteum* (Lat. "orange-yellow body"). This development is regulated by the *luteinizing hormone* of the pituitary. The cell mass produces another hormone, *progesterone* (Gr. "before giving birth"), which continues the preparation of the uterus to receive the egg. If no fertilized egg reaches the uterus, as is generally the case, the corpus luteum begins to degenerate. Soon afterward the uterus sheds its thickened mucous mem-

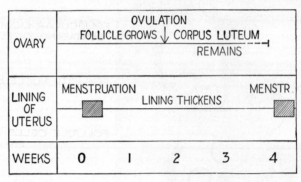

Fig. 249.   Diagram relating changes in the ovary and uterine lining to the human menstrual cycle.

brane and returns to the resting state, a process known as *menstruation* (from Lat. "month," Fig. 249). The follicle-stimulating hormone from the pituitary then causes another follicle to develop, the egg is discharged, the uterus wall thickens, and, assuming that fertilization does not occur, there is another shedding of the lining of the uterus which initiates another menstrual period.

If, on the other hand, a fertilized egg reaches the uterus, the corpus luteum continues to secrete progesterone which, while inhibiting the development of more follicles and preventing further menstruation, continues to enlarge the uterus and the mammary glands and to regulate other changes essential to the growth of the embryo and the eventual birth of the child. This hormone is often administered by physicians during the period of pregnancy to prevent abortion.

Pregnancy tests. During early pregnancy, probably to stimulate continued secretion of progesterone, the outer membrane (*chorion*) of the embryo secretes a hormone known as *chorionic gonadotropin*, which seems to be similar to the luteinizing hormone. This appears in the urine and constitutes the basis of tests to reveal pregnancy long before other signs are apparent. Injection of pregnancy urine into female rats, mice, or rabbits causes the ovaries to enlarge and develop follicles. Its injection into the male of certain frogs and toads leads to the discharge of sperms.

EXERCISES

1. How does a frog compare with man as regards the relative importance of reflex action in behavior?
2. There is a tendency, as we go up the vertebrate evolutionary scale, for the red corpuscles to become smaller. Explain.
3. The neurons of invertebrates are distributed among many centers or ganglia of almost equal importance, whereas in vertebrates, especially man, most of them are closely grouped within the cortex of the brain. Why is the latter arrangement more favorable than the former for the development of intelligence?
4. State three functions of the liver. Name the functions of the spleen.
5. Why is there so little fossil evidence concerning the ancestry of the Subphylum VERTEBRATA?
6. Distinguish the terms vertebra, vertebral column, and vertebrate. Distinguish between notochord and nerve cord.
7. Why are the lungs of a mammal so much more complex than those of a frog?
8. What are the names of the bones of the middle ear of man and how were these names suggested?
9. Determine the dental formula of (a) dog, (b) rabbit, (c) rat, (d) horse. How is variation in the teeth of these mammals related to their food habits?
10. What is meant by *estrus cycle?* In what animals does it occur, and how does it vary from one species to another? What is the *menstrual cycle,* and in what mammals does it occur?

REFERENCES

Baitsell, G. A., *Human Biology*, McGraw-Hill Book Company, Inc., 2nd ed., 1950.

Carlson, A. J., and Johnson, V., *The Machinery of the Body*, Univ. of Chicago Press, 3rd ed., 1948.

Corner, G. W., *The Hormones in Human Reproduction*, Princeton Univ. Press, 1942.

Eaton, T. H., Jr., *Comparative Anatomy of the Vertebrates*, Harper & Brothers, 1951.

Greisheimer, E. M., *Physiology and Anatomy*, J. B. Lippincott Company, 6th ed., 1950.

Holmes, S. J., *The Biology of the Frog*, The Macmillan Company, 4th ed., 1927.

Hyman, L. H., *Comparative Vertebrate Anatomy*, Univ. of Chicago Press, 2nd ed., 1942.

Kahn, F., *Man in Structure and Function*, Alfred A. Knopf, Inc., 2 vols., 1943.

Noble, G. K., *The Biology of the Amphibia*, McGraw-Hill Book Company, Inc., 1931.

Parker, G. H., *Animal Color Changes and Their Neurohumors*, Cambridge Univ. Press, 1948.

Quiring, D. P., *Functional Anatomy of the Vertebrates*, McGraw-Hill Book Company, Inc., 1950.

Romer, A. S., *Man and the Vertebrates*, Univ. of Chicago Press, 3rd ed., 1941.

Romer, A. S., *The Vertebrate Body*, W. B. Saunders Co., 1949.

Turner, C. D., *General Endocrinology*, W. B. Saunders Co., 1948.

Walls, G. L., *The Vertebrate Eye*, Cranbrook Institute of Science, 1942.

Williams, J. F., *Anatomy and Physiology*, W. B. Saunders Co., 7th ed., 1943.

Chapter XVIII

ANIMAL ONTOGENY

Ontogeny (Gr. "origin of the individual") concerns the development of the organism from egg to maturity. Before the developing animal leaves the protection of the egg covering or of the mother's body it is called an *embryo;* the study of its development during this period is called *embryology.* If after being freed from this covering, it has not yet attained a form similar to that of the adult, it is known as a *larva,* and there is then an appreciable postembryonic part to its development. This chapter will consider certain aspects of the very early ontogeny of animals, special attention being given to the embryonic development of several vertebrate types.

Studies in ontogeny commenced about the time of the ancient Greek naturalist Aristotle (384–322 B.C., Fig. 36). During the eighteenth century there was considerable debate between advocates of the *preformation theory,* who believed that the individual existed completely formed, but in miniature, in either the sperm or the egg, and advocates of the *epigenesis theory,* who claimed that the individual developed, organ by organ, through the action of a vital force upon an unorganized egg. We now know that the truth lies between these two extreme views. While the egg shows no differentiation into parts corresponding to the organs of the adult, it contains in its nucleus a set of genes, which, under suitable conditions, direct its development into an organism with definite organs and definite characteristics.

Stages in Development. The course of development varies widely in detail in different animals; nevertheless, it follows to a remarkable extent the same general pattern. It is a continuous process, but may for convenience be considered to consist of the stages here listed.

1. *Fertilization.* The union of egg and sperm combines in the offspring genes from both parents, and also supplies the stimulus that initiates further development.

313

2. *Cleavage.* The egg divides by mitosis into two cells, subsequent divisions giving four- and eight-celled embryos. Continued subdivision results in a mass of undifferentiated cells, the *blastula* (Gr. "little bud"). This mass is typically spherical, one-layered, and more or less hollow.

Variations in cleavage are determined largely by the amount of food or *yolk* contained in the egg (Fig. 250). In some this is small in quantity and is equally distributed through the cytoplasm. Such eggs are called *homolecithal*

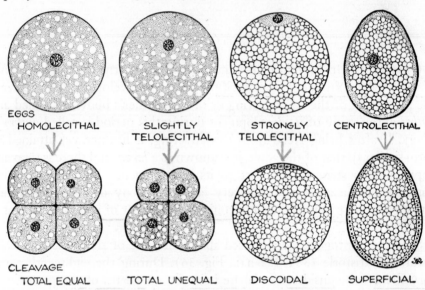

Fig. 250. Types of eggs, showing diagrammatically the yolk distribution and early cleavage characteristic of each type. Cytoplasm is represented by the uniform stippling; yolk, by the white globules.

(Gr. "uniform yolk"). To this type belong the eggs of many of the lower invertebrates, such as *Hydra*, the flatworm, and the starfish; of some of the lowest chordates, such as the lancelet; and of all mammals except the PROTO-THERIA. In such eggs, the early cleavage is *total* (all the way through) and *equal* (the resulting cells alike or nearly so in size). As the cells continue dividing, they push one another away from the center; hence the blastula is, in general, a hollow sphere containing a *cleavage cavity* or *blastocoel*.

If the yolk is unevenly distributed, more being concentrated in one hemisphere than in the other, the egg is *telolecithal* (Gr. "yolk at end"). The pole with little or no yolk is called the *animal pole*, and that with much yolk is the *vegetal pole*. The egg of an earthworm, a clam, a fish, or a frog is slightly telolecithal. Its cleavage is *total* but *unequal*, the cells that form at the animal pole being considerably smaller than those at the vegetal pole. The egg of a squid, a reptile, a bird, or an egg-laying mammal is strongly telolecithal and undergoes *partial, discoidal* cleavage, the partition walls extending only through the protoplasm at the animal pole and forming a disk-like group of cells.

A third type of egg is the *centrolecithal* (Gr. "yolk in center"), in which the yolk occupies the greater part of the interior of the egg. At the center of the yolk is a portion of the cytoplasm enclosing the nucleus; the greater part of the cytoplasm lies just within the egg membrane. This type is found in insects. The central nucleus undergoes a number of divisions; the daughter nuclei migrate to the surface, whereupon part of the cytoplasm is cut off about each nucleus, forming a complete layer of cells which surrounds the yolk. This is *partial, superficial* cleavage.

3. *Gastrulation.* In gastrulation the one-layered blastula becomes a two-layered *gastrula* (Gr. "little stomach"); its outer layer is called the *ectoderm* and its inner layer the *endoderm*. The latter partially or completely surrounds a hollow called the *archenteron* (Gr. "beginning of intestine"). The opening from the archenteron to the outside is the *blastopore*.

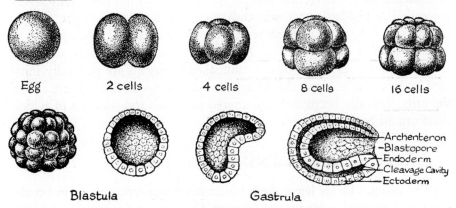

Egg   2 cells   4 cells   8 cells   16 cells

Blastula   Gastrula

Archenteron
Blastopore
Endoderm
Cleavage Cavity
Ectoderm

Fig. 251. Cleavage and formation of germ layers of a homolecithal egg, as in that of *Amphioxus*. (Adapted from Guyer, *Being Well-Born;* copyright, Bobbs-Merrill.)

Typical gastrulation, as was stated on page 99, is brought about by growth in such a manner that one side of the blastula—that on which the cells are beginning to be somewhat larger—is first flattened, then arches toward the opposite side, the whole becoming a two-layered cup (Fig. 251). It may be roughly illustrated by flattening one side of a hollow rubber ball, then pushing it against the opposite side. In some cases there are modifications of this process, as we shall see in the frog, in which gastrulation involves mainly an overgrowth of the ectoderm; in birds, in which the edges of the disk-like ectoderm are tucked under to form the endoderm; and in mammals, in which ectoderm and endoderm are established when the flat embryonic shield is formed by the appearance of amnion and yolk sac cavities.

4. *Formation of the Mesoderm.*   A third germ layer, the *mesoderm*, develops in all animals above the sponges and coelenterates. In most of the phyla the mesoderm arises from bands of tissue that bud off from a few cells along the border line between ectoderm and endoderm; but in the echinoderms and chordates it arises as a series of pouches pushed outward from the endoderm into the space between this layer and the ectoderm. In the former group of phyla it soon splits; in the echinoderms and chordates its origin from pouches makes it a two-layered structure from the beginning. The two layers, in either case, are known as the *splanchnic* (Gr. "visceral"), which surrounds the endoderm of the alimentary tract, and the *somatic* (Gr. "pertaining to the body"), which forms the inner part of the body wall. The cavity between these layers is the *coelom* (Gr. "a hollow"). The epithelial lining of the coelom is the *peritoneum* (Gr. "stretched around"). Animals with three germ layers are called *triploblastic* to distinguish them from the *diploblastic* forms, which have only two. Animals with a coelom are called *coelomates*.

5. *Formation of Organs and Tissues.*   From the germ layers are derived all the tissues of the mature animal. The organs are generally initiated by local thickenings, infoldings, or outfoldings of these layers. Then the cells gradually become differentiated into the various tissues of which these organs come to consist.

ONTOGENY OF THE FROG

Egg-Laying.   Frogs leave their hibernating quarters, appear in ponds, mate, and lay their eggs in early spring. On leaving the female, the eggs are fertilized by sperms discharged over them by the clasping male. The two or three layers of jelly deposited on the egg thicken by absorption of water, and hold all the eggs of one female together in a gelatinous mass. This jelly serves as a protection; the food is contained in the yolk. The egg is of the telolecithal type, for the yolk is accumulated mainly at the whitish, vegetal pole. The darker animal pole contains the nucleus and most of the cytoplasm; it is lighter in weight, hence is uppermost as the egg floats in the water. Its dark color helps it to absorb the heat of the sun, which accelerates development.

Cleavage.   Cleavage is complete, the first cleavage furrow beginning to appear about three hours after the egg is laid. The third division is unequal, making the four cells at the animal pole smaller than the four at the vegetal pole. Henceforth the cells at the animal pole divide much more rapidly than do those at the vegetal, and proportionally become much smaller (Fig. 252). At the end of the first day the embryo consists of twelve to sixteen cells.

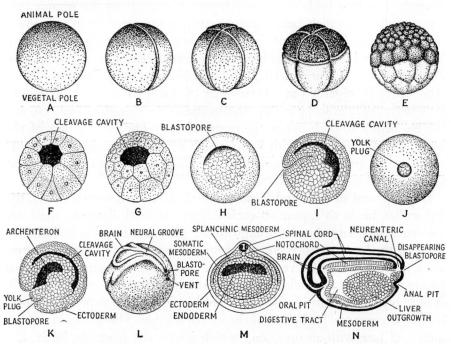

Fig. 252. Early development of the frog egg. *A* to *D*, Cleavage stages. *E*, Blastula; *F*, section of same. *G*, Section of later blastula. *H*, Gastrula; *I*, section of same. *J*, Yolk plug stage; *K*, section of same. *L*, Neural groove stage. *M*, Neural tube stage, cross section; *N*, same, longitudinal section. (After Guyer.)

Blastula and Gastrula. The cleavage cavity of the blastula is comparatively small because of the large amount of yolk. The gastrula stage is completed at the end of the third day. Its formation is modified by the presence of yolk. A crescent-like indentation appears on the surface of the spherical blastula along the line between the smaller and the larger (or yolk) cells. By rapid division the former then begin to grow over the latter. The yolk cells are soon visible on the surface only as a white disk, the *yolk plug*, which closes the blastopore. Before gastrulation is completed, the mesoderm arises from near the edge of the blastopore and pushes in between ectoderm and endoderm, finally separating these two layers. The mesoderm exists in two layers, one of which is applied to the endoderm and the other to the ectoderm, leaving the coelomic cavity between.

Neural Groove. The embryo now elongates, and about the fourth or fifth day two folds appear near its mid-dorsal line. Between these is the *neural groove*. An embryo with the neural groove apparent is called a *neurula*. The two folds now grow together, converting the groove into the *neural tube*, which later becomes entirely separated from the superficial ectoderm. The wall of this tube forms the beginning of the brain and spinal cord. Certain cells lying immediately ventral to this tube have meanwhile become organized into a rod-like structure, the *notochord*, which may be regarded as a forerunner of the spinal column. The head now begins to take shape at the anterior end of the elongated embryo, and the tail begins to push out at the posterior end. The ventral part of the body is still bulged out with yolk, which continues to supply food. At this stage the embryo rotates within the gelatinous envelopes by means of cilia, which disappear after hatching.

Development of Gills and Head. Shortly afterward several ridges, the *gill arches*, begin to appear on each side of the head. Between these are grooves which later break through to the pharynx, forming *gill slits*. In front of the latter a depression arises on either side; then the two depressions move toward the ventral surface and unite to form the ventral sucker. Just above the sucker a pit appears which later becomes the mouth. A little higher up on each side of the head is a thickened depression representing the external beginning of the lens of the eye. This grows inward to meet and fuse with an optic cup which grows out from the brain. External gills bud from the gill arches. Invaginations which appear above them form the vesicles of the internal ears. Nasal pits at the anterior dorsal surface of the head form the external nares. In the meantime the tail has elongated, and V-shaped muscle bands, *myotomes*, begin to appear along the sides of the dorsal portion of the body and of the tail.

Hatching. At this stage, about the eighth day, the larva hatches and immediately attaches itself to the surface of water plants or the sides of an aquarium by means of its ventral sucker (Fig. 253). It is now a *tadpole* (Anglo-Saxon, "a toad that is all head"). It may cling to its support, keeping up wriggling movements, for about two days, still feeding on the yolk. As it releases its hold and begins to swim about, further changes occur. The mouth depression pushes inward and finally unites with the blind primitive gut which has formed inside. Meanwhile the blastopore, at the posterior end of the embryo, closes, and just below it another pit develops and pushes inward to unite with the posterior end of the primitive gut. The anterior folding, the front of which is the mouth, may be called the *stomodaeum* (Gr. "the way to the mouth"); the posterior invagination, which becomes the anus, is the *proctodaeum* (Gr. "the way to the anus"). Soon the external gills disappear; meanwhile gill slits have developed between the gill arches, and four pairs of internal gills have

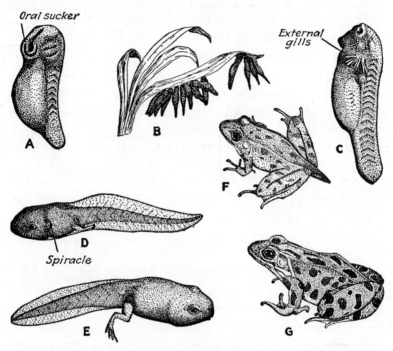

Fig. 253. Development of frog from the time of hatching. *A,* Tadpole just hatched; *B,* young tadpoles clinging to a plant by means of the oral (ventral) sucker; *C,* external gill stage; *D,* internal gill stage showing spiracle opening from gill chamber; *E,* hind legs developed; *F,* tail nearly absorbed; *G,* adult leopard frog. (The scale varies.) (From Wolcott, *Animal Biology;* copyright, McGraw-Hill.)

formed as membranous folds on the sides of the gill arches. Water entering through the mouth passes back to the pharynx, thence outward over the gills and through the gill slits. While the slits are forming, a fold of skin called the *operculum* (Lat. "lid") grows around the body just behind the head, covering the slits on both sides and leaving an opening on the left side as an exit for the water. This opening is the *spiracle* (Lat. "breathing pore"). The young tadpole now begins to feed on algae and other vegetable matter growing on leaves or other surfaces; it scrapes this food from the surface with the horny rim of its toothless mouth.

Internal Changes. In the meantime the systems of essential internal organs have been developing. The wall of the alimentary canal is made up of an epithelium derived from the endoderm, together with a muscular layer and a peritoneum derived from the mesoderm. Several organs are developed from this canal by an outfolding of the wall. A fold in the ventral wall of the pharynx develops into the larynx and the lungs; another fold posterior to this forms the beginning of the liver. In a similar way are formed the pancreas, the thymus, and the thyroid glands. The intestine becomes much coiled in the abdominal region. The heart and the

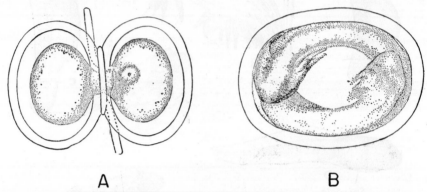

A   B

Fig. 254. A fertilized newt's egg was constricted nearly completely by a fine hair loop (*A*). At the 16-cell stage one of the cleavage nuclei migrated across the constriction and started development on the other side. Both halves developed into normal larvae (*B*). (After Spemann, *Embryonic Development and Induction*, copyright, Yale University Press.)

blood vessels develop very early in the embryo and provide an active circulation to the gills, as well as to other parts of the body. The heart is at first two-chambered, as in the fishes, and the whole course of circulation is similar to that of the fishes, the blood going from the heart to the gills, then to all parts of the body, and finally back to the heart. These fish-like characters furnish a significant illustration of the recapitulation theory, which will be discussed later.

The nervous system develops from the neural tube, hence is ectodermal in origin. Constrictions in the anterior end of this tube indicate the three embryonic regions of the brain: the *forebrain*, the *midbrain*, and the *hindbrain*. The first of these regions gives rise to the *cerebral hemispheres* and the *diencephalon;* the second, to the *optic lobes;* the last, to the *cerebellum* and *medulla*. The posterior part of the neural tube narrows into the *spinal cord*. From brain and cord, nerve fibers gradually push their way among the cells until all portions of the body are reached. The skeletal system develops late, and the muscular system adapts itself to the structure of the skeleton.

Appearance of Legs. The hind limbs appear first, budding out, about the sixth to the eighth week, from the posterior part of the body. Later the fore limbs come into view. The left one first pushes its way through the spiracle; the right one breaks through the wall of the gill pouch soon afterward. The tail diminishes in size and disappears, being partly absorbed by the body and partly enclosed within the body. When the legs and lungs have attained their development the tadpole is a completely organized frog, although small compared with the adult. In the final change

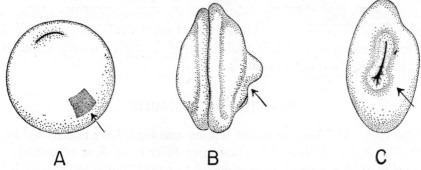

A   B   C

Fig. 255. The dorsal lip of the blastopore of a newt embryo was transplanted onto another embryo (*A*). This resulted in the induction of secondary neural folds on the host embryo (*B* and *C*). The arrows indicate the positions of the graft and the induced neural folds. (After Spemann and H. Mangold; *B* and *C* redrawn from Young and Stebbins, *The Human Organism and the World of Life*, rev. ed., copyright, 1951, Harper & Brothers.)

from gill-breathing to lung-breathing there is a readjustment of the circulation; the internal gills are absorbed and the gill pouch disappears. A little time elapses between the gill-breathing and the lung-breathing period, during which breathing takes place wholly through the vascular skin. Some species complete their metamorphosis in a single season; others (such as the bullfrog) require two or three.

Experimental Embryology. Frogs and other amphibians are very favorable for experiments designed to investigate early development in animals. Of special interest are the experiments of the German embryologist Spemann on the early embryos of newts (Order Urodela). By tying a very fine hair loop around a fertilized newt's egg he produced cleavage on the side of the egg containing the nucleus but not on the other. However, by loosening the loop and permitting a nucleus to migrate to the other side, he produced cleavage on the other side also; eventually two

fully formed newt larvae were derived from the single fertilized egg
(Fig. 254). Such an experiment is of interest because it demonstrates the
ability of a single zygote to produce more than one individual, a process
which must sometimes take place spontaneously in the formation of identical twins in man and other animals. Spemann also transplanted bits of
tissue from one embryo to another, using differently colored species so
that the transplanted tissue could be distinguished from that of the host. A
remarkable result of these studies was the demonstration of a special or-
ganizing property of the dorsal lip of the blastopore of an early gastrula.
A piece of tissue from this region was found to cause the formation of an
additional neural groove in the region of the host into which it had been
transplanted (Fig. 255). Because of this the dorsal lip of the blastopore
has been called an *organizer*. Organizers of other kinds have also been reported in embryos, and it is probable that they play a very important
part in the development of animals.

REPTILES AND BIRDS

The Egg. We have seen that reptiles and birds have telolecithal eggs
and that cleavage is discoidal. These eggs differ from those of amphibians
in that they have a much greater amount of yolk, the cytoplasm with its
nucleus being easily seen as a small disk on the yolk of a hen's egg. Cleavage takes place only within this disk, hence is discoidal (Fig. 256).

A reptile has the usual two functional ovaries; a bird has only one, the
left, because the right one becomes atrophied at an early stage. The egg
proper, including the yolk, forms in the ovary. As it moves down the
oviduct, the glandular cells lining this passage secrete the albumen (white
of the egg), a useful food reserve; the posterior part of the oviduct then
secretes two shell membranes and (in birds) the outer calcareous shell.

In the development of these eggs, which occurs out of water, three
membranes appear; they have an important part in the protection, nourishment, respiration, and excretion of the embryo. These membranes are
(1) the *amnion*, (2) the *yolk sac*, (3) the *allantois*.

The Amnion, a Protective Membrane. The blastula is a disk two or
three layers of cells in thickness. In gastrulation, the edges of the ectoderm
are tucked underneath the main disk and form the endoderm. A line
through the center of the disk, the *primitive streak*, becomes the embryo
proper. The mesoderm outside the embryo splits to form a cavity, the
extra-embryonic coelom, whereupon the ectoderm and mesoderm above
this cavity become folded all around the embryo (Fig. 256 D) and close in

as a dome over the latter (E), the inner layer of the fold becoming a membranous sac called the *amnion* (Greek name). This sac is filled with amniotic fluid, which plays an important part in protecting the embryo from severe temperature changes, drying, and mechanical shock. Since develop-

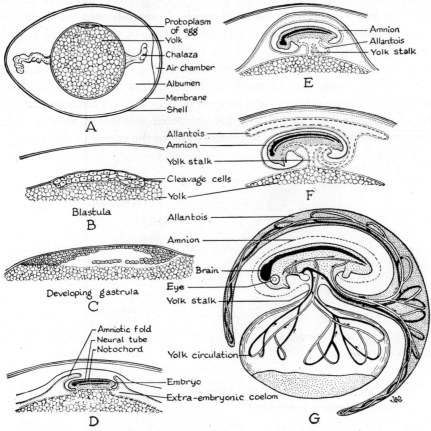

FIG. 256. Structure and development of a hen's egg. *A*, Longitudinal section of egg when laid, natural size. *B* to *G*, various stages in development during the first few days of incubation, all magnified. (*D* to *G* redrawn from Wolcott, *Animal Biology;* copyright, McGraw-Hill.)

ment takes place away from water, each embryo is provided with what we might regard as its own little private pool of water within the amnion.

The Yolk Sac, a Nourishing Membrane. While the amnion is forming, the mesoderm beneath the extra-embryonic coelom is tucked in under the embryo proper until there remains only a narrow cord, the *yolk stalk,* connecting the latter with the yolk. Through blood vessels developed in this stalk, the food of the yolk is conveyed to the growing embryo.

The Allantois, a Respiratory and Excretory Membrane. The embryo in its earlier stages is able to absorb sufficient oxygen directly through its surface; but later, as the need for oxygen increases, a special membrane develops and facilitates the process. This membrane, the *allantois* (Gr. "sausage-shaped"), is formed by an outpushing from the floor of the hind gut just posterior to the yolk stalk. It spreads into an umbrella-shaped structure and follows the curved surface of the egg shell until it nearly surrounds the embryo and the yolk sac. A blood circuit develops from the embryo to the allantois and back to the embryo. Since the egg shell and membrane are permeable to gases, carbon dioxide diffuses from the allantois to the exterior, and oxygen in turn diffuses from the air into the allantois. In later embryonic life, excreted substances are conveyed from the embryo by way of the cloaca and into the cavity of the allantois.

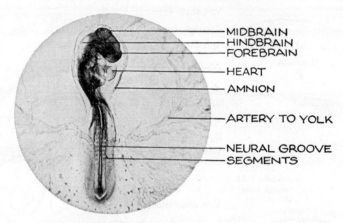

MIDBRAIN
HINDBRAIN
FOREBRAIN

HEART

AMNION

ARTERY TO YOLK

NEURAL GROOVE
SEGMENTS

Fig. 257. Chick embryo 48 hours old. The amnion encloses the anterior part of the embryo. (Copyright, General Biological Supply House, Inc., Chicago.)

Other Features. The internal organs of the embryo develop much as in the frog. An infolding of the ectoderm forms the neural groove, later the neural tube, which develops into brain and spinal cord (Fig. 257). The notochord buds off from the endoderm about the time that the mesodermal pouches appear, and lies just ventral to the neural tube. As the lungs develop, a pulmonary circulation is established to take the place of the early allantoic circulation. When the organism is ready to hatch, it breaks through the amnion and the shell, casting off these no longer useful structures. The food has been for the most part used up, although enough yolk remains connected with the intestine to provide food for a short time after hatching. In most birds and reptiles a small point known as the egg tooth develops near the tip of the bill and helps the shell to break.

MAMMALIAN EMBRYOLOGY

Fertilization. Eggs of mammals (except PROTOTHERIA) are homolecithal and very small (they average 0.15 mm. in diameter in man). A sperm which has been introduced in copulation and has traveled up the oviduct by the lashing of its tail, meets an egg near the distal part of the oviduct and fertilization takes place.

Early Stages. The main steps in human development are shown in Fig. 258. The zygote undergoes total equal cleavage, resulting in a solid sphere of cells called a *morula* (Lat. "little mulberry"). A cavity now develops, resulting in the formation of an outer cell layer, the *trophoblast* (Gr. "nourishing germinal tissue"), and an inner *cell mass*. These processes require eight or ten days; during this time the embryo, now a blastula, passes down the oviduct and reaches the uterus. With the aid of a tissue-dissolving enzyme secreted by the trophoblast, the embryo becomes embedded in the soft mucous wall of the uterus.

Formation of embryonic membranes. Within the inner cell mass two cavities form, the *amniotic cavity* and the *yolk sac*. The former is lined with ectoderm, the latter with endoderm. Between these two cavities the cells form a flat plate, the *embryonic shield*, from which the embryo proper develops. Mesoderm begins to form between ectoderm and endoderm in the embryonic shield, as well as around the amniotic cavity and yolk sac. The amniotic cavity develops into an amniotic sac containing fluid which protects the embryo, as in reptiles and birds. The yolk sac contains no yolk and has no significant role in development, but it persists until birth as a vestigial structure.

The Chorion and the Placenta. On the appearance of the mesoderm, the trophoblast, together with part of the mesoderm, constitutes the outer embryonic membrane, the *chorion* (Greek name). Its outer, absorbing surface is increased by the development of root-like processes, or *villi*. As the embryo grows, the villi disappear from the side of the chorion that bulges into the cavity of the uterus, but become very pronounced over a disk-like area where the chorion remains in contact with the thickened wall of the uterus; this part of the chorion and the wall together make up the *placenta*. The allantois is rather rudimentary in man, though it contributes in part to the formation of the *umbilical cord*, which connects the embryo with the placenta. In this cord are three large blood vessels, two conveying the blood of the embryo to the capillaries of the placenta, the other returning it to the embryo. After about two months the embryo has taken on a definitely human form, although it is still very small. It is generally called a *fetus* (Lat. "offspring") from this time until birth, after about nine months of development. The placenta functions as

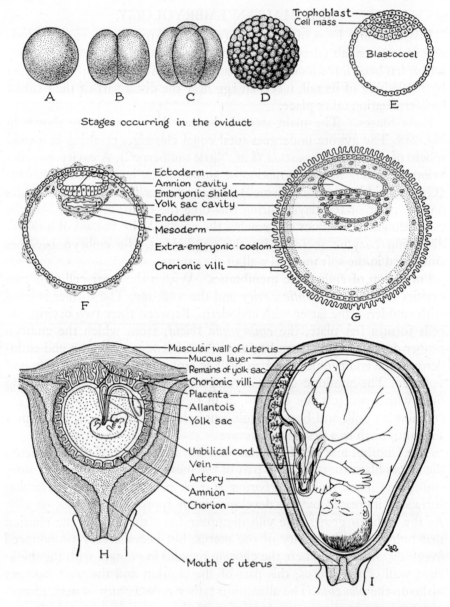

Stages occurring in the oviduct

Trophoblast
Cell mass
Blastocoel

Ectoderm
Amnion cavity
Embryonic shield
Yolk sac cavity
Endoderm
Mesoderm
Extra-embryonic coelom
Chorionic villi

Muscular wall of uterus
Mucous layer
Remains of yolk sac
Chorionic villi
Placenta
Allantois
Yolk sac
Umbilical cord
Vein
Artery
Amnion
Chorion
Mouth of uterus

Fig. 258. Significant stages in human development. (*A* to *G*, highly magnified; *H*, × 1½; *I*, × ⅙; *E*, *F*, and *G* are median sections.) *A*, Fertilized egg; *B*, 2-celled stage (after about a day); *C*, 4-celled stage (after about 2 days); *D*, blastula (after about 6 days); *E*, section of blastula (after about 8 days, at the time of implantation in the uterus wall). *F*, After about 12 days the amnion cavity and yolk sac cavity are appearing in the cell mass, and germ layers are being differentiated. *G*, After about 16 days; the trophoblast, now the chorion, is developing villi which extend into the tissue of the uterus. The embryonic shield marks the region where the embryo proper is developing. *H*, After 38 days; the embryo, still embedded in the tis-an organ for anchorage, nutrition, respiration, excretion, and endocrine transmission between mother and fetus.

Differences Among Mammals. The placenta varies widely in different mammalian types. In man it is saucer-shaped and covers a large area in the wall of the uterus. In other mammals it may be a small disk, a band, or scattered patches. Soon after the birth of the young, the fetal part of the placenta (in the pig) or the whole placenta (in most mammals, including man) is expelled as the afterbirth. However, a few mammals, such as the bat, resorb the placenta. The *period of gestation*, or time of embryonic development, is roughly correlated with the size of the mammal. It is about 21 days in the mouse, 60 in the cat and dog, 147 in sheep, 280 in man, and about 20 months in the elephant. The extent of development of the young at birth also varies widely. Horses, cattle, sheep, and jackrabbits have *precocial* young, with hair and open eyes. They are soon able to walk, although they depend, as do all mammals, upon the milk of the mother. Cats, dogs, and mice are *altricial*, being born blind, with little or no hair, and unable to walk or care for themselves for a considerable period. Human young demand parental care for a longer period than do the young of any other animal.

Summary of Sources of Tissues and Organs. In general the tissues or organs that develop from each of the three germ layers are as follows:

1. *From ectoderm.* Epidermis, with such modifications as hair, nails, feathers; skin glands; nervous tissue; parts of eye and ear; lining of mouth and anus.
2. *From mesoderm.* Connective tissue, skeleton, most of the muscles, circulatory system, reproductive and excretory organs.
3. *From endoderm.* Mucous lining of digestive tract (except mouth and anus); lining of respiratory system; digestive glands, including pancreas and liver.

RECAPITULATION THEORY

The existence of an animal ordinarily begins with a single cell, usually a fertilized egg. The PROTOZOA, as a rule, stop at this level of development, but some of the colonial forms of this group suggest the early cleavage stages of the embryo. A species of *Gonium* is a four-celled colony; *Pandorina*, a sixteen-celled sphere; and *Volvox*, a many-celled hollow sphere

sue of the uterus, has produced a bulge on the uterus wall and is filling the cavity. The villi are enlarging in the region that is to become the placenta, and will soon disappear from the rest of the chorion. The embryo proper shows brain region, gill slits, tail, and beginnings of eye, ear, and limbs. The allantois has appeared, but is essentially limited to the umbilical cord. *I,* After nine months (just before birth); the chorion, with its surrounding uterine mucous layer, has been pressed against the walls of the uterus on all sides. The arteries carry deoxygenated blood from fetus to placenta, and the vein carries oxygenated blood from placenta to fetus.

resembling a blastula. *Hydra* stops at a stage comparable to the gastrula, whereas all the higher Metazoa continue to the development of the third germ layer (Fig. 58).

We have seen many examples of certain structures which are well developed in one group and which still appear but have little or no function in the next higher group. Such structures are called *vestigial*. Among

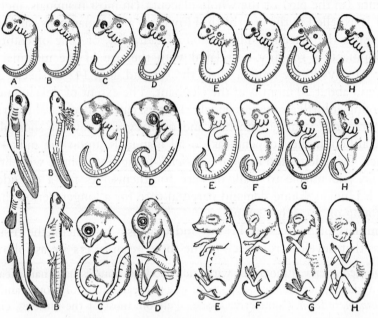

Fig. 259. Parallelism in the development of vertebrates: *A*, fish; *B*, salamander; *C*, turtle; *D*, chick; *E*, pig; *F*, calf; *G*, rabbit; *H*, man. In the first row the embryos are much alike, but as development proceeds they become more unlike. In the early stages, prominent features are gill arches, gill slits, three-lobed brain, eye, ear, tail, and some evidence of body segmentation. (From Romanes, *Darwin and After Darwin*; Open Court Publishing Company and Longmans, Green; after Haeckel.)

them are the yolk sac, which is important in the reptilian ancestors of mammals but has little or no use in the latter, and the vermiform appendix, which is a prominent digestive pouch in various mammals (e.g., the opossum) but is functionless in man.

We have also seen that the larvae of certain forms suggest the general structure of a lower group, although this disappears in the adult. This is shown in the fish-like circulation and the other fish-like characters of the tadpole.

With the development of the science of embryology more than a century ago, these facts began to be noticed. It was found further that if a series of stages in the development of an individual (*ontogenetic series*) were placed side by side with a series of present living animals (*taxonomic series*), arranged in systematic order from the simplest to the more and more complex, the two series showed a remarkable resemblance. The study of fossils showed also that a third similar series might be obtained by arranging these fossils in the order in which they appeared through geological ages, as shown by the rock strata in which they were found (*phylogenetic series*).

These considerations have led to the formulation of what is known as the *recapitulation theory*. This theory has been tersely stated in the now familiar expression, *Ontogeny recapitulates phylogeny*, ontogeny being defined as the development of the individual and phylogeny (Gr. "race origin") as the development of the race from its earliest ancestors.

Considerable criticism has been directed against this idea because many have tried to make its application too rigid and detailed. In accepting the theory, we must take into account that the phylogenetic series has developed through countless ages, whereas the individual crowds all its changes into the brief time of a few days or months, telescoping centuries together as it were. It is true, therefore, that the principle holds only in a general way, with great numbers of phylogenetic stages crowded out or greatly modified in ontogeny. Furthermore, we find that the young forms of higher animals rarely resemble the adult forms of lower groups. The resemblance is rather to the early developmental stages of these groups, suggesting features which we might expect in the common ancestor of the two groups (Fig. 259). But in spite of criticism, the theory has been of great service in clarifying animal relationships; and, most important of all, it has led to an understanding of the great unifying principle of all biology, *evolution*, which is now considered the fundamental law of the development of all life.

EXERCISES

1. What type of egg is produced in each of the following animals, and what protection is provided the eggs in each case: salamander, fish, turtle, bird, grasshopper, snake, rabbit, snail?
2. Compare the temperatures at which these eggs incubate, or develop.
3. What is the composition of the yolk of eggs, and what foods can it furnish?
4. Explain the process by which the nervous system is derived from the ectoderm in invertebrates; in vertebrates.
5. What is the significance of the fact that gill slits develop in the embryonic stage of many of the vertebrates and later disappear in the adult?
6. What changes in the tadpole determine the time when it leaves the water for the land?

7. Why do tadpoles cling to the side of an aquarium for some time after hatching from the jelly?
8. Trace the course of the water which passes over the internal gills in the tadpole. Explain what determines the direction of the current, and show what force causes the movement.
9. What causes double-yolked eggs in birds? What would develop if such an egg were incubated?
10. How would you account for the fact that hens sometimes produce eggs without any shell (soft eggs)?
11. What is the origin of the afterbirth which occurs in connection with the birth of most mammals?
12. Explain how the embryos of mammals obtain food and oxygen during embryonic development.
13. What harmful influences might possibly reach the human fetus from the mother and how might they reach it?
14. Is there justification for the belief that a mother's experience during pregnancy may produce birthmarks on the child? Give reasons for your conclusions.
15. What technique practiced by the patriarch Jacob indicates the belief, prevalent at that time, in prenatal influences? See Genesis XXX:37–39.

REFERENCES

Arey, L. B., *Developmental Anatomy*, W. B. Saunders Company, 5th ed., 1946.

Barth, L. G., *Embryology*, The Dryden Press, 1949.

Corner, G. W., *Ourselves Unborn*, Yale Univ. Press, 1944.

DeBeer, G. R., *Embryos and Ancestors*, Clarendon Press, 2nd ed., 1952.

Dodds, G., *The Essentials of Human Embryology*, John Wiley & Sons, Inc., 3rd ed., 1946.

Gilbert, M. S., *Biography of the Unborn*, Williams and Wilkins Co., 1938.

Holmes, S. J., *The Biology of the Frog*, The Macmillan Company, 4th ed., 1927.

Huettner, A. F., *Comparative Embryology of the Vertebrates*, The Macmillan Company, rev. ed., 1949.

Patten, B. M., *Development of the Chick*, The Blakiston Company, rev. ed., 1946.

Patten, B. M., *Human Embryology*, The Blakiston Company, 1946.

Rugh, R., *The Frog—Reproduction and Development*, The Blakiston Company, 1950.

Shumway, W., *Vertebrate Embryology*, John Wiley & Sons, Inc., 4th ed., 1942.

Spemann, H., *Embryonic Development and Induction*, Yale Univ. Press, 1938.

Waddington, C. H., *How Animals Develop*, W. W. Norton & Company, Inc., 1936.

Chapter XIX

THE PLANT KINGDOM

Plants differ from animals in commonly possessing the ability to make carbohydrates from the inorganic substances, carbon dioxide and water, by the process of photosynthesis; in generally being attached; in the less definite number and looser coordination of parts; and in the low degree of development of sense organs and nervous system.

PHOTOSYNTHESIS

The process of photosynthesis has been considered as a building up, or anabolic, phase of metabolism that takes place in all chlorophyll-containing plants. It utilizes as raw materials carbon dioxide and water, employs sunlight as its energy source, and produces sugar, containing stored or potential energy, and oxygen as a by-product. Since this process is the ultimate source of practically all food for both plants and animals, the utilization of native plants and the growth and improvement of cultivated plants are world-wide occupations. An understanding of plant life is therefore most important from the economic standpoint.

Mechanisms Concerned. Chlorophyll is a complex substance that contains carbon, hydrogen, oxygen, nitrogen, and magnesium. The molecular formula for one of its two forms is $C_{55}H_{72}O_5N_4Mg$, for the other one $C_{55}H_{70}O_6N_4Mg$. It is generally contained in definite bodies, the *chloroplasts*. In the lower forms these are usually distributed over the entire plant; but in the higher, they are largely localized in the leaves. With chlorophyll are associated two yellow pigments, *carotene* and *xanthophyll*. Some algae have blue, red, or brown pigments in addition. These as well as the yellow pigments may be of some aid in photosynthesis, but their specific function is not clearly understood.

Sunlight. Since photosynthesis is an energy-storing process, it requires a source of external energy; this is furnished by *sunlight*. If a leaf is fitted with a light screen which excludes light from a part of it but does not interfere with the entry of carbon dioxide or water, the leaf on removal from the plant after a period in sunlight will be found to contain starch in only those portions that were exposed to the light. Sunlight can be resolved, by passage through a triangular prism, into the colors of the spectrum. If it is first passed through chlorophyll solution, part of the spectral colors will be replaced by dark bands, principally in the red and the violet region. This shows that these portions of the light are the ones absorbed by the leaf. Since practically none of the green is absorbed, the leaf appears green. Only about 4 percent of the absorbed light is actually used in bringing about the chemical union; hence the leaf is not a highly efficient factory. This lack in efficiency is largely offset, however, by the tremendous amount of light that the sun is continually sending to the earth. It is estimated that in a single second the solar energy reaching the earth is approximately twenty-five times the energy released by all the coal burned on the earth in the course of a year. The energy displayed in the growth and activity of all organisms, as well as that produced by most of our forms of combustion, has its origin in the sun and is made possible by this unique process of green plants—photosynthesis. It is estimated that the sugar manufactured by all the plants on earth in a single year has a volume of about nine cubic miles.

Finished Product.   Glucose is the first carbohydrate food to appear in the leaf. When it accumulates rapidly, much of it is changed by the enzymes present in the leaf cell and assumes the form of one or more starch grains inside each chloroplast, for it must be removed from solution to prevent its clogging the cell and interfering with cell activities. Gradually, however, it is digested to glucose by the same enzymes and transported to some other part of the plant for utilization or for storage. Often starch disappears entirely from the leaf cells during the night. In some plants, sucrose, inulin, oils, or other storage forms occur, instead of starch.

The By-product.   From submerged water plants on a sunny day, bubbles may be seen rising freely. These can be shown by test to consist of oxygen. From ordinary foliage in the air, this gas comes just as steadily even though not visibly. Water and carbon dioxide together contain more oxygen, in proportion to the other elements, than is used in sugar; so the surplus oxygen is discarded. Although respiration involves the same interchange of gases in plants as in animals, green plants use more carbon dioxide in photosynthesis than they discard in respiration, and discard more oxygen in photosynthesis than they use in respiration. The gas exchange connected with photosynthesis should not be confused with respiration, for it is the reverse. At night, plants do not carry on photosynthesis; only the respiratory exchange of gases goes on. The by-product of photosynthesis is not regarded as a waste in the economy of nature; it is of immense importance in the maintenance of both plant and animal life upon the earth. Without oxygen to make possible the liberation of energy there could be no life. The oxygen content of the air is kept from depletion by, and only by, the process of photosynthesis.

Chemistry of Photosynthesis. The function of chlorophyll is to absorb sunlight and bring about chemical reactions whereby its *kinetic energy* is changed to *potential energy* (page 34). Although the process of photosynthesis has been extensively investigated, the nature of the chemical steps involved is not fully understood. The view now prevailing is that carbon dioxide and water are in some way joined to the chlorophyll molecule, and detached from it later in a combined form, the chlorophyll thus serving as a catalyst (though other catalysts must also be necessary). The equation for the process as a whole may be written:

$$6CO_2 + 6H_2O + \text{Energy of sunlight (4.1 kilocalories per gram of sugar produced)} \xrightarrow{\text{Chlorophyll}} \underset{\text{Glucose}}{C_6H_{12}O_6} + 6O_2$$

The energy on the left is present as potential energy in the glucose on the right.

PLANT HORMONES

Plants as well as animals secrete growth-regulating substances (*hormones*) which, like the hormones of animals, move from one part to another to influence growth and metabolism. Plant hormones include:

1. *Growth hormones* (*auxins*), substances that hasten or retard the growth of the plant parts in which they accumulate. When an erect plant is placed in a horizontal position, the auxin produced by the cells in the elongating portions of its root and stem tips accumulates, under the influence of gravity, in what is now the lower sides of these organs. Stem growth is accelerated by the concentration of this hormone, whereas root growth is retarded. Therefore the stem tip turns upward, the root tip downward, orienting these parts of the plant anew into the proper position with reference to gravity (Fig. 260). While the terminal shoot of a plant is growing, the growth of the lateral buds is often retarded or completely inhibited. If the tip of the shoot is cut off, the restraining influence is removed and the lateral buds are induced to develop branches; hence the retardation appears

to be due to a hormone produced in the growing terminal shoot and moved downward to the region of the lateral buds.

2. *Flowering hormones*, which determine the period of flowering and fruiting. The production of these substances seems to be regulated in part by the relative length of day and night; hence these hormones determine that some species bloom when daylight periods are long, others when they are short (Fig. 413). That they are transferred from one part of the plant to another is indicated by the fact that the exposure to short daylight periods of only one branch of a plant that blooms under short-day conditions may cause the entire plant to bloom.

3. *Wound hormones*, produced by injured tissues and instrumental in the healing of wounds.

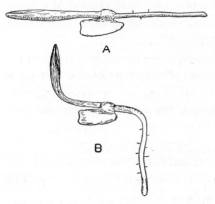

Fig. 260. Growth hormones and their effect. A corn seedling is placed in a horizontal position (*A*). Shading shows the tendency of the hormones to accumulate on the lower side. This accumulation accelerates the growth rate of the shoot, but retards that of the root, resulting in the bending of these parts (*B*).

Various chemicals which have been applied to plants experimentally have the same effect as natural hormones. The use of these chemicals, as well as of vitamin B_1 (thiamine), is becoming common in horticultural practice as a means of stimulating the germination of seeds, the development of roots on cuttings, and the acceleration of growth that has been interfered with by transplanting.

CLASSIFICATION OF PLANTS

The fossil record of plants has been less thoroughly studied than that of animals, and there is considerable difference of opinion as to how they may be classified to express their relationships. The classification customarily used in recent years divides the plant kingdom into four great groups, or phyla:

1. THALLOPHYTA, thallus plants.
2. BRYOPHYTA, moss plants.
3. PTERIDOPHYTA, fern plants.
4. SPERMATOPHYTA, seed plants.

Research in plant history, as revealed by fossils, and in the development and structure of present-day plants shows that the so-called fern plants consist of three groups—ferns, club mosses, and horsetails—which are related not at all, or only very distantly. All three may be traced back to a very early period in land plant development. It is also evident that the so-called seed plants are far more closely related to ferns than to club mosses or horsetails. Therefore botanists are pretty generally coming to adopt a classification scheme somewhat like that here outlined in brief. (For further detail, see the Appendix.) Fig. 261 shows hypothetical relationships of some of the prominent groups.

I. Phylum THALLOPHYTA (thallus plants). This is a large assemblage including several apparently unrelated lines, and probably should be divided into several phyla. These plants vary from minute microscopic forms, such as bacteria, to immense seaweeds. On the whole, they agree in not having much differentiation into organs, such as roots, stems, and leaves. There are more than 100,000 named species. We shall divide them into three subphyla.

A. Subphylum SCHIZOPHYTA (fission plants). These represent the lowest or simplest plant forms. Their cells lack specialization into nucleus, cytoplasm, and plastids. Reproduction is asexual, by fission. They include the blue-green algae and the bacteria.

B. Subphylum ALGAE. These plants usually live in water. They have specialized cells which contain one or more plastids or color bodies and which carry on photosynthesis. Reproductive processes are generally more complex than in the first group.

C. Subphylum FUNGI. This large group has cells which are specialized, but lack plastids and the power of photosynthesis. They obtain food from living organisms (as parasites) or from nonliving organic matter (as saprophytes).

II. Phylum BRYOPHYTA (moss plants). These plants represent a higher degree of differentiation than the thallus plants, and usually a better adaptation to life on land. Since they lack vascular systems for conveying food and water, none of them are very large. In their life histories the sexual generation is usually more prominent than the asexual. They consist of liverworts and mosses. There are about 23,000 species, the mosses being in the majority.

III. Phylum TRACHEOPHYTA (vascular plants). These plants have elongated cells or tubes for conveying food and water; hence they often reach tree-like proportions. In their life history the asexual generation is the prominent one. They are divided into three subphyla.

A. Subphylum LYCOPSIDA (club mosses). This group has many small leaves and produces spores in sporangia in the axils of some of these leaves,

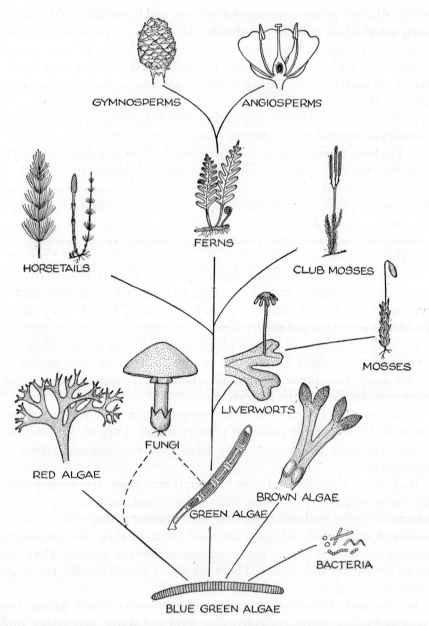

GYMNOSPERMS   ANGIOSPERMS

HORSETAILS   FERNS   CLUB MOSSES

MOSSES

FUNGI   LIVERWORTS

RED ALGAE   BROWN ALGAE

GREEN ALGAE

BACTERIA

BLUE GREEN ALGAE

FIG. 261. Principal groups of the plant kingdom showing hypothetical relationships by descent from the primitive to the advanced. The blue-greens, bacteria, algae, and fungi are thallophytes; the liverworts and mosses are bryophytes; and all those above this in the diagram are tracheophytes.

which usually form a cone. Once prominent tree-like forms, they are losing ground and are not a conspicuous feature of modern vegetation. There are about 1000 species.

B. Subphylum SPHENOPSIDA (horsetails). These were important when our principal coal beds were forming, but are now limited to a single genus, *Equisetum* (the horsetail), which has only about 30 species. The rather rough or fluted stems have circles of scale-like leaves united into collars.

C. Subphylum PTEROPSIDA. This group, with larger leaves, includes three important classes: (1) Class FILICINAE, the ferns, consist of some 9000 species, ranging from small herbs to trees. They are generally alike in having spores in sporangia (cases) which are in groups on the under surface of the leaf. (2) Class GYMNOSPERMAE, the gymnosperms, include about 600 species which are mostly trees, the best known being the conifers which are of vast importance in our lumber supply. They produce naked seeds on scale-like leaves, the latter often grouped into a cone. (3) Class ANGIOSPERMAE, the angiosperms or flowering plants, constitute the great bulk of our present vegetation—some 200,000 species. Their seeds are enclosed in a fruit, which is a development from a structure known as a flower.

Main Steps in Plant Evolution. The fission plants represent the most ancient and most primitive members of the plant kingdom. Nucleus and cytoplasm have not been differentiated, and the simplest mode of reproduction is employed. The algae and fungi include a large number of relatively simple but largely unrelated forms. The algae live for the most part in water, the fungi in or on the moist bodies of living organisms or decaying organic matter. They have advanced in reproductive processes to spore formation and the fusion of sexual cells. Some have developed an alternation of asexual and sexual generations. The moss plants represent the first definite adaptation to life on land and the establishment of alternation of generations. The vascular plants, because of their conducting systems, represent a more complete adjustment to land life, and have developed structures which enable some of them to become large trees. The gymnosperms, with their seeds which permit the rapid establishment of the young plant, and the development of a pollen tube which brings the sperm to the egg by a growth process rather than leaving it to the hazard of swimming, represent a substantial advance in plant evolution. Further advances occur among the angiosperms, the now dominant group, because they have developed a variety of methods to secure the transfer of pollen from plant to plant, and because a fruit wall surrounds the seed or seeds, thus giving additional protection as well as additional dispersal facilities.

Plants are named as are animals (page 73) by the Linnaean binomial system, the genus name being followed by the species name.

EXERCISES

1. Most rapidly growing stems, if placed in one-sided illumination, will bend toward the light. How might this be explained on the hormone basis?
2. Will the continued removal of CO_2 from the air by green plants eventually reduce its amount to such an extent that green plants will no longer grow? Explain.

REFERENCES

Boysen-Jensen, P., *Growth Hormones of Plants*, McGraw-Hill Book Company, Inc., 1936.

Franck, J., and Loomis, W. E., *Photosynthesis*, Iowa State College Press, 1949.

Hylander, C. J., *The World of Plant Life*, The Macmillan Company, 1939.

See also the botany texts listed in the Appendix.

Chapter XX

THALLOPHYTES—FISSION PLANTS

In this and the two following chapters the Phylum THALLOPHYTA (Gr. "thallus plants") will be considered. A thallus is a plant body that is only slightly, or not at all, differentiated into organs such as roots, stems, and leaves. As was said in the last chapter, the various groups are widely different, and may well have had different origins.

The SCHIZOPHYTA (Gr. "fission plants") are the most primitive and simple of the thallophytes. They are one-celled and have the simplest form of asexual reproduction—*fission*, or division of the parent cell into equal halves. In many species the cells adhere to form colonies. They lack specialization into nucleus, cytoplasm, and plastids.

The group consists of two classes:

1. SCHIZOPHYCEAE (Gr. "fission algae"), with photosynthetic pigments, hence independent; blue-green algae.
2. SCHIZOMYCETES (Gr. "fission fungi"), generally lacking photosynthetic pigments, ordinarily dependent; bacteria.

SCHIZOPHYCEAE

These plants, known as the blue-green algae, may be found in shallow water, often in the form of gelatinous globules or masses, or as a slimy coat on moist soil. The color is usually blue-green, for with the chlorophyll is associated a blue pigment known as *phycocyanin* (Gr. "alga blue"). These substances are not in plastids, but diffused through the cell. The stored product of photosynthesis is *glycogen*, a carbohydrate not commonly found in plants. The cell wall consists of cellulose surrounded by a layer of *pectin*, which becomes gelatinous on contact with water. There is no distinction between nucleus and cytoplasm; but in the center of the cell or scattered through its protoplasm are granules which appear to be chromatin and to carry on a nuclear function. In reproduction, which is asexual, by fission, these granules take a position near the cell center and split; and as the halves separate, a new partition forms between them (Fig. 263).

Forms Without Cell Differentiation (Figs. 262, 263). *Gleocapsa* has separate spherical or ovoid cells enclosed in gelatinous sheaths which tend to hold them together for a time after cell division. *Oscillatoria*, inasmuch as its partition walls all form in the same direction, assumes the form of filamentous colonies of cylindrical or disk-like cells. It gets its name from

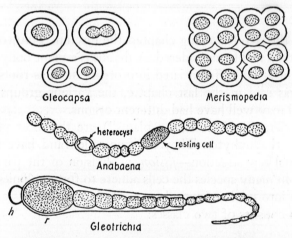

Fig. 262. Blue-green algae. *Gleocapsa* consists of separate cells, each with gelatinous coats; *Merismopedia* is a flat plate of cells; *Anabaena* is a filament with differentiated heterocyst and resting cell; *Gleotrichia* has a terminal heterocyst followed by a resting cell and a tapering filament.

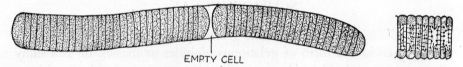

Fig. 263. *Oscillatoria*, a common blue-green alga. Left, the cylindrical filament, showing an occasional cell in the process of division, also the breaking up of the filament by the death of a cell. Right, detail of cell division, showing that the chromatin granules behave much as do chromosomes in plants that have organized nuclei. (Right figure redrawn from Olive.)

the swaying movement of the filaments. In *Merismopedia* the cell partitions form in two directions at right angles to each other; consequently the colonies are flat, rectangular plates.

Beginnings of Differentiation. *Nostoc* shows in its necklace-like colonies a suggestion of differentiation in what is known as the *heterocyst* (Gr. "different cell"). This is an occasional cell which differs slightly from the others in size and structure. Its function is uncertain, except that it is the usual breaking point in the multiplication of colonies. *Anabaena* has in addition an occasional *resting cell* which carries the organism through a season unfavorable for growth. *Gleotrichia* has a tapering filament.

General Remarks. Some blue-green algae contain red pigment in addition to blue and green; this greatly predominates in *Trichodesmium*, the alga that gives the Red Sea its name. The simplicity of their cell structure enables the blue-greens to endure a wider range of conditions than is possible for most plants. Some of them grow at temperatures as high as 87°C.; such forms constitute the principal vegetation of hot springs and geyser basins, giving attractive colors to these features in Yellowstone National Park. The oldest known plant fossils, estimated at more than a billion years of age, are believed to represent blue-green algae.

BACTERIA (SCHIZOMYCETES)

Widespread Occurrence and Importance. Bacteria are found in enormous numbers in soil, in all open waters, in decomposing organic matter, on and often in plant and animal bodies. So important are they to human life for good and for ill that the study of them, *bacteriology*, has assumed great importance as a science. This science is often expanded to include the study of other organisms found in similar situations and studied by similar techniques—certain protozoans, the yeasts, certain fungi called molds, small bodies called Rickettsiae, and the viruses. It is therefore more properly designated *microbiology* (Gr. "study of small life"). Small organisms in general may be called *microorganisms* or *microbes*.

Form and Structure. Bacteria are of three general forms (Fig. 264): the *bacillus* (Lat. "little stick"), which is rod-shaped; the *coccus* (Gr. "grain-like body"), which is spherical; and the *spirillum* (Gr. "coil," Fig. 265), which is corkscrew-shaped. The bacterial cell consists of a thin *wall* composed largely of *chitin*, the substance that forms the outer covering of crustaceans and insects, and a *protoplast* which is not differentiated into cytoplasm and nucleus. Outside the wall in many species is a gelatinous sheath or capsule (plague bacillus, Fig. 264). Some are held together in a continuous gelatinous mass called a *zooglea*. Many kinds of bacteria, especially among the bacilli and spirilla, have *flagella* by means of which they move through a liquid medium. These are variously arranged in the differ-

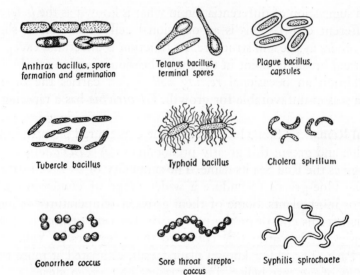

Anthrax bacillus, spore formation and germination

Tetanus bacillus, terminal spores

Plague bacillus, capsules

Tubercle bacillus

Typhoid bacillus

Cholera spirillum

Gonorrhea coccus

Sore throat strepto-coccus

Syphilis spirochaete

FIG. 264. Various species of pathogenic bacteria. Note that anthrax and tetanus bacilli produce spores which enable them to live longer in a dry condition than do most disease germs. The plague bacillus is enclosed in a gelatinous capsule. Typhoid bacilli are provided with flagella. (All highly magnified.)

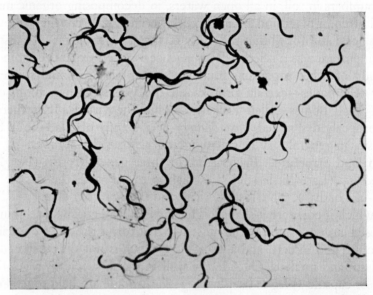

FIG. 265. *Spirillum volutans*, an organism from stagnant water, stained to show flagella, of which there is a tuft at each end (× 610). (Copyright, General Biological Supply House, Inc., Chicago.)

ent forms, and are generally invisible except with special staining. In some forms the contents of the cell occasionally condense into a thick-walled and resistant resting body, or *spore* (anthrax and tetanus, Fig. 264).

Size. Next to the viruses (of doubtful organic status) and the Rickettsiae, the bacteria are the smallest of organisms. The average bacillus is about three microns (thousandths of a millimeter) in length, the coccus one-half to one micron in diameter. If the world were reduced to the size of a sphere eighty feet in diameter, its human inhabitants would, on the

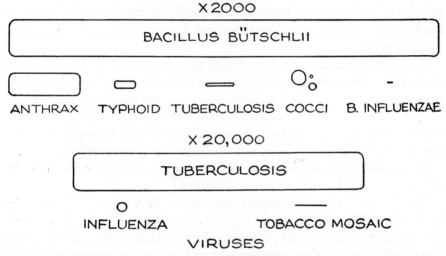

FIG. 266. Comparative sizes of bacteria (above); virus particles compared with tuberculosis bacillus (below). *Bacillus butschlii* is found in the intestine of the cockroach. *Bacillus influenzae* and the influenza virus are associated with different types of influenza.

same scale, be about the size of the average bacillus; the same reduction would make a pumpkin a foot in diameter the size of the average coccus. A chain of 4000 cocci would just reach across an ordinary pinhead, and to cover the top of the pinhead one layer deep would take 12,000,000 of them. There is considerable range in size between the largest and the smallest bacteria (Fig. 266), roughly comparable to that between an elephant and a mouse.

Reproduction. Bacteria reproduce asexually by fission, in which simple, equal division of the cell occurs. The rods and spirals divide transversely; the spheres elongate slightly and constrict in the middle. After division the rods often remain united in filaments; the spheres may remain grouped in pairs (*diplococci*), in chains (*streptococci*), in irregular masses (*staphylococci*), in flat plates, or in cubes. Under favorable conditions of temperature and food supply, divisions as rapid as one every fifteen minutes have been observed. Thus the powers of bacteria to fill the available growing medium are tremendous. It has been estimated that starting with a bacterium weighing one ten-millionth of a milligram and allowing uninterrupted division once each hour, it would take only six days for the progeny of the one cell to equal the earth in mass. Of course shortage of food, accumulation of wastes, and environmental conditions otherwise unfavorable would check cell division long before this point.

Some experiments in which mixtures of bacteria with different characteristics gave rise to new bacteria with combinations of these characteristics suggest a kind of sexual reproduction. Further investigation is needed to confirm this.

Relationships. Bacteria have much in common with the blue-green algae. Both groups consist of members which are one-celled, lack an organized nucleus, multiply by fission, often develop gelatinous sheaths, and often form resting cells (spores). Similar cell forms (cylindrical, spherical, and spiral) are found in both groups. Some of the blue-greens utilize organic matter when light is not available for photosynthesis. Certain species of both groups endure temperatures approaching the boiling point of water, and withstand extreme desiccation.

Metabolism. Certain bacteria that grow in water which contains hydrogen sulfide resulting from organic decay are provided with a purple pigment that enables them to carry on photosynthesis. Other kinds oxidize certain chemicals in their environment and utilize the energy, which the oxidation liberates, for building up their carbohydrate supply; this process is known as *chemosynthesis* (Gr. "putting together by chemical action"). Among these are the *nitrite bacteria*, which secure their energy by oxidizing ammonia to nitrites; the *nitrate bacteria*, by oxidizing nitrites to nitrates; the *sulfur bacteria*, by oxidizing sulfur or hydrogen sulfide; and the *iron bacteria*, by oxidizing iron compounds to the rust-colored deposits often seen in water.

Aside from these few types, whose nutrition is called *autotrophic* (Gr. "self-nourishing"), all bacteria require organic food, and may be considered either *parasites* (Gr. "eating beside"), which get their food from living organisms, or *saprophytes* (Gr. "decay plants"), which get their food from nonliving organic matter. They secrete various enzymes which bring about chemical changes in the organic matter, living or nonliving, on which they feed. Those that attack living organisms destroy the tissues of the host, interfere mechanically with some function such as the flow of blood, or produce *toxins* (Gr. "poisons"), wastes from the metabolism of the bacteria, and thereby harm the body of the host. Those that live on nonliving matter bring about various changes collectively known as *decay* (Lat. "breaking down"). Decay of carbohydrates, which is usually associated with the evolution of gas, is called *fermentation* (from Lat. "to boil"); that of proteins, manifested by the production of foul odors, is *putrefaction* (Lat. "making rotten").

Some of the products of bacterial action are desirable; hence bacteria are important in certain industries. The changes involved in the making of butter, cheese, sauerkraut, silage, and vinegar, the tanning of leather, and the retting of flax to permit the separation of the fibers, are all processes involving bacteria or other microorganisms.

Methods of the Bacteriologist. The existence of bacteria was unsuspected until 1683, when the keen eye of Leeuwenhoek, the Dutch lens maker (page 15), enabled him to find them, by the use of his crude microscopes, in tartar from his teeth (Figs. 7, 267). Bacteria are of hundreds of different sorts, some being injurious to man, some beneficial, and the large majority indifferent. They are so small and simple that it is not as easy to classify them on the basis of appearance as it is the higher plants. Hence the bacteriologist isolates them in pure cultures and grows them on such media

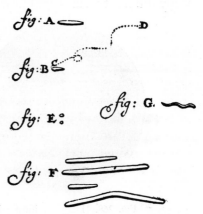

Fig. 267. Leeuwenhoek's figures of bacteria, 1683, the first illustrations of bacteria ever published. *E*, Cocci; *G*, spirillum; the others bacilli. The dotted line from *C* to *D* shows the irregular path described by the form at *C*. (From Zinsser and Bayne-Jones, *General Bacteriology;* copyright, D. Appleton-Century.)

as gelatin, agar, potato, or broth, which have been sterilized by heat and kept in a covered Petri dish (Fig. 268) or in a flask or test tube provided with a plug of cotton to filter out foreign organisms. An inoculating needle sterilized by passage through a flame is used in handling bacteria. The size, shape, and color of the colonies that develop, and the effects of the bacteria on the various cultural media serve as diagnostic characters. Organisms suspected of being responsible for disease may be inoculated into laboratory animals and their effects observed.

Viruses. Viruses are particles much smaller than bacteria; they possess certain properties in common with organisms and perhaps represent organisms of a very primitive type, though this is still regarded as an unsettled question. If blood serum from a cow affected with foot-and-mouth disease is passed through an unglazed porcelain filter which will remove all microscopically visible particles, the filtrate will produce the disease when injected into a healthy cow, and the same disease can be likewise transmitted from this animal to others. Thus we have evidence that the disease is caused by something which, although invisible with an ordinary microscope, has the power of multiplication. Viruses grow only in living organisms; they cannot, like bacteria, be grown on sterile culture media, but they are being grown successfully on embryonic tissue of chickens. Many different viruses are known, including the causative factors for yel-

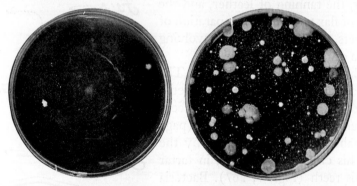

Fig. 268. Diagram illustrating methods of cultivating and counting bacteria. Sterile agar is poured when warm into glass Petri dishes. To the one at the left was added a measured quantity of milk which had been kept cool; to that at the right, the same quantity from a warm place. The dishes were then covered, and the agar was allowed to harden by cooling, then to stand for two days. Each of the introduced bacteria has now grown into a colony. The number of colonies is approximately that of the original bacteria. (From Smallwood, Reveley, and Bailey, *New Biology;* copyright, Allyn & Bacon.)

low fever, infantile paralysis, measles, mumps, smallpox, influenza, encephalitis (often called "sleeping sickness"), cold sores, ordinary colds, and warts; for such animal diseases as parrot fever, hog cholera, rabies, and distemper of dogs; for such plant diseases as peach yellows and tobacco mosaic.

Bacteriophages. In 1917 d'Herelle, a Frenchman, passed cultures of dysentery bacilli through porcelain filters and found that the filtrate, if applied to a colony of the same bacilli on a Petri dish, would check the growth and cause the dissolution of the bacteria. He concluded that the filtrate contains a virus which causes a disease of bacteria; he called this virus a *bacteriophage* (Gr. "bacteria eater"). Similar viruses infect and destroy other kinds of bacteria. Attempts have been made to employ bacteriophages in fighting bacterial disease, but without much success, because they are ineffective in the presence of blood, pus, and fecal matter.

Extending the Range of Microscopic Observation. The physical nature of the light wave does not permit the separation with the ordinary microscope of two points that are closer together than one-tenth of a micron;

Fig. 269. Electron microscope, by means of which such small objects as virus and bacteriophage particles can be photographed. (Photo, courtesy of Dr. G. D. Cummings, Director of Laboratories, Michigan Department of Health.)

hence microscopes cannot give sharp definition at magnifications of more than about 2000 diameters. Our range of vision has been greatly increased by the recent invention of the *electron microscope*, in which a source of electrons replaces the light source of the ordinary microscope, and magnetic fields take the place of lenses in focusing the electron waves on the image plate (Fig. 269). Since the wave length of the electron ray is much shorter than that of light, it is possible with the new instrument to increase magnification greatly beyond that of the light microscope. Photographs up to 100,000 diameters have been taken. Such magnification is ample to reveal the size and form of virus and bacteriophage particles (Fig. 270).

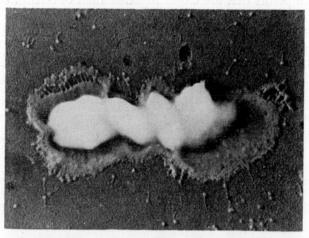

FIG. 270. Bacteriophage particles attacking necklace-like colony of *Streptococcus lactis*. The bacteria (the white object in the center) are disintegrating, as shown by the surrounding gray zone. The bacteriophage particles are shaped somewhat like tadpoles. ($\times$ 17500.) (Photo, courtesy of Iowa State College.)

Borderline Organisms. Viruses have some of the properties which we ordinarily associate with organisms. They bring about specific changes upon their hosts, they reproduce, and, like organisms, they are subject to mutations (sudden changes in character). Research by W. M. Stanley, however, has shown that at least one of them, the virus of tobacco mosaic disease, is a single chemical compound, a nucleoprotein, which is obtainable in crystalline form. Since ordinary protoplasm is a complex colloidal system, it may be regarded as doubtful whether viruses are actually living things. They remind us of a statement attributed to Aristotle: "Nature makes so gradual a transition from the inanimate to the animate, that the boundary lines which separate them are indistinct and doubtful."

Biology of Decay. Bacteria, yeasts, and molds all take part in the processes of decay. In the larger sense, decay is a valuable process in the economy of nature. If there were no such process, the earth would be filled with the bodies of past organisms, leaving little room for present organisms; and the carbon, nitrogen, and other elements essential to life would be locked up or kept from circulation. The existence of decay, supplemented by other processes to be noted shortly, makes it possible for the atoms of these elements to be used over and over in cycle after cycle of life. Of course the decay of our foods is troublesome or injurious. Aside from the fact that organisms of decay destroy food and develop disagreeable odors and flavors, they may produce poisonous substances by breaking down the proteins on which they grow, or as the wastes of their own metabolism. Hence several ways have been found to keep them out or to check their growth.

1. *Low temperature.* Microbes remain dormant at or below the freezing point of water, and grow only slowly at slightly higher temperatures. Hence freezing and cold storage are popular methods of keeping food.
2. *Drying.* Microbes, like all other organisms, are unable to grow without water. Therefore the drying of foods, such as grains, fruits, vegetables, and meats, is an effective means of preservation.
3. *Heating and sealing.* In the widespread use of the food-canning process, food is heated to a high enough temperature to kill organisms, then sealed to prevent their later entrance. In this procedure it is important to remember that nonacid foods may be contaminated with spores of the bacillus that causes botulinus poisoning. Such foods should be heated in a pressure cooker, which permits heating to a temperature higher than the boiling point of water. In the *pasteurization* of milk and other liquid foods, sufficient heat is applied for a sufficient time to destroy infectious bacteria and to reduce greatly the number of those that will cause decomposition.
4. *Chemicals.* Certain chemicals may serve as *antiseptics* (Gr. "against putrefaction") to prevent the growth of microorganisms. Those which may be safely used are salt, sugar, vinegar, and spices. Formaldehyde, sodium benzoate, and some other chemicals have been used in this way, but they are known or suspected to be detrimental to the health of the food consumer.

Spontaneous Generation. Belief in *spontaneous generation*, i.e., that life can arise from lifeless matter, was common in ancient and medieval times. Aristotle and other early scientists believed, as did others of their day, that frogs could come from the mud of ponds, maggots from decaying meat, and eels from the slime rubbed off the skin of fishes. Even as late as 1600, a scholar wrote a recipe for the production of mice; he said that they might be obtained by leaving wheat and a few greasy rags together in a jar for a few days. Another writer cautioned his readers against smelling a certain kind of mint for fear scorpions would be generated in the brain and insanity result.

As late as the 17th century it was generally believed that maggots were generated spontaneously from the substance of meat that had been exposed for some days. But Francesco Redi, an Italian, suspected that they hatched from eggs that were laid on the meat by flies. Surmising that meat protected from flies might not develop maggots, he put pieces of meat in several jars, some of which he screened from flies by parchment or gauze (Fig. 271). After a few days, maggots appeared in the uncovered

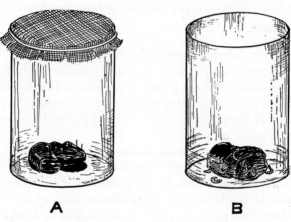

FIG. 271. Redi's experiment. Maggots did not appear on the meat in the gauze-covered jar, *A*, but did appear on that in the open jar, *B*.

FIG. 272. Louis Pasteur (1822–1895) the founder of bacteriology. (From Haggard, *Devils, Drugs, and Doctors;* copyright, Harper.)

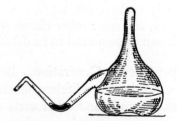

FIG. 273. Flask used by Pasteur in experiments on spontaneous generation. The open top was sealed after broth was introduced. Although the side tube was left open, the condensed steam accumulating in its curve prevented the entrance of airborne organisms; hence the broth did not spoil. (From Shull, *Principles of Animal Biology;* copyright, McGraw-Hill; after MacFarland.)

meat, but not in that which the flies could not reach; thus Redi's idea was supported by the results of his controlled experiment. Consequently the belief in spontaneous generation began to break down so far as the macroscopic (larger than microscopic) organisms are concerned.

It persisted two centuries longer for microorganisms because their almost universal presence in dust was not recognized and because, in attempts to sterilize with heat, account was not taken of the fact that certain microorganisms form spores which withstand boiling temperatures. A controversy on the subject continued for years until Louis Pasteur (1822–1895, Fig. 272) showed by a series of carefully planned experiments that yeasts, molds, and bacteria are not generated in the substances in which they grow but must be introduced in some manner. He put nutrient broth in a flask sealed at the top but provided with a bent side tube (Fig. 273), then boiled the broth. The water that condensed in the lower bend of the tube excluded organisms; consequently the broth did not decompose. He also exposed flasks of sterile culture media to the air of a Paris street, and other flasks to the air of an uninhabited mountain top; the air of the former locality proved to be full of bacteria, that of the latter almost free from them. It is now generally recognized that, within our experience at least, life comes only from life.

Bacteria and the Carbon Cycle. The carbon cycle of nature is outlined in Fig. 274. The *carbon dioxide* supply of the air is the great reservoir from which the organisms of the world secure all of their carbon by means of *photosynthesis* in *green plants* and *chemosynthesis* in a few *bacteria*. Four different channels return carbon dioxide to this reservoir: *respiration in plants, respiration in animals, burning of plant products,* and *microbial decomposition*. If there were no microbes, there would be an insufficient return to the reservoir. Carbon compounds would accumulate, and carbon dioxide would become too scanty to support green plants.

Bacteria and the Nitrogen Cycle. The *nitrogen cycle,* which is more complex, is shown in Fig. 275. Here *nitrates* ($-NO_3$ compounds of certain metals) constitute the reservoir from which green plants draw their nitrogen, making it available for other forms of life. *Plant proteins* are used as food by *animals* and reconstructed into *animal proteins*. *Decay bacteria* break down both plant and animal proteins, the process involving several steps but ending with *ammonia* (NH_3). The nitrogen products of catabolism in plants are probably used again by the same plants; in animals the main product of catabolism is urea, $(NH_2)_2CO$, which, through the agency of urea bacteria, readily unites with water and breaks down into NH_3 and CO_2. The nitrogen in ammonia is not yet available to green plants, but must go through two further steps—the oxidation of ammonia to *nitrites* (-NO$_2$ compounds), carried on by the *nitrite bacteria*, and the oxidation of nitrites to *nitrates* (-NO$_3$ compounds), carried on by the *nitrate bacteria*. Hence nitrite and nitrate bacteria are as important as

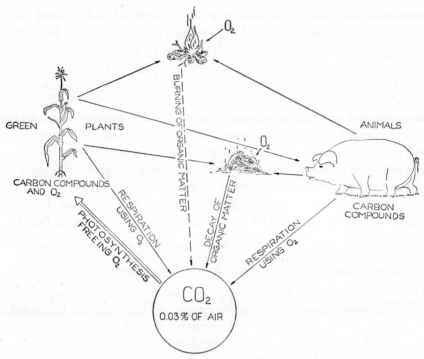

Fig. 274. Carbon cycle. Diagram showing the principal carbon and oxygen changes in connection with organisms and organic substances. Plants, by photosynthesis, remove CO$_2$ from the air (thick arrow). This gas is returned to the air by plant respiration, animal respiration, and the burning and decay of organic matter (thin arrows).

decay bacteria for the completion of the cycle. Since they require oxygen in their chemical processes, they thrive best in soils well supplied with oxygen. On the other hand, waterlogged or uncultivated soils are likely to contain *denitrifying bacteria* which remove oxygen from nitrates and nitrites, reducing them to ammonia or free nitrogen. They therefore decrease the quantity of nitrogen which is in a form available to green plants. It is noteworthy that thorough cultivation, aside from its other benefits, is helpful in encouraging the useful (nitrite and nitrate) and discouraging the harmful (denitrifying) bacteria.

Nitrogen Fixation. By the removal of nitrogen compounds in crops harvested from the land, by the leaching of the soil by flowing water, as well as by denitrification, the amount of nitrogen available to green plants constantly tends to decrease. This tendency is overcome by a group of

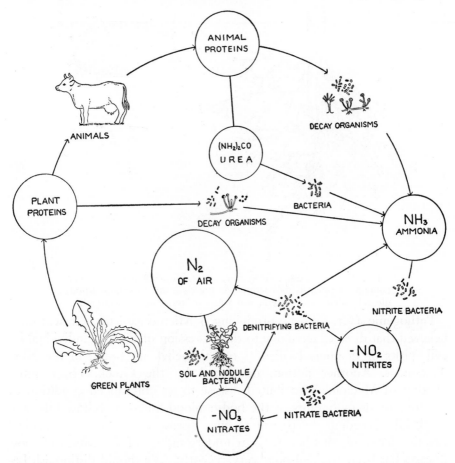

Fig. 275. Nitrogen cycle. Diagram showing sample organisms and chemical processes concerned in the transformations of nitrogen in living things.

organisms known as *nitrogen-fixing bacteria*, which bring an equivalent amount of atmospheric nitrogen back into the cycle and make it available again for green plants. Some of these bacteria live in the soil, unassociated with the higher plants. Others, which are better known, form nodules on the roots of plants of the Pulse family (legumes), such as clover, alfalfa, and soybeans (Fig. 276). The association of the two plants is mutually beneficial, for the legume furnishes the bacteria with carbohydrates made by photosynthesis, and is in turn provided with nitrates. To the nitrogen-fixing power of these bacteria is attributed much of the value of legumes as enrichers of the soil.

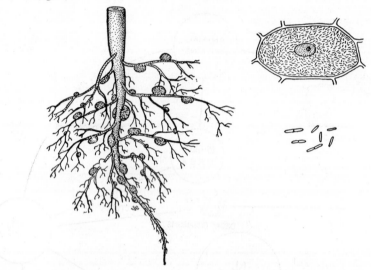

Fig. 276. Soybean root system (left), showing nodules which contain nitrogen-fixing bacteria. At the right are an enlarged nodule cell filled with bacteria and a few bacteria highly enlarged.

Pathogenic (Gr. "disease-producing") **Microorganisms.** It was once believed that diseases were due to the possession of the sick individual by evil spirits or demons. Evidences of this belief are found in the New Testament. Another notion, developed by the Greek, Hippocrates, "Father of Medicine," attributed disease to an unbalanced condition of the four fluids or humors of the body: blood, phlegm, yellow bile, and black bile. Bleeding the patient to cure disease was a common medical practice based on this belief. Clear understanding of the causes of most diseases has been attained only very recently. We should distinguish between two great groups of diseases. *Noninfectious diseases* are those not caused by microorganisms. They may be caused by dietary deficiencies, as scurvy; by endocrine deficiencies, as diabetes; or by the wearing out of some organ, as heart failure. *Infectious diseases* are caused by microorganisms and hence may be transmitted from person to person. Some of the earlier investigators thought microorganisms to be the result rather than the cause of disease. We owe our knowledge of their role as disease producers, and the association of specific diseases with specific organisms, mainly to the researches of the Frenchman, Pasteur, and the German, Robert Koch (1843–1910).

Koch's Postulates. Before any microorganism is accepted as the specific cause of a disease, it must comply with the following conditions which were outlined by Koch:

1. The specific organism must be present in every case of the disease.

2. It must be isolated from the diseased individual and cultivated in pure culture.

3. The pure culture when inoculated into a susceptible host must produce the disease.

4. The organism must again be present in the diseased host and be reobtained in pure culture.

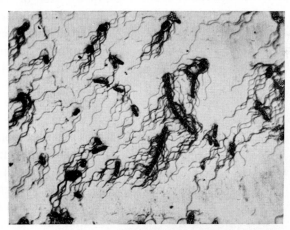

FIG. 277. Bacillus of typhoid fever (*Eberthella typhi*), stained to show flagella (× 1500). (Photomicrograph, copyright, General Biological Supply House, Inc., Chicago.)

To cite an example, the small bacillus discovered by Koch in the sputum of tubercular patients may be grown as a pure culture on sterile blood agar, and a portion of the growth inoculated into a guinea pig which will then gradually develop symptoms of tuberculosis and from which the same bacilli may be reobtained for microscopic examination. It is not always possible to apply all these tests, particularly the second, but they set a standard which investigators try to apply.

Bacterial Diseases. Well-known diseases due to bacteria and allied forms, the microorganisms of some of which are illustrated in Fig. 264, are:

Coccus forms: Boils, blood poisoning, sore throat, pneumonia, gonorrhea, scarlet fever.

Bacillus forms: Anthrax, tetanus, plague, tuberculosis, leprosy, typhoid (Fig. 277), diphtheria.

Spirillum forms: Cholera.

Rickettsias: Typhus fever, Rocky Mountain spotted fever, and some other diseases are attributed to these rod-like or spherical bodies, which are much smaller than ordinary bacteria.

Spirochetes: Syphilis and relapsing fever are caused by spiral organisms which are more slender and flexible than the spirilla, lack flagella, and travel by a snake-like motion (Fig. 278). In some respects they resemble Protozoa.

Sources of Disease Germs and Avenues of Infection. Germs may be transmitted from diseased animals to man by handling, as parrot fever from parrots; by bites, as rabies from dogs; or by flesh or other products used as food, as tuberculosis from the meat of diseased animals, or undulant fever from the milk of diseased cows. But most diseases travel directly or indirectly from person to person. They may come from sick or convalescent persons, or from "carriers" who, although apparently well, harbor in their bodies germs that cause disease in others. They may be conveyed by excreta, by sputum, by droplets of saliva or mucus forcibly expelled in coughing, sneezing, or talking, by germ-containing matter from skin eruptions and wounds, or by blood transfer from a victim through the agency of certain insects. We have already seen the part played by mosquitoes in the spread of malaria, and by the tsetse fly in carrying African sleeping sickness. The rat flea carries the plague bacillus; typhus, a disease frequently prevalent in army camps, is carried from victim to victim by the body louse (Fig. 136). Flies, because of their indiscriminate habit of feeding on filth and foods, are pernicious germ carriers (Fig. 142). Germs may enter our bodies by way of the mouth, nose, or other mucous surfaces, or through skin wounds. The quaran-

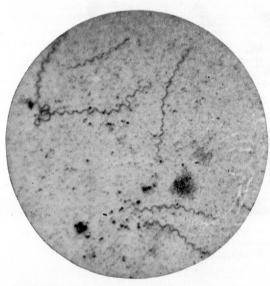

Fig. 278. Organism of syphilis (*Spirochaeta pallida*) from smear of diseased tissue (× 2500). There is some uncertainty whether the organism, a slender spiral thread, is a bacterium or a protozoan. (Photomicrograph, copyright, General Biological Supply House, Inc., Chicago.)

tining of the sick, proper sewage disposal, care as to sources of food and water, and the use of antiseptics on wounds are common precautions that should be taken against illness. Typhoid fever bacteria occur in the body wastes of typhoid patients and are transmitted to healthy individuals, usually by the contamination of drinking water with sewage, or of foods by fingers or flies. Once a very common and dreaded disease, it has been almost eliminated in this country by improvements in sewage disposal and water supply.

Early Research in Immunity. During the last quarter of the 18th century, when smallpox was a very common disease, Edward Jenner (1749–1823), an English physician, noticed that those who worked among cattle sometimes developed a mild form of smallpox through contact with animals having cowpox, and that this protected them against future attacks of the virulent or severe form. This observation led to the discovery of *vaccination* (from Lat. for "cow"), which is still the recognized procedure for smallpox prevention. But the principle behind Jenner's discovery was not understood at the time, and it was almost a century before Pasteur applied it to other diseases.

Work of Pasteur. Pasteur's researches in chemistry developed in him an interest in problems relating to fermentation and disease. In his study of chicken cholera, a deadly disease of poultry, he injected into some chickens bacteria from a cholera culture that had aged in the laboratory. Instead of dying, the chickens were scarcely affected. The same chickens were later inoculated with a fresh culture and escaped with only a very mild attack of the disease, although chickens inoculated without previous treatment with the old culture died. Pasteur then applied the idea gained from this experiment to anthrax, a disease that was causing great consternation among French farmers because of its deadly effects upon sheep and cattle. He isolated the anthrax bacillus, grew it in cultures, inoculated animals with these, and devised ways of weakening the cultures so they would confer immunity on animals treated with them. He met with much opposition and ridicule. Finally he was challenged to come out of his laboratory and put his fantastic theories to a practical test. Sixty sheep were set aside for a public demonstration; twenty-five of them were vaccinated with the weakened culture. Then, in the presence of a large crowd, these vaccinated sheep and twenty-five nonvaccinated ones were inoculated with a fresh, deadly culture of anthrax. A week later, when the crowd reassembled, the vaccinated sheep were in as good health as the ten untreated animals, whereas the twenty-five nonvaccinated but inoculated sheep were all dead. Later, Pasteur applied similar methods to rabies, treating with success a boy that had been bitten by a mad dog. Since his time such techniques have been found applicable to many other diseases.

Antiseptic Surgery. *Joseph Lister* (1827–1912), an English surgeon, made an immensely valuable practical application of Pasteur's discoveries by introducing antiseptic surgery, thus reducing materially the previously heavy death rate from gangrene following surgical operations. Pasteur, Koch, and Lister may well be regarded as the great triumvirate in the campaign against disease. They carried us far toward the realization of Pasteur's assertion that man has it in his power to cause all contagious disease to disappear from the earth. Their accomplishments have undoubtedly been a leading cause in the addition of about twenty years to life expectancy within the past half century.

Disease Resistance. In the long course of evolution, plants, animals, and man gained the power to survive the attacks of their many organic enemies by developing various means of protection. Our microbial enemies have waged their warfare for countless eras, during which various defensive adaptations against them have developed. These adaptations collectively constitute what is commonly called *immunity*. One important factor in the defense of the body is the epithelium, which covers the body surface and all of its canals and cavities, and which, where protection is most required, consists of many overlapping layers of cells. Most bacteria and many poisons are harmless as long as they are outside of an intact epithelium. Along the passages of the respiratory system, a particularly vulnerable part of the body, the epithelium is supplemented by a mucous secretion and by a covering of cilia which vibrate in such a manner as to keep secretion and foreign particles, such as bacteria, moving upward. Furthermore, the body is well provided with cells whose business is to devour and destroy invading germs. These are the *phagocytes* (Gr. "eating cells"), thought of generally as white corpuscles of the blood, but not confined to the blood, inasmuch as they occur in great numbers in the lymph nodes and are present all through the lymph which bathes all the body cells. They are ameboid cells, and ingest microbes of all sorts much as *Amoeba* ingests food. When bacteria enter the tissues by way of a wound, inflammation occurs; i.e., the blood vessels dilate, permitting the ready approach of leucocytes to the spot to carry on their warfare against the bacteria. The *lymph nodes*, which are often located where danger of infection is greatest, may be thought of as important rallying places for these defenders of the body, and as filters which remove many of the invading bacteria. The *liver* and *spleen* serve as large blood filters; the cells that line their capillaries remove microorganisms from the blood.

Antibodies. The protection afforded by the epithelium, mucus, and leucocytes is supplemented by that afforded by various types of chemicals formed by the cells of the body as the result of stimulation by microorganisms or their toxins. The substances thus formed tend to destroy or remove the microorganisms or toxins which have stimulated their formation; hence they are commonly designated as *antibodies*. The toxins or other substances which stimulate the cells to form antibodies are called *antigens*. Antibodies include:

1. *Antitoxins* (Gr. "against poisons"), which counteract the *toxins* or *poisons* produced by disease germs, much as a base counteracts or destroys the properties of an acid. In Pasteur's experiment, the toxin of the anthrax bacillus induced the formation of an antitoxin in the body of a sheep.
2. *Lysins* (Gr. "dissolution"), which, in solution in blood serum, kill and dissolve the particular kind of germs that have caused their formation.
3. *Agglutinins* (Lat. "gluing-together substances"), which cause the clumping of the bacteria that have caused their formation.
4. *Precipitins*, which precipitate or immobilize the bacteria that stimulate their formation.
5. *Opsonins* (Gr. "caterers" or "banquet preparers"), which, in solution in the serum, cause the bacteria that stimulate their formation to be devoured more readily by the phagocytes.

Disease germs or their poisons, by causing the host to produce one or more of the substances mentioned, have the power to confer immunity which, according to the type of disease and the circumstances, may be only temporary or may last for life. It may be noted that germs are not the only agents that form such substances. The antigens of human red blood cells have already been discussed (page 283). In the case of some of these, antibodies already exist in certain people; and in others, transfusion may result in antibody formation. Various foreign proteins are also known to induce antibodies.

Active and Passive Immunity. Immunity may be classified as follows:

I. *Active*, in which the organism possesses or develops its own antibodies:
   A. *Natural*, present from birth, as a matter of inheritance.
   B. *Acquired*, secured by some incident after birth:
      1. By recovering from the disease in question (duration of the immunity varying greatly for different diseases).
      2. By having a mild form of the disease, the germs having been attenuated or weakened by:
         a. Growth in a different animal species, as in the case of vaccine from cattle, used in immunizing man against smallpox.

    b. Heat or drying, such as the rabbit nerve tissue used in the Pasteur treatment for rabies.

    c. Age or exhaustion of culture. (This is illustrated by Pasteur's chicken cholera experiment.)

3. By injecting dead organisms containing endotoxins (poisons in the organism), such as typhoid vaccine, which consists of typhoid bacteria grown on agar, then killed by heating, but still retaining the poison which has formed in them.

4. By injecting exotoxins (poisons that have diffused from the microorganism into the surrounding medium) after treating them chemically in such a way as to destroy their poisonous properties but to allow them to retain the power of stimulating antitoxin production. An example is *toxoid*, the substance now widely used for immunizing against diphtheria. In the preparation of toxoid, the toxin of diphtheria is destroyed by treatment with formaldehyde. The substance which remains is separated from the liquid by precipitation with alum and, on introduction to the human body, induces the formation of antitoxins.

The weakened organisms, dead organisms, or modified toxins (2, 3, 4) introduced to fight or prevent disease are known as *vaccines*, because of their resemblance to the substance used by Jenner in immunizing to smallpox.

II. *Passive*, in which antibodies produced by another animal are introduced, through a blood serum, into the individual to be immunized. An example is tetanus antitoxin, used as a preventive on persons who have received a deep wound. To prepare this antitoxin, tetanus bacilli are grown in broth, which is then passed through a porcelain filter to separate the toxin. This toxin is then injected into a horse in several gradually increasing doses. After the horse has developed a considerable degree of immunity, blood is drawn from it, the corpuscles are allowed to settle, and the serum is used to immunize human patients. Diphtheria antitoxin, a common cure for diphtheria, is prepared in a similar manner.

Chemotherapy. *Chemotherapy* signifies the treatment of disease by means of chemical agents that have a specific effect upon the organisms causing the disease. Many well-known germicides, such as phenol and formaldehyde, cannot be applied to germs in the body because of their poisonous effect upon body tissue. The long quest for chemicals which kill microorganisms without harming the patient was first rewarded by the discovery of germicides for protozoan and related parasites. Ehrlich (1854–1915) was a pioneer in this field, with his discovery that arsphenamine, a compound of arsenic, kills the spirochete of syphilis. We now have as established remedies quinine for malaria, and Bayer 205 for African sleeping sickness. More recently the *sulfa drugs* (sulfonamides) have assumed importance in treating diseases (e.g., pneumonia) and in guarding against infection from wounds or following operations. Such compounds as sulfanilamide, sulfapyridine, and sulfathaladine are widely used, and research is constantly developing new ones. Some of them are toxic, at least to certain individuals; hence they should not be used except on the advice of a physician.

Antibiotics. A new era in medical science has been initiated by the discovery that certain microorganisms produce substances that destroy microorganisms of other species. Such substances are known as *antibiotics* (Gr. "against life"). *Penicillin* was discovered in England in 1929, when Alexander Fleming noticed that colonies of bacteria on a Petri dish were destroyed when invaded by a green mold (*Penicillium*), that grew from spores which had accidentally fallen on the culture medium. It was not used as a remedy until 1941, when World War II created a large demand for it. In producing it, a species of *Penicillium* is grown immersed in a fluid culture medium under carefully controlled conditions, and the penicillin is then extracted and purified. High-yielding strains have been selected from mutations (hereditary changes) produced by exposure to x-rays, and production techniques have been facilitated to the extent that a 100,000-unit dose which cost $20 wholesale in 1943 cost less than 5 cents in 1950. Penicillin has proved very effective in the treatment of syphilis, of skin and wound diseases, and of various other diseases, particularly those caused by coccus bacteria. *Streptomycin* is produced from *Streptomyces griseus*, an organism intermediate between bacteria and molds. It has proved effective for tuberculosis and several other diseases that do not yield to penicillin. *Aureomycin, terramycin,* and *chloramphenicol* are produced from other species of *Streptomyces* and have been found useful in a wide range of diseases. Doubtless great advances are yet to be made. Already the death rate from certain diseases and from intestinal operations has been reduced to one-tenth what it was before these remedies were discovered.

Progress in the Control of Infectious Diseases. Since the beginning of the 20th century, understanding and control of bacteria have brought about an amazing reduction in the death rate from bacterial diseases, as is shown in the accompanying graph (Fig. 279). Distances above the base line represent the average annual number of deaths from the specific diseases per 100,000 of the population of the United States for each five-year period from 1901 to 1950. For the bacterial diseases, each period shows a decrease from the preceding one, except for pneumonia which increased as the aftermath of the severe influenza epidemic of 1918. Diarrhea is primarily a disease of infants. Its marked decrease ensues from the better care and feeding of babies. Diphtheria and typhoid fever have dwindled almost to the vanishing point. In 1949, 222 times as many people were killed in motor vehicle accidents as died of typhoid. The death rate from cancer is increasing; its cause is unknown, its control not completely

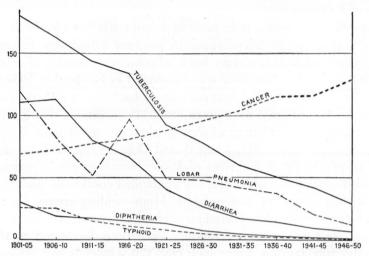

Fig. 279. Graph showing trend of death rate in the United States for the first half of the century, from five bacterial diseases and cancer, a disease of unknown cause. The numbers on the left indicate deaths per 100,000 per year. Note the downward trend for the bacterial diseases and the slight upward trend for cancer. For explanation, see text. (Data from U.S. Census Bureau.)

solved (high-energy radiation and surgery are used to remove certain cancerous growths), and more people who formerly would have died early in life from other causes now live to an age at which cancer is likely to appear.

Bacterial Diseases of Plants. While bacteria are less important than true fungi as causative organisms of plant disease, they are responsible for several prevalent and destructive maladies. One of the best known of these is *fire blight* of apples and pears. This causes first blackening of the leaves, then dying of twigs, limbs, and eventually the whole tree. Bacteria that ooze from diseased tissues are carried to other trees, mainly by insects. Diseased branches should be carefully pruned away and burned. Another disease, *black rot* of cabbage, causes the edges of the cabbage leaf to turn yellow and the veins to blacken. In commercial fields, losses as high as 90 percent are attributed to this disease. *Wilt* of cucumbers and melons is caused by bacteria growing in and clogging the water vessels, thus cutting off the flow of water to the vine. It is believed that the bacteria which cause this disease are transferred from one vine to another by the yellow-and-black cucumber beetle. *Crown gall* is a bacterial disease that is manifest by swellings on the stems of various fruit or ornamental trees and shrubs.

EXERCISES

1. What species of bacteria is responsible for the souring of milk? For the making of vinegar?
2. What type of germ causes leprosy? Scarlet fever? Bubonic plague? Syphilis? Pneumonia? Barber's itch?
3. What diseases are spread by house flies? Fleas? Body lice?
4. Why is it that the possible rates of increase of bacteria for considerable periods of time are seldom realized?
5. Distinguish between an antiseptic and a germicide, and name two or three of each.
6. What is meant by pasteurization, and why is it so called?
7. What are some of the diseases that confer lasting immunity on people who recover from them? Some that do not?
8. Secure further information about the life and work of Jenner, Pasteur, Koch. What was contributed to the science of health by Ehrlich? By Noguchi?
9. How do the methods of fighting disease today compare with those of Shakespeare's time? What improvements may we expect in the next century?
10. What diseases have spread by unsanitary drinking water? What precautionary measures are now being taken for most city water systems?
11. What is the bacteriological principle of the septic tank for sewage disposal?
12. Discuss botulinus poisoning, stating source, symptoms, and preventive measures.
13. Mention instances in which microorganisms of the same species produce at times mild, and at times severe, disease. State the probable reasons.
14. What is meant by ptomaine poisoning?
15. From the standpoint of soil bacteria, what is the advantage to the farmer in the thorough plowing and cultivation of the soil?
16. In what organisms does cancer occur? Is it ever caused by microorganisms? By other known environmental factors?

REFERENCES

Bayne-Jones, S., *Man and Microbes*, The Williams & Wilkins Company, 1932.
Bryan, A. H. and C. G., *Principles and Practice of Bacteriology*, Barnes & Noble, Inc., 3rd ed., 1942.

Buchanan, R. E. and E. D., *Bacteriology*, The Macmillan Company, 5th ed., 1951.

Burdon, K. L., *Textbook of Microbiology*, The Macmillan Company, 3rd ed., 1947.

Burrows, W., *Jordan-Burrows Textbook of Bacteriology*, W. B. Saunders Company, 15th ed., 1949.

Calder, R. M., *Microbiology*, W. B. Saunders Company, 1943.

Clifton, C. E., *Introduction to the Bacteria*, McGraw-Hill Book Company, Inc., 1950.

de Kruif, P., *Microbe Hunters*, Harcourt, Brace & Company, 1924.

Dobell, C., *Antony von Leeuwenhoek and His Little Animals*, Harcourt, Brace & Company, 1932.

Epstein, S., and Williams, B., *Miracles from Microbes: The Road to Streptomycin*, Rutgers Univ. Press, 1946.

Fairbrother, R. W., *Textbook of Bacteriology*, Heinemann, 1942.

Frobisher, M., *Fundamentals of Bacteriology*, W. B. Saunders Company, 4th ed., 1949.

Greaves, J. E. and E. O., *Elementary Bacteriology*, W. B. Saunders Company, 4th ed., 1940.

Kelly, F. C., and Hite, K. E., *Microbiology*, Appleton-Century-Crofts, 1949.

Park, W. H., and Williams, A. W., *Pathogenic Microorganisms*, Lea & Febiger, 1939.

Rahn, O., *Microbes of Merit*, The Jaques Cattell Press, 1945.

Salle, A. J., *Fundamental Principles of Bacteriology*, McGraw-Hill Book Company, Inc., 2nd ed., 1943.

Sarles, W. B., and others, *Microbiology*, Harper & Brothers, 1951.

Smith, K. M., *The Virus*, The Macmillan Company, 1940.

Swingle, D. B., and Walter, W. G., *General Bacteriology*, D. Van Nostrand Company, 1947.

Thompson, L. R., *Introduction to Microorganisms*, W. B. Saunders Company, 1944.

Vallery-Radot, R., *Life of Pasteur* (translated), Doubleday & Co., Inc., 1928.

Zinnser, H., and Bayne-Jones, S., *Textbook of Bacteriology*, Appleton-Century-Crofts, 1939.

Chapter XXI

THALLOPHYTES—ALGAE

Algae are thallophytes that have chlorophyll, and sometimes other pigments, which they use in the process of photosynthesis. Their cells are organized into nucleus, cytoplasm, and plastids; hence they represent an advance over the fission plants. Reproduction may take place by fission, but in addition many of them carry on asexual reproduction by spore formation and/or some form of sexual reproduction. The principal classes are:

1. CHLOROPHYCEAE (Gr. "green algae"), green algae.
2. BACILLARIOPHYCEAE (Gr. "rod-like algae"), diatoms.
3. PHAEOPHYCEAE (Gr. "brown algae"), brown algae.
4. RHODOPHYCEAE (Gr. "red algae"), red algae.

Although the names of 1, 3, and 4 refer to the prevailing colors and that of 2 to a common shape, the more significant differences are found in structure and life history.

GREEN ALGAE (CHLOROPHYCEAE)

Protococcus, a Unicellular Type. Protococcus, one of the most common algae, forms the familiar coat of green seen on the bark of trees and on unpainted buildings and fences. It is made up of microscopic spherical cells, some separate, others in clumps of two to a dozen or more (Fig. 280). The cell has a relatively thick wall of cellulose, a central nucleus, and a *chloroplast* that almost fills the cytoplasm. Since this plant, unlike most algae, is exposed to the air, and since it could not be waterproof and still be able to absorb water, it has the power of remaining alive but dormant when dry. It thrives best where water is longest retained, along with sufficient light for photosynthesis, as on the shaded side of tree trunks.

Protococcus reproduces asexually by fission. The nucleus divides by mitosis, whereupon a partition membrane and a wall form across the middle of the cell. The primary layer of the wall consists not of cellulose but of calcium pectate, which is soluble in water. After cell division this layer begins to dissolve and the cells gradually separate. Since conditions are often such that cell separation does not quite keep up with cell division, many of the cells occur in groups of two, four, or larger numbers. The new partition walls form in various directions; therefore these cell

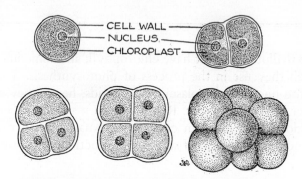

Fig. 280. *Protococcus viridis*, a simple green alga that is common on the bark of trees, showing detail of cell structure, division of cells, and the formation of aggregates as the result of such division. The single large chloroplast is usually cup-shaped. (Highly magnified.)

aggregates are clumps instead of filaments. This alga is thought to be a simplified descendant of some filamentous green alga.

Spirogyra, a Filamentous, Isogamous Type. Slimy masses of dark green thread-like algae are often found floating in lakes and sluggish streams. When handled, they slip through the fingers. They are the pond scums, of which there are several genera, the best known being *Spirogyra*, named for its spiral chloroplasts (Fig. 281). Its colony consists of an unattached, unbranched filament made up of cylindrical cells end to end. The cytoplasm is restricted to a layer against the wall, a layer around the centrally placed nucleus, and strands that connect these two layers and suspend the nucleus in its central covering of cytoplasm. Most of the cell volume is a large vacuole that contains sap. The most remarkable feature of the cell is the chloroplast, a wavy-edged spiral ribbon that winds about just beneath the wall from one end of the cell to the other. Some species have more than one such chloroplast in the cell. Equally spaced along the chloroplast are a number of globular protein bodies, the *pyrenoids* (Gr.

"kernel-like"), which function as centers for starch accumulation during active food manufacture. As the filament grows in length, the cells divide mitotically and new cross walls appear parallel to the old, as in *Oscillatoria*. Now and then new filaments are formed by the breaking up of old ones.

Thus far among plants we have observed only *asexual reproduction*, in which new cells come about through the division of old cells. *Spirogyra* has in addition a *sexual* process, which involves the union of cells to initiate the new individual. Usually this takes place by the development of projec-

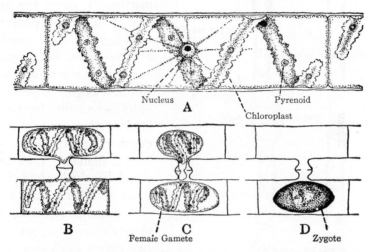

FIG. 281. The common pond scum (*Spirogyra*). *A*, Vegetative cell, showing its attachment to the adjoining cells. Note that the nucleus is suspended by cytoplasmic strands in the center of a large vacuole. *B*, *C*, *D*, Steps in conjugation. (Highly magnified, from Mottier, *Textbook of Botany;* copyright, Blakiston.)

tions on the proximal surfaces of cells in two neighboring parallel filaments, the fusion of these projections, the dissolution of the contact wall to form a conjugating tube, the flowing of one of the protoplasts through the tube, and its union with the other protoplast (Fig. 281, B, C, D). A wall forms around the fused cell, and there results a spherical or ovoid *zygote* (Gr. "yoked"), which has the power of growing a new filament. The bodies that enter into the sexual process are called *gametes* (Gr. "spouse"). In *Spirogyra* all the vegetative cells have the power to function as gametes. Since the two uniting cells are alike in shape, size, and appearance, the type of sexual reproduction is known as *isogamy* (Gr. "equal marriage"). This is the more primitive or ancient form of sexual reproduction. There is, however, a difference in behavior, for one of the gametes moves through the tube while the other remains in the cell that originally contained it. When conjugation involves a number of cells on the two filaments, as is usually the case, one of them contains all the zygotes, the other being left practically empty. There is evidently something in the nature of the cell which determines whether it shall be active (*male*) or receptive (*female*). The plant therefore represents *isogamy* with leanings toward *heterogamy* (Gr. "unequal marriage"). Since the nucleus of each of the two conjugating cells has the same number of chromosomes, the zygote has twice as many as are needed. But as it begins to grow, it divides meiotically, forming four haploid nuclei. Three of these degenerate; the fourth grows into a filament, each cell of which has the haploid chromosome number. The retained chromosomes represent a random selection from each of the two parent cells; therefore the new filament combines hereditary factors from both parents and is not exactly like either. The pond scums illustrate another phenomenon which is generally associated with sexual reproduction among the algae but not inseparably bound up with it. The zygote is protected against unfavorable conditions, and rests through the dry or the cold season; it does not grow until favorable conditions return.

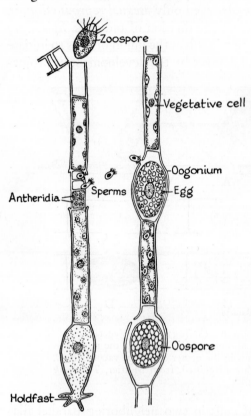

Fig. 282. Filaments of a dioecious species of *Oedogonium* (× 350). Left, male plant, producing sperms. Right, female plant, showing an egg approached by a sperm, and a thick-walled oospore or fertilized egg. Filaments of both sexes have holdfasts and may produce zoospores (as shown in plant at left).

Part of this power is probably due to the smaller water content, for obviously considerable water must be extracted before two protoplasts can occupy a smaller space than was originally occupied by one.

Some Heterogamous Types. *Oedogonium* (Fig. 282) is a filamentous alga which is generally found attached to submersed water plants. One cell at the end is modified into a holdfast for attaching the filament. Since the plant usually grows in moving water, the lack of an attachment would probably result in its being carried to a less favorable environment. In view of the slight division of labor among the cells, we might regard the filament of *Oedogonium* as near the border line between the colony and the multicellular individual. Asexual reproduction in this plant differs from that in the algae previously described. Some of the cells of the filament organize each a single *zoospore* (Gr. "animal spore"), which escapes from the cell, swims about by means of a crown of cilia, and eventually settles down to grow into a new filament. In its sexual reproduction there are two advances over *Spirogyra*. In the first place, whereas any vegetative cell of *Spirogyra* may become a gamete, this possibility is limited in *Oedogonium* to only a small number of the cells, and these cells undergo certain modifications to become sex organs. In the second place, the sexual cells of *Oedogonium* are differentiated into two sexes, distinguishable in size and appearance as well as in behavior; it represents a clear-cut case of *heterogamy*. At intervals in the filament a cell becomes bulged as its protoplast rounds up into a food-containing *egg;* this cell is an *oogonium*. Elsewhere on the same or another filament are small groups of disk-like cells, the *antheridia*, each of which contains two *sperms*. The sperms break out from the antheridium when mature and swim toward the egg by means of a crown of cilia. Apparently they are attracted by a chemical stimulus. Finally a sperm enters by way of a little pore in the wall of the oogonium and fuses with the egg. The resulting zygote may rest for a time, but ultimately it divides into four zoospores, each with half the chromosome number of the zygote; these zoospores grow into filaments. The differences in the gametes represent specialization in function; one is efficient in *food storage*, the other in *motility*.

Vaucheria (Fig. 283), the green felt plant, forms a harsh, felty mass of coarse green filaments in shallow water, on wet soil along the edges of the water, and on pots in the greenhouse. It differs from the other algae we have studied in the fact that the plant body is a *coenocyte;* i.e., there are no walls or membranes separating cell from cell. The nuclei, each of which really represents a cell, are scattered through the continuous protoplasmic mass. In this plant the reserve food takes the form of oil rather than of starch. Occasionally a wall forms across the filament near the end of a branch, and the contents of the end portion escape as a large zoospore covered with flagella. After swimming about for a time this body grows into a new filament. Sexually the plant is heterogamous, there being a hook-like antheridium which contains many motile sperms, and a knoblike oogonium with a single egg. *Vaucheria*, like a number of other green algae, varies in its reproductive behavior with changes in the environment. When there is plenty of water as a swimming medium for the zoospores, asexual reproduction prevails. When the habitat begins to dry, making a resting condition imperative, the sexual process occurs, resulting in the thick-walled zygote which carries the plant through to the next moist season.

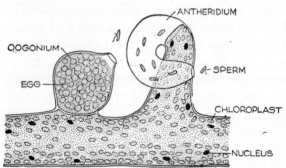

FIG. 283. *Vaucheria sessilis*, a coenocytic green alga (× 240); portion of a filament showing antheridium with escaping sperms, and oogonium, which has a perforated beak facilitating the entrance of the sperm.

General Considerations. The green algae are the most widespread and best known of the groups of algae. From the resemblance of their pigments to those of the higher plants and from the similarity of their motile reproductive bodies to the swimming sperms of mosses it seems probable that green algae were the ancestors of the higher groups of the plant kingdom. Among green algae there are a great variety of body forms, such as simple and branching filaments, flat plates, spheres, and nets; but all are alike in being fairly simple and, in most cases, restricted to water. The series of colonial forms, including *Sphaerella*, *Gonium*, *Pandorina*, *Pleodorina*, and *Volvox*, that were used to illustrate the transition from one-celled to many-celled organisms (Fig. 57) are often regarded as green algae. *Ulva*, the sea lettuce, is a leaf-like genus widespread along seashores.

DIATOMS (BACILLARIOPHYCEAE)

The student should have at least a passing acquaintance with algae that are as abundant as the diatoms are. They are found in both fresh and salt water, often as a brown sediment on larger plants or debris. They are usually unicellular, but sometimes form linear colonies. In the various genera the cells may be triangular, circular, boat-shaped, cigar-shaped, or fiddle-shaped. The cell has a central nucleus and usually two golden-brown longitudinal plastids. The cell wall is impregnated with silica and consists of two parts (*valves*) which fit together like a candy box and its overlapping lid (Fig. 284). During the process of fission two new valves are formed, each of which, with one of the old outer valves, forms the wall of each new cell. The surface of the wall is often delicately grooved.

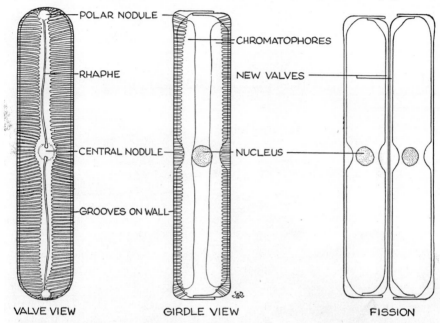

POLAR NODULE

CHROMATOPHORES

RHAPHE

NEW VALVES

CENTRAL NODULE

NUCLEUS

GROOVES ON WALL

VALVE VIEW   GIRDLE VIEW   FISSION

Fig. 284. A common fresh-water diatom (*Pinnularia*), shown from two points of view; also in the process of reproduction by fission ($\times$ 540). The chromatophores are golden brown.

Diatoms furnish food for PROTOZOA, which in turn are eaten by larger animals; hence they form an important starting point for the chain of food-demanding organisms that occupy both sea and fresh water. They are one of the most valuable foods for the oyster. On the death of the cells. their siliceous valves drop to the bottom and form deposits of diatomaceous earth that are sometimes hundreds of feet in thickness. This porous and finely gritty material is used as scouring powder, for filtering liquids, and for absorbing nitroglycerin in the making of dynamite.

BROWN ALGAE (PHAEOPHYCEAE)

The brown algae are multicellular, are limited almost entirely to sea water, and usually have more differentiation in structure than is found among the green. The pigment is located in plastids within the cells and consists of chlorophyll and a brown substance, *fucoxanthin* (Gr. "alga-yellow"), which partially or completely masks the green.

Rockweeds. Rockweeds are branching plants that are very abundant on rocks between high and low tide levels (Figs. 285, 286). *Fucus*, probably the best-known genus, has a flattened, dichotomously branched (fork-

Fig. 285. Marine algae on the rocky coast of New England, seen at low tide. The rocks are covered mainly with *Fucus*, the common rockweed. In the middle foreground may be noted *Laminaria*, a kelp (the long leaf-like form), and the red alga, *Chondrus*, Irish moss (the small dark form). (Photo of an exhibit; copyright, Chicago Natural History Museum.)

ing) thallus with paired *air bladders* (floats) and swollen reproductive tips. In these tips are flask-like depressions (*conceptacles*) in which are borne the reproductive organs. The sexes are usually on separate plants. The male conceptacle is crowded with much-branched filaments that bear on the tips of the branches the antheridia containing the biciliate sperms; the female conceptacle contains several oogonia, each of which produces eight eggs. The sperm and egg unite after their discharge from the conceptacle, the fertilized egg growing into a new plant. *Sargassum*, the gulfweed, is a rockweed that is abundant in the Gulf of Mexico; it is often torn loose from the rocks and floated by the Gulf Stream in masses to various parts of the ocean. Its thallus shows considerable differentiation into stem-like and leaf-like parts, and air bladders which superficially resemble small berries.

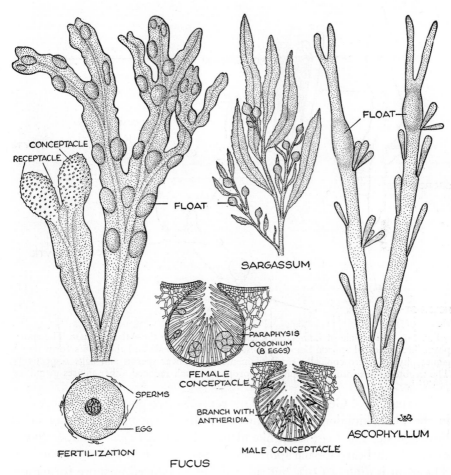

Fɪɢ. 286. Common rockweeds, representatives of the brown algae, growing attached to rocks, usually between low and high tide lines (about natural size). Reproductive details, shown here (magnified) for *Fucus*, are similar in *Ascophyllum* and *Sargassum*.

Kelps. Kelps are the larger brown algae. The plant usually consists of a holdfast, which clings to a rock, a more or less elongated stalk, and an entire or lobed blade. *Laminaria* (Fig. 287) is the most common genus along our Atlantic coast. It may reach a length of ten feet. Some of the kelps of the Pacific shoreline, notably *Macrocystis* with its blade divided into many strap-like parts, may grow as much as 200 feet long. Kelps are of economic value as fertilizers of the soil, as a source of potash and iodine, and for the production of medicines that utilize their rich mineral and vitamin content.

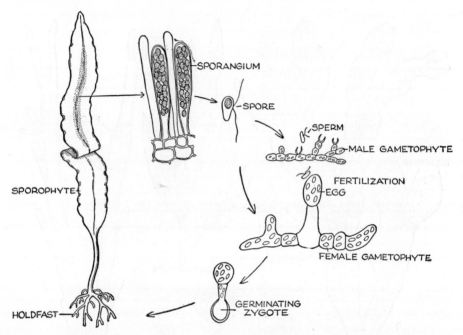

Fig. 287. Life cycle of *Laminaria,* a kelp common along the Atlantic coast. The sporophyte bears asexual spores. Some of these spores form male and the others form female gametophytes, microscopically small filaments which bear sperms and eggs respectively. The zygote grows into a sporophyte. Sporophyte much reduced, other figures magnified.

Alternation of Generations. This reproductive phenomenon prevalent in the plant kingdom is well illustrated by *Laminaria* and many other brown algae. The large strap-like plant is the *asexual generation,* or *sporophyte,* for it bears asexual *spores* in club-shaped *sporangia* on its surface. The plant is *diploid* (2*n*), but the number is reduced in spore formation; hence each spore has the *haploid* (*n*) number. Each spore is capable of growing into one or the other of two kinds of microscopic filamentous *sexual* plants—the male and female *gametophytes.* These are haploid plants bearing, respectively, *sperms* and *eggs.* The fertilized egg, or *zygote,* then grows into the sporophyte. There are two critical points in the life cycle— *fertilization,* which combines the chromosomes of the sperm with those of the egg and brings about the change from the haploid to the diploid condition, and *reduction division,* which restores the haploid number. All organisms that reproduce sexually have alternation in chromosome numbers, but in some algae, such as *Spirogyra* and *Oedogonium,* the real plant body is haploid, because the diploid stage occurs only in the zygote and undergoes immediate reduction when the zygote begins to grow.

RED ALGAE (RHODOPHYCEAE)

The red algae are usually filamentous, ribbon-like, or leaf-like in form and rather delicate in structure (Fig. 288). Associated with chlorophyll in their plastids, and often masking it, is a red or purple pigment, *phycoerythrin* (Gr. "alga-red"). If the plant has been torn from its moorings, the red pigment, being soluble in water, often washes out first, leaving the green pigment visible. The life history of these algae generally involves an alternation of generations similar to that in *Laminaria*. This complicated life history is of biological interest because it suggests what we shall find in the higher groups of the plant kingdom, including the mosses, the ferns, and the seed plants. But the brown and red algae themselves may be regarded as evolutionary blind alleys which lead to nothing higher.

Among the red algae are certain contributors to the world's food supply, such as Irish moss (*Chondrus*) and the sources of agar (*Gelidium* of Japanese coasts, and some other genera). Agar is a vegetable gelatin much used in food and medicine; it is also employed as a cultural medium for bacteria and other microorganisms.

EXERCISES

1. What is the relation of the algae to aquatic life in general? What is their significance as a primary source of human food?
2. Discuss the development of kelp utilization, especially along the west coast of the United States.
3. Heterogamy is more prevalent than isogamy today in the plant world. Give a probable reason.
4. Zoospores of algae swim toward the light rather than away from it. Explain.
5. Why are algae more abundant on a rocky coast than on a sandy one?
6. The large and coarse brown algae are more common in northern seas than in southern ones. Explain.
7. Seaweeds that grow between tide levels are often very gelatinous. Explain.
8. Why cannot algae be found more than a few hundred feet below the ocean surface?

REFERENCES

Prescott, G. W., *Algae of the Great Lakes Region*, Cranbrook Institute, 1951.
Smith, G. M., *Cryptogamic Botany*, McGraw-Hill Book Company, Inc., 1938. Vol. I.

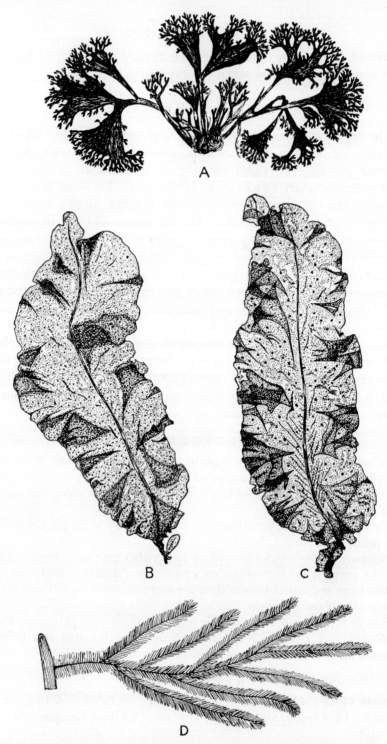

FIG. 288. Red algae. *A*, *Chondrus*, or Irish moss; *B*, *Grinnellia*, a leaf-like form, asexual plant; *C*, same, female plant; *D*, *Dasya* (reduced ⅓).

Smith, G. M., *The Fresh-water Algae of the United States*, McGraw-Hill Book Company, Inc., 2nd ed., 1950.

Taylor, W. R., *Marine Algae of the Northeastern Coast of North America*, Univ. of Michigan Press, 1937.

Tiffany, L. H., *Algae, the Grass of Many Waters*, Charles C. Thomas, Publisher, 1938.

Tilden, J. E., *Algae and Their Life Relationships*, Univ. of Minnesota Press, 1935.

Chapter XXII

THALLOPHYTES—FUNGI

The fungi, thallophytes with specialized cell structure but without chlorophyll, consist of thousands of species, constituting the following classes:

1. Myxomycetes (Gr. "slime fungi"), slime molds.
2. Phycomycetes (Gr. "alga fungi"), alga-like fungi.
3. Ascomycetes (Gr. "bladder fungi"), sac fungi.
4. Basidiomycetes (Gr. "little base fungi"), basidia fungi.

Fungi Imperfecti, a miscellaneous group of those not otherwise classified.

SLIME MOLDS

Though not well known except to the botanist, the slime molds are widespread, and are of interest because in their life cycle they go through a plant-like and an animal-like phase (Fig. 289). As the spore germinates, it liberates through its ruptured wall a naked bit of protoplasm. This soon elongates, develops a flagellum, and swims about like a flagellate. Soon it loses its flagellum and begins to crawl about and engulf food in an ameba-like fashion. Many of these ameboid bodies fuse together to form a naked mass of protoplasm with many nuclei. This is the *plasmodium;* after moving about on leaf mold, decaying wood, or grass, from which it engulfs particles of food, it becomes transformed into a large mass of spores (some genera), or into many stalked or stalkless *sporangia.* These vary greatly in form and color in the different genera. The spores are often supported by an intricate network of threads. By some these organisms have been regarded as animals and called Mycetozoa (Gr. "fungus animals"). This curious combination of plant and animal characteristics illustrates the lack of a sharp boundary between the two kingdoms.

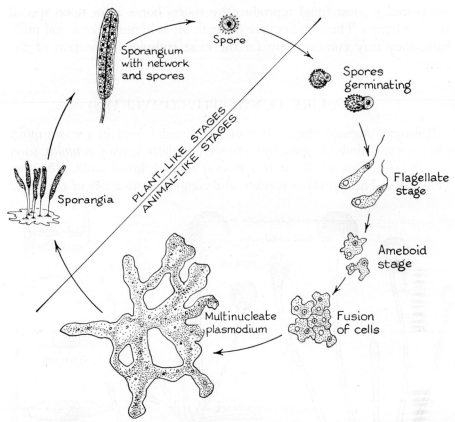

Fig. 289. Diagram of the life cycle of a slime mold, showing the animal-like nutritive stages and the plant-like reproductive stages.

TRUE FUNGI

In the remaining classes, the true fungi, the vegetative body is known as the *mycelium* (Gr. "mushroom"); it is a mass of branching filaments, each one of which is a *hypha* (Gr. "web"). The mycelium ramifies through the *substratum* (Lat. "strewed under"), which is the source of food for the fungus. From the standpoint of nutrition there are two types of fungi—*parasites*, in which the substratum is part of a living plant or animal, the *host*; and *saprophytes*, in which it is dead organic matter, such as an animal body, a decaying log, or humus-containing soil. A few fungi may live as either parasites or saprophytes. The hyphae of plant parasites may either spread over the surface of the host or force their way between its cells. They usually make their contact with the cells by thrusting through the cell walls absorbing structures called *haustoria* (Lat. "drinking places"). Most fungi reproduce by spores borne in or upon special fruiting bodies. These bodies may be small or, as in mushrooms and puff-balls, they may constitute by far the most conspicuous portion of the fungus.

ALGA-LIKE FUNGI (PHYCOMYCETES)

Rhizopus, Asexual Stage. If a slice of bread is kept in a warm moist place, several kinds of saprophytic fungi, popularly known as *molds*, soon appear on it. One of the more common is black bread mold, *Rhizopus* (Fig. 290). The mycelium spreads all through the substance of the bread

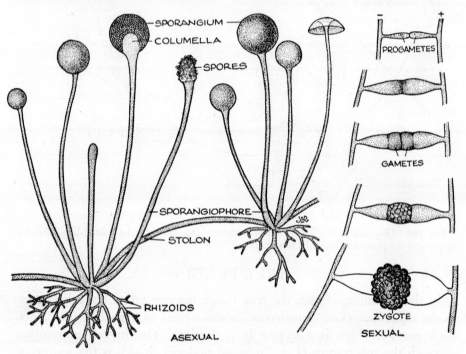

FIG. 290. The black bread mold (*Rhizopus nigricans*), showing vegetative and asexual structures at left, sexual structures at right.

and forms a white cottony coat over its surface. Changes in the odor and flavor of the bread are caused by metabolic products of the fungus. Special hyphae known as *sporangiophores* (Gr. "sporangia bearers") project, often in small clusters, from the main mycelium. *Rhizoids* anchor these clusters to the substratum, and *stolons* reach out to establish new clusters. On the tips of the sporangiophores are *sporangia* (Gr. "spore receptacles"), which begin as small white knobs and turn dark as the spores ripen. The hypha, as in all PHYCOMYCETES, is a coenocyte (without cross walls); but while the sporangium is developing, the spore-bearing portion is cut off from the stalk by a wall enclosing the dome-shaped *columella* (Lat. "little column"). Because of the aerial habitat, water cannot serve in spore dispersal as it does in many of the algae; air currents pick up the spores after the bursting of the sporangium wall. Those that chance to settle where moisture, food, and temperature are satisfactory germinate, forming hyphae.

Sexual Stage. The sexual stage of *Rhizopus* is comparatively rare; it occurs only when strains of two contrasting types of the mold, known as *plus* and *minus*, chance to be on the same substratum. Along the line where mycelia from the two strains meet, a club-like branch (*progamete*) from one comes in contact with a similar branch from the other. A *gamete* is cut off by a cross wall from the end of each branch, and the two gametes unite to form a *zygote* with a thick rough wall. This zygote later germinates to produce a short filament bearing one or more sporangia. Since the gametes are alike in structure though differing physiologically, this plant, like *Spirogyra*, illustrates isogamy with a tendency toward heterogamy.

White Rusts, Downy Mildews, and Wilts. Many PHYCOMYCETES are plant parasites, some of which cause great damage to cultivated plants. The *white rusts* (*Albugo*) can be recognized by white blister-like patches produced on the leaf or stem of the host by masses of developing sporangia; one common species attacks members of the Mustard family. After the sporangia separate from their stalks, their contents break up into several flagellate spores which use as their swimming medium the film of water that covers the host after a dew or rain. The *downy mildews* are so called because their large branching sporangiophores project from the diseased area to give a downy appearance. One destructive species attacks the grape. Near Bordeaux, France, it was discovered that a solution of copper sulfate and lime, which had been used as a spray to prevent theft of the fruit, was effective in preventing mildew on the grape vines. This solution, now known as *Bordeaux mixture*, is extensively used in the control of fungus diseases. It is most effective in killing the spores, or the young hyphae which develop from the spores to enter the leaf or stem by way of the stomata. After it enters the tissues, a fungus is not easily reached by sprays. Potato blight is one of the downy mildews. It attacks potato leaves and stems, blackening them and eventually killing the entire plant and greatly reducing the yield. Its ravages in Ireland in 1845 produced a severe famine which brought about an extensive migration of the Irish to

America. The best known of the *wilts* is that which causes damping off of seedlings. It can be checked by lowering atmospheric humidity, by baking the soil of the germination box, or by treating the seeds with germicides.

SAC FUNGI (ASCOMYCETES)

Cup Fungus and Morel. Cup fungi (*Peziza* and related genera) grow as saprophytes in decaying wood or leaf mold, and form exposed fruiting bodies resembling cups or saucers; these vary in size for the different species, and are often brightly colored (Fig. 291). The cup is lined on the inside by the *hymenium* (Gr. "membrane"), which is a compact layer of spore sacs (*asci*) interspersed with slender sterile filaments known as

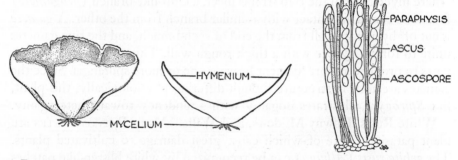

FIG. 291. A cup fungus (*Peziza vesiculosa*), natural size; same in cross section; portion of the hymenium (× 200) showing asci and paraphyses.

paraphyses (singular, *paraphysis*, Gr. "growth beside"). Each ascus contains eight spores in a row. It bursts when mature, probably aided by turgor pressure exerted by the paraphyses, and ejects the spores with sufficient force to facilitate their distribution by air currents. Closely allied is the well-known edible morel or "sponge mushroom" (*Morchella*, Fig. 292). The pits of the sponge-like head of its fruiting structure are covered with the hymenium in which develop asci with spores.

Yeasts, Structure and Reproduction. The yeast plant (*Saccharomyces*, or "sugar fungus") is a one-celled fungus so small that it may be regarded as one of the "microbes" and handled in the laboratory in much the same way as are bacteria. It is supposed to be a simplified descendant of a more typical ascomycete. The cell is ovoid and is provided with a nucleus (rendered visible by stains) and one or more vacuoles. Its usual mode of reproduction is asexual, by budding (Fig. 293). A bulge appears on the cell surface, gradually enlarges, receives one of the halves of the dividing nucleus, and ultimately breaks off as a separate cell. When separation does not quite keep up with division, short chains of cells appear. Yeast is regarded as a sac fungus because, under certain unusual environments, the cell divides internally and becomes an ascus with four or eight spores.

Fig. 292. Morel (*Morchella esculenta*), or "sponge mushroom," an edible ascomycete. (Photo by L. O. Overholts.)

Yeasts, Physiology. As has been noted (page 65), yeasts break down simple sugar, which forms a portion of their food, into carbon dioxide and alcohol. Since it does not involve free oxygen, this mode of energy release is *anaerobic respiration,* and is much less efficient than ordinary (aerobic) respiration. If oxygen is at hand, yeast may grow, in part, as an aerobe. Hence we call it a *facultative anaerobe,* in contrast with such organisms as tetanus bacteria, which are *obligate anaerobes* and cannot grow unless oxygen is practically absent. The chemical process of sugar disintegration, as carried on by yeast, is known as *alcoholic fermentation.* It is brought about through the agency of an enzyme, *zymase* (really a complex of enzymes), secreted by and retained in the yeast cell. If yeast cells are ground thoroughly with fine sand, the resulting liquid, containing the enzyme, has the power to ferment sugar in the absence of living cells.

Economic Aspects. Fermentation is a common process in nature, for yeasts of various types occur everywhere and are almost certain to attack

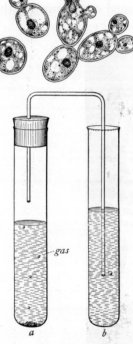

FIG. 293. Yeast plants (above), showing dark-stained nuclei, vacuoles, cell walls, and bud formation. Apparatus (below) to demonstrate carbon dioxide formation in fermentation. The gas arising from a culture of yeast in sugar solution (*a*) is conducted through lime water (*b*), to which it gives a milky precipitate, the test for CO_2. (Upper figure from Buchanan, *Elements of Biology;* copyright, Harper; lower, from Conn, *Bacteria Yeasts and Molds in the Home;* copyright, Ginn.)

any exposed liquid containing sugar. As agents in sugar destruction they take their part with bacteria in the decay portion of nature's cycle of change. *Alcohol*, one of the products of yeast activity, is an important commercial product. When prepared for beverage purposes, the quality varies not only with the material fermented but with the kind of yeast that is employed in the process. When the alcohol present in the liquid reaches about 15 percent, yeast activity stops, and it is necessary to resort to distillation to secure higher concentrations. In making bread, yeast is introduced for the production of carbon dioxide to render the bread porous. Generally, tested strains of cultivated yeast are utilized, but salt-rising bread depends upon wild yeasts. Before the days of yeast cultivation it was customary for the housewife to make use of *leaven*, a little unbaked dough held over from one baking to introduce yeast plants into the next batch of bread.

Green and Yellow Molds. *Penicillium* (Lat. "a small brush") and *Aspergillus* (Lat. for the brush used in the Catholic church for sprinkling holy water) are common saprophytic molds or mildews; the former is bluish green and the latter varies from yellowish green to dark brown. They are found on fruit, leather, and all sorts of plant and animal matter; they often cause much damage. The usual method of reproduction is asexual, by spores known as *conidia* (Gr. "dust"), which are pinched off successively from the tips of special hyphae known as *conidiophores* (Gr. "conidia-bearers"). The difference in the conidiophore structure of the two organisms is shown in Fig. 294. Asci are rarely formed by these molds. The widely publicized drug, *penicillin*, is produced from a species of *Penicillium* (page 361).

Powdery Mildews. The powdery mildews are sac fungi which are external parasites on a number of the higher plants, such as clover, rose, and willow. They may be illustrated by *Microsphaera alni,* common on lilac (Fig. 295). The mycelium, which is on the surface of the host, gives a white powdery appearance to the leaf or stem. It is connected with the epidermal cells by means of haustoria. The fungus is extensively distributed all summer by means of white conidia. Toward the close of the season, dark specks appear scattered over the white mycelium. Each of these is a closed *ascocarp* (Gr. "ascus fruit"), inside of which are several asci containing the usual ascospores. As in a number of ascus fungi, the ascusforming hypha of powdery mildew is the result of the sexual fusion of a plus and a minus nucleus which come together by the union of tips of filaments, somewhat as in *Rhizopus.* Powdery mildews can be kept in check by the use of Bordeaux mixture.

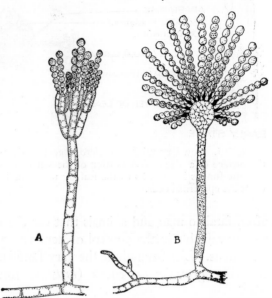

FIG. 294. Two ascomycete molds which are common on foods and other organic substances, showing fruiting stalks (conidiophores) bearing chains of asexual spores (conidia). *A, Penicillium,* a blue-green mold. *B, Aspergillus,* varying from yellow-green to black. Ascus formation is rare in these molds. (From Stanford, *Economic Plants;* copyright, D. Appleton-Century.)

Other Ascomycete Diseases. *The canker blight* of the chestnut was introduced into New York City in 1904, presumably on nursery stock from China. From this point it has spread throughout the chestnut area of the eastern states, almost exterminating one of our most valuable forest trees. Probably the best hope of a solution lies in finding a strain of the chestnut immune to the disease. The Dutch elm disease (so called because it was first investigated in Holland) was brought to our Atlantic ports about 1930 on elm logs imported from Europe and has since destroyed many American elms in the region surrounding New York City. Its carrier is an elm bark beetle. Other economic diseases in this group are *brown rot* of peaches and plums, which causes the fruit to decay and ultimately to shrivel on the trees; peach *leaf curl,* which distorts the leaves and causes their early fall; and *black knot* of plum and cherry, which produces knotty enlargements on the twigs. These diseases can be controlled by spraying at proper intervals. Another is *ergot,* which attacks rye and other grasses and causes a large, dry, mycelium-filled body to replace some of the grains on the head. Ergot is poisonous and

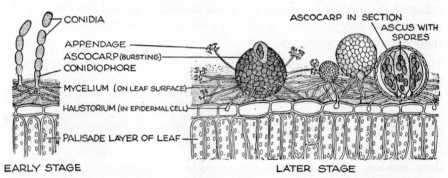

Fig. 295. Powdery mildew (*Microsphaera alni*), an ascus fungus, much enlarged, on the surface of a lilac leaf. A portion of the leaf is shown in cross section. It will be noted that the fungus is attached to the leaf by means of haustoria (absorbing organs) which enter the epidermal cells.

often fatal to man and animals that eat the diseased grains. It also yields a drug valuable in the control of hemorrhage.

Lichens. Lichens include the very familiar gray-green or yellow-green crust-like growths on rocks (*crustose forms*), the wrinkled leaf-like

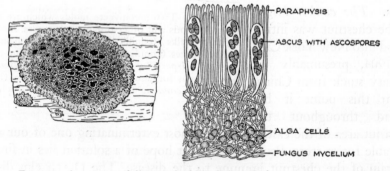

Fig. 296. A common foliose or leaf-like lichen. Left, on bark, natural size, showing ascocarps as dark spots; right, detail of section through ascocarp, highly magnified.

growths on the bark of trees (*foliose forms,* Fig. 296), and the stem-like growths on barren soil or hanging in tufts from the branches of trees (*fruticose forms,* some of which are popularly known as "reindeer moss" and "old-man's-beard"). A lichen is not a single plant but a combination of two species, a *fungus* and an *alga*, which live together in a mutually beneficial relationship, somewhat similar to that of the clover plant and its nodule bacteria. The fungus is generally an ascomycete and bears typical spore sacs in exposed, often saucer-like fruiting bodies. The alga, which is enmeshed among the fungus hyphae, is usually unicellular and belongs to either the blue-green or the green group. In many lichens it is *Protococcus*. The alga furnishes the fungus with part of the food which it has manufactured, and in turn benefits from the protection and water-retaining power possessed by the fungus. The two partners may therefore be considered as exchanging board for lodging. Cooperating thus, they have built up a highly successful combination, for lichens are found the world over at the very outposts of vegetation—bare rocks, infertile soil, the frozen polar regions, the practically plantless deserts—where they may be preparing the way for the entrance of other and higher types of plant life. Lichens reproduce vegetatively by the separation from the plant body of little tufts of fungus, each containing a few cells of the alga. Ascospores grow to form fungus filaments; but unless the proper algae are obtained, the fungus dies without becoming a lichen. Litmus, used as an indicator of acids and bases (page 41), and certain other dyes are obtained from lichens.

BASIDIA FUNGI (BASIDIOMYCETES)

Mushrooms. Basidia fungi are characterized by a reproductive structure strikingly different from the ascus. It is the *basidium* (Gr. "little base"), a club-like body bearing at its apex four slender stalks, *sterigmata* (singular *sterigma*, Gr. "support"), each of which pinches off a spore at its tip. One of the best-known subgroups is that of the *gill fungi*, popularly known as toadstools and mushrooms (Fig. 297). The mycelium permeates decaying organic matter and bears above the surface a rather large fruiting body, the *sporophore* (Gr. "spore-bearer"). Thus wind and insects are available for spore distribution. The sporophore consists of a stalk or *stipe* and an umbrella-like cap or *pileus* (Lat. "felt cap"). On the underside of the cap, radiating from center to margin, are many flat *gills*. Both sides of the gill are lined with the hymenium, consisting of many thousands of basidia, from which develop the spores. Some of the species have an *annulus* (Lat. "little ring"), a ring-like remnant of the *veil* that originally covered the gills; some have a cup, the *volva*, at the base of the stalk. Some species are valued as food, whereas others, such as members of the genus *Amanita* (Fig. 298), are dangerous. The edible ones are popularly called mushrooms, the poisonous ones toadstools. There is no sure rule for distinguishing the poisonous sorts; hence one should not eat any gill fungus unless he knows that the species is edible. An interesting result of the

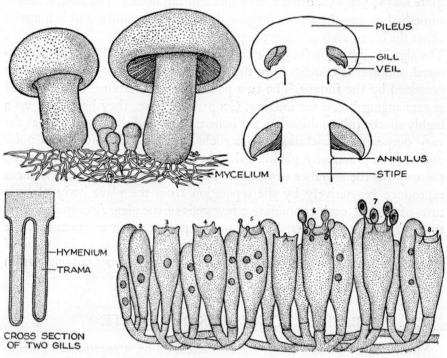

PILEUS

GILL
VEIL

MYCELIUM

ANNULUS
STIPE

HYMENIUM
TRAMA

CROSS SECTION
OF TWO GILLS

Fig. 297. The edible mushroom (*Agaricus campestris*). Upper left, mycelium and fruiting bodies in various stages; upper right, longitudinal sections of young and older fruiting bodies; lower left, low-power section of two gills; lower right, gill surface (hymenium), highly magnified. Note in the successively numbered basidia that two nuclei, regarded as male and female, fuse; the fusion nucleus undergoes two successive divisions; then the four resulting nuclei migrate into the spores which are pinched off the tip of the basidium. Further constriction results in the shedding of the spores.

growth of several types of mushrooms that live on the humus of grasslands is the formation of a "fairy ring" (Fig. 298). This is caused by the development of sporophores around the margin of an ever-widening circle of mycelium.

Bracket Fungi. Bracket fungi are saprophytes that live on dead timber and on the heartwood (nonliving tissue) of living trees. Spores may germinate on any portion of the heartwood that is left exposed, as by the breaking off of a limb in a windstorm. The fungus attacks the wood of the cell walls, which it softens and causes to crumble away altogether, leaving the tree hollow. The sporophores usually take the form of brackets on the surface of the trunk or limb (Fig. 299). Several families are represented in this habitat group, but the most common are the *pore fungi*, in which the sporophore is made up of many small parallel tubes **that open** by pores on its lower surface. The tubes are lined with the layer of basidia. These fungi cause great damage to timber and shade trees; tree surgery is

Fig. 298. Left, fruiting body of *Amanita verna*, a poisonous gill fungus. Note the annulus just below the cap, and the volva at base. Right, "fairy rings" of gill fungi, resulting from the extension of the mycelium in ever-widening circles. The circles shown here are two or three feet in diameter, but they range up to a hundred feet. Above, the field mushroom (*Agaricus campestris*); below, the inky cap (*Coprinus comatus*). The entire cap of the latter dissolves into a black inky mass when the spores are ripe. (*Amanita* photo, courtesy of E. B. Mains; fairy ring photos, courtesy of L. O. Overholts.)

largely directed toward repairing their ravages. Damage can be prevented to a large extent by painting or cementing diseased areas after cleaning out the infected tissue, and similarly treating wood exposed by pruning or by injuries to the bark.

Closed Basidia Fungi. Puffballs (Fig. 300) are familiar fungi; they bear their basidia on the surfaces of many small enclosed chambers. They burst when ripe, discharging the spores as a copious brown dust. The giant puffball is one of the most prolific of plants, producing millions of millions

Fig. 299. Pore fungi of the bracket type which cause great damage to timber by attacking the heartwood. Above, left, fruiting bodies of *Fomes applanatus* on a beech tree. Right, section of a fruiting body showing three years' growth of the tubes, which are lined with the microscopic basidia (not visible in photo). Below, left, wood of spruce affected with pocket rot as the result of *Fomes pini;* only heartwood is attacked, showing cottony tufts of cellulose which remain after the destruction of the lignin. Right, fruiting bodies of *Polyporus sulfureus*, the sulfur-colored pore fungus, growing in an old wound on an oak tree. (Photos, courtesy of L. O. Overholts.)

of spores. The *stinkhorn*, when its sporophore bursts, emits an odor exceedingly disagreeable to us but attractive to flies, which are important agents in spore dispersal.

Wheat Rust. The rusts and the smuts are important parasitic fungi belonging to the basidomycete group. They are sometimes called HEMI-BASIDIOMYCETES (Gr. "half-basidiomycetes") because their basidium differs from the typical kind described above; it is a filament several cells in length. The best known and probably the most troublesome of these fungi is *Puccinia graminis*, which causes black stem rust of wheat (Fig. 301). This rust has a complicated life history, including stages on two widely different host plants and a stage independent of a host; there are five different kinds of spores in the life cycle. The stages of wheat rust were once

Fig. 300. Some common basidia fungi with enclosed basidia. Above, left, *Calvatia gigantea*, the giant puffball, with a fruiting body a foot in diameter and containing approximately a million million spores. Right, *Lycoperdon gemmatum*, and below, left, *Lycoperdon pulcherrimum*, smaller puffballs. Right, *Dictyophora ravenelli*, the stinkhorn, a fungus that bursts its envelope and exposes a slimy mass of ill-scented spores which are dispersed by flies. (Photos, courtesy of L. O. Overholts.)

thought of as different fungi; the old names given to some of them are now used for spore types in the life history. While infected wheat is ripening, spores break through the epidermis of the stem or leaf sheath in dark vertical lines. These are *winter spores*, or *teliospores* (Gr. "end spores").[1] They are provided with a very thick wall which protects them

[1] *Teleutospore, sporidium, pycniospore, aecidiospore,* and *urediniospore* are alternative terms sometimes used instead of *teliospore, basidiospore, spermatium, aeciospore,* and *uredospore,* respectively.

through the winter, and they are really double spores, since the two cells germinate independently. In germinating, the hypha pushes its way through a thin place in the wall. The result is a four-celled filament, the *basidium*. Each cell has a sterigma, at the tip of which is pinched off a *basidiospore*. This minute spore is carried by the wind, and if it reaches a

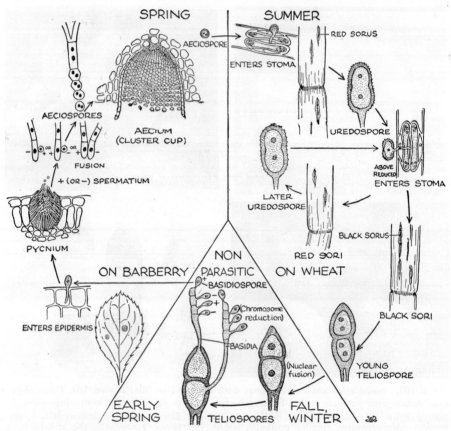

Fig. 301. Diagram of the life cycle of black stem rust of wheat (*Puccinia graminis*).

plant of the common (European) barberry (not to be confused with the Japanese barberry of cultivation) it germinates in the film of moisture on the leaf, its hypha penetrating the epidermis and ramifying among the leaf cells; this causes the leaf to be much swollen in the infected area. Flask-like *pycnia* appear, most commonly on the upper surface of the leaf, and bear, pinched off from small filaments, many minute bodies known as *spermatia*. These germinate on other barberry leaves, to which they may be carried by insects attracted by a nectar-like secretion of the pycnium. Commonly on the under surface of the leaf appear cluster cups or *aecia* (Gr. "injury"), in which are crowded together many chains of *aeciospores* cut off in succession from tips of spore-bearing filaments. These are carried by the wind to the wheat plant and germinate on the leaf, the hyphae entering by way of stomata. The presence of the parasite on the wheat is first evident when patches of spores of a rusty brown color, the *summer spores* or *uredospores*, appear through the bursting epidermis. These are scattered to other wheat plants, spreading the rust. Later in the season teliospores are mixed in among the uredospores, and still later the former appear in black patches by themselves. It will be noted that the mycelium in wheat produces both of these spore types, one earlier and the other later. In cool temperate climates it has been discovered that breaking the life cycle by eliminating the barberry puts an end to the rust; consequently the U.S. Department of Agriculture has for several decades been waging a relentless war against the barberry. In the southern part of our country, uredospores survive the winter and germinate the following spring on wheat; hence the removal of the barberry is less effective than in the north.

Until very recently the spermatia were thought to be degenerate or functionless sperm cells, but it is now known that they have a sexual function. Of the four basidiospores produced on a single basidium, two are *plus* (female) and two are *minus* (male.) The mycelium from a plus basidiospore produces plus spermatia; that from a minus basidiospore, minus spermatia. Aeciospores are not produced until there is a fusion of plus and minus cells. This fusion occurs when plus and minus mycelia happen to be close together within the leaf, or when a spermatium of one sexual type comes in contact with a mycelium of the opposite type. Cell fusion is not accompanied by nuclear fusion; therefore the cells of the aeciospore-bearing filament as well as the aeciospores themselves each contain two haploid nuclei. As the teliospore matures, the two nuclei in each of its two cells fuse and form a diploid nucleus, thus completing the sexual process. On the germination of the teliospore, reduction division takes place, thus restoring the haploid condition with the basidiospores.

The sexual process leads to the development of new strains of rust having new combinations of hereditary factors (Chapter XXVIII). One such strain spread through the wheat belt in 1950, attacking all commercial varieties of wheat. Elimination of the barberry would stop this development and enable the plant breeder to cope with existing strains by originating resistant varieties of wheat.

Other Rusts. A common rust on the red cedar produces brown knotty bodies known as cedar apples. In rainy spring weather these bodies protrude long gelatinous processes filled with teliospores. These spores pro-duce basidiospores which germinate on apple or hawthorn, producing aecia on the leaves and often damaging the fruit. Damage to the apple may be controlled by removing all red cedar trees from the vicinity of orchards. White pine forests of New England and adjoining areas have been seri-ously depleted by a blister rust, for which white pine is the host for the aecia and pycnia. Uredospores and teliospores form on various species of currant and gooseberry. Much effort has been directed by the forestry interests toward eradicating currant and gooseberry from white pine areas.

Smuts. The grains (such as corn, wheat, and oats) and some other plants are attacked by fungi allied to the rusts and known as smuts. Some portion of the plant, often the fruit, swells enormously, then becomes a powdery mass of spores. The greatly enlarged smutted grains on occa-sional ears of corn are familiar over most of the country. Affected tissues should be destroyed wherever found; and if infections are serious, crop rotation may be desirable. Smut of oats is controlled by treatment of the seed with formaldehyde or a copper salt. Chemical treatment is not effec-tive in loose smut of wheat because the spore has germinated on the stigma at flowering time and the mycelium has permeated the grain. Here the established procedure is to immerse the seed in water at 129°F. for ten minutes. This kills the mycelium but does not injure the wheat embryo.

FUNGI IMPERFECTI

In the two preceding classes, the ascus and the basidium are regarded as the perfect stages. As has been noted, many of the forms also reproduce by conidia (a so-called imperfect stage). This is the more common type of reproduction in *Penicillium* and *Aspergillus*, for example. There are some 25,000 fungi for which a perfect stage has not been found, and in many of these it probably does not occur. These are lumped together as FUNGI IMPERFECTI. Some will doubtless be found to belong to either the ASCO-MYCETES or the BASIDIOMYCETES. Among the imperfect fungi are several responsible for human disease, such as thrush, a disease of the mouth and throat; and ringworm, barber's itch, and athlete's foot, all of which affect the skin.

EXERCISES

1. Bread is usually wrapped in paraffin paper before it is marketed. State the advantages.
2. The fruiting body of a mushroom develops almost overnight. How do you account for this rapidity in development?

3. Why are fungus diseases of plants more prevalent in wet weather than in dry?

4. Which would probably cause greater injury to the host: a disease like rose mildew, which remains on the surface of the leaf, touching only the epidermal cells, or one like potato blight, which penetrates the entire host tissue?

5. Cite some instances of the control of plant disease by the development of resistant varieties.

6. When cider ferments in a stoppered jug, the cork is sometimes blown out. Explain.

7. Is wind or water the common agency for the distribution of reproductive bodies of the algae? Of the fungi? Explain.

8. Which are more important economically, algae or fungi? Why?

REFERENCES

Bessey, E. A., *Morphology and Taxonomy of Fungi*, The Blakiston Company, 1951.

Christensen, C. M., *The Molds and Man*, Univ. of Minnesota Press, 1951.

Crowder, W., "Marvels of the Mycetozoa," *Nat. Geog. Mag.* 49:421, 1926.

Fink, Bruce, *Lichen Flora of the United States*, Univ. of Michigan Press, 1935.

Heald, F. D., *Manual of Plant Diseases*, McGraw-Hill Book Company, Inc., 2nd ed., 1933.

Krieger, L. C. C., *The Mushroom Handbook*, The Macmillan Company, 1936.

Leach, J. G., *Insect Transmission of Plant Disease*, McGraw-Hill Book Company, Inc., 1940.

McKenny, Margaret, *Mushrooms of Field and Wood*, John Day Company, 1929.

Marshall, Nina L., *The Mushroom Book*, Doubleday & Co., Inc., 1929.

Smith, G. M., *Cryptogamic Botany*, McGraw-Hill Book Company, Inc., 1938, Vol. I.

Thomas, W. S., *Field Book of Gilled Mushrooms*, G. P. Putnam's Sons, 1928.

Wolf, F. A. and F. T., *The Fungi*, John Wiley & Sons, 2 vols., 1947.

Chapter XXIII

BRYOPHYTES—MOSSES AND LIVERWORTS

Pioneer Land Dwellers. Unlike the miscellaneous aggregation known as thallophytes, the BRYOPHYTA (Gr. "moss plants") constitute a relatively small group with considerable similarity among its members. Whereas most of the algae live in water, either permanently or during their period of activity, the bryophytes may be regarded as a group that has ventured out of water to make its home on land. A land environment usually necessitates a more complex plant structure than does a water environment. In the latter, the same cells can admit water, carbon dioxide, and sunlight, whereas on land certain cells beneath the surface must be differentiated for the absorption of water and minerals, and those above the surface, where light is available, must either be waterproofed to prevent drying, or be able to withstand drying without injury. The lack of a vascular system and the fact that they are dependent upon water for fertilization have kept these plants from becoming as successful as land dwellers as have the more prominent and abundant vascular plants.

The phylum is divided into mosses (MUSCI) and liverworts (HEPATICAE).

MOSSES (MUSCI)

Mosses are the better-known bryophytes. They differ from liverworts in that the leaves of the gametophyte are distributed around the stem (in a sort of radial symmetry), the rhizoids are several-celled, and the spore capsule generally opens by a lid. In using the term "moss" in its strict botanical sense we must exclude certain plants that are popularly called mosses, as, for example, "reindeer moss" (a lichen), "water moss" (often used for algae and aquatic seed plants), "club moss" (*Lycopodium*), and "Spanish moss" (*Tillandsia*, a seed plant of the Pineapple family). Mosses grow in a wide variety of habitats, such as water, bogs, forest soil, sand, rocks, and the bark of trees.

One of the larger mosses is *Polytrichum*, the hairy-cap moss (Fig. 302). The erect leafy stem may range from one to several inches in height. The thin leaves usually have a midrib, but neither they nor the stem have tubes

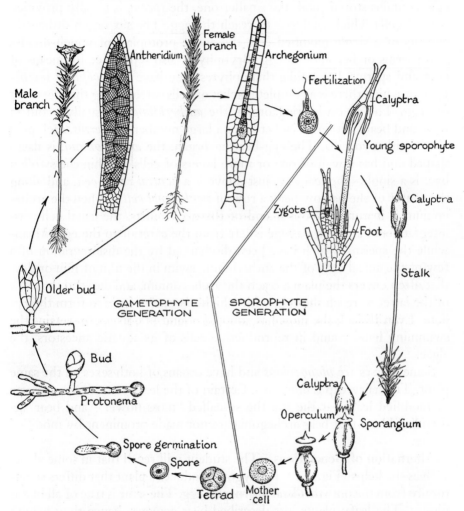

Fig. 302. Life cycle of the hairy-cap moss (*Polytrichum*). All cells of the gametophyte have *n* chromosomes, those of the sporophyte, 2*n*.

for conduction of food and water, the bryophytes being without a vascular system. Root-like filaments known as *rhizoids* anchor the plant to the soil.

Many-Celled Sex Organs. It will be remembered that among the algae and fungi are *isogamous* (Gr. "equal marriage") types, in which two

gametes, alike in shape and size, unite in the sexual process; and *heterogamous* (Gr. "unequal marriage") types, in which there is a marked difference in form, size, and behavior of the gametes. The larger gamete, the
egg, contains stored food; the smaller one, the *sperm*, is usually provided
with flagella which enable it to reach the egg. The sex organ ordinarily
consists of a single modified cell, the entire protoplast of which divides
into sperms or becomes an egg. Bryophytes also reproduce by means of
eggs and sperms, but unlike thallophytes they have *multicellular sex organs*, in which there is a complete jacket of cells surrounding the sperms or
the egg. The sperm-bearing organ, the *antheridium*, is usually ovoid in
form and bears within its jacket layer a large number of *sperms*, each provided with two cilia. The egg-bearing organ, the *archegonium*, is flask-
shaped and has a wall of one or more layers of cells. Within the swollen
base is a single spherical *egg*, just above it a *ventral canal cell*, and along
the center of the narrow neck a row of *neck canal cells*. When the archegonium is mature, the upper end of the neck bursts, the canal cells disintegrate, and an open passage is left from the exterior to the egg. Meanwhile the sperms, which have been discharged by the disintegration of a
few of the apical cells of the antheridium, swim in the film of rain or dew
that often covers the plants, reach the archegonium, and descend the neck
of the latter to reach the egg, with which one sperm fuses to form the zygote. Even though the moss has adopted a land life, its sperm retains the
swimming habit found in reproductive cells of its aquatic ancestors, the
algae.

Some mosses are *monoecious* and have organs of both sexes on the same
plant. The hairy-cap is *dioecious*. Certain of the leafy stems have a rosette
of modified leaves at the tip, the so-called "moss flower," and bear antheridia. Those that bear archegonia are not made prominent by modified
leaves.

Alternation of Generations.   The student will recall that in some algae,
such as the kelps (Fig. 287), the zygote produces a plant that differs structurally from the ones that bear sperm and egg. The same is true of all bryophytes. The leafy plants just described bear gametes; hence they belong
to the *gametophyte* or sexual generation. The zygote grows into a very
different plant, the *sporophyte* or asexual generation. The moss sporophyte (Fig. 303) has a pointed *foot* which joins it to the top of the leafy
gametophyte, a *stalk* which lifts the spores high enough to facilitate wind
dispersal, and a *capsule* which contains the *spores*. In the early stages of
sporophyte growth, the archegonium wall enlarges, but it is finally torn
away and carried as a cap, the *calyptra* (Gr. "head covering"), which

partly encloses the capsule. The hairy texture of the calyptra gives the name "hairy-cap" to this moss. When the spores are ripe, a lid, the *operculum* (Lat. "lid"), breaks away at the summit of the capsule. The tissue just beneath the lid then breaks into a fringe of teeth called the *peristome*

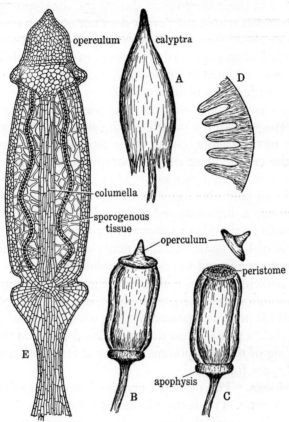

FIG. 303. Capsule of hairy-cap moss: *A,* with calyptra; *B,* with calyptra removed; *C,* with operculum removed, showing peristome; *D,* a few teeth of the peristome; *E,* longitudinal section of capsule, showing sporogenous tissue.

(Gr. "around the mouth"). In wet weather these teeth close the spore-containing part of the capsule; in dry weather, when conditions are favorable for spore dispersal by wind, they bend back and allow the spores to escape. When supplied with moisture and a favorable temperature, the moss spore germinates into a filament which branches freely and constitutes the beginning of the sexual generation. This filamentous growth, the *protonema* (Gr. "first thread"), resembles a green alga and suggests, on the principle of recapitulation, that algae may have been the ancestors of the mosses. The leafy sexual branches mentioned at the beginning of this paragraph develop from buds formed on the branches of the protonema.

Retention of Zygote and Embryo. As has just been observed, the zygote is retained in the archegonium during the development of the embryo. This retention within the parent does not occur in thallophytes but is found in both the higher groups—bryophytes and tracheophytes. This may be regarded as an additional adaptation to land life, because the developing zygote is retained in a moist environment during its early stages, when it would suffer from desiccation if exposed.

Changes in Chromosome Number. As was noted in the discussion of brown algae (page 374), the gametes each furnish the haploid number of chromosomes to the zygote, giving it the diploid number; this continues through all the cell divisions of the sporophyte generation until, at the time of spore formation, a meiotic division restores the haploid number. This is true in all plants having alternation of generations. In the young moss sporophyte, a barrel-shaped layer of cells which surrounds the central *columella* is set aside as a *sporogenous tissue*. After a series of divisions, the cells of this tissue become *spore mother cells*. The nucleus of each undergoes meiosis and forms four haploid nuclei. A cell wall forms around each nucleus, producing a *tetrad* or group of four spores. Since a spore has n chromosomes, the gametophyte into which it grows has n in each of its cells. It produces gametes with n, which, on uniting in fertilization, resume the $2n$ phase. Thus the two critical points in the life history are the doubling of the chromosome number at fertilization and its reduction to half at spore formation.

Kinds of Mosses. The principal orders of mosses are (1) *bog mosses* and (2) *true mosses*. The former belong to the genus *Sphagnum;* they bear numerous drooping leafy branches from a constantly elongating main stem (Fig. 304). The leaves are usually of a light green color because of the fact that between the chlorophyll-bearing cells are large empty cells provided with pores and capable of absorbing water like a sponge. This property renders the moss valuable for use in packing plants for shipment, for surgical dressings, and for other absorbent purposes. *Sphagnum* grows over large areas, mostly wet land or shallow water, particularly in the northern portions of America, Europe, and Asia, where it is the principal plant in the familiar acid bogs. As the stem continues growth, the lower part dies and gradually becomes transformed into peat. The formation of a mat by the moss over a water surface gives rise to quaking bogs.

The *true mosses* consist of two great groups—the *terminal fruited*, such as the hairy-cap, which are erect and bear the sporophyte at the summit of the leafy gametophyte; and the *lateral-fruited*, which are prostrate and bear the sporophyte on a short lateral branch of the gametophyte. The latter often cover the bases of forest trees, and persist on stumps and logs.

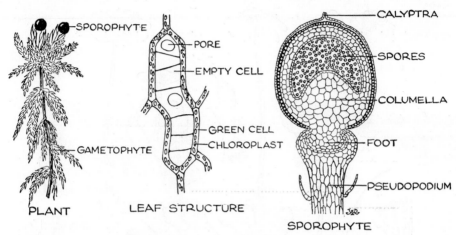

FIG. 304. The bog moss (*Sphagnum*), showing habit, leaf structure, and detail of sporophyte, the foot of which is embedded in the pseudopodium or upward extension of the gametophyte.

LIVERWORTS (HEPATICAE)

Liverworts have generally been regarded as more primitive than mosses, but there is now a tendency to question this hypothesis. In general they differ from mosses in (1) the dorsiventral structure of the gametophyte body, which is generally flattened against the substratum, (2) unicellular instead of multicellular rhizoids, (3) the reduced sporophyte, which is usually more fully dependent upon the gametophyte than in mosses, (4) the opening of the capsule by valves or irregularly rather than by a lid.

Some liverworts have leaves and resemble small prostrate mosses. Unlike most mosses, the leaves lie in two distinct lateral rows on the stem and are without midribs. In another group the gametophyte is a flattened, branching, ribbon-like body.

A familiar example of the latter group is *Marchantia* (Fig. 305). The gametophyte is dioecious, the male plant bearing stalked antheridial branches with antheridia sunken in pits in the disk-like upper surface. The corresponding structure of the female plant bears radiating arms which suggest the ribs of an umbrella. In a cushion beneath the bases of these arms are the archegonia, which in their structure are much like those of mosses. The sporophyte is small and hangs from the lower surface of the archegonial branch. In addition to the characteristic alternation of generations, *Marchantia* produces asexual reproductive buds, *gemmae*, which are

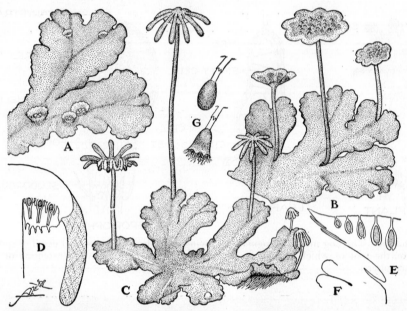

FIG. 305. *Marchantia polymorpha*, a common liverwort on moist soil. *A*, Part of thallus, bearing, in small cups, *gemmae* (buds for vegetative reproduction); *B*, male plant with antheridial branches; *C*, female plant with archegonial branches; *D*, portion of vertical section of archegonial branch, showing archegonia below; *E*, portion of vertical section of antheridial branch, showing antheridia sunken in pits; *F*, sperm; *G*, sporophytes which have developed from fertilized eggs and protrude from the lower surface of the archegonial branch (see *C*). The lower one has burst and is discharging the spores. (From Transeau, Sampson, and Tiffany, *Textbook of Botany;* copyright, Harper.)

borne in little cups on the upper surface of the gametophyte thallus. On being dispersed, these grow into new gametophytes.

SUMMARY

Bryophytes are intermediate between thallophytes and tracheophytes in structural complexity. They differ from the former in (1) differentiation of tissues adapting them to land life, (2) complex multicellular sex organs, (3) retention of the developing zygote within the mother plant. Alternation of generations, found in some algae and fungi, becomes well marked in the bryophytes. Unlike tracheophytes, they have no vascular systems, and the sporophyte has not become independent of the gametophyte nor has it developed roots or leaves. Apparently the mosses are remote descendants of the green algae. They may in turn have led to the vascular plants, but the evidence on this point is rather obscure. From the standpoint of human values, the mosses are builders of certain soils, such as muck. They have an important place in the economy of nature, for they often serve as pioneers on otherwise barren sand, on exposed rocks, and in shallow water, helping to prepare the way for a more stable and permanent vegetation.

EXERCISES

1. What algae or fungi can you recall to which the term "alternation of generations" may be appropriately applied?
2. What is the elater of a liverwort? What does it accomplish that may be of value to the plant?
3. Look up the life history of the horned liverwort (*Anthoceros*). What are its unique characters?
4. What plants usually precede the mosses in the occupation of barren rocks, sand hills, and tree trunks? (See Chapter XXII.)

REFERENCES

Conard, H. S., *How to Know the Mosses*, Wm. C. Brown Co., 1944.

Grout, A. J., *Mosses with a Hand-Lens*, published by the author, 3rd ed., 1924.

Marshall, Nina L., *Mosses and Lichens*, Doubleday & Co., Inc., 1914.

Smith, G. M., *Cryptogamic Botany*, McGraw-Hill Book Company, Inc., 1938, Vol. II.

See also the botany texts listed in the Appendix.

Chapter XXIV

VASCULAR PLANTS—CLUB MOSSES
AND HORSETAILS

Significance of a vascular system. The plants hitherto considered lack tubes for the transmission of water, minerals, and foods. Such transmission is not important in underwater plants such as the large kelps, but in non-vascular land plants size is restricted by the slow process of diffusion or osmosis from cell to cell. Mosses do not ordinarily grow to more than a few inches in height. In this and the three following chapters will be considered the TRACHEOPHYTA (from "trachea," a water vessel), or vascular plants. These plants have systems consisting either of greatly elongated cells or of tube-like structures which were originally rows of cells. These cells or tubes conduct water or food. Many of these plants reach tree-like proportions.

Their classification follows:

A. Subphylum LYCOPSIDA, club mosses.
B. Subphylum SPHENOPSIDA, horsetails.
C. Subphylum PTEROPSIDA, the prevailing or "modern" plants.
   1. Class FILICINAE, ferns.
   2. Class GYMNOSPERMAE, gymnosperms.
   3. Class ANGIOSPERMAE, angiosperms, or flowering plants.

The three subphyla represent divergent evolutionary lines. The first two reached their highest development in the latter part of the Paleozoic Era, more than 200,000,000 years ago, and are responsible for much of the coal formed at that time, but have since greatly declined in numbers and size. The club mosses (*Lycopodium, Selaginella*, and a few smaller genera) are the living representatives of the LYCOPSIDA; the horsetails or scouring rushes (*Equisetum*), of the SPHENOPSIDA. The PTEROPSIDA are the prevailing plants of today.

Types of Vascular Plant Tissues. Since these are the first plants with highly developed tissues, it is well to notice here the characteristics of the types of plant tissue. There are striking differences between plant tissues and those of the higher animals. The lack of movement and of the close coordination associated with the ability to move makes it unnecessary for the plant to have muscular and nervous tissues. The tissues essential to a

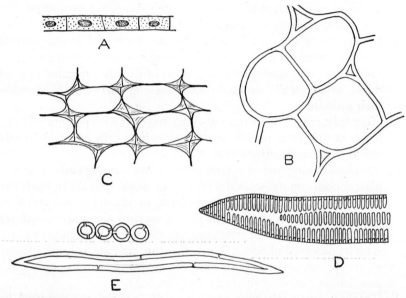

Fig. 306. Some cell modifications in plants. *A*, Cambium, a meristematic tissue; *B*, parenchyma cells, large with rather thin walls; *C*, collenchyma cells, walls thickened at the angles; *D*, portion of a scalariform (ladder-like) tracheid; *E*, cross and longitudinal views of fibers, a type of sclerenchyma. Cell contents are shown only in *A*.

plant are those (1) for the absorption of water and dissolved minerals, (2) for the manufacture and storage of foods, (3) for strength, (4) for conduction. Plant tissues may be classified as follows (Fig. 306):

I. *Meristems* (Gr. "divisible"): any tissues that are undergoing division and adding new cells to the plant. Such regions of cell addition are generally more localized in the plant than in the animal. A meristem cell is small and thin-walled, and has a nucleus that takes up a considerable part of its bulk. Meristems include:

    A. *Terminal meristems:* near the tips of roots and stems, including undeveloped leaves that are situated near the tips of the stems.

    B. *Cambium* (Lat. "exchange"): dividing tissue that brings about increase in diameter of roots and stems (found in conifers and in dicots).

II. *Parenchyma:* tissues made up of thin-walled cells which are about as broad as they are long. Special types of parenchyma are:

    A. *Epidermis:* mainly for <u>absorption</u> in underground parts, and for <u>protection</u> in parts above ground.

    B. *Cork:* in older plants supplanting the epidermis as a <u>protective</u> tissue.

    C. *Storage tissue:* such as <u>pith</u> and pith (<u>medullary</u>) rays.

    D. *Chlorenchyma:* green, carbohydrate-manufacturing tissue, mostly in leaves, to some extent in stems; in leaves, also called *mesophyll.*

III. *Prosenchyma:* made up of elongated cells.

    A. *Collenchyma:* cells thickened at the angles; useful in strengthening growing parts, since it is capable of elongation as the stem grows.

    B. *Fiber tissue* (*sclerenchyma*): consisting of greatly elongated cells with thick, woody walls; useful in <u>strengthening parts</u> that have attained their growth.

    C. *Sieve tubes:* made up of rows of elongated cells with perforated (sieve) plates in the walls, usually at the ends where cells adjoin each other; useful in <u>carrying manufactured foods.</u>

    D. *Tracheids:* elongated cells with pointed, overlapping ends. The protoplast deposits on the walls thickenings of wood (lignin) in the form of spirals, rings, or ladder-like structures, or involving the entire wall with the exception of pits. The protoplast then dies and the cells serve the twofold purpose of <u>strengthening the stem and conducting water with its dissolved minerals.</u> These elements are especially prominent in all groups below the angiosperm level. Pine wood, for example, is composed almost entirely of tracheids (Fig. 322).

    E. *Tracheae, or vessels:* rows of lifeless cells in which the end walls have dissolved, leaving continuous tubes. The woody side walls are variously thickened, as in tracheids (Fig. 337). The characteristic water-conducting elements of angiosperms.

Further discussion of these tissues and their characteristic arrangement in the groups concerned will be given in the following chapters.

CLUB MOSSES (LYCOPSIDA)

During the late Paleozoic this class was represented by large trees, mostly of the genera *Lepidodendron* and *Sigillaria,* the strap-like leaves of which left distinct scars on the trunk (Fig. 399). Its present members, however, are small, branching, scaly-leaved plants, of which the best-known genera are *Lycopodium,* the club moss or ground pine extensively used for Christmas greens, and *Selaginella,* the little club moss. The <u>spores</u> of these plants are in <u>sporangia</u> borne singly at the axils of the leaves. <u>Spore bearing leaves,</u> *sporophylls,* are usually somewhat differentiated

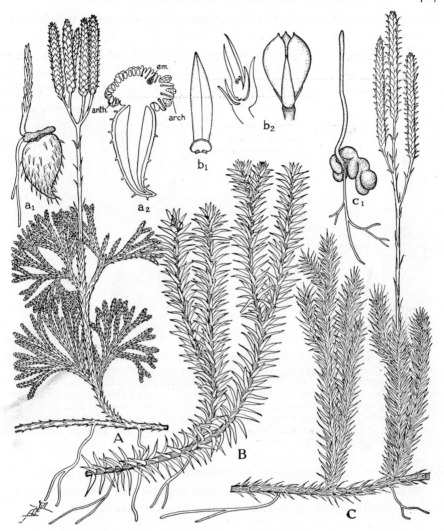

Fig. 307. *Lycopodium*, the club moss or ground pine. *A, L. complanatum; a₁,* gametophyte with young sporophyte attached; *a₂,* section of gametophyte containing young embryo (after Bruchmann). *B, L. lucidulum,* a species without distinct cone; *b₁,* the sporophyll, resembling a foliage leaf but slightly smaller, with sporangium at the base; *b₂,* reproductive buds, sectional and surface view. *C, L. clavatum; c₁,* gametophyte with young sporophyte attached. (From Transeau, Sampson and Tiffany, *Textbook of Botany;* copyright, Harper.)

from foliage leaves and grouped together into cones. Each of them bears a single *sporangium* in its axil. In *Lycopodium* the spores are all alike and grow into tuberous gametophytes, all of which usually bear both antheridia and archegonia (Fig. 307). In *Selaginella,* however, an advance evolutionary step has been taken in the differentiation of spores, which are of two distinct kinds that differ markedly in size (Fig. 308). The small ones, called *microspores*, grow into *male gametophytes;* the larger, known as *megaspores*, produce *female gametophytes*. This habit of producing two distinct kinds of spores is known as *heterospory* (Gr. "different spores").

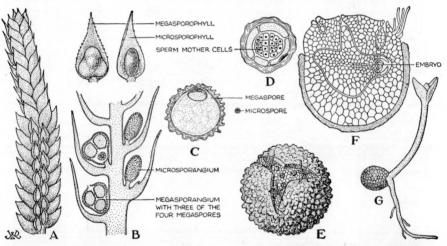

MEGASPOROPHYLL
MICROSPOROPHYLL
SPERM MOTHER CELLS
D
EMBRYO
MEGASPORE
MICROSPORE
F
C
MICROSPORANGIUM
MEGASPORANGIUM WITH THREE OF THE FOUR MEGASPORES
G
A   B   E

Fig. 308. *Selaginella*, the little club moss. *A*, Leafy branch with cone at tip (× 5); *B*, enlarged longitudinal section of a portion of the cone; *C*, megaspore and microspore, showing comparative size; *D*, developing male gametophyte within microspore wall; *E*, female gametophyte bursting through megaspore wall, showing rhizoids and necks of archegonia; *F*, section of female gametophyte, showing archegonium at left, very young embryo at right, and more advanced embryo at center; *G*, embryo with root and shoot protruding from megaspore wall. (From Transeau, Sampson, and Tiffany, *Textbook of Botany;* copyright, Harper.)

We shall see that heterospory is developed independently in some of the ferns (Subphylum Pteropsida), and that it persists in the gymnosperms and angiosperms, making possible the structure known as a seed.

HORSETAILS (SPHENOPSIDA)

During the coal age there existed a widespread group of branching plants with circles or whorls of leaves on their jointed ridged stems. They are placed in the group Sphenopsida (Gr. "wedge appearance," because some of the members had wedge-shaped leaves). Their only living descendants are the horsetails, all of which belong to the genus *Equisetum*. The various species grow in marshes, in shaded woodlands, or on barren soil such as railway ballast. The conspicuous generation, the sporophyte, consists of a horizontal underground stem with simple or branched upright stalks. The leaves are reduced to collar-like whorls of scales, the green stems taking over the process of photosynthesis. Because of the rough coats of silica on their stems, these plants were formerly used for polishing kitchen vessels, which has given them the popular name of scouring rushes. Vascular bundles, consisting of phloem and xylem, are rather poorly developed, but the stem has conspicuous air spaces.

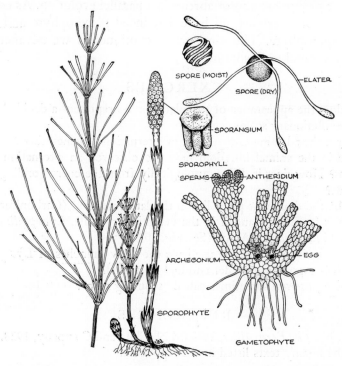

Fig. 309.   The field horsetail (*Equisetum arvense*); sporophyte reduced one-half, and gametophyte much enlarged. The sketch of the sporophyte includes a fertile and two young sterile shoots. An older sterile shoot is shown detached at left.

At the apex of the stem (in some species, of specialized reproductive stems only, Fig. 309) is borne a cone made up of hexagonal shield-like sporangium-bearing plates. Projecting inward from the edges of the hexagon are several sac-like *sporangia*. The globular spores are wound about by two spiral bands, the *elaters* (Lat. "jumpers"). These bands are uncoiled when dry, but coil tightly around the spore when slightly moistened. These hygroscopic movements may aid in the distribution of the spores. When it falls in a suitable place, the spore germinates to form an almost microscopic gametophyte shaped like an irregularly branching ribbon. On this are found antheridia containing sperms, or archegonia containing eggs, or both. The sperm is provided with a tuft of cilia which enables it to swim to the egg. The fertilized egg (zygote) grows into the conspicuous sporophyte.

The relative size and complexity of gametophyte and sporophyte generations are approximately the same in horsetail, club moss, and fern; hence these groups are almost abreast in a parallel evolution. As compared with a moss or liverwort, all have a reduced gametophyte and a large, complex sporophyte. The same trend continues as we advance to the gymnosperms and angiosperms.

EXERCISES

1. Why does the appearance of vascular bundles represent a decided advance in the evolutionary scale?
2. What are the advantages to a plant of alternation of generations?
3. Where in the animal kingdom have we observed an alternation of generations? How does it differ cytologically from the corresponding process in plants?
4. Describe the dominant plant life in the late Paleozoic (Carboniferous).
5. Which is further advanced in the evolutionary scale, *Lycopodium clavatum* or *L. lucidulum?* Why? (See Fig. 307.)
6. What extensive commercial use have the leafy branches of *Lycopodium?* What is lycopodium powder and how is it used?
7. Why is *Equisetum* sometimes called "scouring rush"?

REFERENCES

Clute, W. N., *The Fern Allies*, Willard N. Clute and Company, 1928.
See also the botany texts listed in the Appendix.

Chapter XXV

VASCULAR PLANTS—FERNS

The subphylum PTEROPSIDA (Gr. "feather-like," since many ferns have feathery leaves) is by far the largest subdivision of vascular plants, and the one that has attained the highest development. It includes the ferns, the gymnosperms, and the angiosperms. The oldest class is FILICINAE (from Lat. for "fern").

The familiar fern plant is the sporophyte generation. In the better-known members, it consists of a horizontal underground stem, the rhizome, from which arise roots and leaves. The latter, also called fronds, are strikingly larger and more complex than those of club mosses and horsetails, and are often pinnately compound (divided into parts called leaflets, with a feather-like arrangement, Fig. 310), although they may be simple (Fig. 313), or more than once compound.

Stem Structure. We have noted that vascular plants are characterized by the possession of conducting tissues. The arrangement of these varies considerably in the different ferns, but a common type is found in the bracken (*Pteridium aquilinum*), a familiar large fern of our woodlands. The chestnut brown rhizome of this fern runs for many feet underground, and has a prominent ridge on each side. A cross section (Fig. 311) reveals the following tissues: (1) *epidermis,* consisting of small cells whose walls are considerably thickened; (2) *outer sclerenchyma,* or *fiber sheath,* a layer of dark, thick-walled cells, several cells thick, which give rigidity to the rhizome; (3) *parenchyma,* or large, thin-walled food-containing cells which make up the major portion of the central area; (4) *inner sclerenchyma,* or *fiber bundles,* two large, elongated groups of cells similar to those of the fiber sheath; (5) *vascular bundles,* circular or oval groups of rather large cells serving mainly for conduction. Each bundle consists of a central mass of *xylem* completely surrounded by *phloem*, outside of which are two layers of parenchyma called, respectively, *pericycle* and *endodermis.* The xylem carries water and dissolved minerals from the roots to the leaves, and the phloem distributes over the plant the food manufactured by the leaves. The xylem is made up mainly of *ladder tracheids*, elongated empty cells with pointed ends and ladder-like thickenings in the woody walls. The phloem consists chiefly of *sieve tubes*, which are

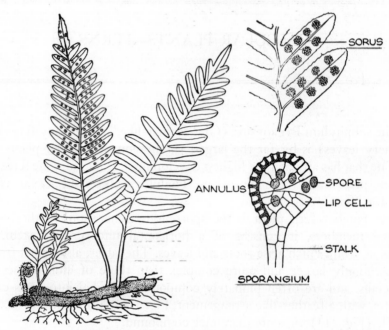

SORUS

ANNULUS

SPORE

LIP CELL

STALK

SPORANGIUM

Fig. 310. Polypody fern (*Polypodium virginianum*), a common species on shaded rock cliffs and sand banks. Left, entire plant, about natural size, showing underground rootstock, and leaves which unroll in developing. Right, above, enlarged detail of the pinnately compound leaf, showing sori, which are bunches of sporangia; the indusium is absent in this species. Below, a single sporangium beginning to rupture by the straightening of the annulus.

longitudinal rows of thin-walled cells with sieve plates in the side walls. No cambium layer, such as is found in the cone-bearing trees and many of the flowering plants, occurs in the fern stem. There is therefore no increase in the thickness of the stem after the cells have attained full size; further growth takes place entirely at the tip.

Leaf Structure. As fern leaves develop, they unroll from base to tip, a habit rare among seed plants. In cellular structure (Fig. 312) they resemble the leaves of flowering plants (Fig. 346); they consist of *upper epidermis, palisade cells, vascular bundles* or *veins, spongy tissue,* and *lower epidermis* perforated with *stomata.* The walking fern (Fig. 313) has a long, tail-like tip to the leaf which it uses in vegetative reproduction. On striking the ground, this tip takes root and develops a new plant.

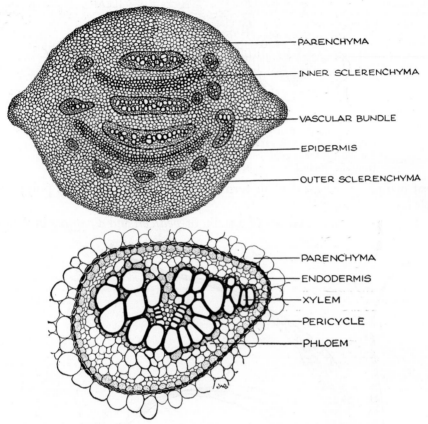

Fig. 311. Cross section of the rhizome of bracken fern (*Pteridium*) above; enlarged view of a single vascular bundle below.

Spore Formation. The leafy fern plant, as we have noted, is the sporophyte; it produces spores in sporangia which grow on the under surface of the leaf. In some ferns, all the leaves function as spore-bearing organs; in others, only certain leaves or certain parts of leaves assume this role. Such leaves, known as *sporophylls*, may closely resemble or be strikingly different from the leaves whose only function is to manufacture food. The sporangia may cover the entire lower leaf surface, but more frequently they are grouped into bunches called *sori* (singular, *sorus*, Gr. "heap," Figs. 312, 314). The sorus is often covered by a membrane called the *indusium* (Lat. "undergarment"). This is shield-shaped in the shield fern, an elongated flap in the chain fern, and merely an inturned portion of the

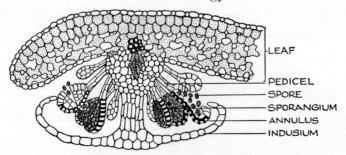

LEAF
PEDICEL
SPORE
SPORANGIUM
ANNULUS
INDUSIUM

Fig. 312. Section of leaf and sorus of a shield-fern (*Dryopteris*), showing location of the latter on one of the smaller veins. Sporangia are shown in various stages of development; some are being opened by the straightening of the annulus. The name is derived from the shield-like form of the indusium.

leaf margin in the maidenhair fern and *Pteris* (Fig. 314). The polypody has no indusium.

Each sporangium consists of a stalk, or *pedicel*, and a *capsule* in which

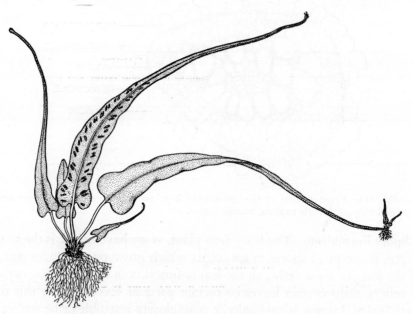

Fig. 313. Walking fern (*Camptosorus rhizophyllus*), showing the sori on the under surface of the simple (undivided) leaf, and the habit of vegetative reproduction by rooting at the leaf tip.

spores are developed. This capsule is a flattened, somewhat oval sac. Around one edge is a single row of cells that form the *annulus* (Lat. "little ring"). The inner and radial walls of these cells are thickened; the outer walls are thin. The annulus varies in different families of ferns. In most of our native ferns it is only a partial ring, extending rather more than half-way around the edge of the capsule (Figs. 310, 312). The remainder of the edge consists, as do the sides, of thin-walled cells, two of which, rather larger than the others, are called *lip cells*. When the capsule is mature, the evaporation of water from the cells of the annulus, and the consequent shortening of their thin outer walls, result in a tendency to straighten the annulus. This bursts the capsule between the lip cells. Then the annulus snaps forward again, throwing the spores for a considerable distance. The

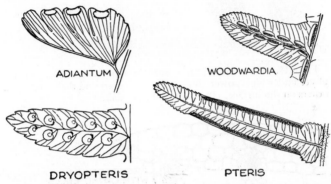

Fig. 314. Types of sori and indusia in various ferns. The indusium consists of the inturned portions of the leaf margin in *Adiantum* (maidenhair fern) and *Pteris;* it is shield-like in *Dryopteris* (shield fern) and flap-like in *Woodwardia* (chain fern).

spores are formed in groups of four from a spore mother cell, which undergoes reduction division in the process. They are provided with an inner membrane and a roughened outer wall, and are so small and light that they are carried long distances by the wind.

The Gametophyte Generation. Fern spores may live for a considerable time in the dry condition. When moisture and temperature are favorable the spore germinates, pushing out the inner membrane in the form of a tube which develops into a green filament. The terminal cell of the filament then begins to divide in such a way that it grows into a thin flat thallus with an apical notch. This thallus, which is about ¼ inch across and is easily overlooked, is the gametophyte plant (Fig. 317); it is often called the *prothallus* because it precedes the sporophyte, or commonly recognized fern plant. *Rhizoids* grow out from its base and under surface; they anchor it to the soil and absorb water, as do the very similar root hairs found in the sporophyte generation of most vascular plants. Except in the somewhat thickened central portion, the prothallus is one layer of cells in

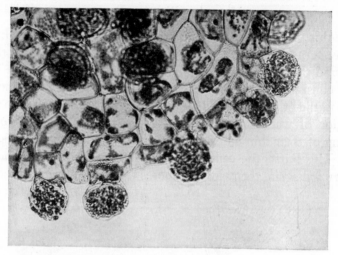

FIG. 315. Fern antheridia, as seen in a portion of the gametophyte under high power. Several are shown around the margin and others on the surface. (Photo by E. B. Wittlake.)

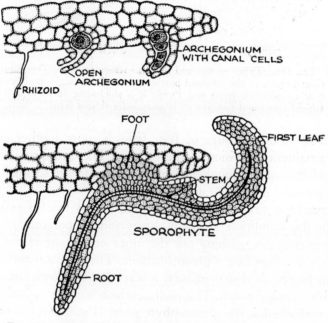

FIG. 316. Above, longitudinal section of the apical portion of a fern gametophyte, showing the archegonium before and after disintegration of the canal cells. The former contains egg, ventral canal cell, and two neck canal cells. The latter contains only the egg. Below, a young sporophyte developing from the fertilized egg. In this early stage it is absorbing food from the gametophyte by means of the foot.

thickness. In the notch is the *apical cell*, which is the origin of all new cells contributing to the growth of the thallus.

Sex Organs.   Ferns, like mosses, have two kinds of sex organs: the *archegonium*, which bears the *egg*; and the *antheridium*, which bears *sperms*. Both sex organs arise from single superficial cells on the under side of the

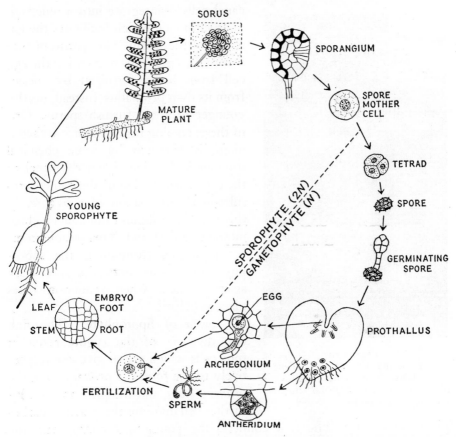

Fɪɢ. 317.   Life cycle of a fern (*Polypodium*).

prothallus, the archegonia appearing near the free edge just back of the notch, and the antheridia developing at the base, mostly among the rhizoids. The *antheridium* (Fig. 315) is a simple, dome-shaped structure that consists of a thin, transparent jacket of three cells, within which, by repeated divisions of a central cell, a large number of sperms are produced. The sperms are released by the bursting of the jacket. Each consists of a spirally coiled body, at one end of which are attached many long flagella;

by means of these they swim in the film of water often present where the prothalli grow, and perchance reach archegonia.

The *archegonium* (Fig. 316) is a flask-shaped organ with its base embedded in the thallus, and its projecting neck curved by the unequal growth of the *neck cells*. The base contains the single spherical *egg* and a *ventral canal cell*; the neck, two *neck canal cells*. As the egg matures the canal cells disintegrate into a mucilaginous substance which facilitates the entrance of the sperm. The sperms mature before the eggs, thus preventing the egg cell from being fertilized by sperms from its own prothallus. Instead, nearby younger prothalli furnish sperms. One of these, coming near a mature archegonium, is attracted by some chemical stimulus and swims down the canal to the egg, where union of the gametes results in the formation of a *zygote*. In this union the diploid number of chromosomes is restored. This double number continues throughout the sporophyte generation until the spores are again formed, when reduction takes place as before.

Fig. 318. Tree ferns (*Alsophila glauca*) in the Taiping Hills, Federated Malay States. (From Smith, *et al.*, *Textbook of General Botany;* copyright, Macmillan.)

Growth of Sporophyte. The first two divisions of the zygote result in four cells which are to give rise respectively to the *foot*, the *primary root*, the *primary stem*, and the *primary leaf*. By further cell divisions these structures begin to take form. The foot connects the young sporophyte with the gametophyte and absorbs food and water for the former until it is able to live independently, after which the gametophyte dies and disintegrates.

Comparison with Bryophytes. Alternation of generations in the fern is similar to that in the moss. There is, however, one important difference. In the moss the gametophyte is the dominant, food-manufacturing generation upon which the sporophyte depends for existence; in the fern the sporophyte has become dominant and has well-developed roots, stems, and leaves, the gametophyte being only a simple and inconspicuous plant. Although simple, this gametophyte can manufacture sufficient food for its own needs and for the young sporophyte which is parasitic upon it until enough developed to live independently (Fig. 317).

Other Ferns. Ferns are most abundant in moist tropical regions, the home of the *tree ferns* (Fig. 318), the delicate *filmy ferns*, and several other families. In temperate America the *sensitive fern* and *cinnamon fern* are of special interest in that they show a striking differentiation between

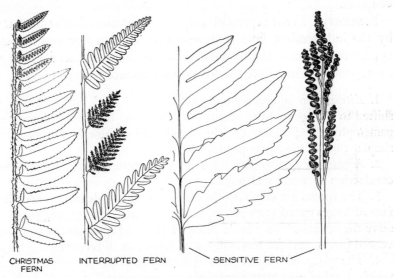

CHRISTMAS FERN   INTERRUPTED FERN   SENSITIVE FERN

Fig. 319. Portions of fern fronds, showing tendency toward the differentiation of spore-bearing leaves (sporophylls) from foliage leaves. In the Christmas fern (*Polystichum acrostichoides*), the upper leaflets of the fronds are decidedly smaller and bear the sori; in the interrupted fern (*Osmunda claytoniana*), some of the middle leaf divisions are highly modified into spore-bearing structures; and in the sensitive fern (*Onoclea sensibilis*), entire leaves serve as sporophylls. In the two latter, the leaf is divided into small globular spore-bearing leaflets wrapped around the sporangia.

foliage leaves and *sporophylls* (spore-bearing leaves). The foliage leaves of both these ferns are wide-spreading; the leaflets of the sporophylls are compactly rolled about the sporangia and soon lose their chlorophyll (Fig. 319). In the *interrupted fern*, only the middle divisions of some of the pinnate leaves are modified for spore production; hence the name, for the green leaflets are interrupted in this middle region.

Water Ferns and Heterospory. The water ferns, which include *Marsilea*, a rooted form with a leaf suggesting a four-leaf clover, and some smaller floating forms, have proceeded a step in advance of the other ferns by developing heterospory, which was mentioned in the last chapter as a characteristic of *Selaginella*. The large megaspore grows into a female gametophyte, the small microspore into a male. As in *Selaginella*, the megaspore contains food, which is largely retained through the gametophyte generation and gives the following sporophyte generation a rapid start. Thus the way is paved for the appearance of the seed, which is the characteristic structure in the two classes discussed in the following chapters.

Summary. Ferns represent a stage in evolution similar to that attained by the independent lines represented by club mosses and horsetails, but appear to be more closely related to the dominant seed plants than are those groups. They have the following characteristics:

1. *Alternation of generations*, as in bryophytes, but with the emphasis shifted to the sporophyte generation. This soon becomes independent of the gametophyte and attains a fairly complex development. The gametophyte is simpler than in most bryophytes.

2. A *vascular system*, lacking in the bryophytes, serves in the ferns for the conduction of water and food.

3. The spores are contained in *sporangia*, which develop on the lower surface of leaves called *sporophylls*. In the majority of ferns, the leaves (fronds) serve the common function of foliage leaves and sporophylls; in the more advanced forms, parts of leaves or entire leaves are differentiated as sporophylls.

4. The spores of some (the water ferns) are differentiated into *microspores*, which develop into *male gametophytes*, and *megaspores*, which develop into *female gametophytes*. This introduces *heterospory*, a differentiation found in all gymnosperms and angiosperms.

EXERCISES

1. To what generation in mosses does the leafy fern plant correspond? To what does the prothallus correspond?
2. In what respects does the leaf of a fern differ from that of a horsetail or club moss? The sporangium?
3. Of what use to a fern is the indusium?
4. Would the trunk of a tree fern be suitable for lumber? Explain.
5. What is the advantage to certain ferns in having separate leaves or leaf parts for photosynthesis and for spore production?

REFERENCES

American Fern Journal, quarterly publication of American Fern Society.
Clute, W. N., *The Fern Allies*, Willard N. Clute and Company, 1928.
Comstock, A. B., *How to Know the Ferns*, Comstock Pub. Co., Inc., 1918.
Durand, H., *Field Book of Common Ferns*, G. P. Putnam's Sons, 1928.

Eames, A. J., *Morphology of Vascular Plants, Lower Groups*, McGraw-Hill Book Company, Inc., 1936.

Roberts, E. A., and Lawrence, J. R., *American Ferns*, The Macmillan Company, 1935.

Smith, G. M., *Cryptogamic Botany*, McGraw-Hill Book Company, Inc., 1938, Vol. II.

Wherry, E. T., *Guide to Eastern Ferns*, The Science Press Printing Company, 1937.

See also botany texts listed in the Appendix.

Chapter XXVI

VASCULAR PLANTS—GYMNOSPERMS

Seed Plants. Descended, apparently, from some of the early ferns are plants which, instead of disseminating their spores as do the ferns, retain them on the parent sporophyte pending the growth of the gametophyte and the formation of a somewhat complex structure, the *seed*. This structure consists of (1) the *embryo*, or young sporophyte; (2) the *endosperm*, or food reserve; (3) the protecting *coat* (two in angiosperms). Being thus partly developed and provided with food, the new plant (sporophyte) can establish itself more quickly and surely. With this advantage, seed-bearing plants have become the dominant members of the plant kingdom. Moreover, the storage of food in seeds has proved to be of immense value to the higher animals and man, for seeds make up the major portion of their food.

Gymnosperms and Angiosperms. These are the seed-bearing classes of PTEROPSIDA. GYMNOSPERMAE (Gr. "naked seeds") consist of only about 500 living species, but they have a long fossil record and are evidently the ancestors of the ANGIOSPERMAE, which are the leading plants of today and include some 200,000 species. The ovules (undeveloped seeds) of a gymnosperm are exposed on the surface of a modified leaf (the sporophyll); those of an angiosperm are enclosed in a modified leaf which might be regarded as wrapped around the seeds, like a bean pod (Fig. 320).

The Pine Tree. Like the fern plant, the pine tree, with its roots, trunk, branches, and needles, is the sporophyte generation. The gametophyte is far simpler than that of the fern; it is microscopic in size. A pine tree may live for hundreds of years. Its main axis grows more vigorously than its branches, and thus a conical form is maintained. The needles grow in clusters of five (white pine), three, or two (most of our common species). This cluster is really a little branch which is limited in its growth; it is known as a *short shoot*. It grows in the axil of a hard and woody scale-like leaf; around its base, just below the attachment of the needles, there is a sheath of several thin leaves which may be considered the *bud scales* of the short shoot. At the tip of the pine branch is a *terminal bud*, and near it are several *lateral buds*. Both are winter buds and are protected by many over-lapping brown scales. Circles of scars at intervals on the stem show where the terminal buds of previous winters were located, and lateral branches indicate the positions of former lateral buds. Hence, in most species, a whorl of branches represents each year of the age of the pine tree. If trees are crowded together in a forest, however, the lower branches tend to disappear.

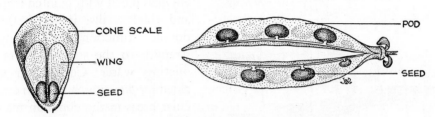

FIG. 320. A gymnosperm and an angiosperm compared. Left, cone scale (sporophyll) of pine, showing two naked seeds. Right, pod (ripened carpel or sporophyll) of bean, with several seeds attached alternately to the two edges of the modified leaf. When ripe, the pod splits along both the midrib and the united margins of the leaf.

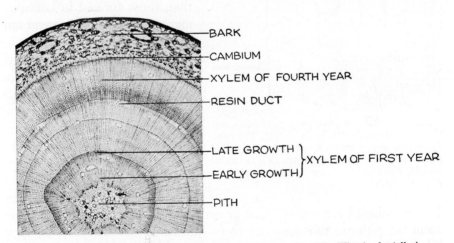

FIG. 321. Cross section of a four-year-old pine stem (× 25). The bark (all tissue outside of the cambium) consists of phloem, cortex, and epidermis, and includes large resin ducts. (Photomicrograph, copyright, General Biological Supply House, Inc., Chicago.)

Stem Structure. The stem of the pine is made up of three general regions: *bark, wood,* and *pith* (Fig. 321). Between the bark and the wood is a layer of actively dividing cells, the *cambium layer*, the function of which is to add new tissue to the bark and wood by continuous division of its cells. The bark consists of the single-layered *epidermis*, which disappears as the stem grows older; the *cortex*, made up principally of thin-walled cells; and the *phloem* (Gr. "bark"), composed (except its oldest portion) of the bark cells produced by the cambium and serving mainly for the conduction of manufactured foods. The woody part of the stem, or *xylem* (Gr. "wood"), lies just inside the cambium and is made up of *tracheids*. A

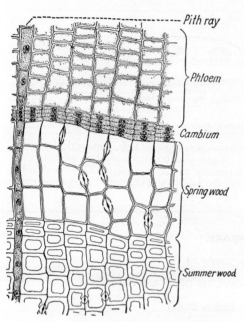

Fig. 322. Stem of pine, portion of cross section ($\times$ 500) made during the spring. The cambium, later in the summer, will add thick-walled tracheids to this season's growth. (From Chamberlain, *Elements of Plant Science;* copyright, McGraw-Hill.)

tracheid is an empty, much elongated cell with pointed ends and thick walls; it serves the double function of giving strength to the stem and conducting water. Conduction is aided by *pits*, which are thin circular areas in the common wall of two adjoining cells. The tracheids formed in the spring are large in diameter and are especially adapted for water conduction; those formed in late summer are smaller in diameter and thicker-walled, and are especially adapted to giving strength to the stem (Fig. 322). The spring and late-summer tracheids together constitute the *ring of annual growth*, which is clearly distinguished from the ring denoting the growth of the preceding and following years; hence the age of a tree may be determined by counting these growth rings. Radiating in all directions from the pith are thin strips of tissue known as *medullary (pith) rays*. Their cells are elongated radially, and serve for the radial conduction of water and foods. Throughout both bark and wood is a network of *resin ducts* which contain the resin that oozes so copiously from a broken pine twig. This resin is said to protect the tree against destructive insects and organisms of decay.

Leaf Structure. The foliage leaf or needle of the pine is retained on the tree for several years. Since it must remain unharmed during the winter, when water absorption by the roots nearly or quite ceases, it is almost as thick as it is broad, and is well waterproofed by a thick, waxy, outer epidermal wall (Fig. 323). As an added protection, the stomata are sunk in pits. Underneath the epidermis is the *sclerenchyma*, consisting of one or more rows of thick-walled supporting cells, beneath which is a rather compact chlorophyll-bearing tissue. In the center is a vein, or *vascular cylinder*, which contains two *vascular bundles*.

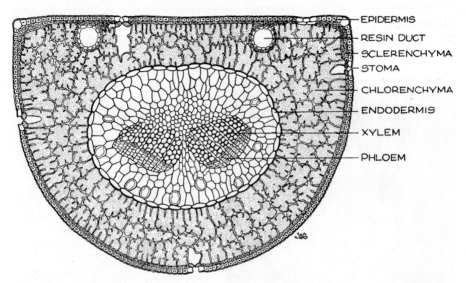

EPIDERMIS
RESIN DUCT
SCLERENCHYMA
STOMA
CHLORENCHYMA
ENDODERMIS
XYLEM
PHLOEM

FIG. 323. Cross section of leaf (needle) of pine showing types of cells and adaptation to dry conditions ($\times$ 80).

Reproductive Structures. It will be recalled that the spores of a club moss or fern are borne in *sporangia*, which grow on leaves, and that in some they are restricted to specialized leaves known as *sporophylls*. Pine also has sporophylls; they are grouped into structures called *cones*, or *strobili* (Lat. "pine cones"). Like *Selaginella* and the water ferns, pine is heterosporous; i.e., it has two kinds of spores. They form in different sporangia on different sporophylls which are grouped into separate cones. The cone is the counterpart of the flower of an angiosperm. Because flower parts were named and these names were extended to gymnosperms before their analogies to structures in the lower vascular plants was understood, we have the following synonymy of terms:

Microsporophyll cone	Staminate (male) cone (flower in angiosperms)
Microsporophyll ("leaf bearing small spores")	Stamen
Microsporangium ("sac containing small spores")	Pollen sac

Microspore	Pollen grain
Male gametophyte	Pollen tube (with two sperm nuclei)
Megasporophyll cone	Carpellate (female) cone (flower in angiosperms)
Megasporophyll	Carpel
Megasporangium	Nucellus of ovule (part within the coat)
Megaspore	Embryo sac
Female gametophyte	Mature embryo sac with one or more eggs

FIG. 324. Cluster of staminate cones of red pine (*Pinus resinosa*). Needles are in bundles of two. Those of last year are below the cones, and the developing ones of the present season are above. (Photo, courtesy of E. B. Mains.)

Staminate Cones. Clusters of staminate cones appear at the bases of the new shoots in the spring (Fig. 324). Each of their closely crowded sporophylls has two sporangia bulging from the lower surface. The pollen grains are very abundant and appear as clouds of yellow dust when mature cones are shaken. These grains are microspores that grow into male gametophytes. To achieve their function they must be carried by the wind to the ovules on the carpellate cones. Their buoyancy in air is increased by two hollow air sacs on each grain. We shall discuss later their growth into gametophytes.

Carpellate Cones. The carpellate cone appears singly or in groups of two or three at the tip of the new growth of the season. Since two years are needed for the full development of the seeds, cones of three ages may be present on a branch at any one time (Fig. 325). Each scale (megasporophyll) of the young cone has two ovules on its upper surface. Each of these is covered by a *coat*, through which a small opening, the *micropyle*, is directed toward the base of the sporophyll. Within the coat is a tissue called the *nucellus* (or megasporangium); near the center of it a *megaspore mother cell* forms and divides meiotically into a row of four megaspores. Only one of these is functional. Gymnosperms, unlike *Selaginella* and water ferns, retain the megaspore on the parent sporophyte while it grows into the female gametophyte, a structure which we may regard as parasitic upon the sporophyte. Wind-borne pollen drifts into the micropyle and lodges in the *pollen chamber*, a small cavity between coat and nucellus.

FIG. 325. A branch of Austrian pine (*Pinus laricio*) in late spring. At the tip of the leafy shoot of the present season are two carpellate cones ready for pollination; at the tip of last year's growth are two year-old ones at about the stage in which fertilization of the egg occurs; near the base is the two-year-old cone, with ripe seeds. A cluster of staminate cones may be seen on the branch at the right. (From Transeau, Sampson, and Tiffany, *Textbook of Botany;* copyright, Harper.)

Growth of Gametophytes (Note life cycle diagram, Fig. 326). Pine requires two growing seasons between pollination and the ripening of the seed; it differs in this respect from most gymnosperms. By the end of the first year the pollen grain has undergone several cell divisions and has begun to elongate into a structure known as the *pollen tube*, or *male gametophyte*, a thread of protoplasm which penetrates the nucellus, absorbing from its tissue. Meanwhile the functional megaspore has enlarged at the expense of the surrounding cells, and has undergone free nuclear division. Early in the second season the nuclei are separated by developing cell walls, and the structure becomes a *female gametophyte*. At the end nearest the micropyle are several *archegonia* which resemble those of a moss or

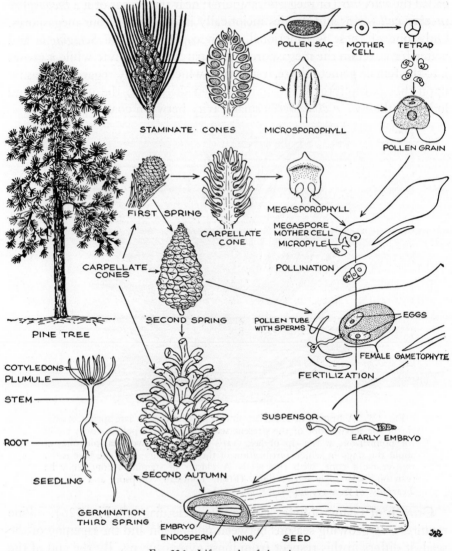

STAMINATE CONES

MICROSPOROPHYLL

POLLEN SAC

MOTHER CELL

TETRAD

POLLEN GRAIN

FIRST SPRING

CARPELLATE CONE

MEGASPOROPHYLL

MEGASPORE MOTHER CELL

MICROPYLE

POLLINATION

CARPELLATE CONES

SECOND SPRING

POLLEN TUBE WITH SPERMS

EGGS

FEMALE GAMETOPHYTE

PINE TREE

FERTILIZATION

COTYLEDONS
PLUMULE

STEM

SUSPENSOR

ROOT

EARLY EMBRYO

SEEDLING

SECOND AUTUMN

GERMINATION THIRD SPRING

EMBRYO
ENDOSPERM WING SEED

FIG. 326. Life cycle of the pine.

fern; however, they are simpler, in keeping with the reduced size of the whole gametophyte. The *neck*, which is very small, consists of about eight cells. There are no neck canal cells and the *ventral canal cell* is represented by a disintegrating nucleus. The *egg cell* is large. By the time the egg is mature, one of the pollen tubes has grown down, bringing a *sperm nucleus* (of which there are two) so near the egg nucleus that sperm and egg fuse (*fertilization*). In the pine, therefore, the sperm and egg are brought together by a growth process rather than by the swimming process retained in the mosses and ferns from their old aquatic ancestry. Thus the plant kingdom developed a more effective mechanism for survival under drier conditions and made it possible for the land to be covered with vegetation. It is interesting to note that although some of the more ancient gymnosperm types, such as *Ginkgo* and the cycads (described later), have pollen tubes like all other gymnosperms, they still retain cilia on the sperms. They may be considered transitional, in this respect, between ferns and pines.

Growth of Embryo. After fertilization, the egg cell undergoes a series of divisions and forms an elongated *suspensor* and an *embryo* proper. The suspensor pushes the embryo into the center of the gametophyte, from which it obtains its nourishment. The gametophyte tissue is known as the *endosperm* (Gr. "within seed"). At the close of the season, both the embryo and the surrounding structures stop growing and the *seed* is mature. At some later time, usually the following spring, the cone scales, or sporophylls, which are now hard and woody, spread their tips and the seed drops off, carrying with it a portion of the surface of the scale in the form of a *wing* which facilitates wind dispersal. If the seed falls in a favorable place, it germinates and the young sporophyte develops into a pine tree.

Parts of Seed. A pine seed is made up as follows:

I. *Embryo*, or *young sporophyte*, developed from fertilized egg, and consisting of:
   A. *Cotyledons*, or *seed leaves*, several in a whorl.
   B. *Hypocotyl* (Gr. "below cotyledons"), which grows into the root and the lower portion of the stem.
   C. *Epicotyl* (Gr. "above cotyledons"), which grows into the trunk and branches of the tree (also called *plumule*).
II. *Endosperm*, or *female gametophyte*, which has become a mass of food-containing cells surrounding the embryo.
III. Remains of *nucellus*, a thin layer surrounding the endosperm.
IV. *Seed coat*, for protection, developed from the coat of the ovule, hence like the nucellus a part of the old sporophyte.

It is interesting to note that the seed is a very complicated structure that includes portions of three successive generations.

Classification. Aside from three extinct orders that lived in the Paleozoic era, there are four orders of gymnosperms with living representatives; all are woody plants.

1. CYCADALES (*cycads*, Fig. 327), a group widespread in the Mesozoic era (age of reptiles). They now grow in widely scattered tropical and subtropical

FIG. 327. A cycad (*Dioon edule*) at Chavarrillo, Mexico. Staminate plant on left with small dried cones; carpellate on right with large seed-bearing cone. Plants about 7 feet high. (Photo, courtesy of C. J. Chamberlain.)

FIG. 328. A famous bald cypress (*Taxodium mucronatum*) at Tule near Oaxaca, Mexico. It has a diameter of 50 feet, and its age is variously estimated at from 2000 to 6000 years. (Photo by Don Glassman; courtesy of the New York Botanical Garden, and of Transeau, Sampson, and Tiffany.)

areas; in temperate regions they may be seen in conservatories. They have a palm-like aspect, with large pinnately compound leaves growing in a rosette at the top of a cylindrical trunk, which is generally marked by the bases or scars of former leaves. They have apparently evolved from the "seed ferns," one of the extinct orders of gymnosperms which bears a marked resemblance to the ferns. The cycads and ginkgoes have ciliated sperms, a fern-like character wanting in the two more advanced orders.

Fig. 329. *Welwitschia mirabilis* (Order Gnetales), a remarkable gymnosperm of the southwest African deserts. Cones are developing along the edge of the disk which forms the upper surface of the obconical trunk. The two large leaves, which are the only leaves the plant ever has with the exception of the two cotyledons, grow continually at the base; the older portions break into strap-like woody segments that sprawl on the ground for a radius of several feet from the trunk. (Photo, copyright, Chicago Natural History Museum.)

2. Ginkgoales, another ancient order which has only one surviving species, the *maidenhair tree* (*Ginkgo biloba*). This tree, which probably represents the oldest tree genus now living, is native to the hills of western China, but is fairly common in cultivation in our country. Its broad fan-like leaves somewhat resemble the leaflets of the maidenhair fern and are deciduous (Fig. 345). Its survival in more recent times may have been aided by the protection given it by the Buddhist monks, who regard it as sacred.

3. Coniferales (*conifers*) to which belong all of our better-known gymnosperms. They are narrow-leaved trees, most of them evergreens, such as *pine, spruce, fir, hemlock, arbor vitae,* and *juniper. Tamarack* and *bald cypress,* also in this order, are deciduous. The order includes the largest trees in the world. The *sequoias* of the Pacific states and the *Douglas fir* are the tallest and bulkiest,

one of the latter in British Columbia being reported as 417 feet high. The *bald cypress* at Tule, Mexico, is probably the largest in trunk diameter (Fig. 328). Conifers are said to supply three-fourths of the wood used for structural purposes.

4. GNETALES includes a small number of shrubby forms which in some respects resemble angiosperms. Among them are *Ephedra*, which furnishes the drug ephedrine, and the curious southwest African *Welwitschia* (Fig. 329).

SUMMARY OF GYMNOSPERMS

1. The gymnosperms undergo alternation of generations, as do the bryophytes and the more primitive vascular plants.

2. The sporophyte is a conspicuous, independent plant, usually a tree. The gametophyte is a microscopic nongreen plant concealed within and parasitic upon the sporophyte.

3. The sporangia occur on modified leaves, or sporophylls (as in some less advanced vascular plants). They are of two sorts, which contain megaspores and microspores respectively. In nearly all species they are grouped into cones of two sorts.

4. The sperm is brought to the egg by a growth process (pollen tube), rather than by swimming, the method mainly used in the preceding groups.

5. The young sporophyte, with the food-containing gametophyte and the protecting coats, forms a seed which generally falls from the old sporophyte in a dormant state. The seed is not enclosed in a fruit wall, as it is in the angiosperms.

EXERCISES

1. Look up and describe briefly the extinct groups of gymnosperms—CYCADO-FILICALES, CORDAITALES, and BENNETTITALES. Which group has a cone most nearly approaching the flower of the angiosperms?
2. Discuss the importance of the gymnosperms from the standpoint of lumber production. Distinguish hardwoods from softwoods.
3. What gives the bluish color to the Colorado blue spruce, often grown on lawns? Examine the tree.
4. What cycad may be found in the United States, and where?
5. Where is *Ephedra* found, and what is its use?
6. Give the distribution of the two existing species of *Sequoia*. What reason have we for thinking that this is a vanishing genus?
7. Why are staminate cones much more numerous on coniferous trees than are carpellate?
8. Suppose that 20 is the sporophyte chromosome number in pines. How many are in the tube nucleus of the male gametophyte? In the embryo sac cell? In an endosperm cell?

REFERENCES

Chamberlain, C. J., *Gymnosperms*, Univ. of Chicago Press, 1935.
Chamberlain, C. J., *The Living Cycads*, Univ. of Chicago Press, 1912.
Penhallow, D. P., *North American Gymnosperms*, Ginn and Company, 1907.
See also the botany texts listed in the Appendix.

Chapter XXVII

VASCULAR PLANTS—ANGIOSPERMS

Contrast with Gymnosperms. It has already been noted that the seed-bearing plants include the *gymnosperms* and the *angiosperms*. In the latter group the seed is contained within a closed structure called the *ovary*, the wall of which may be regarded as one or more sporophylls wrapped around the *ovule* or *ovules*. When developed, the ovary becomes a *fruit;* the ovule, as in gymnosperms, a *seed*. Usually there are accessory leaves, such as *sepals* and *petals*, growing with the sporophylls on a short modified branch which may be regarded as equivalent to the pine cone. Such a branch is called a *flower;* hence the term *flowering plants* is often applied to the angiosperms. The two subclasses, distinguished primarily by the number of seed leaves, are:

1. MONOCOTYLEDONEAE (monocotyledons, or monocots): one seed leaf; stems generally with scattered bundles lacking cambium; leaves generally parallel-veined; parts of the flower generally in 3's; corn, lily.
2. DICOTYLEDONEAE (dicotyledons, or dicots): two seed leaves; stem generally with bundles arranged in a cylinder and provided with cambium; leaves generally net-veined; parts of the flower generally in 4's or 5's; bean, oak.

VEGETATIVE STRUCTURES

The 200,000 known species of angiosperms present an infinite variety of sizes and forms, yet are built on a rather uniform structural plan which may be illustrated by the petunia plant (Fig. 330). It will be noted that this plant consists of an axis partly beneath and partly above the ground level, and structures branching from it. Growth in length is restricted to the terminal portions of the axis and its branches, and continues during most of the life of the plant. The underground portion is the *root system*, which serves for anchorage and the absorption of water and dissolved minerals. The portion above ground is the *shoot system*. It is differen-

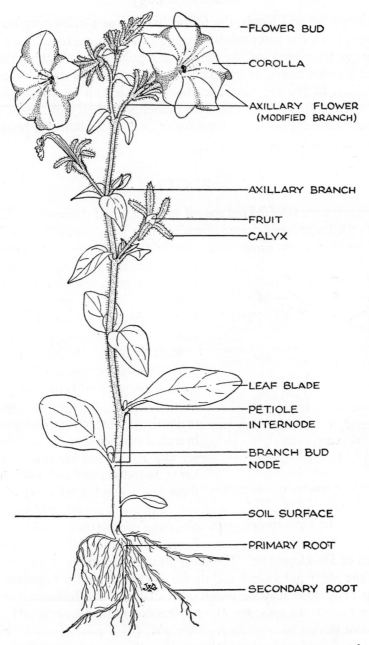

FLOWER BUD

COROLLA

AXILLARY FLOWER
(MODIFIED BRANCH)

AXILLARY BRANCH

FRUIT

CALYX

LEAF BLADE

PÉTIOLE

INTERNODE

BRANCH BUD

NODE

SOIL SURFACE

PRIMARY ROOT

SECONDARY ROOT

FIG. 330. A petunia plant, showing the characteristic structures of flowering plants.

tiated into *stem* and *leaves*, the former serving as a supporting and conducting system, the latter manufacturing carbohydrate food by the aid of
the energy from sunlight. At somewhat regular intervals along the stem
are points called *nodes*. From each of these grow one or more leaves (two
in petunia). In the *axil*, or angle above each leaf, is an *axillary branch*.
This, in turn, may bear leaves with branches in their axils. Some of the
branches (flowers) are specialized for reproduction. Before a branch develops, it is a *bud*.

ROOTS

Roots serve the twofold purpose of anchorage and absorption. The main
root is called a *primary root;* branching from it are *secondary roots. Adventitious roots* often grow from stems and occasionally from leaves. Ex-

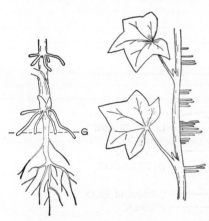

amples are the prop roots at the base
of a corn stalk, the clinging roots of
poison ivy, and the roots that develop
from a geranium stem cutting (Fig.
331).

Root Systems.   Root systems are of
two main types, the *tap root system*
and the *fibrous root system* (Fig. 332).
In the former, the primary root remains the prominent one and sends out
branches smaller than itself. Examples
are the radish and dandelion. In the
latter, found in corn and other grasses,
there are a number of roots of equal
size. Tap roots are adapted to absorption from deep in the soil; fibrous roots,
from the more superficial portions.

Fig. 331. Examples of adventitious
roots. Left, prop roots shown on corn
plant at two nodes just above the
ground level, *G;* right, clinging roots
of English ivy.

Zones of Development.   The chief absorbing portion of a root is near
its tip; the older parts serve mainly for anchorage and transportation. A
root tip (Fig. 333) may be roughly divided into the following regions:
(1) a *root cap* at the apex, serving as protection to the tender growing cells
as the root pushes its way through the soil; (2) a *zone of cell division* in
which mitosis occurs freely; (3) a *zone of cell enlargement*; (4) a *zone of
cell differentiation* in which the different root tissues are developing.

Root Hairs.   On the surface of the last-named zone are important structures known as *root hairs*. These are merely outpushings of epidermal cells,

and must not be confused with branch roots, which are multicellular. The cytoplasm and the enclosed large vacuole extend into the hair, and usually the nucleus migrates into it, apparently controlling its growth in length. Root hairs enable the plant to bring into contact with the soil particles a surface several times as great as would be possible without them, and hence

greatly increase the rate of absorption. By osmosis and diffusion, water and soil minerals enter the hair and are transferred from the epidermal cell to the cells within, ultimately reaching the water vessels of the xylem. The dissolving of soil minerals is aided by carbon dioxide given off in the respiration of the root. As the root elongates, the old hairs progressively die and new ones are progressively formed toward the tip, enabling the root to absorb from parts of the soil in which the water supply has not become exhausted. It is sig-

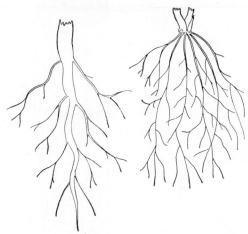

Fig. 332. Tap root system (left) showing branch roots all arising from a main vertical (tap) root; fibrous root system (right) consisting of a number of branching roots of approximately equal size.

nificant that elongation of the root takes place in advance of the hair zone; otherwise the hairs would be snapped off in the process. When plants are transplanted, most of the root hairs and smaller roots are broken off unless a ball of soil is taken up with the root system; hence thorough watering and shading are necessary to get the plant reestablished.

Cross Section of Root. The cross section of a root, made in the zone of differentiation, reveals the following layers (Fig. 334): (1) an outer, single layer of *epidermal cells*, showing vestiges of root hairs, which are usually destroyed in the preparation of the section; (2) the *cortex*, several cells thick, made up of large, thin-walled parenchyma cells useful for food storage; (3) a *central vascular cylinder*, or *stele*, surrounded by a single layer of small, thin-walled cells, the *endodermis*, within which are alternating bundles of *xylem* and *phloem* surrounded by a few parenchyma cells. The xylem is often a continuous star-like area, the phloem lying between its arms. The epidermis and cortex are the outer bark, and the stele constitutes the conducting system; the xylem conducts water and soil minerals to the stem and leaves, and the phloem distributes food elaborated by the leaves. As the root of a dicot grows older, a layer of thin-walled, elongated cells develops between xylem and phloem. This is the *cambium;* its cells continue dividing to add to the thickness of the root.

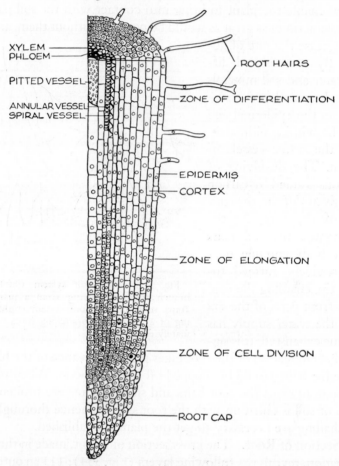

Fig. 333. Diagram of a root tip, quartered and arranged to show both longitudinal and cross sections. The zones indicated blend gradually into each other. Note particularly the structure of root cap and root hairs, and the relation of the latter to the conducting elements.

Extent of Root System. Because the root system is not ordinarily exposed to observation, and because so much of it is cut or broken off when the plant is dug or pulled, we do not ordinarily realize that it may be far more extensive than the part of the plant above ground. A wheat plant three feet high may have roots extending nine feet below the soil surface. A recent study revealed that a single rye plant four months old had a total of thirteen million roots with a combined length of 387 miles. These, with their hairs, presented a surface contact with the soil of over six thousand square feet. From such figures we can understand why a cover of vegetation is so effective in preventing soil erosion.

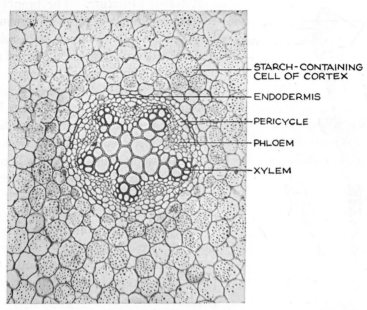

Fig. 334. Inner portion of cross section of the young root of buttercup (a dicot), showing the stele and part of the cortex. The epidermis is not shown. The primary xylem is at the five points of the star. (Photomicrograph by E. B. Wittlake.)

STEMS

Function. The stem bears the leaves, displays them to the air and sunlight, and provides a means of transportation for supplying water and dissolved salts to the leaves, and distributing elaborated foods to all parts of the plant. Like roots, stems often store food. Most young stems contain some green tissue by means of which sugar can be manufactured.

Types. In their direction of growth, stems may be erect, ascending, reclining, prostrate, or climbing. Climbing stems may wind about a support, or develop structures such as tendrils or adventitious roots for clinging. On the basis of stem size and amount of woody tissue, plants may be designated as *herbs, shrubs,* and *trees.* Herbs as a rule die back at the end of each growing season and are therefore relatively soft, with little wood or cork, whereas shrubs and trees develop much strengthening wood and protecting cork that enable them to live through successive seasons. Shrubs are relatively low and have slender stems that usually branch freely at or near the ground; trees are tall and usually have a single trunk which becomes much thickened.

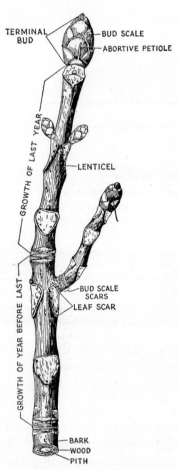

TERMINAL BUD
BUD SCALE
ABORTIVE PETIOLE
GROWTH OF LAST YEAR
LENTICEL
GROWTH OF YEAR BEFORE LAST
BUD SCALE SCARS
LEAF SCAR
BARK
WOOD
PITH

FIG. 335. Stem of horse chestnut in the winter condition. Note the buds in the axils of last year's leaves, and the branch that grew last season from one of the axillary buds of the previous season.

External Structure. The branching of roots is irregular, but the arrangement of leaves and branches on the stem follows a definite pattern. A *node* is a point of leaf attachment, an *internode* the space between two nodes. As regards position, a *bud*, or undeveloped branch, may be *terminal* (at the tip of the stem), *axillary* (at the angle just above the leaf), or *adventitious* (coming out at unusual places). Woody plants of temperate climates have *winter buds* (Fig. 335) which form in the late summer and remain dormant till spring, when they unfold into shoots or flowers. These buds are provided with *bud scales*, which are hard, compactly fitting, protective leaves. In many plants, such as poplar and horse chestnut, these scales are sealed with a sticky cement which must be dissolved by enzymes as the bud resumes growth. As the bud opens the scales drop off, leaving a ring of scars to mark the place of their attachment. When leaves drop in autumn, leaf scars show where they were attached. Regularly arranged dots on these scars mark the location of *leaf traces*, which are the vascular bundles extending from the stem into the leaf.

Since branches ordinarily come out at the axils of leaves, it follows that branch arrangement must correspond with leaf arrangement. In some trees, such as the columnar poplars, growth from the terminal bud constantly maintains its dominance over that from the lateral buds, the result being a conical top with a straight, cylindrical shaft. Such a stem is said to be *excurrent*. In others, such as elm, the terminal bud dies before the end of the season's growth, and the growth of the following year comes entirely from lateral buds. This causes the tree to form a broad, diffuse top. This is *deliquescent* growth.

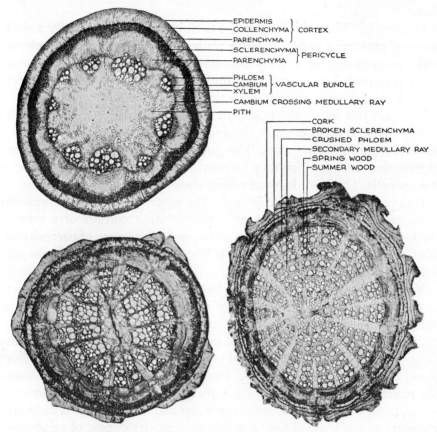

EPIDERMIS
COLLENCHYMA } CORTEX
PARENCHYMA

SCLERENCHYMA } PERICYCLE
PARENCHYMA

PHLOEM
CAMBIUM } VASCULAR BUNDLE
XYLEM

CAMBIUM CROSSING MEDULLARY RAY
PITH

CORK
BROKEN SCLERENCHYMA
CRUSHED PHLOEM
SECONDARY MEDULLARY RAY
SPRING WOOD
SUMMER WOOD

Fig. 336. Cross sections of stem of *Aristolochia,* or pipe vine (a dicot), 1 year old (top), 3 years (lower left), 7 years (lower right); magnified about 15, 10, and 6 diameters respectively. (Photomicrographs by E. B. Wittlake.)

Internal Structure of Dicotyledonous Stems. At the growing tip of a dicotyledonous stem the cells are practically alike, have breadth about equal to the length, are actively dividing, and constitute the *terminal meristem* (Gr. "divisible"); but as we pass to the older portions, we find them becoming gradually differentiated into various types of tissue, chief among which are protective, supporting, conducting, storage, and growth tissues. A cross section (Fig 336) reveals three distinct regions: the *bark* (consisting usually of epidermis, cortex, pericycle, and phloem), the *wood* (xylem), and the *pith*. The bark is separated from the wood by a layer of thin-walled cells, the *cambium*, the function of which is to add new wood to the outside of the old wood and new bark to the inside of the old bark. In herbaceous stems, however, the cambium may be lacking or unimportant.

Epidermis. The *epidermis*, on the outside surface, is ordinarily a single layer of protective cells, the outer walls of which are usually thickened and waterproofed by a waxy substance called *cutin*. As woody stems grow older, this layer is stretched until it cracks. About this time cork is formed to replace it as a protective tissue.

Cortex. Just inside the epidermis is the cortex. Its outer portion, the *collenchyma*, consists of strengthening tissue that is capable of elongating somewhat as the stem grows. The greater portion is thin-walled parenchyma, the cells of which may be provided with chloroplasts or serve as storage cells. The inner layer of cells in the cortex is the *endodermis*.

Pericycle. The pericycle is really the outer portion of the vascular cylinder. In some stems (such as *Aristolochia*) it consists of a zone of thick-walled *sclerenchyma*, or bast fibers, enclosing a zone of parenchyma; in others it is entirely parenchyma. It is not always sharply differentiated from the cortex.

Vascular Bundles. The vascular bundles of a dicotyledonous stem, as in the pine stem, are arranged in the form of a cylinder. Each bundle is made up of three groups of cells. On the outside, just beneath the pericycle, is the *phloem*, the principal cells of which constitute *sieve tubes* (Fig. 337), rows of elongated, thin-walled cells with perforated sieve plates constituting the end walls. The function of these tubes is to carry the manufactured foods. The inner part of the bundle is the *xylem*, or wood, made up of tubes which carry water and soil minerals to the working parts of the plant. These water tubes (*vessels*) consist of cells which have lost their protoplasts and their end walls. They are designated, according to the nature of the thickenings laid down on the side wall before the death of the protoplast, as *spiral, annular,* or *pitted*. Associated with them are wood fibers and woody-walled storage cells. Between xylem and phloem the cambium layer is formed. This tissue usually not only extends through the center of the bundle, but continues between the bundles to form a complete cylinder. It consists of one or more layers of flattened, thin-walled active cells, and constitutes the growing region of the stem. Its cells divide rapidly during the growing season and constantly add to the thickness of the bark on the outside and of the wood on the inside. The tissues developing from the terminal meristem constitute the *primary growth;* those from the cambium, the *secondary growth*. The portion of the cambium extending from bundle to bundle forms new medullary ray cells. As the stem develops, these cells elongate radially and facilitate the passage of both food and water from the vascular bundles to the cortex or the pith. These rays are strikingly revealed in quartered oak lumber, which is prepared by cutting the logs into quarters and then sawing off boards radially from the two cut sides of each quarter, so that the rays appear on the surface of the boards, thus giving a characteristic mottled effect.

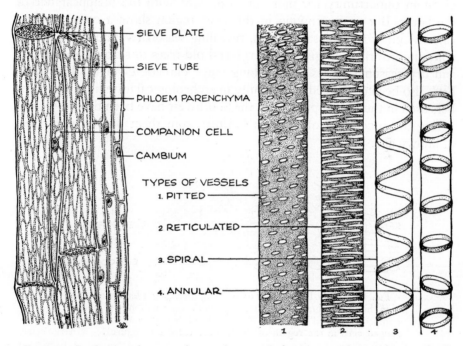

SIEVE PLATE

SIEVE TUBE

PHLOEM PARENCHYMA

COMPANION CELL

CAMBIUM

TYPES OF VESSELS

1. PITTED

2 RETICULATED

3. SPIRAL

4. ANNULAR

1   2   3   4

Fig. 337. Conducting elements of an angiosperm. Left, elements of the phloem and cells of cambium in longitudinal section. Right, four types of xylem vessels in longitudinal view. All are highly magnified. Vessels of the annular and spiral type develop in young and elongating portions of stems; hence they are next to the pith in an older stem.

Pith. The *pith*, which occupies the center of the stem, is made up of large parenchyma cells that give it a somewhat spongy texture; it is of some value for food storage. As the stem grows older, the pith often disappears, leaving the stem hollow.

Rings of Annual Growth. Woody stems which grow in localities where the growing season is terminated by cold or very dry weather add a distinct layer of wood each year through the activity of the cambium (Fig. 336). In spring and early summer large vessels predominate, making the inner portion of this layer open or porous. Later in the summer the growth becomes retarded; this results in a compact portion, made up mainly of wood fibers. This differential growth results in a distinct separation of one year's growth from the next, and makes it possible to determine the age of the tree by counting the rings. Variations in the thickness of the rings are evident in any woody stem. These variations reflect differences in the growth conditions of different years. Sometimes these differences are localized, as when a tree is suppressed by being shaded by larger trees, then given an opportunity for more rapid growth with the disappearance of the latter. But trees growing in the same region show a corresponding ring thickness for the same years, revealing seasonal variations. This enables the information given by large and old trees to throw light on wet and dry seasonal cycles and on long-range climatic changes. Tree rings have also been employed successfully in archeological investigations. Timbers used in the Indian pueblos of the Southwest have been dated by comparing the succession of rings in borings from them with that in trees of known age.

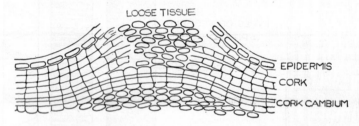

Fig. 338. Cork layer of a woody stem, including a lenticel, shown in a highly magnified section. The cork cambium has produced compactly placed cork cells (each side of figure) and loosely arranged cells in the region of the lenticel (center of figure).

Cork and Lenticels. A second region of lateral growth is formed in most woody perennial dicots. When the stem is about a year old, a layer of divisible tissue is cut off from the inner faces of the epidermal cells, or the outer faces of the outermost collenchyma cells. This is the *cork cambium*. Its continued division forms many layers of cork cells. These cells, which have waterproofed walls, soon die, become empty and serve for protection in place of the epidermis when the latter is stretched to the breaking point. Here and there in this impervious tissue are small areas of porous tissue, the *lenticels* (Fig. 338), which facilitate the interchange of gases between the internal air spaces and the outside air. Commercial cork is thick cork tissue stripped from the cork oak, which grows in the Mediterranean region.

Monocotyledonous Stems. Branching is rather less frequent in monocotyledonous stems than in dicotyledonous stems, and the nodes and internodes are often more sharply marked. The stem is not differentiated
into bark, wood, and pith; instead, its *vascular bundles* are *scattered*
through a pith-like parenchyma. A cross section of the cornstalk shows
this (Fig. 339). There is a hard external epidermis which is impregnated

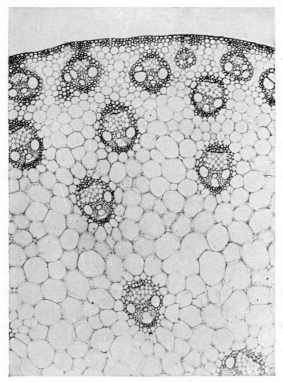

Fig. 339. Corn stem (a monocot), portion of cross
section (× 65). Each of the scattered fibrovascular
bundles consists of phloem (above) and xylem (below,
with about four large water tubes). There is no cambium. Fibrous supporting tissue lies just beneath the
epidermis and also surrounds each bundle. (Photomicrograph, copyright, General Biological Supply House,
Inc., Chicago.)

with silica. Underneath are several layers of fibers which form a supporting tissue. The whole interior contains vascular bundles distributed somewhat irregularly among the parenchyma cells; they are more numerous
near the cortex than toward the center. The vascular bundles resemble
those of dicotyledons in the arrangement of xylem and phloem, but no

cambium is present. The entire bundle is surrounded by a thick-walled bundle sheath. The sieve tubes are eight-sided; on four of their sides are small square cells known as *companion cells*. The xylem has four large vessels and a number of smaller, thick-walled cells. The lack of a cambium and the limitation of growth to the enlargement of cells already differentiated are the distinctive characteristics of the stems of monocotyledons.

LEAVES

Leaf Characters and Functions. Leaves generally agree in being green in color, thin and flat, and arranged in such a way as to give an extensive surface exposure both to light and to the carbon dioxide of the air. Certain

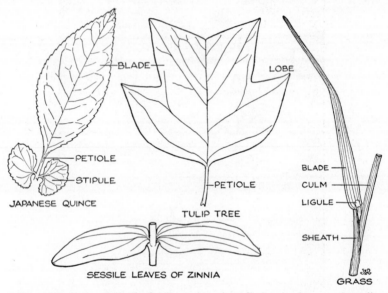

Fig. 340. Parts of the leaf. The quince has all the usual parts, the tulip tree lacks stipules when mature, and the zinnia has neither petiole nor stipules. The petiole of a grass leaf is a sheath that partly surrounds the stem. The ligule is a small appendage at the junction of sheath and blade.

leaves are not green, but these serve other functions than photosynthesis; the bud scales, for example, are modified leaves that protect the tender parts of the bud. Exceptions to the usual thinness of leaves are found among succulent plants, which commonly prevail in dry areas. In them efficiency in photosynthesis is sacrificed to protection against drought. Leaves are also rather thick in evergreens; this adapts them so they can persist through the winter when conditions are unfavorable for water absorption.

Parts of a Leaf. The flat, spreading part, in which most of the work of the leaf is done, is the *blade* (Fig. 340). It is usually attached to the stem by means of a *petiole*, or stalk. Leaves without a stalk are said to be *sessile*. Variations in the length of the petiole are often effective in spacing the leaves so that each has access to light. Leaves lower on a twig, for example, may thereby be brought out beyond the shade of those that stand above them. Many leaves, but not all, have at the base a pair of outgrowths known as *stipules*. These may be leaf-like, membrane-like, reduced to minute vestiges, or absent. Sometimes they are modified into tendrils or thorns (Figs. 350, 351).

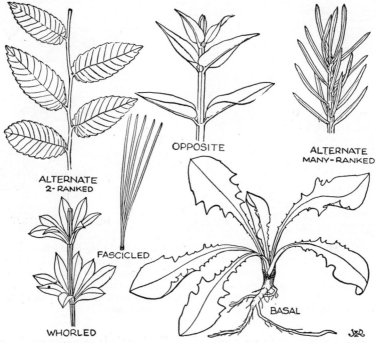

Fig. 341. Types of leaf arrangement. Upper row: elm, mint, spruce; lower row: bedstraw, pine, dandelion.

Arrangement of Leaves (Fig. 341). The position of leaves on the stem is fixed as though with mathematical precision. In many plants there is a single leaf at a node, and consecutive leaves are so placed that a line drawn through their points of attachment forms a spiral around the stem. This is the *alternate* arrangement. For any species, a definite number of intervals between leaves and a definite number of turns around the stem locates a leaf which is directly above the starting point. For example, in the elm (upper left) one complete turn of the spiral around the stem covers two of these intervals; hence each leaf is one-half the circumference of the stem from the one next to it, and there are two longitudinal rows of leaves. The spruce (a gymnosperm, upper right) has a greater number of longitudinal rows, and it is a significant fact that its leaves are narrower. The *opposite* arrangement is that in which there are two leaves at a node, located di-

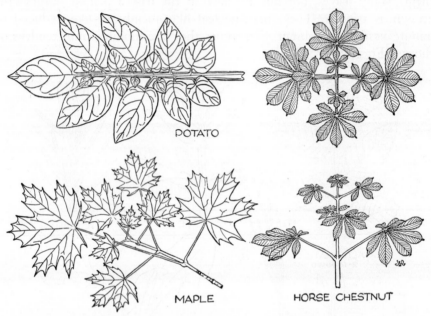

POTATO

MAPLE HORSE CHESTNUT

Fig. 342. How leaves are displayed to light. The vertical twig of the horse chestnut (shown in top and side views) and the horizontal twig of maple both bear opposite leaves. Whatever the stem position, the length and position of the petioles in both enable the leaves to display almost their entire upper surface area to the light. In the potato, the small leaflets fill the gaps left by the larger ones. (Based in part on Guyer, *Animal Biology*, Harper.)

rectly across the stem from each other. Each pair is at right angles to the preceding one; thus on a vertical twig the shading of the leaves by one another is largely prevented (as in the horse chestnut, Fig. 342). On a horizontal twig, opposite leaves are generally brought into a flat plane by the twisting and sometimes the elongation of the petioles (as in the maple, same figure). The *whorled* arrangement (as in bedstraw, Fig. 341) is that in which three or more leaves encircle the stem at the node. Some plants, such as the dandelion, have greatly shortened internodes, causing all their leaves to come from near the ground level. Such leaves are said to be *basal* in arrangement. In the pine, the leaves are in bundles, or *fascicled*. Whatever the fundamental plan of arrangement, the effect is to give each leaf a position that enables it to receive sunlight over at least a considerable portion of its surface, and permits the whole leaf system to use advantageously the space within a certain radius of the stem.

Degree of Division of Leaf Margin. A *compound leaf* is one whose blade is divided into distinct parts, or *leaflets* (Fig. 343). If the leaflets

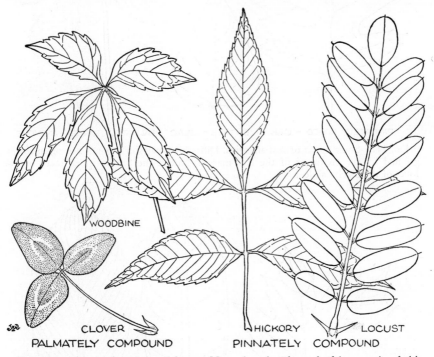

WOODBINE

CLOVER · HICKORY · LOCUST

PALMATELY COMPOUND · PINNATELY COMPOUND

Fig. 343. Types of compound leaves. Note that the clover leaf has a pair of thin stipules at its base, and that the locust leaf has stipular spines, a motor organ (swollen base of petiole), and hair-like stipels (secondary stipules) at the bases of the leaflets.

come from one point, suggesting the radiating of the fingers from the palm, the leaf is *palmately compound;* if they are spread along an axis, suggesting the barbs of a feather, the leaf is *pinnately compound*. If the leaf falls just short of being compound, it is *parted* (Fig. 344); and if the incisions go about halfway or less, it is *lobed*. Many leaves have *teeth*, which may be coarse or fine, sharp or blunt. *Entire* leaves are those without teeth or lobes. Differences between leaves illustrate the great variability in the plant world and form an important means of distinction among the different species. As compared with the leaf, a flower is a stable and conservative structure. The latter is of more value in the recognition of plant

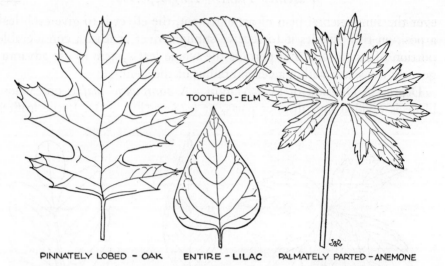

TOOTHED - ELM

PINNATELY LOBED - OAK   ENTIRE - LILAC   PALMATELY PARTED - ANEMONE

FIG. 344. Some types of leaf margins. Different species of a genus are often distinguished by the character of the leaf margin. Notice the bristle-tipped teeth on the lobes of the black oak leaf.

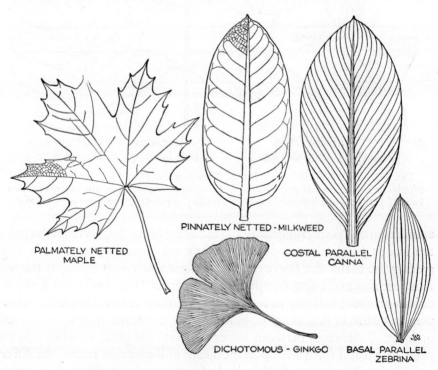

PINNATELY NETTED - MILKWEED

PALMATELY NETTED
MAPLE

COSTAL PARALLEL
CANNA

DICHOTOMOUS - GINKGO   BASAL PARALLEL
ZEBRINA

FIG. 345. Principal kinds of leaf veining. The network in the netted leaves is only partially filled in.

families, whereas the former serves to differentiate otherwise closely related species.

Leaf Veining. The veins of a leaf form its framework and contain the extensions of the xylem and phloem. When a leaf is held to the light, the veins are seen to form so extensive a system that no part of the leaf is more

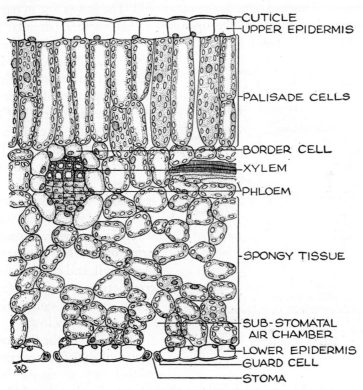

CUTICLE
UPPER EPIDERMIS

PALISADE CELLS

BORDER CELL
XYLEM
PHLOEM

SPONGY TISSUE

SUB-STOMATAL AIR CHAMBER
LOWER EPIDERMIS
GUARD CELL
STOMA

Fig. 346. Cross section of a typical leaf. The chloroplasts are the small bodies shown in white in the cells of the palisade and spongy tissue. The leaf vein (vascular bundle) consists of the border cells, xylem, and phloem. To the right of the vein shown in cross section is a portion of one of its branches shown in longitudinal section.

than a few millimeters away from its nearest vein. As the streets of a city give access to all its houses, so the veins provide for the conveying of raw materials to and foods from every part of the leaf. *Dichotomous,* or repeatedly forking, veins are restricted to many ferns and some gymnosperms, such as *Ginkgo.* Angiosperms have in general two types of veins (Fig. 345). Most monocots have *parallel,* or nonintersecting, veins. These may run from base to tip as in *Zebrina* (wandering Jew), or from midrib to margin as in *Canna.* Most dicots have *netted* veins, the finer branches of which form a network. These may be arranged *pinnately* (from a single midrib), as in milkweed, or *palmately* (from several main ribs), as in maple.

Leaf Structure. A typical leaf (shown in cross section in Fig. 346) is bounded by the upper and lower epidermis, which are waterproofed by a waxy cuticle deposited outside the outer wall. The lower one in particular is perforated by many slit-like openings called *stomata* (singular *stoma*, Gr. "mouth"). The tissue between the two epidermal layers is the *mesophyll* (Gr. "midleaf"); it consists of thin-walled cells, each containing several *chloroplasts* (Gr. "green bodies"). The upper cells of the mesophyll, known as the *palisades* (French "picket fence"), are rather compact and at right angles to the leaf surface; the lower ones are more loosely arranged and constitute the *spongy tissue*. The veins of the leaf permeate the mesophyll, and consist of water-conducting tissue (*xylem*) above, and food-conducting tissues (*phloem*) below.

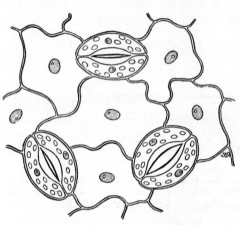

FIG. 347. Surface view of the lower epidermis of the garden geranium, showing three stomata (slit-like openings, each bounded by two guard cells) and several of the ordinary epidermal cells. The lower right stoma is open because of an increased turgor of the guard cells.

Operation of the Stomata. A *stoma*, of which there may be a million on a single leaf, is bounded on each side by a kidney-shaped guard cell (Fig. 347). Unlike the other epidermal cells, these cells contain chloroplasts. When the sun is shining they manufacture sugar, which, dissolved in the cell sap, increases the flow of water from adjoining cells, thereby increasing the turgor of the guard cells. This turgor tends to bulge the thin outside walls of the guard cells, and this results in drawing the thick inside walls apart and opening the stoma. As long as carbon dioxide is being used for photosynthesis in the leaf, it passes in through the open slit. Its molecules dissolve in the film of water on the outside of the mesophyll cells and diffuse through the wall and membrane into the protoplast. Each gas in a mixture tends to diffuse from its lesser to its greater concentration; hence although CO_2 constitutes only 0.03 of 1 percent of the air, it diffuses into the leaf as long as it is used in photosynthesis without involving the entry of the other gases of the air.

Utilization and Loss of Water. Water, the other raw material used in photosynthesis, is supplied by the tracheids, which constitute the xylem of the leaf vein. Since the stomata must be open to admit carbon dioxide, much water evaporates from the moist outer walls of the mesophyll cells and is lost to the leaf. This loss is *transpiration*. A corn plant is said to lose forty gallons of water by transpiration during its growing season. Transpiration is not a useful process but an unavoidable danger which threatens the life of the plant during periods of water shortage, and which the plant must guard against by the regulatory action of its stomata. These tiny openings close not only at night, but also in dry weather when water is not easily secured to give turgor to the guard cells.

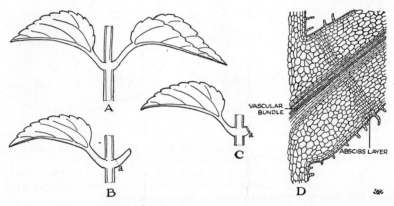

FIG. 348. Leaf fall. *A*, A pair of opposite leaves in *Coleus; B*, one of the leaves pinched off; *C*, the pinching has hastened the disintegration of the cell walls of the absciss layer (*a*), causing the petiole to drop within a day or two; *D*, detail of petiole base, magnified, showing absciss layer.

Autumn Colors and Leaf Fall. *Carotene* and *xanthophyll*, the yellow pigments associated with the green chlorophyll in the chloroplasts, are less complex and more stable than chlorophyll and hence remain after the latter has decomposed. Yellow is therefore a prominent color in aging leaves. Reds and purples are due to pigments known as *anthocyans* (Gr. "flower blue"), which appear as decomposition products in certain leaves, especially those which, like the maple, are rich in sugar. Low temperature and sunlight seem to favor their formation. They are in solution in the cell sap, and are red in an acid medium, blue in a basic. Browns may be due to the accumulation of tannins, or to decomposition products of the protoplasts or of the cellulose walls. During the growth of the leaf, a layer of cells, the *absciss* (Lat. "cutting off") *layer*, forms transversely across the base of the petiole (Fig. 348). Gradually the partition walls of the cells of this layer disintegrate, a gust of wind snaps the vascular bundles, and the leaf falls. This separation of the leaf prepares the tree for winter, for during this season absorption is practically at a standstill, and if the leaves were retained, the loss of water from them would be disastrous to the plant.

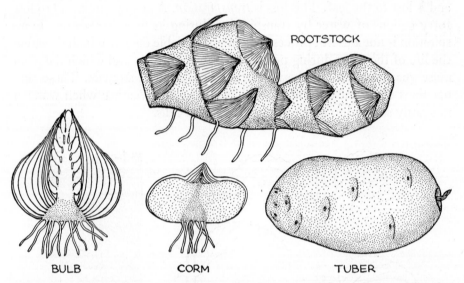

ROOTSTOCK

BULB   CORM   TUBER

Fig. 349. Underground stems which serve for the storage of food and the continuation and multiplication of the plant. Rootstock of canna, with prominent scale-like leaves; bulb of hyacinth, made up chiefly of fleshy leaf bases and containing flower-bud cluster; corm of crocus, tuber of potato, indicating that the eye represents a much reduced leaf with a bud in its axil. Bulb and corm are shown in longitudinal section.

Modifications of Stems and Leaves. Stems may depart widely from their usual structures and functions. The edible part of the common potato is not part of the root system, but a modified stem known as a *tuber* (Fig. 349). Like any stem it has buds (the eyes) growing in the axils of leaves (the little protruding scale from each eyebrow-like ridge) and these are at regularly arranged nodes (alternate in the potato). The tuber develops not on the root, but on an elongated stem above the root system. A more slender underground stem, known as a *rhizome* or *rootstock*, such as we have noted as the common type of stem among ferns, is found in Solomon's seal and many other plants. A *corm*, such as that of crocus or Jack-in-the-pulpit, is a compact, upright rhizome; a *bulb*, such as that of the onion, is a similar structure but is made up mainly of scales or coats which constitute the fleshy bases of leaves.

Sometimes stem branches are modified into *tendrils* which coil around a support and hold the plant in place; but some tendrils are modified leaves,

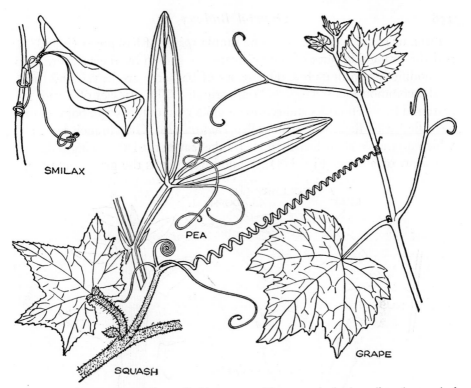

FIG. 350. Types of tendrils or climbing organs. They are stipules in smilax, the terminal part of the compound leaf in perennial pea, modified stems in squash and grape. Observe the reversals in the direction of the coil in the squash.

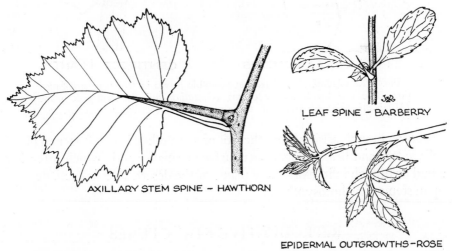

FIG. 351. Spines and prickles, modified parts serving for the defense of plants against grazing animals. The spine of hawthorn grows in a leaf axil, hence may be interpreted as a modified axillary branch. That of barberry bears a very short leafy branch in its axil and therefore is regarded as a modified leaf. The prickles of rose are epidermal outgrowths that come out anywhere on the internodes.

leaflets, or stipules (Fig. 350). The simple *spines* of hawthorn (Fig. 351) and the branching ones of honey locust are shown by their structure to be modified stem branches. The spines of barberry are leaves, and those of the common locust (Fig. 343) are stipules. The *prickles* of a rose are scattered between nodes and represent epidermal outgrowths. Some plants have fleshy or flattened stems called *cladophylls* (Gr. "branch leaves"), which do the work ordinarily done by the leaves, the latter being reduced, transient, or absent (Fig. 352). A good example is the greenhouse plant

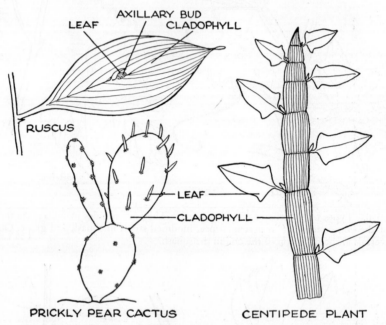

Fig. 352. Cladophylls, stems that resemble leaves in structure and function. The real leaves of the cactus (*Opuntia*) and the centipede plant (*Muehlenbeckia*) are transient; those of *Ruscus* are reduced to scales.

Ruscus; a branch arising from the axil of a scale-like leaf is flattened like a foliage leaf and bears on its upper surface a smaller scale which often has a bud or branch in its axil. Many plants of the desert, such as cacti, depend upon stems for photosynthesis.

REPRODUCTIVE STRUCTURES

In the preceding chapters we have seen that in horsetails, club mosses, ferns, and gymnosperms, the sporophyte generation produces asexual *spores,* contained in sacs called *sporangia* which grow on modified leaves called *sporophylls*. In some forms the sporophylls are grouped on a stem or branch, constituting a *cone*. In the more advanced groups there are two kinds of sporophylls, borne in the same or different cones. The *megasporophyll* bears *megasporangia*, containing *megaspores* which grow into *female gametophytes;* the *microsporophyll* bears *microsporangia*, containing *microspores* which grow into *male gametophytes*. Sometimes there are accessory leaves associated with the cone, especially at its base.

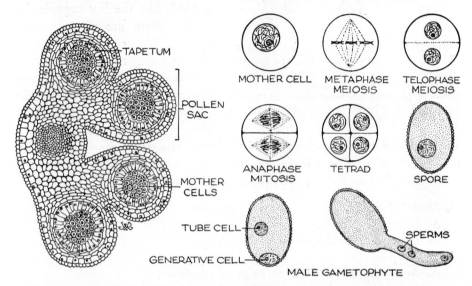

TAPETUM

POLLEN SAC

MOTHER CELLS

TUBE CELL

GENERATIVE CELL

MOTHER CELL

METAPHASE MEIOSIS

TELOPHASE MEIOSIS

ANAPHASE MITOSIS

TETRAD

SPORE

MALE GAMETOPHYTE

SPERMS

Fig. 353. Cross section of lily anther (left), and stages in development from the mother cell to the spore and the male gametophyte (pollen grain and tube).

Parts of a Flower. A flower also is a modified branch bearing *sporophylls*. Unlike the pine cone, which contains only one sort of sporophyll, the flower generally has both kinds. In addition to the sporophylls, the flower usually has two sets of specialized accessory leaves that do not bear spores; they afford protection and, by attracting insects, often help in the distribution of pollen. The outer set is the *calyx*, consisting of *sepals;* the inner set is the *corolla*, consisting of *petals*. The *microsporophylls* are the *stamens;* each is usually differentiated into a stalk, the *filament*, and an enlarged terminal portion, the *anther*. The anther usually consists of four *microsporangia (pollen sacs*, Fig. 353). Sporogenous cells developing in the center of each pollen sac form many *spore mother cells* by repeated division. Each spore mother cell undergoes two nuclear divisions during which the chomosomes are reduced to the haploid number. A wall now develops around each daughter nucleus, and the four resulting cells

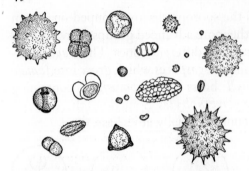

function as separate *microspores*, or *pollen grains* (Fig. 354). The *megasporophyll* (*carpel*) may be a single modified leaf, like the pea pod, or it may be united with others of its kind to form a compound structure known as a *pistil*, like the lily capsule, in which there are three united carpels. The carpel or pistil consists of a swollen base, the *ovary*, containing one or more *megasporangia*, or *ovules*. Above this base is usually a stalk-like part, the *style*, with a somewhat

FIG. 354. Pollen grains of various plants, indicating range in shape and size. The fact that each species has a definite pollen type is put to use in analyzing the atmosphere for the recognition of potential hay fever agents, and also in examining bog sediments to determine the plant types of the past.

roughened pollen-receptive part, the *stigma*. The tip of the flower stalk, sometimes enlarged, is called the *receptacle*.

To recapitulate, a complete flower (see Fig. 362) consists of:

I. Modified stem.
   A. *Peduncle*, or stalk.
   B. *Receptacle*, or flower base.
II. Modified leaves.
   A. Accessory leaves, *perianth*, or *floral envelopes*.
      1. *Sepals*, constituting the *calyx*.
      2. *Petals*, constituting the *corolla*.
   B. Essential leaves, or *sporophylls*.
      1. *Stamens*, or *microsporophylls*.
         a. *Filament*, or stalk.
         b. *Anther*, made up of four (usually) *pollen sacs*, or *microsporangia*, containing *pollen grains*, or *microspores*.
      2. *Carpels*, or *megasporophylls*, constituting the *pistil*.
         a. *Ovary*, the enlarged base, containing one or more *ovules*, *megasporangia*, in which usually only one functional *megaspore* develops.
         b. *Style*, the stalk-like part.
         c. *Stigma*, the pollen-receptive part.

Distribution of Sporophylls. Usually both kinds of sporophylls are present in the same flower; such a flower is known as *perfect*. However in some species, like corn, oak, and melons, the two types are separated into different flowers on the same plant. Such plants are called *monoecious*

(Gr. "one house"). In others, like willow and mulberrry, the stamens and carpels are not merely in different flowers, but on separate plants. These are known as *dioecious* (Gr. "two houses"). Dioecious plants are commonly regarded as male and female; a statement scientifically more accurate is that, though asexual, they produce spores which grow respectively into male and female gametophytes.

Male Gametophyte. When the pollen grain is shed from the anther, it has already commenced its growth into a *male gametophyte* having divided into a large vegetative cell, the *tube cell*, and a smaller reproductive one, the *generative cell* (Fig. 353). The former directs the growth of the *pollen tube*, or completed male gametophyte, and the latter divides into two *sperm nuclei*. The adhesion of the pollen grain to the stigma and its germination into a pollen tube are facilitated by a sticky secretion on the surface of the stigma. The pollen tube, really a protoplasmic thread, absorbs food from the tissues through which it passes as it grows down the stigma and style. The tube nucleus, which governs its growth, leads the way, and the two sperm nuclei follow, the tip of the tube eventually reaching the ovary.

Ovule. An ovary may contain a single ovule or up to many thousands. Starting from the base of the ovule where it joins its stalk, two folds of tissue gradually push their way toward the apex but do not quite close in over it. The folds are the two seed coats and the opening which remains is the *micropyle* (Gr. "small gate"); by way of the latter the pollen tube enters the ovule. In most angiosperms the ovule is inverted, bringing the micropyle close to the stalk. Just inside the coats is the *nucellus*, within which the single large *megaspore mother cell* undergoes reduction division to form four *megaspores*. The three next to the micropyle ordinarily degenerate; the fourth, the *embryo sac*, grows into the female gametophyte.

Female Gametophyte. The functional megaspore undergoes three successive nuclear divisions, resulting in eight nuclei (Fig. 355). Four of these occupy the micropylar end of the large cytoplasmic mass, and four occupy the opposite or antipodal end. One nucleus from each end then migrates to the center; these are known as *polar nuclei*. More or less distinct walls now form around the three nuclei at each end. The three cells at the micropylar end constitute the *egg apparatus*. One of these is the *egg cell*. The other two, the *synergids* (Gr. "co-workers"), as well as the three *antipodal cells*, usually disappear soon after fertilization. One of the sperm nuclei fuses with the egg nucleus to form the *zygote*, which grows into the *embryo;* the other fuses with the two polar nuclei to form the *endosperm nucleus*, a $3n$ structure which grows into the endosperm.

About 30 percent of the angiosperms which have been investigated vary from this type of female gametophyte. In some the gametophyte consists of four nuclei; in others, of 16. In the lily, which is widely used for laboratory studies, all four of its megaspores form the eight-nuclear gameto-

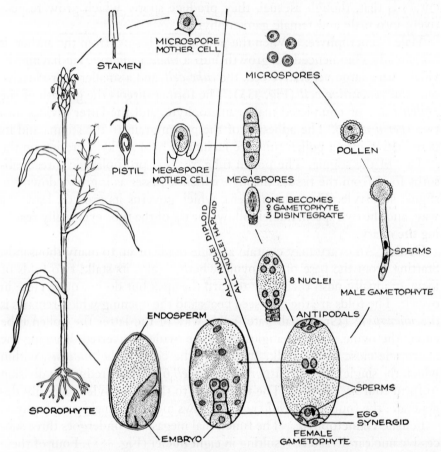

Fig. 355. Life history of a sedge (*Carex*), a monocot of the Sedge family, with the general aspect of a grass, from which it differs by having a triangular stem and closed leaf sheaths. Its gametophyte structures are typical. The two polar nuclei are shown with the sperm in the center of the female gametophyte. The sedge is monoecious, with separate staminate and pistillate flowers which are often, as in this case, in separate spikes.

phyte. Three of them migrate to the antipodal end, pool their chromosomes in the succeeding mitosis, and give rise to four $3n$ nuclei at that end. One of these, as a polar nucleus, fuses with the n polar nucleus from the micropylar end and the second sperm nucleus, to form a $5n$ endosperm nucleus.

Pollination.   Before seeds can develop in the ovary, it is necessary for pollen to be transferred to the stigma from the anther of the same or another flower. This process is called *pollination*. Flowers may undergo *self-pollination* or *cross-pollination*. The former is the placing of pollen on the stigma of the same flower. It occurs regularly in such flowers as the garden pea and wheat, in which the anthers are situated close to the sigma. Some

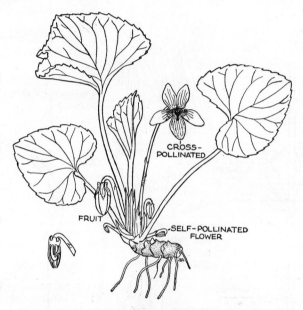

Fig. 356.   Plant of a common blue violet, showing two types of flowers. The showy flowers, opening in spring and sometimes in autumn, are cross-pollinated by insects; the bud-like (cleistogamous) flowers, appearing all summer, are self-pollinated and produce pods without opening. The section of the latter at the left shows how the position of the anther against the stigma facilitates self-pollination.

plants have, in addition to their showy cross-pollinated flowers, bud-like or *cleistogamous* (Gr. "hidden marriage") self-pollinated flowers; an example is the common blue violet (Fig. 356). Self-pollination permits an economy of pollen, of stigma surface, and of petals, odor, and nectar, but it does not ordinarily lead to much variation in offspring. Cross-pollination takes place when the pollen of one flower reaches the stigma of another. Its advantage is that it gives the offspring two separate parents and makes it more likely to vary than if it came from only one parent. The two principal agents of cross-pollination are *wind* and *insects*.

Wind-Pollinated Flowers. Corn (Fig. 357) is pollinated by wind. Its flowers are not very showy, lack sepals and petals, and have no odor, nectar, or other properties that would make them attractive to insects. This plant, as well as many other wind-pollinated and some insect-pollinated

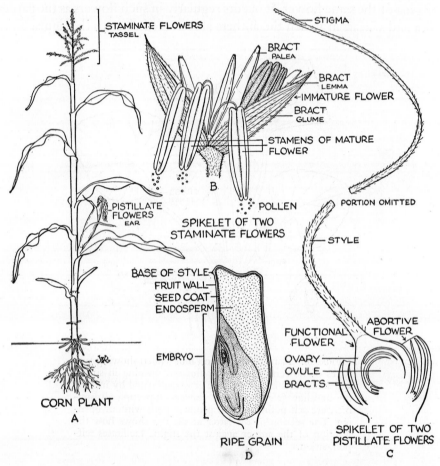

Fig. 357. The corn plant and enlarged details of its flowers and fruit.

plants, is monoecious, having staminate flowers in tassels at the top of the stalk, and pistillate flowers, each a young grain with its silk, on the ear in the axil of a leaf. The staminate flowers produce a great abundance of pollen, which is loose and dust-like, light in weight, and easily carried by air currents. It is deposited on the exposed silks (stigmas) of the same or, more commonly, another stalk. It is necessary for the plant to produce an excess of pollen, because the great majority of the grains never reach a silk.

Insect-Pollinated Flowers. Plants that profit from insect visitors for the carrying of their pollen usually have bright colors or attractive odors, have nectar or excess pollen that serves as an inducement to the insect, and often make insect visits effective by providing special landing places and other special arrangements of flower parts. The garden nasturtium (Fig. 358) is a typical insect-pollinated flower. It has petals which are brightly colored, contrasting strongly with the green leaves and making the flower clearly

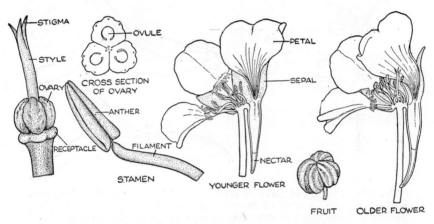

Fig. 358. Flower structure of the garden nasturtium. Compare the younger flower (stamens shedding pollen, stigmas immature) with the older flower (stamens shriveled, stigmas receptive). (Flowers and fruit natural size, details at left × 5.)

visible to insects. In addition to the general color, there may be special guide lines, which are thought to direct the visiting bee to the *nectary*, a spur of one of the sepals wherein the *nectar* is secreted and held. While they are shedding pollen, the stamens are so placed that they are directly in the path of the visiting bee, thus making it certain that the sticky pollen will be picked up. Although stamens and pistil are in the same flower, the stamens shed their pollen before the stigma is ready to receive it. By this means self-pollination is avoided. In the older flower, the three stigmas at the top of the pistil are in about the same location as are the anthers in the young flower. Hence a bee, in moving from a younger to an older flower, is sure to carry pollen from the former to the latter.

Salvia (Sage). The two-lipped flowers of sage (*Salvia*, a member of the Mint family, Fig. 359) grow in terminal clusters, and each flower extends from the main stalk in such a way that the broad lower lip of the corolla serves as a platform on which the bee or other insect can alight easily. The inner portion of the corolla forms a tube in which the nectar is secreted.

At the opening of the tube, on either side of the mouth of the corolla, are two stamens of peculiar construction. Each has a short basal filament with two arms. One arm, which is long, thread-like, and arched, holds a fertile anther and extends upward just beneath the upper lip. The lower arm, which is short and sterile, extends forward, acting as the power arm of a lever. In order to reach the nectar, the bee has to push against both short

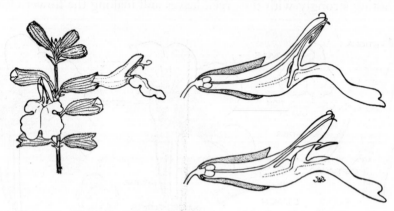

Fɪɢ. 359. Flowers of *Salvia* illustrate a special adaptation favoring cross-pollination. Left, portion of flower cluster with two open flowers; right, flowers in longitudinal section. One of the two stamens is shown in normal position in the upper section, and as tripped by a visiting bee, in the lower.

arms; this pulls the long arms downward so that the anthers with the ripe pollen come in contact with the hairs on the back of the bee, smearing them with pollen. When the anther is shedding its pollen, the pistil is not yet ready for pollination; hence self-pollination cannot take place. In older flowers the stamens have shriveled and the pistil is matured, bringing the stigma into such a position that a bee, sprinkled with pollen from a younger flower, brushes against it, effecting cross-pollination.

Yucca and the Yucca Moth. Another remarkable case is the pollination of *Yucca* by the small, whitish moth *Pronuba* (Fig. 360). Yucca is a member of the Lily family and is abundant in the dry regions of the West; one species is extensively cultivated in gardens. Its large, white bell-shaped flowers have sticky pollen that cannot be distributed by wind. The style tube of the three united carpels is stigmatic only on the inside and extends considerably beyond the tips of the stamens, thus precluding self-pollination. Nectar is scant, and insects seeking it would not come near stamens or stigmas. The only known way in which the flower is pollinated is by the female *Pronuba*. She remains inactive during the day inside of the flower. At dusk she mounts the stamens one by one and, by means of mouth parts adapted to the purpose, gathers a ball of pollen. She then flies to another flower, lights on the pistil, and deposits an egg in one of the six rows of ovules. She immediately crawls to the top of the pistil and spreads on the stigmatic surface in line with this row of ovules some of the pollen which she is holding. The process is then repeated for other rows of ovules in the same pistil. By this means the ovules are fertilized and the seeds de-

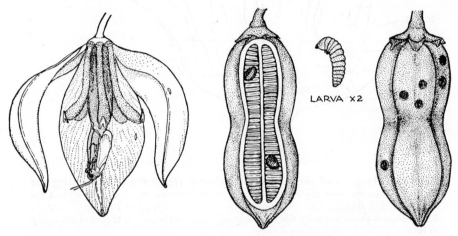

LARVA X2

FIG. 360. Pollination of *Yucca* by the yucca moth, *Pronuba yuccasella*. Left, flower with three perianth divisions removed. The moth is rubbing pollen into the stigma after having laid an egg in the ovary. Note that the anthers are remote from the stigma, making assistance at pollination imperative. Middle, developing pod cut open, showing two moth larvae. Right, ripe pod, showing holes through which full-grown larvae have emerged.

velop. In the meantime, the eggs of the moth hatch into larvae which feed upon the developing ovules until they are ready to pupate. However, the ovary contains so many ovules that enough seeds escape destruction to insure the perpetuation of the yucca plant. Thus mutual benefit results to both the moth and the plant; the two are so intimately related that without the moth the plant could produce no seeds and without the plant the moth could not have progeny. It is not easy to find a complete explanation of this strange relationship; to call it instinct only gives it a name but does not explain it. One writer has said, "It is easy but unscientific to assign to both the moth and the flower the ability to plan, to foresee and to act accordingly. But the scientist must yet search for facts with which to explain such a marvelous phenomenon."

Composite Family. The structure popularly regarded as a flower in the sunflower, daisy, aster, coreopsis, and cosmos (Fig. 361) is really a cluster of many small flowers in a compact head. These plants are representatives of the Composite family, so named because the head was once regarded as

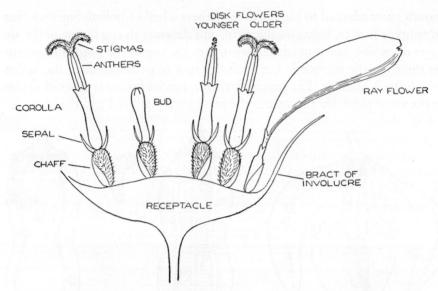

FIG. 361. Diagram of the head of a sunflower (*Helianthus*), representing the Composite family. The ray flower of this genus is sterile and serves to attract insects. The disk flowers shed their pollen into a tube consisting of the united anthers. This pollen is pushed out by the exanding stigmas, which then spread and are ready to receive pollen from younger flowers.

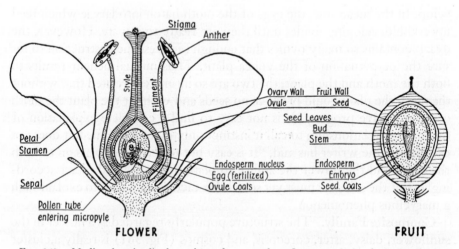

FIG. 362. Median longitudinal section of a complete flower and the fruit developing from it, showing how the various parts of the pistil contribute to the fruit. The fruit is on a smaller scale than the flower.

a compound flower; it is the largest family of seed plants. The sunflower has two kinds of flowers in a head. Those around the margin, with strap-shaped corollas, are *ray flowers;* those packed in the center, with tubular corollas, are *disk flowers.* The ray flowers attract insects to the head; the disk flowers bear the essential organs. The stamens are united by their anthers into a tube surrounding the style and stigmas; the latter as they develop push the pollen out at the upper end of the stamen tube, then spread apart and are ready to receive pollen. Insects carry the pollen from a younger flower, in which it is being discharged, to an older one, in which the stigmas are receptive; thus self-pollination is avoided and cross-pollination assured.

Summary. The following are the more usual characteristics of flowers of the three pollination types:

Insect-Pollinated Flowers	Wind-Pollinated Flowers	Self-Pollinated Flowers
Pollen not abundant	Pollen abundant	Pollen scant
Pollen sticky	Pollen dust-like	
Anthers concealed	Anthers exposed	Anthers against stigma
Stigmas small, concealed	Stigmas large, exposed	Stigmas concealed
Possess petals or other showy parts	Lack showy parts	Often lack showy parts
Possess odor and nectar	Lack odor and nectar	Lack odor and nectar
Often have landing places and guide lines	Lack landing places and guide lines	Lack landing places and guide lines

Fertilization. As the tip of the pollen tube enters the micropyle, its membrane breaks and one of the two sperm nuclei unites with the egg to form the *zygote,* which thus has the diploid chromosome number. Instead of disintegrating, as in the gymnosperms, the other sperm unites with the two polar nuclei to form the *endosperm nucleus,* from which arises the endosperm of the seed. No satisfactory explanation has been found for this triple union. This participation of two sperms in fertilization-like processes is called *double fertilization.* It will be remembered that the endosperm in the pine is gametophyte tissue, with *n* chromosomes. Although the endosperm of an angiosperm does not correspond with this in origin, it has the same function—supplying food to the embryo. The sperm that participates in endosperm formation may contribute to the endosperm characters of the plant that furnished the pollen. This is seen, for example, when white corn that has been planted near yellow corn develops a few yellow grains on its ears.

Formation of Seed. After fertilization is completed, the fertilized egg develops into the *embryo sporophyte*, and the endosperm nucleus develops into the food-containing *endosperm*. The integuments usually harden to form the *seed coats*, and the ovary wall becomes the *pericarp*, or *fruit wall* (Fig. 362). The process of seed formation is well illustrated in shepherd's-purse (Fig. 363). The fertilized egg divides to form a filament of several cells. The cell farthest from the micropyle divides and differentiates to form the *embryo;* then the remaining cells constitute the *suspensor*, the

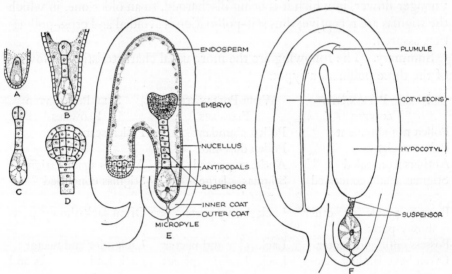

FIG. 363. Development of embryo and endosperm in shepherd's-purse. The fertilized egg (*A*) undergoes several transverse divisions, forming the suspensor (which pushes the embryo well into the endosperm) and the embryo proper (terminal cell in *B*). The latter then divides (*C*) and develops (*D, E, F*). The triple fusion nucleus undergoes free nuclear division and becomes the endosperm, which in this plant is soon reabsorbed by the growing embryo.

function of which is to push the developing embryo farther into the food-containing embryo sac. The embryo soon becomes a globular body and then develops two lobes, which are the beginning of the cotyledons. The epicotyl (plumule) develops between these lobes; the basal portion of the body forms the hypocotyl. Meanwhile, the endosperm nucleus has undergone repeated free nuclear division, forming cells which are spread out near the boundary of the enlarging embryo sac. Later these cells tend to fill the space surrounding the embryo and to develop walls, forming a many-celled tissue. In shepherd's-purse and many other dicots the endosperm is absorbed by the developing embryo before the seed is ripe; but in monocots and many dicots it remains in the seed, being finally absorbed during the process of germination.

The Fruit. As the seed develops, the wall of the enclosing ovary grows and forms the *pericarp* (Gr. "around fruit"). This is thick and fleshy in the tomato, thin and dry in the pea, a firm shell in the acorn, and a very thin membrane on a grain of corn; in a peach it consists of three distinct parts—the skin, the flesh, and the stony pit. A *dehiscent* fruit is one that splits or bursts to discharge the seeds.

The Seed. On the outside of the seed are the two *seed coats*, the *testa* and *tegmen*, developed from the integuments of the ovule. Within these is the food reserve (*endosperm*), unless it has been absorbed before the ripening of the seed. Within or alongside this is the little plant, the *embryo*, which consists of three parts—the seed leaves, or *cotyledons;* the *hypocotyl* (Gr. "below cotyledons"), which is below the attachment of the cotyledons; and the *epicotyl* (Gr. "above cotyledons"), or plumule, which is above their attachment.

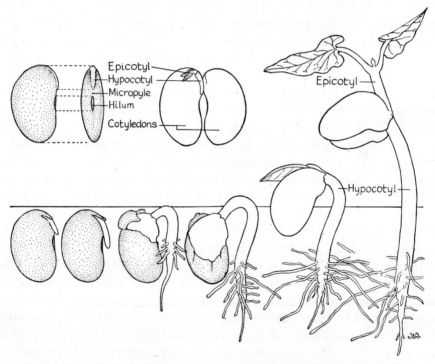

Fig. 364. Lima bean seed, a dicotyledonous seed without endosperm, and its germination. Above, side and edge of seed, and seed with coats removed and cotyledons spread. Below, successive stages in germination.

A Bean and Its Germination.   In the bean the coats are fused together as a tough membrane which covers the seed. Along one edge may be seen the *hilum*, a scar left where the bean has broken from its stalk, and near it the *micropyle*, the opening through which the pollen tube entered the ovule. The endosperm has been absorbed before the seed ripened. The two *cotyledons* are the fleshy halves of the bean (Fig. 364). On germination they and the enlarging plumule are raised above the ground; on exposure to sunlight they turn green and act as the first food-making leaves. But they are too thick to become very efficient, and soon drop. In some plants, such as the pea, the cotyledons remain below ground and disappear when the supply of food is exhausted.

The hypocotyl first grows downward, and the lower part becomes the taproot. The upper part elongates, forms an arch, pulls the cotyledons and plumule out of the ground, and finally straightens.

The *plumule* consists of a short stalk bearing rudimentary leaves. When the arched hypocotyl straightens, these leaves are raised above the ground, ready to expand and function as the food-manufacturing organs of the young plant. In the meantime, the root has become well established and is ready to supply raw materials from the soil; thus the young seedling is prepared to be self-supporting when the food supply of the seed leaves has disappeared.

Corn and Its Germination.   Corn is a monocot with an endosperm-containing seed. A corn grain is a fruit in which the thin fruit wall is scarcely distinguishable from the seed coats. At its upper side is the embryo, marked by an oval depression (Figs. 357, 365). The greater part of the seed is endosperm, consisting of starch and protein. The shield-shaped cotyledon lies in close contact with the endosperm, and in addition to containing food of its own—protein and oil—serves to absorb the food that is stored in the endosperm. The outer leaf of the epicotyl lacks a blade and is merely a protecting sheath.

Seed Dormancy and Factors in Germination.   Seeds are capable of remaining dormant, but alive, over a period of time varying both with the species and with the environment. Seeds of willows and poplars die unless they germinate within a few days after ripening. Germination in corn decreases rapidly from year to year, though some kernels may grow after four or five years. Seeds of some weeds are capable of lying dormant in the soil for more than fifty years. The longevity record is held by seeds of the Indian lotus, which grew after being excavated from a Manchurian lake deposit said to be thousands of years old.

Seeds also differ greatly as to the necessity of a dormant period before germination. Some seeds, such as those of mangrove, a tree of muddy tropical shores, germinate while still on the tree and drop into the mud beneath as well-advanced seedlings. Others, like those of the soft maple, grow immediately after falling; but the majority of seeds do not germinate until after they have gone through a dormant period. This delay may be due to one or more of several causes, such as (1) hardness of the seed coat or fruit wall, (2) slow permeability of the coat or wall to water or to oxygen, (3) immaturity of the embryo, (4) need of a chemical change, perhaps the development of the proper enzymes; this change is often expressed as "after-ripening." Freezing often facilitates germination by softening the coat, rendering it more permeable, or promoting certain chemical changes.

Factors essential to germination are (1) water, which swells the cells of the embryo, softens the seed coats, and makes cell division and growth possible; (2) oxygen, without which no organic activity is possible; (3) temperatures high enough to promote rapid growth; (4) enzymes, which make the reserve food available to the plant; these are normally present in the cells of the seed.

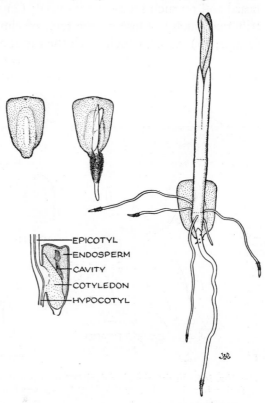

EPICOTYL
ENDOSPERM
CAVITY
COTYLEDON
HYPOCOTYL

Fig. 365. Grain of corn, and two stages in its germination. (For internal structure before germination, see Fig. 357.) The germination stages show the root hairs and the first adventitious roots (those that come from the node at which the cotyledon is joined to the plant axis). Note that the first plumule leaf consists of a sheath only. At left, below, is a section of the germinated grain showing contact of cotyledon with endosperm, and the cavity left by the partial absorption of the latter.

Dispersal by Fruits and Seeds. A species is aided in survival by any agency which removes its young from the crowded situation that would result from their growing too close to the parents, and enables them to colonize new areas. Many of the most successful species are those that have special means by which their seeds or seed-containing fruits are carried. Familiar examples (Fig. 366) are (1) tufts of *hair* that enable the fruit or seed to be carried by wind; these are found on such fruits as goat's beard and on such seeds as milkweed; (2) *wings*, also favoring wind distribution, such as those on the fruit of elm, maple, or ash, or the seed of catalpa; (3) *hooks*, which catch the fur of a passing animal or the clothing

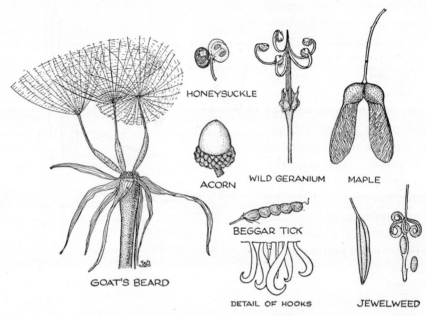

HONEYSUCKLE

ACORN   WILD GERANIUM   MAPLE

BEGGAR TICK

GOAT'S BEARD

DETAIL OF HOOKS   JEWELWEED

Fig. 366. Fruits, showing devices for dispersal. Goat's beard has a dry, one-seeded fruit which is carried by the wind by means of a parachute formed by the modified calyx. The honeysuckle fruit is fleshy; its bright color attracts birds, which feed on the pulp and pass the seeds unharmed from the digestive tract. The acorn (fruit of the oak) is gathered by squirrels, often to be carried for some distance and buried. The maple fruit has a wing-like extension which is caught by the wind. The wild geranium fruit opens by the coiling of elastic strips along the beak, and the jewelweed by the collapse of the elastic wall; these sudden movements result in the hurling of many of the seeds. The beggar tick breaks into one-seeded joints that cling to animals and clothing by means of hooked hairs.

of man, as on beggar ticks and cockleburs; (4) fruits with *seeds edible* by certain animals; the acorn is collected, transported, and often buried by squirrels; (5) fleshy, *edible fruits* with hard, indigestible seeds, such as the grape, raspberry, or honeysuckle berry, the seeds escaping digestion when the fruits are eaten; (6) *explosive fruits*, such as those of wild geranium and jewelweed (touch-me-not), that burst open when mature and throw the seeds to some distance from the parent.

Asexual Reproduction in Flowering Plants. In addition to the reproductive method already discussed, many of the flowering plants have
methods of *asexual* or *vegetative reproduction* (Fig. 367). The *tuber* of the
potato and other familiar underground stems have been considered (Fig.
349). Many plants develop new shoots as sprouts from an old root (as does

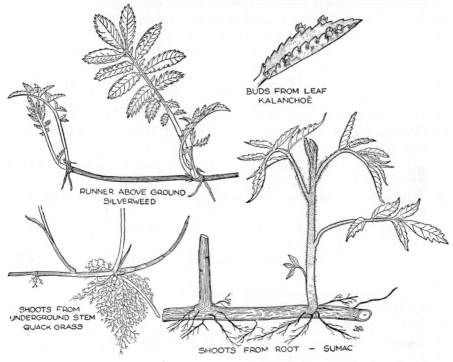

BUDS FROM LEAF
KALANCHOË

RUNNER ABOVE GROUND
SILVERWEED

SHOOTS FROM
UNDERGROUND STEM
QUACK GRASS

SHOOTS FROM ROOT — SUMAC

FIG. 367. Some modes of vegetative (asexual) multiplication among the flowering plants.

sumac). These grow into plants, which may become separated from the
parent. Others have stems which arch over (like the stolon of the black
raspberry) or trail along the ground (like the runner of the strawberry or
silverweed), and strike root to form new plants. Some fleshy leaves, such
as those of *Kalanchoë*, form in the notches buds that develop into plants.
Young plants produced asexually have only one parent and can be depended upon to carry the characteristics of that parent generation after
generation.

EXERCISES

1. Explain how a root hair provides the necessary conditions for osmosis.
2. Why is elongation limited to the very tip of a root, whereas it extends for
   a considerable distance back from the tip of a stem?

3. Why does grass not grow freely under a maple tree?

4. Name five plants with taproot systems; five with fibrous root systems.

5. Name several garden vegetables in which the roots serve as storage organs. Which of these are annuals? Biennials? Perennials?

6. Why do land plants usually die after being covered with water for a few days, whereas water plants may be constantly submerged?

7. Why is a palm stem not adapted to use for lumber?

8. In grafting stems, it is important that the stock (rooted part) and the scion (inserted part) be in contact at their cambium layers. Explain.

9. Why is it that with rare exceptions monocots cannot be grafted?

10. Name several plants with erect stems; with ascending stems; with prostrate stems; with climbing stems.

11. How does quarter-sawed lumber differ from ordinary lumber?

12. Distinguish between heartwood and sapwood. Which makes better lumber? Why?

13. In the spring, the bark of a tree can be easily peeled or slipped from the wood, as is done in making a willow whistle. Explain.

14. Why does the outer bark of a tree often flake off, as does that of shagbark hickory?

15. Look up literature on the use of tree rings in meteorological investigations; in archeological research.

16. Name several plants in which the leaves are used as food. Several in which the petioles are so used.

17. Is there any general correlation between the number of vertical rows of leaves on a stem and the width of the leaves? Between the distance apart in the row and the length? Explain.

18. Although leaves vary greatly in length and breadth, they are rather uniform in thickness. Explain.

19. Account for the excessive thickness of the leaves of a rhododendron; of a live-forever.

20. List ten plants with netted-veined leaves; ten with parallel-veined leaves. Which are dicots and which monocots?

21. The potato is regarded as a modified stem, the sweet potato a modified root. Explain.

22. Name six uses that may be served by leaves in addition to their usual function.

23. What is the significance or use of stipules in the pea; smilax; rubber plant; common locust; elm?

24. Name a plant in which the spines are modified stems; one in which they are modified leaves; one in which they are stipules; one in which the stem is armed with prickles representing epidermal outgrowths.

25. Would you expect greater variation in the progeny of a potato plant when grown from the seed, or when grown from the tubers? Explain.

26. Explain the advantage to the violet in the showy cross-pollinated spring flower; in the bud-like self-pollinated summer flower.
27. List ten flowers adapted to wind pollination; ten adapted to insect pollination.
28. Name five monoecious angiosperms; five dioecious ones. What is a perfect flower? Give examples.
29. Look up and describe adaptations for pollination in milkweed; lady's slipper; fig.
30. In the following fruits name the part or parts that represent the receptacle, the pericarp, and the seed: peach, tomato, walnut, cucumber, pea, orange, apple, strawberry, raspberry, mulberry, fig.
31. A pollen grain of yellow dent corn blown to the silk of white popcorn causes the latter to develop a grain that is yellow, larger than the popcorn. and inferior in popping quality. Explain.

REFERENCES

Clements, F. E. and E. G., *Flower Families and Ancestors*, H. W. Wilson Company, 1928.

Cuthbert, M J., *How to Know the Fall Flowers*, Wm. C. Brown Company, 1948.

Cuthbert, M. J., *How to Know the Spring Flowers*, Wm. C. Brown Company, 2nd ed., 1949.

Fernald, M. L., *Gray's Manual of Botany*, American Book Company, 8th ed., 1950. For the Northeastern and North Central States; similar manuals are available for other areas.

Graves, A. H., *Illustrated Guide to Trees and Shrubs*, published by the author, Wallingford, Conn., 1952.

Hough, R. B., *The Trees of the Northern States and Canada*, published by the author, Lowville, N.Y., 1936.

House, H. D., *Wild Flowers*, The Macmillan Company, 1935.

Jaques, H. E., *How to Know the Trees*, Wm. C. Brown Company, 1946.

Jaques, H. E., *Plant Families: How to Know Them*, Wm. C. Brown Company, 1946.

Lloyd, F. E., *The Carnivorous Plants*, Chronica Botanica Company, 1942.

Maheshwari, P., *Embryology of Angiosperms*, McGraw-Hill Book Company, Inc., 1950.

Mathews, F. S., *Fieldbook of American Wild Flowers*, G. P. Putnam's Sons, rev. ed., 1927.

Otis, C. H., and Burns, G. P., *Michigan Trees*, Univ. of Michigan, 10th ed., 1931.

Pool, R. J., *Flowers and Flowering Plants*, McGraw-Hill Book Company, Inc., 2nd ed., 1940.

Sargent, C. S., *Manual of the Trees of North America*, Houghton Mifflin Company, 1926.

Stover, E. L., *Anatomy of Seed Plants*, D. C. Heath and Company, 1951.

See also botany texts listed in the Appendix.

For tree rings consult papers by A. E. Douglass in *Publications of the Carnegie Institute of Washington*, 1914, 1919, 1928, 1936, and in *Scientific Monthly*, 1925, and *Nature Magazine*, 1928.

Chapter XXVIII

GENETICS

Hereditary Factors. The tendency of related individuals to resemble each other is called *heredity* and constitutes the subject matter of the science of *genetics*. An outstanding achievement of this science has been the demonstration that heredity depends on factors called *genes*, which are carried in the chromosomes of organisms (though cytoplasmic factors, or *plasmagenes*, have also been revealed in a few cases). The nature of these factors has been determined through studies of the transmission of characteristics from generation to generation (*inheritance*) and through observations of cells and chromosomes.

MENDELIAN INHERITANCE

Mendel. The science of genetics is rather new, having undergone most of its development since the beginning of the 20th century. However, it owes a number of its basic concepts to the work of a 19th-century investigator, Gregor Mendel (1822–1884), who performed breeding experiments with garden peas. Mendel (Fig. 368) was a monk and teacher of the city of Brünn (then a part of Austria but now in Czechoslovakia), and his experiments were done in a monastery garden there. In a publication in 1866 he announced the results of these experiments and stated a number of rules of inheritance which have subsequently been found to have wide application.

Breeding Results with One Pair of Contrasting Characters. For his breeding experiments Mendel chose several varieties of garden peas which differed from each other by easily recognizable characteristics (or characters). He recognized seven pairs of contrasting characters involving various attributes of the plants:

1. Form of ripe seeds: round or wrinkled.
2. Color of ripe seeds: yellow or green.

3. Color of seed coat: white or gray.
4. Form of ripe pods: inflated or constricted.
5. Color of unripe pods: green or yellow.
6. Position of flowers: axial or terminal.
7. Length of stem: tall or dwarf.

Fig. 368. Johann Gregor Mendel, whose experiments constitute the foundation of the science of genetics. (From Scott, *Science of Biology;* copyright, Crowell.)

For each of these pairs of characters he made crosses between the differing types. This was done by removing the stamens from flowers of one variety and artificially applying pollen from the other kind to their stigmas, covering them up afterward to prevent accidental pollination by insects. Additional generations were usually derived by self-pollination (which is normal in peas).

The results obtained in the seven cases were essentially similar, so one example is sufficient to illustrate them. When Mendel crossed a variety with round seeds and one with wrinkled seeds, he obtained only round seeds as offspring. However, when another generation was derived (by self-pollination), both round and wrinkled seeds were obtained in a ratio of approximately 3:1 (actual numbers: 5474 round, 1850 wrinkled). These results are shown below, the first and second derived generations being called F_1 (*first filial*) and F_2 (*second filial*) respectively.

	round parent	×	wrinkled parent
F_1		round	
F_2	round		wrinkled
	¾		¼

Explanation of the Breeding Results. These results may be explained by means of the following principles (stated in the terms of modern genetics, though similar to those advanced by Mendel):

1. *Each pair of contrasting characters depends on a pair of genes.* In the example there is a gene for roundness and another one for wrinkledness.

2. *Each individual carries such genes in duplicate.* This is apparent from the nature of the F_1 generation plants. Although these plants exhibit only roundness and consequently must have the gene for roundness, they are capable, when mated to themselves, of having wrinkled offspring

and hence must also carry the gene for wrinkledness. Since roundness is expressed in the F_1 generation to the exclusion of wrinkledness, roundness is called *dominant*, wrinkledness *recessive* (in the above tabulation of seven pairs of contrasting traits, the first character of each pair is the dominant one). The roundness gene may be designated by R, the wrinkledness gene by r; the gene constitution of an F_1 plant is then Rr. The parent plants (i.e., plants of the pure varieties) also have their genes in duplicate, but both members of the gene pair are alike; thus the round parent has gene combination RR, the wrinkled parent gene combination rr.

3. *An individual produces gametes which have only one member of a pair of genes.* Hence the members of a gene pair must *segregate* from each other at some time prior to gamete formation. When the members are alike, all the gametes must be alike, each having one gene of the pair. But in an individual in which the members of a gene pair are different, two kinds of gametes should be produced, and in equal numbers—one kind with one gene and the other kind with the other. Thus, an F_1 plant should produce half its gametes (half its eggs and half its sperms) with gene R and half with gene r (the generations being considered are, of course, sporophyte generations, though the gametes are actually produced by the inconspicuous

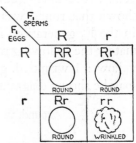

Fig. 369. Diagram explaining the 3:1 ratio obtained by Mendel in the F_2 generation derived from the crossing of round and wrinkled peas.

gametophytes). This principle has been called *Mendel's First Law*, or the *Law of Segregation*.

4. *Fertilization of the gametes restores the duplicate condition of the genes.*

5. *With respect to the genes they contain, gametes enter fertilization at random.* Thus, the combinations of genes in the zygotes depend on chance encounters of the gametes that carry the genes.

On the basis of these principles the breeding results described above are shown in Fig. 369. The kinds of individuals in the F_2 generation (representing different gamete combinations) are shown in subdivisions of a square, at the top of which are the kinds of sperms produced by an F_1 plant and at the left of which are the kinds of eggs produced by such a plant. Since fertilizations occur at random, the four kinds that result in the F_2 generation should occur about equally often. Since three of these result in round seeds and the other one in wrinkled seeds, the ratio of round to wrinkled seeds is expected to be approximately 3:1. Deviations from an exact 3:1 ratio may appear because of chance (just as tossing a coin a number of times may result in an unequal number of heads and tails). However, the effects of chance are minimized by large numbers of individuals (as with coin tosses); and by obtaining many seeds, Mendel satisfied himself that a 3:1 ratio was being approximated.

Breeding Results with Two Pairs of Contrasting Characters. Mendel also studied results of crosses involving two pairs of contrasting characters. When a variety with round and yellow seeds was crossed with one having wrinkled and green seeds, the F_1 generation consisted entirely of round, yellow individuals (consistent with the fact that separate experiments had shown that round was dominant over wrinkled, and yellow over green). In the F_2 generation, four kinds of seeds were obtained and in approximately the following ratio: 9 round, yellow : 3 round, green : 3 wrinkled, yellow : 1 wrinkled, green (actual ratio, 315:108:101:32). These results may be shown diagrammatically:

	round, yellow parent	$\times$	wrinkled, green parent	
F_1		round, yellow		
F_2	round, yellow	round, green	wrinkled, yellow	wrinkled, green
	$\frac{9}{16}$	$\frac{3}{16}$	$\frac{3}{16}$	$\frac{1}{16}$

Explanation of These Results. These results may be explained by the principles already given and by another one.

When there are two pairs of unlike genes, the distribution of the members of one pair to the gametes is independent of the distribution of the other pair. Since each gamete should receive one member of each pair of genes, all the different possible combinations of the genes of the different pairs should occur in the gametes, and these combinations should all be equally likely. Thus, if Y is the gene for yellow seeds and y the gene for green seeds, an F_1 individual resulting from the "round, yellow" and "wrinkled, green" cross should have the gene constitution $RrYy$. With independent distribution (*independent assortment*) of the R-r and Y-y gene pairs, four kinds of gametes should be produced by such a plant— RY, Ry, rY, and ry—and these should be equally frequent. This principle has been called *Mendel's Second Law*, or the *Law of Independent Assortment*.

The results obtained with the two pairs of contrasting characters are shown in Fig. 370. As the diagram indicates, there are sixteen possible combinations of gametes that give rise to the F_2 generation. Moreover, with the gametes uniting at random, these different combinations should be equally likely. Nine of them result in round, yellow seeds; three in round, green ones; three in wrinkled, yellow ones; and one in wrinkled, green ones. Thus, an approximate 9:3:3:1 ratio is expected.

Some Genetics Terms. The discussion of genetics is greatly facilitated by the use of special terms. A number of these are introduced here and illustrated by the breeding experiments just described.

1. *Alleles* (or *allelomorphs*). Genes which are related to each other as members of a pair are called *alleles*. Thus, R and r constitute a pair of alleles, as do also Y and y.

2. *Unit Character.* An attribute of an organism that varies because of a single pair of alleles is called a *unit character*. In the above examples, seed shape (which may be either round or wrinkled) and seed color (either yellow or green) are unit characters. Mendel was fortunate in choosing traits that acted as unit characters for his study, because it now appears that many of the

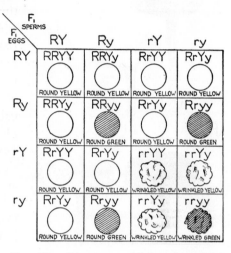

Fig. 370. Diagram explaining the 9:3:3:1 ratio obtained by Mendel in the F_2 generation of the crossing of round, yellow peas and wrinkled, green peas.

attributes of organisms vary depending on numerous genes, so that the actions of the *individual* genes are difficult (if not impossible) to demonstrate.

3. *Phenotype and Genotype.* As in the above examples, individuals may be classified according to their appearance. A class based on appearance is called a *phenotype*. Thus, round seed is one phenotype, wrinkled seed another. With the addition of the yellow-green pair of contrasting characters, more phenotypes become possible—round, yellow; wrinkled, green; round, green; wrinkled, yellow. On the other hand, individuals may be classed according to the genes they possess; a class based on genes is called a *genotype*. Sometimes the genotype is apparent from the phenotype, but often it is not. For example, RR, Rr, and rr are three different genotypes; but RR and Rr are both associated with the round phenotype, rr with the wrinkled one. The 3:1 and 9:3:3:1 ratios are phenotype ratios. However, examination of Figs. 369 and 370 reveals the expected genotype ratios as well. In the case of round-wrinkled variation alone, the F_2 geno-

type ratio is expected to be 1 *RR* : 2 *Rr* : 1 *rr*. In the case involving both round-wrinkled and yellow-green variation, the expected F_2 genotype ratio is 1 *RRYY* : 2 *RRYy* : 1 *RRyy* : 2 *RrYY* : 4 *RrYy* : 2 *Rryy* : 1 *rrYY* : 2 *rrYy* : 1 *rryy*. By allowing his F_2 generation plants to produce another generation, Mendel determined these genotype ratios experimentally.

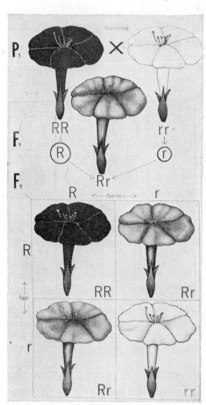

FIG. 371. Diagram showing flower color inheritance in four-o'clocks. Red and white depend on a pair of alleles, *R* and *r*, but neither gene is dominant. Hence the F_1 offspring are pink; the F_2, 1 red; 2 pink; 1 white. (From chart of *General Biology Series* edited by Goddard, Kenoyer, and Hinds; published by Denoyer-Geppert Co., Chicago, by courtesy of the publishers.)

4. *Homozygous and Heterozygous Individuals.* An individual in which both members of a gene pair are alike is said to be *homozygous* for the gene in question, and such an individual is called a *homozygote.* For example, plants of genotypes *RR* and *rr* are *homozygous* for genes *R* and *r* respectively. If the members of a gene pair are unlike, the individual is *heterozygous* for the gene, or a *heterzygote.* For instance, a plant of genotype *Rr* is heterozygous for the genes of the *R-r* pair. An organism may, of course, be homozygous for one gene pair and heterozygous for another, as for instance a "round, yellow" plant of genotype *RRYy.*

Significance of Mendel's Principles. Though Mendel published his results and conclusions in 1866, they received little attention until 1900, thirty-four years afterward. This neglect may have been due partly to the obscurity of Mendel's publication (in the *Proceedings* of the Natural History Society of Brünn), but it must have been due in large part to the fact that the biologists of his day were not prepared to accept his explanation of heredity. In 1900, several investigators working independently of each other rediscovered the principles of inheritance which Mendel had formulated, and Mendel's accomplishments were given the recognition they deserved.

Numerous additional examples of *Mendelian inheritance* were also shown to exist. These were found in many different organisms (cultivated plants, domestic and experimental animals, and man), and this suggested the fundamental nature of his discoveries. However, some exceptional cases were also observed. For example, heterozygotes were sometimes found to have intermediate phenotypes (i.e., lacking dominance). Thus, phenotype ratios corresponding to ratios of genotypes were obtained. This is illustrated by flower color inheritance in four-o'clocks, which is shown in Fig. 371. Another exception to Mendel's rules was lack of independent assortment. This will be discussed later, after the relationship of genes and chromosomes has been introduced. Although exceptions to Mendel's principles are known and much additional information about inheritance has been gained, his idea of hereditary factors behaving as particles has proved to be of far-reaching importance.

GENES AND CHROMOSOMES

Early Investigations. In the latter part of the 19th century, various observations of chromosomes were made which supported the idea that these bodies were the carriers of hereditary factors. It was observed that the chromosomes are precisely divided at mitosis, that their number is maintained with considerable regularity from cell to cell and from individual to individual, that the chromosome number is reduced at meiosis, and that there is a fusion of nuclei (with combination of their chromosomes) at fertilization. The regularity of the behavior and distribution of chromosomes was taken as evidence of their importance in the lives of organisms, and it was suspected that they were the carriers of the factors of heredity. All these studies of chromosomes were made after Mendel's publication of his principles of inheritance; but because of the obscurity of this publication, the interpretation of these studies in terms of heredity must have been made without knowledge of his principles. However, because of these investigations, biologists were well prepared to accept Mendel's laws of inheritance when they were rediscovered in 1900. As will be shown presently, there were remarkable parallels between the behavior of the hereditary factors postulated by Mendel and that of the chromosomes revealed by the microscope.

Meiosis. As was pointed out in Chapter III, *meiosis* (Gr. "making smaller") is a nuclear process that results in the reduction of the chromosomes from the diploid to the haploid number. It is a regular accompaniment of gametogenesis in animals (Figs. 65, 372) and of sporogenesis in plants. This process usually takes place with two successive cell divisions;

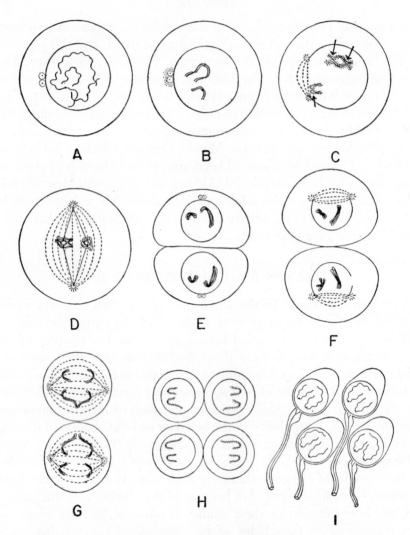

Fig. 372. Diagram illustrating meiosis accompanying spermatogenesis. For simplicity, the diploid chromosome number has been assumed to be four (i.e., two pairs of chromosomes). *A-C*, Prophase of the first division. The cell in *A* is a primary spermatocyte just beginning meiosis. In *B* the members of the chromosome pairs lie side by side in synapsis. In *C* the individual chromosomes have split and chiasmata (indicated by arrows) have appeared. *D*, Metaphase of the first division. *E*, Formation of the secondary spermatocytes. *F*, Prophase of the second division. *G*, Anaphase of the second division, *H*, Four spermatids. *I*, Four sperms. Note that each spermatid (and each sperm) has but one chromosome derived from each of the chromosome pairs shown in the primary spermatocyte. (Redrawn, with modification, from L. H. Snyder, *The Principles of Heredity*, D. C. Heath and Company, 4th ed., 1951.)

hence, four rather than two cells (or nuclei) are ordinarily produced. The nuclear behavior in each of these divisions is superficially similar to that in mitosis, and the names applied to the mitotic stages (prophase, metaphase, anaphase, and telophase) are also used for each of the meiotic divisions. However, there are definite differences between these divisions and ordinary mitotic divisions, especially as regards the chromosomes. During the prophase of the first division of meiosis, a striking feature is the fact that the chromosomes come together in pairs and lie close to each other side by side (Fig. 372 B). Chromosomes which pair in this manner generally look very much alike and are called *homologous chromosomes*, or *homologues*. The pairing process is called *synapsis*. As the metaphase of the first division passes into anaphase, the members (already partly split) of each pair of chromosomes separate from each other, and one member moves to one pole of the spindle and the other member moves to the other pole (Fig. 372 D, E). This *segregation* of the members of the chromosome pairs takes the place of the separation of the chromosome halves which occurs at the corresponding stage in mitosis. In meiosis, the separation of the half chromosomes does not take place until the end of metaphase in the second division (Fig. 372 G). Consequently, since there are two cell divisions and only one division of the chromosomes, each of the four resulting nuclei receives only one chromosome from each chromosome pair (instead of from each chromosome) and thus has only half as many chromosomes as there were in the original cell (Fig. 372 H, I). Two striking parallels between chromosomes and Mendel's hereditary factors are apparent from meiosis: (1) Chromosomes, like genes, exist in pairs in an individual; (2) the members of a chromosome pair, like those of a gene pair, segregate from each other prior to gamete formation.

Fertilization. When gametes participate in fertilization (Fig. 373), their nuclei fuse and their chromosomes are brought together. The chromosomes again exist in pairs (though they may not lie side by side until another meiosis). According to Mendel's conclusions, fertilization restores the duplicate condition of the genes. Thus, fertilization offers an additional parallel between chromosomes and genes.

Sex Chromosomes. Early in the present century it was found that in certain animals there is a definite difference between the chromosomes of the two sexes. An early example of this sort was observed in tiny fruit flies of the species *Drosophila melanogaster* (Fig. 374), an organism which was to feature prominently in the later development of genetics. Flies of this species regularly show four pairs of chromosomes at mitosis, but there is a difference between females and males with regard to one of the chromosome pairs. In females there are two rod-shaped chromosomes (*X-chromosomes*), but in males there is only one of these rods, and this is associated with a J-shaped chromosome (*Y-chromosome*) not present in females. The X- and Y-chromosomes are called *sex chromosomes*. These offer an explanation of the age-old question of why one individual develops into a female and another becomes a male. When oogenesis takes place in a female of this species, each egg receives one of the X-chromosomes

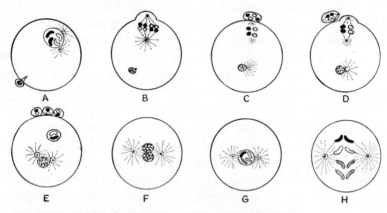

Fig. 373. Meiosis, fertilization, and first division of the zygote as shown in eggs in the uterus of *Ascaris*, a parasitic roundworm. *A,* Entrance of sperm (below, left) into the cytoplasm of the egg; the nucleus of the latter contains two pairs of chromosomes; one of each pair (shaded) has come from the mother and the other (unshaded) from the father of the worm producing the egg. *B,* Metaphase of first meiotic division in which paternal and maternal chromosomes pair in preparation for redistribution as whole chromosomes. They have already split, however, in preparation for the subsequent division. *C,* Telophase of first division. *D,* Second meiotic division. *E,* Egg and three polar bodies; centrosome of sperm nucleus dividing. *F,* Fusion of egg and sperm nuclei. *G,* Prophase of first cleavage of zygote; the chromosomes contributed by the egg are shown above, those by the sperm below. *H,* Anaphase of first cleavage division.

(along with one member of each of the other three chromosome pairs). However, when spermatogenesis occurs in a male, the members of the XY pair segregate, and half the sperms receive an X-chromosome and half a Y. Fertilization of an egg by an X-bearing sperm results in an XX zygote which becomes a female, and fertilization by a Y-bearing sperm produces an XY zygote which gives rise to a male (Fig. 375). Since these combinations of gametes must be equally likely, this shows why females and males are produced in approximately equal numbers. Similar sex chromosomes have been demonstrated in many other animals, including man (Fig. 376).

Sex-Linked Inheritance. Several years after the observation of a chromosome difference between the sexes in *Drosophila melanogaster*, an unusual kind of inheritance was demonstrated in this species by the American geneticist T. H. Morgan (1866–1945). Although flies of this species normally have red compound eyes, Morgan found a number of males with white eyes. When these males were mated to red-eyed females, the offspring all had red eyes. But when the F_1 flies produced an F_2 generation,

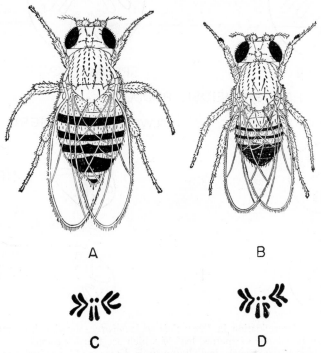

A   B

C   D

Fig. 374. *Drosophila melanogaster. A,* Adult female. *B,* Adult male. *C,* Chromosomes of female as seen at metaphase. *D,* Metaphase chromosomes of male. The rod-shaped chromosome represented twice in the female and once in the male is the *X;* its *J*-shaped partner in the male is the *Y.* (*A* and *B* about 10×, *C* and *D* greatly enlarged.) (*A* and *B* redrawn from Bridges and Gabritschewsky in *Zeits. f. ind. Abst. u. Ver.*)

though the F_2 generation had an approximate 3:1 ratio of red-eyed to white-eyed individuals, all the F_2 females were red-eyed and half the F_2 males were red-eyed and half white-eyed. White-eyed females were also obtained in a later generation, so it was possible to make a *reciprocal cross,* i.e., white-eyed females mated to red-eyed males. This also gave unusual results, but of a different kind. In the F_1 generation, although the females were red-eyed, the males were white-eyed; and in the F_2 generation, instead of a 3:1 ratio, there was a 1:1 ratio of red-eyed to white-eyed flies, half of each sex being of each kind.

PRIMARY GAMETOCYTES

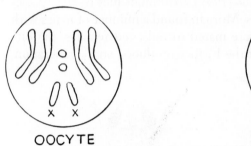

OOCYTE   SPERMATOCYTE

THROUGH MEIOSIS PRODUCE

ONE KIND OF EGG   TWO KINDS OF SPERM

          +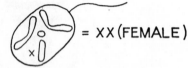

          +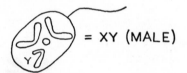

FIG. 375. Sex determination in *Drosophila melanogaster*, showing how meiosis in the male results in two kinds of sperms, half of which are female-producing and half male-producing. Sex in many animals, including man, is determined by a similar mechanism.

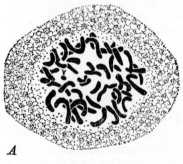   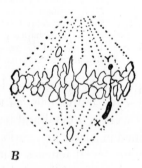

A   *B*

FIG. 376. Chromosomes of human male. *A*, Prophase in one of the divisions of the spermatogenous tissue, the Y-chromosome indicated; *B*, metaphase of meiosis, equatorial view, showing the sex chromosomes shaded, the others in outline. (From Guyer, *Being Well-Born;* copyright, Bobbs-Merrill.)

Explanation of Sex Linkage. Morgan offered an explanation of sex-linked inheritance based on the sex chromosomes of this species. The eye color variation was attributed to a single pair of alleles: W, a dominant gene causing red eyes, and w, a recessive gene causing white eyes. It was assumed that the X-chromosome regularly carried either one or the other of these genes, and that the Y-chromosome carried neither of them and moreover had nothing to do with their expression. Fig. 377 shows how the inheritance of red and white eyes is explained by these assumptions. This explanation offered considerable support for the idea that chromosomes are the carriers of genes, because it provided evidence that a peculiar sort of inheritance could be explained by genes carried by a special kind of chromosome. The demonstration of sex linkage in *Drosophila melanogaster* was the beginning of an extensive investigation of heredity in this insect by Morgan and his co-workers; many more cases of hereditary variation were discovered, and much evidence was obtained concerning the genes responsible for them.

Linkage. As was said earlier, Mendel's 9:3:3:1 ratio may be explained by the assumption that different gene pairs are assorted independently of each other, so that an individual heterozygous for two pairs of genes produces four kinds of gametes with equal frequency. However, it was discovered early in the 20th century that not all gene pairs show independent assortment with respect to each other. An example may be taken from the corn plant. Colored kernels are caused by dominant gene C, white ones by recessive gene c; full kernels depend on dominant gene S, shrunken ones on recessive gene s. Thus, when a plant of a "colored, full" variety was crossed with a "white, shrunken" individual, the offspring were of genotype $CcSs$. When an F_1 plant was mated to a plant of the "white, shrunken" kind (an example of a *backcross*), it was found that a large majority of the resulting kernels (96.4 percent) were of the two parental types "colored, full" and "white, shrunken," whereas only a few (3.6 percent) showed a *recombination* of the characters in the "colored, shrunken" and "white, full" phenotypes. Since the four kinds of offspring of the backcross formed two groups with markedly unequal frequencies, the four kinds of gametes produced by the F_1 plant must have occurred with correspondingly unequal frequencies. The gametes with gene combinations of the kinds originally received from the parents (CS and cs) must have constituted 96.4 percent of all the gametes, those with a recombination of genes (Cs and cS) making up the remaining 3.6 percent. Thus, there was a strong tendency for genes to stay in their original combinations, though they were capable of achieving new combinations with low frequencies. When such a tendency exists, the genes are said to show *linkage* and to be *linked* to each other.

Explanation of Linkage. The phenomenon of linkage may be explained by assuming that the different pairs of linked genes are associated with the same chromosome pair. (Independent assortment may likewise be ex-

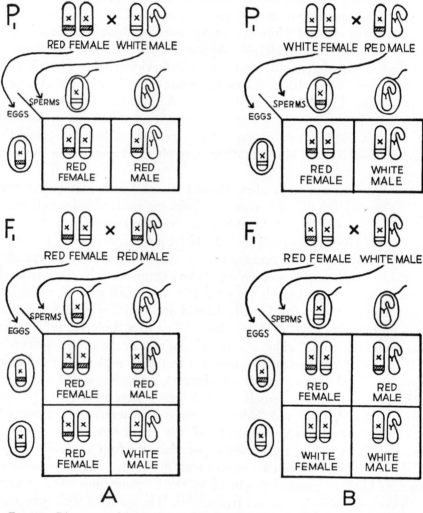

A   B

Fig. 377. Diagram explaining the sex-linked inheritance of red and white compound eyes in *Drosophila melanogaster*, as observed by Morgan. *A*, Derivation of F₁ and F₂ generations following the crossing of red-eyed female with white-eyed male. *B*, Derivation of F₁ and F₂ from crossing of white-eyed female and red-eyed male. The X- and Y-chromosomes are shown and also their distribution in eggs, sperms, and zygotes. On the X-chromosome the presence of the dominant red-eye gene (W) is shown by a shaded bar, that of the recessive white-eye gene (w) by an unshaded bar.

plained by the assumption that different pairs of chromosomes are the carriers of different sets of alleles and that the chromosome pairs are assorted independently of each other.) In the example, the two sets of alleles, *C-c* and *S-s*, must be carried by the same pair of chromosomes. In the original cross, genes *C* and *S* are received together on the same chromosome from the "colored, full" parent, and genes *c* and *s* are similarly received together on the chromosome from the "white, shrunken" parent. The small amount of recombination of these genes in the gametes of the F_1 individual may be assumed to require an exchange of material by the homologous chromosomes (*crossing over*). Recombination must occur with a frequency that reflects the frequency of crossing over. When there is linkage, various frequencies of recombination, and hence of crossing over, are found. Crossing over takes place during meiosis; associated with this process are X-shaped connections (*chiasmata*), which may be seen during the early part of the first meiotic division (Fig. 372C). Fig. 378 illustrates the phenomena of linkage and crossing over in the inheritance of kernel color and shape in corn.

Linkage Groups and Chromosome Maps. Experience has shown that the genes of a species fall naturally into *linkage groups*, within each one of which the genes show linkage to each other. When many of the genes of an organism are known, the number of linkage groups usually corresponds to (and does not exceed) the number of pairs of homologous chromosomes. For example, *Drosophila melanogaster*, with four chromosome pairs, has four linkage groups; and the corn plant, with ten pairs of chromosomes, has ten linkage groups. This correspondence between linkage groups and chromosome pairs is additional evidence that the chromosomes are the carriers of the genes. Within the same linkage group it has been found that the various frequencies of crossing over are related to each other in such a way as to suggest a *linear distribution* of the genes along their chromosomes, with the genes far apart having greater crossing-over frequencies than those close together. On the basis of variation of crossing-over frequencies, *chromosome (genetic) maps* have been constructed to show the distribution of the genes along their chromosomes (Fig. 379).

Chromosome Aberrations. Although chromosomes are distributed from generation to generation with remarkable regularity, occasionally there occur microscopically visible transformations of the chromosomes of a species. Such changes are called *chromosome aberrations*. The number of chromosomes may be altered, or the chromosomes may be broken and parts lost or gained or reassembled in an unusual way. These changes occur spontaneously very infrequently (once in many thousands of gametes

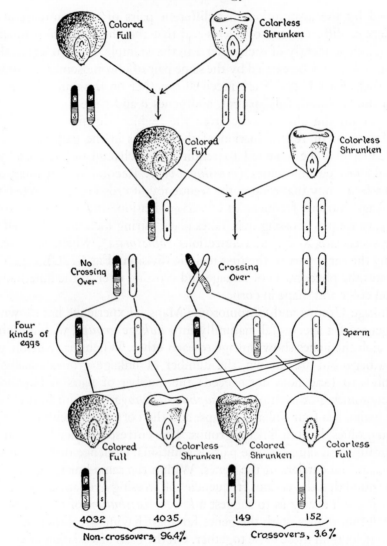

Fig. 378. Diagram explaining the inheritance of kernel color and shape characteristics in corn. The color genes (*C* and *c*) and the shape genes (*S* and *s*) are shown to be *linked*, i.e., carried by the same chromosome pair. When there is heterozygosis for both these gene pairs, recombination of genes occurs through *crossing over* with a frequency of 3.6 percent. (Adapted from Sinnott and Dunn.)

or spores per generation). However, certain environmental agents increase their occurrence tremendously. For example, chemicals are known which alter chromosome number, and x-rays and other high-energy radiations promote chromosome breakage. Chromosome aberrations offer abundant proof of the relationship of genes and chromosomes, because these aberrations are regularly associated with modifications of inheritance and changes in the relations of genes to each other.

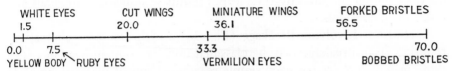

| WHITE EYES | CUT WINGS | MINIATURE WINGS | FORKED BRISTLES |
| 1.5 | 20.0 | 36.1 | 56.5 |

| 0.0 | 7.5 | 33.3 | 70.0 |
| YELLOW BODY | RUBY EYES | VERMILION EYES | BOBBED BRISTLES |

Fig. 379. Partial genetic map of the X-chromosome of *Drosophila melanogaster*. The positions of several mutant genes are indicated by numbers based on frequencies of crossing over. For example, white eyes is assigned position 1.5 because it shows 1.5 percent of crossing over with respect to yellow body (0.0); miniature wings is placed at 36.1 because of showing 36.1 percent of crossing over with respect to yellow body.

Aberrations Involving Change of Chromosome Number (Fig. 380). Prominent among chromosome aberrations are cases of *polyploidy*, in which one or more whole sets of chromosomes are added to the usual number. *Triploidy* is the condition of having three sets of chromosomes ($3n$). It is the normal condition of the endosperm in certain angiosperms (page 459), but it has occurred as an abnormality in various plants and animals. In *tetraploidy* there are four sets of chromosomes ($4n$)—i.e., twice the diploid number. The alkaloid substance *colchicine* has been used to induce tetraploidy in various plants. This substance interferes with mitosis and results in chromosome doubling without cell division; when cell division does take place later, the doubled chromosome number is maintained in the daughter cells. Polyploids of a still higher order are also known. Other kinds of aberrations involving change in chromosome number are *haploidy*, in which only one set (n) of chromosomes is present (as in spores and gametes), and *heteroploidy*, in which one or more chromosomes (but not a whole set) are either lacking or present in excess (e.g., $2n - 1$,

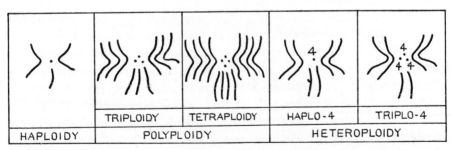

| | TRIPLOIDY | TETRAPLOIDY | HAPLO-4 | TRIPLO-4 |
| HAPLOIDY | POLYPLOIDY | | HETEROPLOIDY | |

Fig. 380. Aberrations involving change in chromosome number, as illustrated by the chromosomes of *Drosophila melanogaster*. Except for haploidy, zygotes of all these kinds have been reported to survive and produce abnormal adult individuals of this species. The tiny, dot-like chromosome is called Chromosome 4.

$2n + 1$). Aberrations involving change in chromosome number are associated with modifications of phenotype and inheritance. For example, polyploids are generally large, haploids small; in breeding experiments the distribution of genes by these types results in unusual individuals and ratios of phenotypes.

Aberrations Involving Breakage (Fig. 381). Chromosome aberrations resulting from breakage may be classified under two main headings: (1) those in which there has been simple rearrangement of material, and (2)

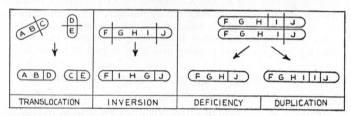

| TRANSLOCATION | INVERSION | DEFICIENCY | DUPLICATION |

Fig. 381. Chromosome aberrations involving breakage and re-attachment of parts. The translocation is shown as a reciprocal transfer between nonhomologous chromosomes. The remaining aberrations involve only one kind of chromosome. For simplicity, only a few genes are indicated by letters.

those involving loss or gain of material. In the first category are *translocations* and *inversions*. A translocation results from transfer of material between nonhomologous chromosomes (unlike crossing over, in which the transfer involves homologues); an inversion results from the removal of a piece of chromosome and its replacement in reverse order. In the second group are *deficiencies*, in which a piece of chromosome is lacking, and *duplications*, in which a piece is present in excess. These aberrations are also associated with changes of phenotype and inheritance. Particularly striking are the alterations of linkage relations associated with rearrangements of chromosome material.

Cytological Maps. In certain species, attempts have been made to determine the actual positions of the genes on the chromosomes. The greatest success has been achieved with the little flies of the genus *Drosophila*. A remarkable feature of these insects is the fact that larvae contain salivary glands in which the chromosomes are enormously large (about 200 times larger than those of other tissues) and exhibit considerable detail (Fig. 382). The chromosomes of the salivary glands show a regular pattern of bands and interband spaces (except for aberrations), and it has been possible to relate the positions of genes to this pattern. Especially helpful in this work have been the aberrations involving breakage, because changes of gene associations (as determined in breeding experiments) have been found to be correlated with clearly visible changes of chromosome material. On the basis of such studies *cytological maps* have been constructed showing the distribution of genes with respect to microscopically visible landmarks. There has been remarkable agreement between these maps and

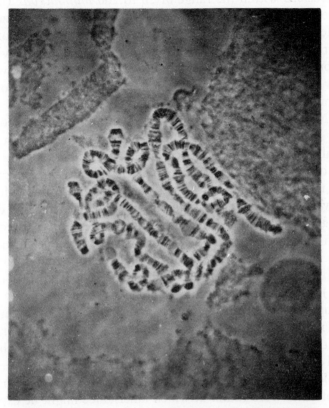

FIG. 382. Salivary gland nucleus of a larva of *Drosophila robusta* (× 520). The long strands having patterns of cross bands of various intensities represent closely paired chromosomes much larger than those of ordinary cells. These unusual chromosomes occur in larval salivary glands in members of the genus *Drosophila* and elsewhere in the Order DIPTERA. (Phase contrast photomicrograph by A. F. Yanders.)

chromosome maps based on crossing-over data alone (though discrepancies indicate that crossing over is not equally likely in all chromosome regions).

Gene Number and Size. The possibility exists that each of the bands of a *Drosophila* salivary gland chromosome represents the position of a gene (though more than one gene might be included in such a band). On the basis of the number of such bands the minimum number of genes in the chromosomes of *Drosophila melanogaster* (haploid set) has been estimated at about 5000 (a much larger number than that of genes with *known* variation). Other organisms with more chromosome material must presumably have more genes than this. A single gene has been estimated to have dimensions within the range of 20 to 200 *millimicrons* (thousandth of a micron) and thus to be of the order of a virus particle in size. Though such dimensions would place the gene well below the limit of visibility with microscopes using light, a particle of this size should be visible with an electron microscope. But the difficulty of distinguishing between genes and other possible chromosome material has stood in the way of attempts to determine genes microscopically.

Gene Mutation. Although genes are duplicated with considerable accuracy from cell to cell and from generation to generation, there are occasional transformations of genes, or *gene mutations*. A gene which has recently come into existence in this way is called a *mutant gene*. Gene mutation may be revealed by the sudden appearance of individuals show-ing a new phenotype. For example, the white-eyed fruit flies discovered by Morgan probably owed their existence to the relatively recent trans-formation of gene W (red eyes) to gene w (white eyes.) Sometimes a mutant gene appears in a portion of the body cells of an individual so that part of the organism exhibits a character different from that of the rest (Fig. 383). Gene mutation occurs spontaneously, but ordinarily with very low frequencies. In 1927 the American geneticist H. J. Muller reported that gene mutation frequencies are enormously increased by x-rays. More recently it has been found that other high-energy radiations, high tempera-tures, and certain chemicals also increase mutation rates.

Multiple Factors. Soon after the rediscovery of Mendel's principles, a number of cases were found in which inheritance might be explained by two or more pairs of genes influencing the same character. For example, the Swedish geneticist Nilsson-Ehle observed that when a white variety of wheat was crossed with a very dark red one, the offspring were of an intermediate shade of red. When an F_2 generation was produced, variation was found from very dark red to white, with several intermediate colors. Inspection of these colors showed there were five different classes with about the following ratio—1 very dark red: 4 dark red: 6 intermediate red: 4 light red: 1 white. This was explained as follows: The original parents differed by two independent pairs of color genes: A and a, B and b. Both A and B caused redness, a and b whiteness. Moreover, there was no domi-nance in either gene pair, and the effects of the different genes were cumu-lative. This explanation is shown diagrammatically in Fig. 384.

Much of the variation of living things is of a kind called *continuous*, or *quantitative*. Individuals appear to show all degrees of variation from one extreme to another, and classification into natural categories is not possible. Many of the important characters of domestic animals and cultivated

Fig. 383. Delphinium plant bearing flowers exhibiting both purple coloration (left) and lavender coloration (right). This plant came about through mutation of the lavender gene to the purple gene at an early stage of development, so that the mutant gene was incorporated into a large part of the plant. (From M. Demerec in *Journal of Heredity*, 24:369, 1933.)

plants are of this sort, e.g., size and weight, yield of products (milk, eggs, grain, etc.). It was once believed that the inheritance of such traits required an explanation quite different from that sufficient for Mendelian inheritance. But it is now generally believed that numerous gene pairs (*multiple factors*) are responsible for such inheritance, the genes indi-

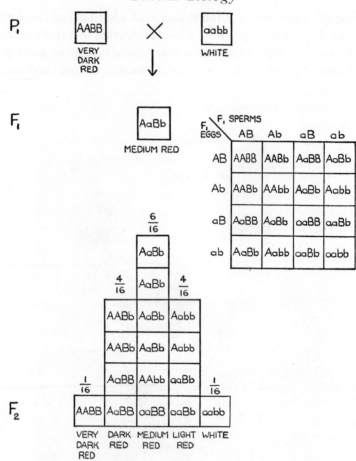

Fig. 384. Diagram explaining inheritance of kernel color in wheat, as observed by Nilsson-Ehle. Two pairs of color factors are shown, with the capital letter genes causing red coloration, dominance lacking, and the effects of these genes cumulative. The combinations of F_1 generation gametes to form an F_2 generation are shown in the large square at the right. Below, the F_2 zygotes are arranged in columns according to the number of color genes (capital letters) present— four of these causing very dark red coloration, three dark red, two medium red, one light red, and none (i.e., four small-letter genes) whiteness.

vidually having slight effects which are cumulative, as with the color factors in wheat.

Genes and Development. On the basis of our present knowledge of inheritance it appears that an organism must have numerous genes that work together to determine its development. Some insight into the operation of these factors has been gained by close examination of the differences in developmental processes associated with gene differences. There is increasing evidence that genes produce their effects by means of enzymes. Many investigations have shown that gene variation is associated with variation in chemical reactions accompanying development. For example, in normal animals of many different kinds the pigmentation of the skin and skin derivatives is due to the presence of a substance called melanin, which is produced from the amino acid tyrosine by a series of reactions. In *albinos* (e.g., white rabbits), which may owe their lack of coloration to a single gene, melanin is diminished or lacking. In normal animals, enzymes that promote the transformation of tyrosine to melanin are present, but albinos lack one or another of them. Thus, the normal allele of an albinism gene may be considered necessary for the presence of such an enzyme; substitution of the gene for albinism results in absence of the enzyme and failure of melanin formation.

GENETICS AND AGRICULTURE

Since early times man has sought to improve domestic animals and cultivated plants by regulating their breeding, selecting superior individuals and rejecting undesirable ones. Genetics is able to offer explanations for some of the difficulties and successes that have been encountered and to give suggestions for further improvements.

Selection. By selecting individuals with desirable characteristics, it is sometimes possible to establish true-breeding stocks that exhibit these traits. One may also combine the good characteristics of different varieties by crossing them and selecting from their descendants. Thus, for example, a wheat grower may take one strain that has good milling quality but is susceptible to disease and another strain with poor milling quality but disease-resistant, cross them, and select from their descendants plants with both good milling quality and disease resistance. This may be explained by recombination of genes following the original cross. On the other hand, because of undesirable recessive genes, selection sometimes runs into difficulty. Unwanted characters may crop up repeatedly, and much continued breeding and selecting may be needed to get rid of them. A number of domestic animals (e.g., cattle) occasionally produce grossly abnormal offspring which die early; some of them are known to depend on recessive genes (examples of *lethal factors*).

Inbreeding. Reproduction involving the mating of close relatives (even self-mating) is called *inbreeding*. Close inbreeding through many generations regularly results in a nearly uniform group of individuals. In certain organisms there is also a marked loss of vigor and the appearance of abnormal traits. It may be shown by Mendelian principles that inbreeding should increase the number of homozyous genes. Thus, the uniformity of

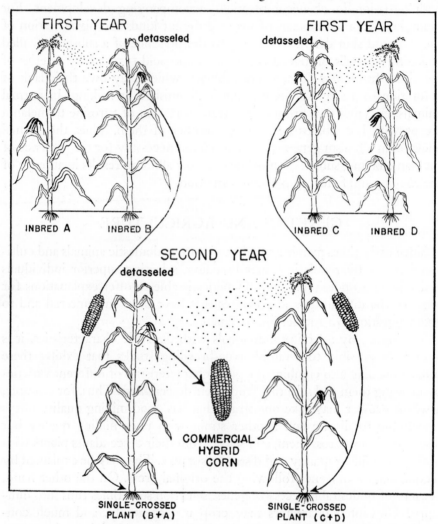

FIG. 385. Diagram illustrating a method commonly used in hybrid corn production. Four inbred lines (A, B, C, and D) contribute to the commercial hybrid corn. (From G. F. Sprague in *Bulletin* P 48, Iowa State College Agricultural Experiment Station.)

individuals derived from inbreeding may be explained as being due to their all being homozygous for many of the same genes. A reasonable explanation of the harmful effects of this system of breeding is that deleterious genes heretofore concealed by heterozygosis are made homozygous.

The desirable feature of inbreeding is the fact that it makes possible both uniform sets of individuals, which may be useful for experimental and practical reasons, and the recognition (and elimination) of harmful genes.

Hybridization. Reproduction involving mating of genetically dissimilar individuals (even members of different species) is called *hybridization*. In contrast to inbreeding, hybridization is frequently associated with marked improvement of vigor. This phenomenon is called *heterosis*, or *hybrid vigor*. It has been explained by assumptions similar to those for the reduction of vigor with inbreeding. Organisms may have numerous genes that are undesirable when homozygous. Crossing genetically very different individuals results in a large amount of heterozygosis for such genes, thus minimizing their deleterious effects.

The principle of heterosis has been effectively employed in recent years in increasing the quality and yield of corn. In this plant, hybridization is preceded by inbreeding, which is accomplished by self-pollination over a number of generations. Although this is accompanied by loss of vigor, it results in genetically uniform strains which may be selected for characters that it is desired to introduce into the hybrids. Several inbred lines are ordinarily combined to produce commercial hybrid corn (Fig. 385), and the vigor lost in inbreeding is much more than compensated for by the resulting heterosis. The importance of hybrid corn to the food supply of this country and of the world can hardly be overestimated. Whereas hybrid corn was still a curiosity in the early 1930's, more than 75 percent of the corn now grown in the United States is of this kind, and hybrid corn has been introduced into other corn-growing parts of the world (e.g., Latin America, southern Europe). The principle of hybridization is also being applied to other plants and to some domestic animals (e.g., poultry).

THE GENETICS OF MAN

Methods of Studying Human Inheritance. The genetics of man presents special problems. Not only is it not possible to control the kinds of matings, but the numbers of offspring obtained in single families are invariably too small to reveal genetic ratios (since chance causes relatively much variation in small groups). Consequently, special methods must be used. *Pedigrees* are often studied. A pedigree is a record of the distribution of one or more traits in a group (or *kindred*) of related individuals. Inspection of pedigrees exhibiting a certain character shows which modes of inheritance may possibly be active. When many pedigrees are in agreement with a proposed mode of inheritance, the mode in question may be considered to be very likely. Another method involves the investigation of large populations of individuals. On the basis of certain simple assumptions, expected relationships of the frequencies of different kinds of individuals may be calculated for different modes of inheritance. Agreement between the observed and the expected frequencies is evidence supporting a proposed mode of inheritance.

Examples of Hereditary Characters. By using such methods it has been possible to determine the nature of numerous hereditary traits. Some of these have been found to have a simple genetic basis. For example, to about 70 percent of the general population the substance phenylthiocarbamide (PTC) has a definite taste, usually bitter, but to the remaining 30 percent it is tasteless. Inability to taste PTC depends on an ordinary recessive gene; the pedigrees of Fig. 386 are consistent with this interpretation. Red-green color blindness, which includes a number of visual abnormalities involving these colors, may be due to any of several recessive genes carried by the X-chromosome (i.e., sex-linked genes). Fig. 387 shows the inheritance of this character; it will be noted that a man with a color-blindness gene must express it, while a woman may have the gene without showing it (i.e., in the heterozygous state). Similarly sex-linked is *hemophilia*, a rare disease in which the blood clots more slowly than usual. Numerous characters appear to depend on two or more pairs of genes. For example, a study carried out on the island of Jamaica, where there had been much interbreeding of white and colored people, suggested that at least two pairs of genes were involved in skin color variation, with dominance lacking and the effects of the color genes cumulative (as in the example of wheat color inheritance). Among other traits that would generally seem to depend on multiple factors are such characteristics as body form and size, susceptibility to disease, and intelligence.

The A-B-O blood groups (page 283) are determined by at least three

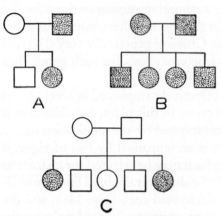

FIG. 386. Three pedigrees showing occurrence of inability to taste phenylthiocarbamide (PTC). Females are represented by circles, males by squares, and affected individuals (i.e., nontasters) by shaded symbols. Inability to taste PTC depends on an ordinary recessive gene. Note that whereas two normal people may have nontaster children (C), two nontasters have only nontaster offspring (B). (From L. H. Snyder, *The Principles of Heredity*, D. C. Heath and Company, 4th ed., 1951.)

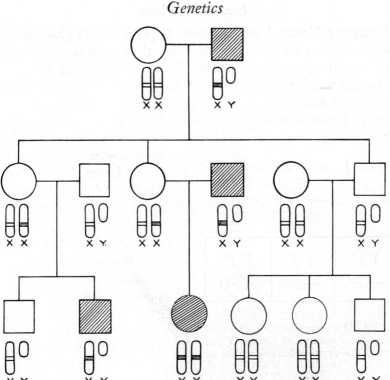

FIG. 387. Diagram in the form of a pedigree showing red-green color-blindness inheritance in a hypothetical family. Circles represent females, squares males; color-blind individuals are designated by shaded symbols. The color-blindness gene is shown by a shaded section on the X-chromosome, the corresponding unshaded section representing its normal allele.

different genes which are alleles to each other. This is an example of *multiple alleles*, cases of which are also known in other animals and in plants. The genes are designated I^A, I^B, and I^O. Since an individual may have only two of these, there are six possible genotypes; these are shown, with their phenotypes (blood groups), in the following table.

Genotype	Blood Group
$I^O I^O$	O
$I^A I^A$	A
$I^A I^O$	A (i.e., I^A dominant over I^O)
$I^B I^B$	B
$I^B I^O$	B (i.e., I^B dominant over I^O)
$I^A I^B$	AB (i.e., both genes effective)

From knowledge of the inheritance of these blood groups it is possible to predict the kinds of offspring from various matings and the kinds that will not appear (barring exceedingly rare mutations). For example, a mating between a Group A and a Group O person could produce either a Group A child or a Group O child (since the Group A parent might be heterozygous) but not a Group B or a Group AB child (Fig. 388). Knowledge of this sort is useful in cases of disputed parentage, in which legal decisions can sometimes be made against a supposed relationship. For instance, a Group B child should not be the offspring of two people who belong to Group A and Group O respectively, and a Group B child with a Group A mother should not have a Group O father. Evidence of this kind is recognized in many courts of law in this and other countries. Inheritance of the Rh factors (page 283) is attributed to a different set of multiple alleles, a number of these genes causing the Rh-positive condition and at least one of them causing the Rh-negative condition, which is recessive. These and other blood groups for which the inheritance is known are also useful in decisions concerning disputed parentage.

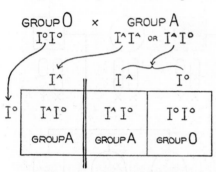

Fig. 388. Diagram showing expected offspring from matings of Group O and Group A. The square at the left represents the offspring expected if the Group A parent is of genotype $I^A I^A$; the two squares on the right, those expected if the Group A parent is of genotype $I^A I^O$. Thus, Group A and Group O children are both possible, but children of Groups B and AB are not expected.

Heredity and Environment. In the development of any characteristic of an organism, both hereditary factors and the environment play a part. Frequently, however, one is much more important than the other in causing variation. Thus far in this chapter we have dealt mostly with characteristics in which variation depends entirely or largely on hereditary factors—shape and color in peas, eye color in fruit flies, blood groups in man. But there are numerous traits in which the environment greatly influences the outcome. Quite evidently, size and vigor are affected by the environment (e.g., the food an animal eats, the water and sunshine available to a growing plant), though the results of breeding experiments show that these characters are also subject to the control of hereditary factors. In many cases it is difficult to decide which type of factor, hereditary or environmental, is more influential in determining a trait; this is particularly true in man, where neither heredity nor environment can rigidly be controlled. Considering people in general, it is usually difficult to explain the role of inheritance in such traits as susceptibility to various diseases, special aptitudes, and intelligence.

Twins. In this country, twins occur in one out of 88 births. About 20 to 30 percent of all twins result from the development of two growing points on a single developing "egg," causing its ultimate division into two complete individuals. Twins of this type are known as *one-egg*, or *identical*, *twins* (Fig. 389). Coming from a single fertilized egg, they should have the same hereditary factors. They are always of the same sex and are remarkably similar to each other. *Two-egg*, or *fraternal*, *twins* develop from different eggs which happen to be fertilized at about the same time; hence,

Fig. 389. One-egg, or identical, twins. (Photo, courtesy of the *Kalamazoo Gazette*.)

in their hereditary factors they are no more alike than ordinary brothers and sisters. Two-egg twins are sometimes of the opposite sex (in about half the cases) and may be very dissimilar.

The existence of these two kinds of twins affords an opportunity to study the relative importance of heredity and environment in the formation of many human traits. A widely employed method is the determination of frequencies of *concordance* (i.e., cases of agreement in the members of a twin pair with regard to a trait) in one-egg and two-egg twins. One-egg twins should be alike in hereditary factors, whereas two-egg twins should be different; but the environments of the members of a twin pair should be about the same for either of the two types of twins. Consequently, a tendency to greater similarity (i.e., a higher frequency of concordance) in one-egg twins than in two-egg twins may be attributed to the fact that one-egg twins are alike as to hereditary factors. On the other hand, a difference (i.e., *discordance*) in one-egg twins may be attributed to the environment. For example, the metabolic disease *diabetes* (page 308) was found to occur in both members of one-egg twin pairs in 84 percent of the cases with at least one member affected, but two-egg twin pairs showed only 37 percent concordance. This suggests a definite influence of heredity in the development of this illness, but it also shows that heredity does not have absolute control. Another kind of twin study involves identical twins reared apart (as may happen when the members of a twin pair are adopted by different families). With regard to intelligence, the average difference in I.Q. (intelligence quotient) was found to be 3.1 points for one-egg twins reared together, 6.0 points for one-egg twins reared apart, and 8.5 points for two-egg twins. This suggests an influence of heredity in determining intelligence, but an influence of the environment is also implied.

Applications of Knowledge of Human Heredity. Reference has already been made to the use of the A-B-O blood groups in predicting kinds of offspring. Similar predictions may be made for other sorts of characteristics. Of special interest are predictions of harmful traits. For example, Huntington's chorea, a serious nervous affection and a form of insanity, which is fortunately very rare, is inherited as an ordinary dominant trait. Because of the rareness of the gene in a population, individuals affected with this disease are almost invariably heterozygous. Consequently, if one parent of an individual develops this abnormality, the chance that the individual will himself show the trait is one-half (since that is the chance of his receiving the abnormal gene rather than its normal allele from the affected parent). Knowledge of the existence of a hereditary ailment in a family may also be helpful in diagnosis and treatment of the disease. For instance, a physician may be prompted to look for the symptoms of diabetes in a patient and to begin early treatment if he knows that relatives of that patient have exhibited the disease.

It was recognized early in the development of genetics that knowledge of human inheritance might be used to improve mankind through regulation of breeding. The application of genetics to human improvement is called *eugenics*. The most obvious opportunities for eugenics have seemed to be the elimination of harmful characteristics that depend on heredity— such traits as certain kinds of feeble-mindedness and insanity, and certain outstanding physical defects. Methods for preventing the reproduction of individuals with such characteristics include: (1) enactment and enforcement of laws prohibiting the marriage of such persons; (2) segregation of the sexes in institutions such as hospitals for the insane and schools and homes for the mentally deficient; and (3) sterilization, accomplished by severing the sperm ducts or oviducts (preventing reproduction but not otherwise interfering with the sexual nature of individuals). With regard to the genetic results of such measures, there has been much uncertainty. The hereditary basis of many of the characteristics with which eugenics is concerned is not well understood; for many of them it must be rather complex. For example, there are different kinds of insanity, presumably depending on various hereditary factors. Recessive genes must often be involved. As was pointed out earlier in connection with the breeding of domestic animals and cultivated plants, recessiveness makes selection difficult. Consequently, selection against an undesirable human trait that depends on one or more recessive genes may be expected to be a very slow process. Nevertheless, though the influence of eugenic measures on a population's gene constitution must be very gradual, the prevention of a relatively few cases of outstanding defects due to heredity would still seem to be worth the effort.

Another matter of concern to those interested in eugenics is the occurrence of deleterious mutant genes. Although mutant genes ordinarily occur with very low frequencies, they may be made to appear more frequently by certain environmental agencies, particularly x-rays and other high-energy radiations. Overexposure to such irradiation, besides being harmful to individuals (cancerous growths sometimes follow such exposure), may be expected to be deleterious to mankind as a whole, causing a rise in the rates of mutation of undesirable genes. Consequently, steps are being taken to keep the exposure to irradiation at a minimum in x-ray laboratories and plants working with atomic energy.

EXERCISES

1. If the F_1 plants from Mendel's cross between round and wrinkled varieties of peas were crossed with the wrinkled variety, what kinds of offspring should result and in what ratio? What is such a cross called?
2. In some animal species, the male has one X-chromosome with no homologous chromosome (XO condition) and the female has two X-chromosomes (XX). Explain the occurence of a 1:1 sex ratio in such a species.
3. A red-green color-blind woman is married to a man who has normal color vision. What kinds of offspring are expected and in what ratio?
4. A white, disk-shaped squash, when self-pollinated, has 28 white, disk; 9 white, sphere; 10 yellow, disk; and 3 yellow, sphere plants as offspring. Explain this result.
5. What should be the offspring (and expected ratio) of a pink four-o'clock pollinated by a red one? Of the pink pollinated by a white one?

6. A black-bodied, long-winged fruit fly was crossed with a gray-bodied, vestigial-winged fly. The first-generation females, mated to black vestigial males, had 283 gray, long; 1340 gray, vestigial; 1355 black, long; 265 black, vestigial offspring. Are the genes for body color and wing length on the same or on different chromosome pairs? Explain.

7. Since man has 24 pairs of chromosomes and crossing over may take place within these chromosome pairs, why is it extremely unlikely that two members of a two-egg twin pair will be genetically identical?

8. The following pedigrees represent three different families. Females are shown by circles, males by squares, and abnormal individuals by shaded symbols. With which of these modes of inheritance of the abnormality are the following pedigrees all consistent: ordinary dominant gene, ordinary recessive gene, sex-linked dominant gene, sex-linked recessive gene?

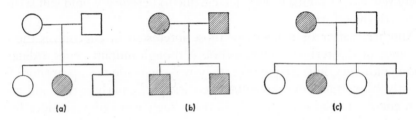

9. If a woman of blood Group AB is married to a man of Group B, what kinds of children may they have? What kind (or kinds) are they expected not to have?

10. Suppose recessive genes *a* and *b* cause a form of hereditary blindness (homozygosis for either one or both of them). Assuming no linkage between these genes, what is the chance of a blind child resulting from a mating of individuals that are both of genotype *AaBb?*

11. Give some examples of inheritance controlled by factors *other than* chromosomal genes. How are these explained?

REFERENCES

Dunn, L. C. (ed), *Genetics in the 20th Century*, The Macmillan Company, 1951.

Gates, R. R., *Human Genetics*, The Macmillan Company, 1946, 2 vols.

Glass, B., *Genes and the Man*, Teachers College, Columbia University, 1943.

Goldschmidt, R. B., *Understanding Heredity*, John Wiley & Sons, Inc., 1952.

Goldstein, P., *Genetics Is Easy*, Garlan Publications, 1947.

Haldane, J. B. S., *New Paths in Genetics*, Harper & Brothers, 1942.

Morgan, T. H., *The Theory of the Gene*, Yale Univ. Press, 2nd ed., 1929.

Osborn, F., *Preface to Eugenics*, Harper & Brothers, 2nd ed., 1952.

Scheinfeld, A., *The New "You and Heredity,"* Frederick A. Stokes Company, 2nd ed., 1950.

Sinnott, E. W., Dunn, L. C., and Dobzhansky, T., *Principles of Genetics*, McGraw-Hill Book Company, Inc., 4th ed., 1950. (Appendix includes English translation of Mendel's publication.)

Snyder, L. H., *The Principles of Heredity*, D. C. Heath & Company, 4th ed., 1951.

Srb, A. M. and Owen, R. D., *General Genetics*, W. H. Freeman and Company, 1952.

Stern, C., *Principles of Human Genetics*, W. H. Freeman and Company, 1949.

Sturtevant, A. H., and Beadle, G. W., *An Introduction to Genetics*, W. B. Saunders Company, 1939.

Winchester, A. M., *Genetics*, Houghton Mifflin Company, 1951.

Chapter XXIX

EVOLUTION

Introduction. According to evolution, the various kinds of living things have been (and are being) derived from previously existing different kinds by descent with modification. Numerous references to this idea have already been made in this book, for many of the aspects of organic variation are made understandable in the light of the evolution concept. Although the idea of evolution is very old, general acceptance of it has come relatively recently—within the last one hundred years. This acceptance has largely depended on the accumulation of evidence for evolution and the formulation of ideas concerning the way it must come about. Of outstanding importance has been the work of Charles Darwin—his presentation of facts supporting evolution and his idea of evolution by natural selection. In this chapter, the evidence for evolution will be presented and summarized, and some proposed evolutionary mechanisms will be discussed.

EVIDENCE FOR EVOLUTION

The evidence for evolution consists of biological facts that can be explained by evolution. This evidence depends greatly on the concept of heredity, that is, on the assumption that the similarities of individuals and groups of individuals are generally based on relationship (though cases of similarity that do not depend on relationship are also recognized). Generally speaking, the evidence for evolution consists of the details of the resemblances of organisms, both among existing forms and among ancient forms of life. Taken together, these details suggest a pattern of variation formed by numerous lines of descent, just as is implied by the evolution idea. In the following sections some of this evidence will be considered.

RESEMBLANCES AMONG EXISTING ORGANISMS

Morphological Resemblances. The classification of plants and animals is generally based upon structure. The kinds that are nearest alike are regarded as species of a common genus, and the genera that are allied are grouped into a family. Related families constitute an order, related orders make up a class, and related classes a phylum. The Phylum Arthropoda, for example, consists of animals which are alike in having an external skeleton, a segmented body, jointed appendages, a dorsal heart, a ventral nerve cord, and certain other features in common. Members of the Class Insecta have a greater number of characters in common, and members of the Order Coleoptera, or beetles, have a still greater number. A beetle is more closely related to another beetle than it is to a fly, whereas beetle and fly are more closely related to each other than either one is to a spider. The taxonomist recognizes these facts by putting all beetles in the Order Coleoptera, by placing the flies in another order, Diptera, both orders belonging to the Class Insecta, and by assigning spiders to a separate class, Arachnoidea, included with Insecta in the Phylum Arthropoda.

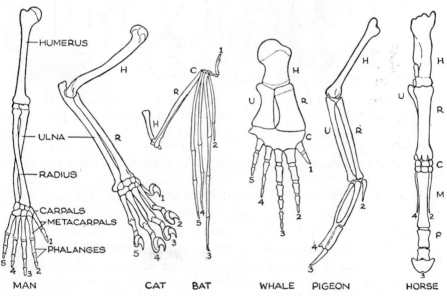

Fig. 390. Right fore-limb skeletons of several vertebrates showing homologies. The bones, except in the left-hand drawing, are indicated by initials, and the digits are numbered, starting with the thumb. Primates (such as man) are unique in having the power to rotate the ulna-radius portion (the forearm). (In part after Woodruff.)

Homologous Organs. To illustrate the nature of structural similarities, let us consider the fore limbs of different vertebrates (Fig. 390). The upper arm bone (*humerus*) of man fits by a ball-like head into a socket in the shoulder blade (*scapula*). At the distal end of the humerus are two forearm bones (*radius* and *ulna*), eight wrist bones (*carpals*), five bones of the palm (*metacarpals*), and fourteen finger bones (*phalanges*). The fore limb of the cat has exactly the same bones, although they differ from the human in form and function. In the bat, bones known by the same names are modified into a slender framework for the support of the wing membrane, and in the whale they form a paddle-like structure for swimming. Human arm, cat fore limb, bat wing, and whale flipper are said to be *homologous* (Gr. "agreeing") organs; they are basically similar in structure, although their functions may be very different. Comparisons of the brains of the different classes of vertebrates (Fig. 391) reveals that the parts (cerebrum,

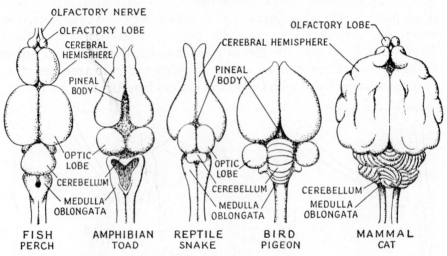

FIG. 391. Comparative study of brains in a series of vertebrates. (After Guyer.)

optic lobes, cerebellum, and medulla) are homologous. The same holds true for any other system of organs. Arthropods, or members of any other phylum, show similar homologies among themselves. According to the idea of evolution, homologous organs are similar because of heredity and hence are useful in erecting a natural system of classification based on relationships.

Analogous Organs. Sometimes two structures have the same function but, though superficially alike, are very different in design—for example, the wing of a bird and the wing of a butterfly. The former is a true limb; the latter originates as a sac-like outgrowth of the chitinous exoskeleton. Structures agreeing in function but basically different in form are said to be *analogous*. The similarities of analogous structures may be attributed to the *adaptation* of different organisms to the same or a similar way of life (e.g., to life in the air, for which wings are useful). Thus, adaptation rather than heredity is sometimes responsible for similarities. The possibility of analogy must always be considered in classifying organisms, since a natural system of classification should make use of homologous rather than analogous structures.

Vestigial Organs. A comparison of the fore-limb skeleton of the horse with that of man (Fig. 390) shows that the former has only one complete digit, the third or middle one. The second and fourth are represented by the metacarpal only, the *splint bone*. The outer two of the original five possessed by the ancestor of the horse have entirely disappeared. The splint bones, which are smaller than the functional metacarpal, are digits that are no longer functional; they are said to be *vestigial*. The short second

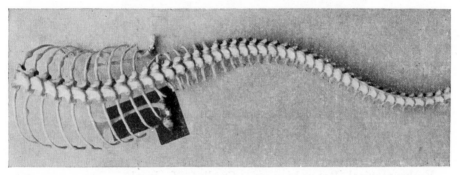

Fig. 392. Python, rear portion of skeleton, showing rudimentary hip girdle and hind limbs in position. The elongated bones under the ribs are the hip bones. The short terminal portion (claw) is all that is visible in the living animal. (Photo, copyright, Chicago Natural History Museum.)

digit of the pigeon wing is also vestigial. Snakes have probably descended from ancestors with limbs. Evidence of this is seen in the fact that snakes of the family which includes the pythons and boas have rudimentary hip girdles and vestiges of hind limbs in the form of short claws that just emerge between the scales (Fig. 392). The human body has retained a large number of vestigial organs which were probably once useful but which now seem to be on the way to complete disappearance. The *vermiform appendix*, at the upper end of the large intestine, is the vestige of a pouch that attains considerable development in the rabbit and some other mammals (Fig. 393). It is proportionally larger in the ape than in man, and in the human embryo than in the adult. The little chain of bones known as the *coccyx* constitutes all that remains in man of what was once a tail. We have numerous muscles that do not function, such as those of the scalp and those that once moved the outer ear. A fold at the inner corner of the human eye represents all that is left of a structure which in reptiles and birds serves as a third eyelid. The minute leaves at the eyes of a potato tuber (Fig. 349), the insignificant sepals of a carrot blossom, and the functionless stamens in the blossoms of some of the mints show that plants as well as animals are undergoing the modification and ultimate loss of certain organs.

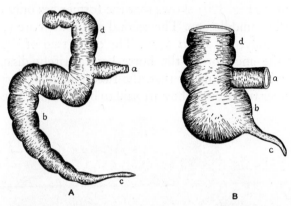

FIG. 393. Vestigial nature of caecum and appendix in man. *A*, Junction of small and large intestine in rabbit, compared with *B*, same in man: *a*, terminal portion of small intestine; *b*, caecum; *c*, appendix; *d*, beginning of colon.

Embryological Resemblances. Studies of development stages may reveal great similarities between otherwise quite different forms. We saw (Chapter XVIII) that a multicellular animal begins life as a fertilized egg and that it undergoes cleavage, and after a time passes through the blastula (hollow sphere) and gastrula (two-layered) stages. We noted that the members of a given phylum, such as chordates, bear a close resemblance to one another at still later stages of development; that at an early stage even the human embryo has gill slits and arterial arches which suggest those of the fish, a brain that is no further developed than that of a fish, a tail, and other primitive characters. Before it has a real backbone, it has a notochord which suggests that of the simplest chordates. This common beginning, followed by gradual divergence, suggests relationship. Without this interpretation, such facts cannot be rationally explained. We have already discussed this principle as the theory of recapitulation expressed in the phrase, "Ontogeny recapitulates phylogeny."

Physiological Resemblances. Function is based largely on structure; hence the organisms which are similar in structure carry on their processes similarly. In our study of the development of plant and animal kingdoms we saw that functions may be carried on before specialized organs are developed to perform them. Certain fundamental processes, such as nutrition, respiration, excretion, coordination, and reproduction, are carried on through the whole range of animal life; in addition to the above, plants carry on photosynthesis. In the smaller groups, functional similarities often extend to many details of activity. For example, birds of many different species show similarities in the selection of breeding territory, in song, in mating and nest-building, in the feeding and care of the young, and in the semiannual migration. We have evidence to show that, in the course of many generations, instincts and habits as well as structures are subject to steady changes. Resemblances in function as well as in form imply relationship. Extensive study is now being made of the habits, domestic life, and mental and emotional reactions of the monkeys and apes in the hope of elucidating the origins of human behavior.

Chemical Resemblances. All organisms show a general resemblance in the chemistry of their protoplasm and owe their activities to similar chemical changes. Wider differences usually exist between different phyla than between different members of the same phylum. Important advances in medicine have been made possible by the fact that certain other mammals are susceptible to bacteria that cause human disease, and that the antibodies which these mammals produce can be used in the prevention or cure of the same disease in man. Some of the bacteria pathogenic to man produce disease in other primates but not in mammals of any other order; hence chemical and physiological similarities must be closer within the order than between this and other orders. These similarities influence the successful utilization of endrocrines from the glands of other mammals in overcoming human endocrine deficiencies (such as cretinism, which is caused by thyroid deficiency). The horticulturist has learned that a pear scion is grafted easily on the stock af a pear, less easily on that of a quince, and rarely if ever on that of a more distantly related species. That there are chemical differences among people is shown by the fact that individuals react differently to poisons, such as that of poison ivy and those of pathogenic bacteria, and to air-borne pollen, dust, and other irritating substances. These differences appear to have a genetic basis.

Use of Precipitins in Determining Relationship. Foreign substances introduced into the body often stimulate the accumulation in the blood of antibodies which tend to counteract or remove the offending substance. This was discussed in connection with bacteria (Chapter XX). A familiar example is the production of antitoxin, which tends to neutralize and destroy the particular kind of bacterial toxin, or poison, that is introduced into the system. When blood of another animal is introduced into the circulatory system of an experimental animal such as a rabbit, the latter animal forms a precipitin which tends to precipitate the foreign blood. Nuttall, an English physiologist, developed a delicate test whereby the degree of relationship, as represented by blood similarities, may be determined. Blood from a donkey was introduced into a rabbit at intervals of several days, until from three to twenty such injections had been made. Several days afterward, blood was drawn from the rabbit and the serum allowed to separate. This serum contained precipitin for donkey blood. A drop of it added to a little donkey blood gave a strong precipitate; when added to horse blood, the precipitate was almost as strong. With zebra blood, however, it was less striking; with pig blood, weak; and with ox blood, lacking. In general, the closer the relationship of the animal whose blood is tested to the animal whose blood has induced the formation of the precipitin, the stronger the precipitate. Nuttall learned from hundreds of such tests that close structural similarity is in general correlated with close blood similarity. Human blood is chemically similar to that of the apes and less similar to that of the monkeys. The chemical reactions of cell sap in plants have been used in a similar way to indicate evolutionary relationships. The precipitin test has been used to help assign doubtful organisms to groups and to learn something of their relationships; for example, such a test has shown that the horseshoe crab is allied to the ARACHNOIDEA, that whales are related most closely to the even-toed hoofed animals (ARTIODACTYLA), and that rabbits (LAGOMORPHA), suspected on other grounds to be distinct from RODENTIA, are markedly different in their blood reactions.

Similar Parasites on Similar Hosts. Additional evidence of chemical similarity is provided by the fact that a parasite which feeds habitually upon a particular animal or plant may thrive upon a closely related animal or plant. The Colorado potato beetle formerly fed upon a spiny weed (*Solanum rostratum*); but when the potato (*Solanum tuberosum*) was introduced into Colorado, the insect left the former host for the potato. A species of louse which in the Old World is parasitic on the camel, feeds upon the llama, a related animal, in South America. Presumably this louse lived upon the common ancestor of the camel and the llama before migration led to the separation of their two lines of descendants. During the vicissitudes which brought about a gradual change in both branches of the progeny of this early ungulate, the louse continued to live, practically unchanged, on its victims of both branches.

EVIDENCES FROM ANCIENT FORMS

Fossils. *Paleontology* (Gr. "ancient-life science") is the study of the past history of life, based on *fossils*. A fossil (Lat. "something dug up") may be:

1. A portion of the actual substance of an animal or plant, such as a bone, a tooth, or a piece of carbonized wood (coal).
2. A *petrifaction* (Lat. "making rock") in which mineral matter has been deposited, bit by bit, to replace the substance of the organism as the latter decays. Wood is often preserved in this way, the microscopic structure of

Fig. 394. Portion of the trunk of an extinct conifer (*Araucarioxylon*), in the Petrified Forest, Arizona. The wood is petrified, or replaced by stone, but retains the minute details of its original structure. Note the rings of annual growth. (Photo, courtesy of C. A. Arnold.)

the fibers being reproduced in the mineral matter (Fig. 394).
3. An *impression* left by the organism in mud or other soft material which has since hardened; or a *cast* of mineral matter which fills such an impression after the decay of the organism (Fig. 395).

Fossils are found mainly in sedimentary rock deposited through the agency of water, wind, or glaciers; or in accumulations of organic remains, such as peat, coal, and limestone. Since the later deposits are, in general, above the earlier ones, the relative position of the deposit gives a clue to the age of the fossil. At no one place on the earth's surface do we find strata representing all geological periods, because any given place has usually been exposed for long periods to erosion during which it receives no deposits. If we could bring together in one place all the known rock strata, we should have a mass about seventy miles in thickness. If all the past types of life had left remains preserved in this mass, we could, on passing from bottom to top, read the complete history of life on the earth. But our historical record is very fragmentary, for probably not more than one organism out of many thousand dies in such a location and under such conditions that it leaves a permanent trace of its existence. Since only the hard parts are capable of preservation under most conditions, those species of organisms which were without skeletal structures have left few fossils. Moreover, certain extensive geological periods of the past either have left no strata, or have left them only in places which lacked the forms of life whose evolution we desire to trace. Furthermore, until recently, no organized effort has been made to search for the fossil remains in the earth's crust. Those that have been collected were found mainly by accident, being uncovered either by erosion or by excavations made for other purposes. In other words, we have only scratched the surface of the earth in our search for remains of life. Recently, however, our knowledge has been greatly extended by organized projects which are backed by liberal endowments; the continuance

Fig. 395. Rock concretion, broken open, showing impression of the leaf of a Paleozoic fern. (From Brown, *The Plant Kingdom;* copyright, Ginn.)

of such efforts will, without doubt, vastly increase the completeness of our knowledge. In spite of the scarcity of evidence, we can ascertain the general trend of the story and see that the specialized types of today developed from simpler or more generalized types that lived in earlier periods. Within the various groups, moreover, we can often follow rather fully the details of the evolutionary changes.

Estimation of Geological Time. The actual length of the geological eras can be only roughly estimated, the rates of present geological processes being used as clues. For example, we have evidence that Niagara Falls began cutting its gorge at Lake Ontario at the close of glacial times. If we divide the length of the gorge (in feet) by the present rate of recession of the falls (in feet per year), making corrections for estimated differences between the present rate and that of former years, we learn that no less than 25,000 years have elapsed since the Glacial period. In a similar manner we may use the rate of deposition of silt by streams entering lakes or oceans, and the rate of increase of salt lakes in saltiness. Chemical analyses throw light on the ages of some of the older rocks. Through spontaneous decomposition, uranium loses half its weight in 4,500,000,000 years, evolving helium and becoming lead with an atomic weight of 206 (an isotope or form slightly lighter than ordinary lead). By analyzing a rock which contains uranium and this isotope of lead, it is possible to tell how long the uranium has been decomposing, and hence estimate the age of the rock. On the basis of such calculations, it is generally believed that the time since the earliest forms of life appeared upon earth is certainly more than a billion years, probably approaching two billion.

Eras of Geological Time. The accompanying table gives the names of the eras, the estimated time since the beginning of each one, and its prevailing animal and plant groups:

Era	Time Since Beginning	Animals	Plants
Cenozoic	60 million years	Mammals, man	Angiosperms
Mesozoic	200 " "	Reptiles, earliest birds and mammals	Gymnosperms, earliest angiosperms
Paleozoic	540 " "	Amphibians, fishes, and invertebrates	Primitive tracheophytes, including earliest gymnosperms
Proterozoic	1200 " "	Invertebrates (sponges, worms)	Algae
Archeozoic	2000 " "	Protozoa	Unicellular algae, bacteria

Archeozoic (Gr. "beginning of animals") **Era.** This era, of long duration, is represented by the igneous and metamorphic rocks, such as granites, basalts, and slates, so commonly exposed in mountainous areas. Our knowledge of the life of this period is hazy, for we have no direct evidence of it. Indirect evidence, however, is furnished by deposits of carbon (graphite) and of calcium carbonate, the accumulation of which we ordinarily associate with organisms. It is highly probable that these early organisms were simple unicellular forms, and that such remains as accumulated have been largely obliterated by the heat and pressure to which most of these rocks have been subjected.

Proterozoic (Gr. "earlier animals") **Era.** This era, also of long duration, is represented by metamorphic rocks containing a few fossils, all of which represent simple plants, such as blue-green algae and bacteria, or simple animals, such as protozoans, sponges, and worm-like forms. It is the period of the development of invertebrate animals and of the simpler aquatic plants.

Paleozoic (Gr. "ancient animals") **Era.** The Paleozoic is the earliest era that affords abundant evidence of life. It is subdivided into seven periods. In strata of the *Early Paleozoic* (including the *Cambrian* and *Ordovician*

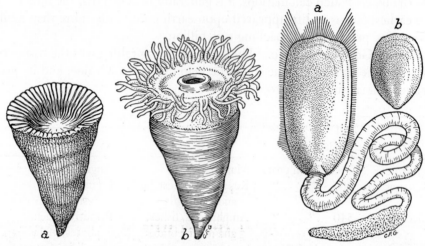

FIG. 396.   Horn coral, a coelenterate, from the Silurian period; *a*, the fossil skeleton; *b*, with soft parts restored. (Drawn by Carl F. Gronemann; courtesy of Chicago Natural History Museum.)

FIG. 397.   Brachiopods or lampshells; *a*, a living type; *b*, a fossil from the Cambrian period. (Courtesy of Chicago Natural History Museum.)

periods) are found fossils of protozoans, sponges, coelenterates (Fig. 396), mollusks, brachiopods (Fig. 397), annelids, and trilobites (an early class of arthropods, Fig. 398). The Ordovician marks the appearance of the first insects, the nautilus-like mollusks, and the earliest fishes. During the *Middle Paleozoic* (*Silurian* and *Devonian*), fishes representing the more ancient subdivisions of the class were abundant; they represent the "lords of creation" of that time. During the *Late Paleozoic* or *Carboniferous* (*Mississippian*, *Pennsylvanian*, and *Permian*) arose the amphibians, the earliest land vertebrates. Vascular plants, which were evolving in the early part of the era, now reached their culmination. Ferns, horsetails, and club mosses were abundant, many of them being of tree-like proportions (Fig. 399). The great coal beds of the world consist of partially decomposed and carbonized remains of these early plants, which formed great Paleozoic forests. Meanwhile the first reptiles were appearing, and seed-bearing gymnosperms were represented by "seed ferns."

Mesozoic (Gr. "middle animals") **Era.** During the *Mesozoic*, reptiles rose to a dominant position. Of about sixteen orders then living, only four now remain. The dinosaurs (Gr. "terrible reptiles," Fig. 400) were sometimes 100 feet long and larger than any modern animals except certain whales (Fig.

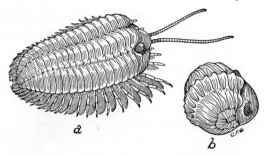

FIG. 398. Trilobites representing an early arthropod type from the Silurian period; *a*, extended position; *b*, coiled into a protected position. The soft parts are restored. (Courtesy of Chicago Natural History Museum.)

210). Fossilized eggs of one of the smaller dinosaurs were discovered by a scientific expedition that explored Mongolia in the 1920's (Fig. 401). The flying reptiles were unique in the possession of wings, each consisting of a membrane from the greatly extended fifth finger to the body and the hind limbs. The first birds (Fig. 194) and the earliest opossum-like mammals appeared during the Mesozoic, but these groups did not be-

FIG. 399. Restoration of a carboniferous swamp forest. Trunks of giant club mosses, fern leaves, and the leaf of "seed fern," a gymnosperm, may be seen at the left; a giant horsetail at the right. Notice the cockroaches on the tree trunks, the giant dragonfly flying near the horsetail, and a small salamander on the log in the immediate foreground. (Copyright, Chicago Natural History Museum.)

come abundant until the Cenozoic. Gymnosperms, such as cycads and *Ginkgo*, were the prevailing plants during the *Early Mesozoic* (*Triassic* and *Jurassic* periods); angiosperms appeared in the *Late Mesozoic* (*Cretaceous*) when many of our modern genera of trees prevailed.

Fɪɢ. 400. Restoration of *Triceratops*, a three-horned dinosaur, and *Tyrannosaurus*, a carnivorous dinosaur which reached a length of 47 feet and is the largest known flesh-eating animal of all time. The skeletons have been found in close proximity, suggesting that *Tyrannosaurus* preyed upon *Triceratops*. (After a painting by Charles R. Knight; copyright, Chicago Natural History Museum.)

Fɪɢ. 401. Two skeletons of *Protoceratops*, a dinosaur ancestral to *Triceratops*, and a nest of eggs in the sand. Restored from fossils found in Mongolia. (Courtesy of the American Museum of Natural History.)

Cenozoic (Gr. "recent animals") **Era.** The large reptiles had disappeared by the beginning of this era, and mammals were now numerous. During the *Early Cenozoic* (*Tertiary* period) the giant ground sloth (Fig. 402), bulky ungulates, and the saber-toothed tiger are noteworthy. We can trace the development of the modern horse, starting with a little ani-

Fig. 402. Giant South American mammals of the Pleistocene or Glacial period. Left, ground sloth (*Megatherium*), related to the tree sloths of the present but living on the ground and as large as an elephant. Right, *Glyptodon*, related to the armadillos but with a solid domed shell of bony plates; the tail is a remarkable spiked club. Both animals are edentates. Photo, copyright, Chicago Natural History Museum.)

mal named Eohippus, which lived in the early Cenozoic (Fig. 403). This creature not only was small but it differed from modern horses in its teeth, skeleton, feet, etc. For example, it had four complete digits and a splint of the first on each forefoot, three and a splint of the fifth on each hind foot. Descending from this ancient form were a number of lines including larger and more horse-like animals in which first and fifth digits had entirely disappeared. Eventually one of these lines gave rise to modern horses, with their characteristic teeth and skeleton, and the presence of only one functional digit (the third) on each foot, two others (the second and fourth) being reduced to splint bones. Development can likewise be traced for the elephant, the camel, and other modern mammals. The primate lines appeared shortly after the beginning of the era. The *Late Cenozoic* (*Pleistocene* or *Quarternary* period) was marked by successive advances of continental glaciers, giving what is now our northern states area somewhat the aspect of Greenland of today. Its main biological event was the evolution of man. The early Cenozoic plants were mainly wind-pollinated angiosperms; plants specialized for insect pollination as well as pollinating insects —bees and butterflies—came late in the era.

THE EVOLUTION OF MAN

Distinctive Human Characteristics. Man, a member of the Order Primates, has much in common with the other members of this order. He agrees with other primates, except some of the lower forms, in the possession of stereoscopic vision (both eyes directed forward), in the use of the

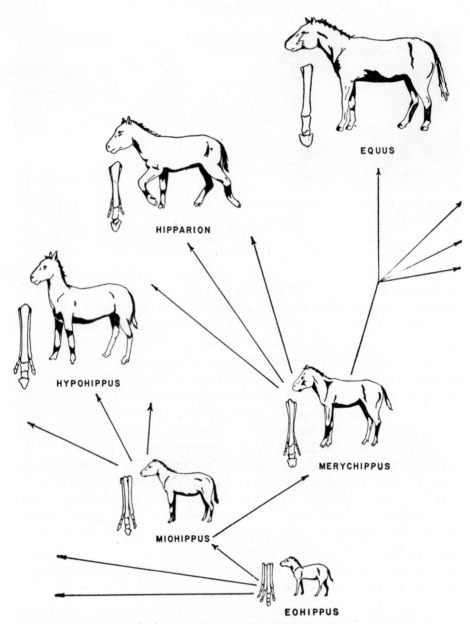

EQUUS

HIPPARION

HYPOHIPPUS

MERYCHIPPUS

MIOHIPPUS

EOHIPPUS

FIG. 403. Diagram illustrating the evolution of the horse family. Only a few of the many types are shown here; and of these, only the genus *Equus* exists at the present time. Lines of evolution were more numerous and complex than the arrows indicate. In front of each "horse" are shown the lower bones of the right fore foot. Thus, it may be seen that in the descent of the modern horse from the small Eohippus of the Eocene Epoch there was a reduction of the number of digits from four, through three, and finally to one. Modifications of bones and teeth also took place. (Based largely on G. G. Simpson's *The Meaning of Evolution*, Yale Univ. Press, 1949.)

hands for manipulating (instead of solely for locomotion, as in most mammals), and in the considerable development of the cerebral cortex, the part of the brain concerned with reasoning. Man greatly exceeds other primates in the latter feature. This permits him, instead of being confined to a limited range, to spread all over the world and occupy many kinds of ecological habitats; to construct and use tools far beyond the ability of the highest apes, and therefore to assert in a marked way his dominance over nature; and to develop both oral and written means of communication, which not only makes possible extensive cooperation with his fellows but enables each generation to build upon the achievements of the past.

Prehuman Development. Primates are first found as fossils in the early Cenozoic, apparently as descendants of the tree shrews of the Order IN-SECTIVORA. The earlier forms were lemurs, which had dog-like muzzles, and tarsioids which, like the tarsier (Fig. 211), had stereoscopic vision. About the middle of the era, branches gave rise to the various families of monkeys, and to certain tree-inhabiting forms, such as *Dryopithecus* (northern India). Because its characteristics seem more generalized than are found in the four modern apes (gibbon, orang, gorilla, and chimpanzee) and in man, *Dryopithecus* may have been the ancestor of these various lines. A fossil which in some respects appears to be between the prehuman and the human has been found in South Africa and named *Australopithecus* (Gr. "southern ape").

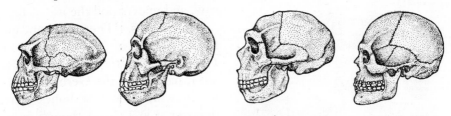

PITHECANTHROPUS ERECTUS • EOANTHROPUS DAWSONI • HOMO NEANDERTHALENSIS • HOMO SAPIENS
Java man　　　　　　　Piltdown man　　　　　　Neanderthal man　　　　Cro-Magnon man

Fig. 404. Restored skulls of four of the best-known types of primitive man, placed in chronological sequence. Note that forehead height, brain capacity, and prominence of chin tend to increase, while eyebrow ridge and mouth protrusion decrease from earlier to later stages.

Earliest Humans. The Java Man (*Pithecanthropus erectus*, "erect ape-man"; Fig. 404) is probably the earliest organism that may be called human. A careful study of associated fossils assigns this creature to the early part of the glacial period, approximately half a million years ago. Although somewhat erect in posture, he had several ape-like characters, such as a low, receding forehead, prominent brow ridges, protruding mouth, and

Fig. 405. Neanderthal man (*Homo neanderthalensis*), from a restoration. (Photo, copyright, Chicago Natural History Museum.)

receding chin. Portions of some three dozen similarly primitive skeletons have been found in caves near Peiping, China. This form has been named *Sinanthropus pekingensis* ("Chinese man of Peking"), but some authorities place it in the same genus as Java man.

Showing some structural advances over these, and probably belonging to a somewhat more recent date are the Piltdown man (*Eoanthropus dawsoni*) of southern England and the Heidelberg man (*Homo heidelbergensis*) of Germany. Our knowledge of these two species is based on portions of a single skull of each, but we know from accumulated evidence that these and other "dawn men" used crude tools of stone, bone and deer antlers, split the leg bones of animals to obtain the marrow, and understood the use of fire.

Later Types. There is abundant fossil evidence of Neanderthal man (*Homo neanderthalensis;* Figs. 404, 405), named for the German locality in which the first bones were discovered in 1856. Although more like modern man than were his predecessors, he had the primitive facial features of a low forehead, prominent brow ridges, protruding mouth, and receding chin; a small skull cavity; he lacked a strictly erect posture, lived in rock shelters, and chipped out crude stone tools. His range extended over much of Europe and into Asia and northern Africa. He lived about a hundred thousand years ago.

The first comers of the present species (*Homo sapiens*) were the Cro-Magnon men (named for a cave in France), who lived some fifty thousand years ago. They closely resembled modern man in stature and skull shape, but were a little taller and had a slightly larger cranial capacity than most of the modern races. They made more refined stone tools than did their predecessors, and decorated their cave walls with pictures of the hairy

FIG. 406. A Cro-Magnon (*Homo sapiens*) artist decorating the walls of his cave. Using a tube made from bone, he blows powdered red ocher around his fingers to make an imprint of his hand. Note the imprints above his head, also the outlines of mammoth and bison. The cave is lighted by the wood fire and a primitive lamp at the artist's left. Reproduction of a cave of the Aurignacian cultural period in southwestern France. (Photo, copyright, Chicago Natural History Museum.)

elephant, the hairy rhinoceros, and other animals now extinct (Fig. 406). Possibly they were the result of a drastic process of natural selection, later mitigated somewhat by civilization which has permitted a slight physical deterioration. The capacity of the race to build culturally on the achievements of past generations has, however, led to immense cultural gains since that time.

GEOGRAPHICAL DISTRIBUTION OF ORGANISMS

Few organisms are world-wide in their distribution. Most kinds are re-stricted to limited areas, some being confined to a single small island, valley, or mountain peak. All kinds of organisms have the means of spreading from place to place, but the means are far more ample in some than in others. Migration to a new region, moreover, does not always mean con-tinuation, for the new environment may not be suitable. There are thus two factors that restrict the range of a given species: the *unsuitability of environments* and the *presence of barriers.* In two separated land areas, such as, for example, a continent and a neighboring island that was once con-nected with the continent, the diversity between the land organisms is, in general, proportional to the time that the areas have been separated. The same holds true for marine species separated by a land barrier. The British Isles have been separated from the mainland of Europe for only a short time, geologically speaking; therefore the organisms of the former do not differ greatly from those of the latter. Australia has been separated from the other land masses of the world since the Mesozoic era. During that era the only mammals existing on earth were primitive types, similar to those now found in Australia. When the first English settlers reached that con-tinent, the only placental mammals they found were primitive men, dogs (possibly descended from those which the early human inhabitants brought in with them), rats and mice, which may have arrived on drifting debris or with man, and bats, which had flown across the ocean barrier. Aside from these, the mammalian population consisted of the two genera of PROTOTHERIA, and many diverse types of marsupials (METATHERIA) adapted to many modes of life (Fig. 407). Shut off from the rest of the land areas of the world and thus protected from competition with more advanced forms, these primitive types had held their own. Darwin began his speculations on evolution when he traveled as a naturalist to and around South America, where the facts of animal distribution seemed to call for an evolutionary explanation. Particularly significant were his studies in the Galápagos Islands, which lie seven hundred miles west of Ecuador. Their fauna and flora resemble those of South America more closely than of any other continent, but in many respects they are unique. Species that are restricted to land vary slightly on the different islands of the group, sug-gesting that since their original dispersal they have had time to develop along independent lines in the isolated localities. South America differs from Africa in its living forms far more widely than does North America from Europe and Asia, for in comparatively recent geological times land bridges connected the northern lands, but it has been much longer since the southern lands were connected. In general, the distribution of organisms over the earth is about what we should expect on the assumption that there has been evolutionary development of more specialized from more generalized types, along with migrations and interruptions of migration.

THE FACTORS OF EVOLUTION

Various theories have been advanced concerning the causes of evolution. For example, it has been suggested that the environment in which organisms live has a direct effect on them, producing modifications which are inherited. However, there has been little supporting evidence for the *inheritance of acquired characters*, so the idea is now mainly of historical interest. On the other hand, hereditary variation is known to come about through spontaneous changes of chromosomes and genes (*chro-*

FIG. 407. Koala (*Phascolarctus*), an Australian marsupial differing widely in structure and habits from the kangaroo. It lives in eucalyptus trees, feeding upon the leaves. (Photograph by the New York Zoological Society.)

mosome aberrations, gene mutations), and it is widely believed that these are important factors of evolution. Outstanding among the theories of the causes of evolution is Darwin's idea of *natural selection*, which explains the establishment in nature of hereditary characteristics favoring survival and reproduction. Though other factors influencing the establishment of hereditary characteristics have been suggested (*mutation pressure, chance,* etc.), natural selection is still considered important. It has also been recognized that the origin and preservation of distinct groups of organisms (species and higher groups) must require *reproductive isolation* between the members of these groups, thus preventing the free intermingling of their hereditary factors (with consequent loss of identity of the groups).

Inheritance of Acquired Characters. It is common knowledge that the environment causes modifications of individuals; e.g., exposure to strong light may cause pigmentation of the skin. It is a very old belief that such modifications may be inherited, and the idea of the *inheritance of acquired characters* has been offered at various times as an explanation for evolution. For example, the dark-skinned peoples of the earth might be accounted for by the repeated darkening of their ancestors' skin by exposure to the sun. Since the idea of the inheritance of acquired modifications had a prominent place in the writings of the French naturalist Jean Baptiste Lamarck (1744–1829), it has come to be called the Lamarckian doctrine. But the idea was current long before Lamarck and has been favored by other biologists since his time. Moreover, Lamarck restricted himself to the inheritance of modifications due to use or disuse; thus, vestigial organs might be explained by long disuse of these parts.

Though the idea has played a prominent part in the history of evolutionary thought, the inheritance of acquired characters is now generally rejected (although elevated to the position of an official doctrine in the U.S.S.R. and other communist countries). There has been no conclusive supporting evidence for it; moreover, the findings of the science of genetics make such a process seem most unlikely. For example, there is no evidence for the inheritance of mutilations. The binding of the feet of Chinese girls has not made the feet of their descendants any smaller, nor has the cutting off of the tails of domestic and experimental animals for numerous generations resulted in individuals born with short tails. Although biologists have from time to time published experimental evidence which seemed to them to substantiate the transmission of acquired characters, this evidence has failed to withstand the scrutiny of critical analysis. Stated in terms of hereditary factors, the inheritance of an acquired character means that a special environment capable of modifying the bodies of individuals may also influence their hereditary factors so that these give rise to the same sort of modification in later generations even in the absence of the special environment. This is hardly to be expected from the known properties of genes. Genes are quite stable, though they do occasionally mutate. The fact that certain environmental agencies (x-rays, high temperatures, certain chemicals) are capable of increasing the frequency of gene mutation is not relevant, because the mutant genes produced by such agencies do not necessarily cause modifications of the kinds induced in individuals by these factors. For example, there is no evidence that mutations promoted by high temperature have any special relationship to individual modifications caused by heat treatment. Finally, the inherited modifications that seem to be derived from acquired characters (e.g., hereditary dark skin) may be explained by mutation and natural selection, as will be shown.

Chromosome Aberrations and Gene Mutations. Hugo de Vries (1848–1935), a Dutch botanist, once noticed that a few plants of the evening primrose, a weedy plant that had been introduced into Europe from America, differed strikingly from the others. He collected seed from several kinds of these altered individuals and planted it; their progeny were true to the new types. He attributed these new types to *mutations,* and he advanced the theory that it is by such sudden and discontinuous changes that new species arise. Subsequent analysis of the types studied by de Vries showed that several different genetic processes were responsible for them —including chromosome aberrations, gene mutations, and even gene recombination. Although modern biologists have departed somewhat from de Vries' extreme view that sudden, striking changes of hereditary material ordinarily give rise directly to new species, it is generally believed that chromosome aberrations and gene mutations are important in evolution because they furnish the hereditary variation which is the "raw material" of evolution. With regard to the characteristics they produce, such changes of hereditary material are of many different kinds. In addition to those producing clearly recognizable changes of phenotype, there are many which cause early death (*lethal factors*), and probably many more that cause very slight modifications (thus influencing continuous variation). Studies of such changes in experimental animals (particularly *Drosophila*) and plants show that these changes are generally deleterious, but not invariably so. Although much remains to be learned about the details of changes of hereditary material, at present it seems reasonable to consider such changes as more or less random with regard to the effects they produce.

Natural Selection. For the establishment of new hereditary types in nature, the theory of evolution by *natural selection* was advanced by Charles Darwin (Fig. 408) in his *Origin of Species,* published in 1859. This idea, which has been most influential in developing an understanding of evolution, involves the following facts and conclusions drawn from them.

1. Organisms tend to reproduce themselves in such a way as to increase their numbers indefinitely.
2. However, the numbers of organisms either remain about the same from year to year or increase at rates far less than their reproductive potentialities would permit.
3. Consequently, there must be a *struggle for existence.* Organisms must struggle with their environment for survival and the opportunity to reproduce, and many must fail. Elimination of these must come about because of the physical environment and because of other organisms (competitors, predators, parasites).

4. There is variation in traits among organisms—among individuals of the same species, and even among offspring of the same parents.
5. Consequently, the organisms that are best adapted to meet the conditions of their environment survive (the *survival of the fittest*); the others perish.
6. The hereditary characteristics that enable organisms to survive in the struggle for existence must persist and increase, i.e., become established in nature.

Fig. 408. Charles Darwin (1809–1882), originator of the theory of evolution by natural selection. (From Scott, *Science of Biology;* copyright, Crowell.)

Natural selection offers an explanation for the remarkable *adaptations* of organisms to the environments in which they live. For example, plants have special ways of dispersing their seeds (e.g., the parachutes of goat's beard, Fig. 366); animals are often colored so as to resemble their backgrounds, thus being inconspicuous to their enemies or prey (e.g., polar bears and other white animals of arctic regions, Fig. 425); among human beings, the natives of tropical regions are usually dark-skinned and relatively well protected from the burning effects of the sun. Various other adaptations have already been mentioned in this book, and more will be pointed out in the next chapter. According to natural selection, though many different hereditary types may have arisen during the evolution of these organisms, the individuals having special adaptations that enabled them to survive and reproduce more readily than their competitors, have transmitted their characteristics to numerous descendants, thereby establishing these traits in nature. Thus, the idea of natural selection may be offered to explain adaptations which once seemed to require the inheritance of acquired modifications (though Darwin himself believed that acquired characters might be hereditary). For example, it is not necessary to suppose that the dark-skinned peoples of the earth originated because their ancestors' skin was repeatedly darkened by strong sunlight. With the appearance of hereditary dark skin through mutation, natural selection may be expected to have established the character in many individuals in regions in which the trait is an advantage.

Artificial Selection. As was mentioned in the preceding chapter, it has long been a practice to control the breeding of domestic animals and cultivated plants, selecting certain individuals for breeding and rejecting others. Accompanying this process has been considerable change in these animals and plants, and the development of numerous breeds and varieties that differ widely from the ancestral types and from each other (Figs. 409, 410). For example, the large, meat-producing fowl, like the Cochin; the specialist in egg-laying, like the Leghorn; the gamecock, and the tiny

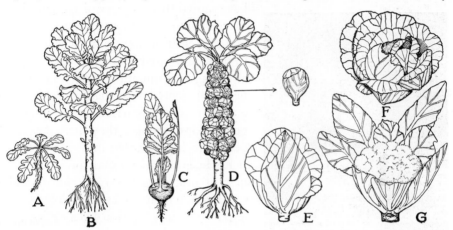

Fig. 409. Wild European cabbage (*Brassica oleracea*) and its varieties produced under cultivation. *A*, wild cabbage; *B*, kale; *C*, kohlrabi; *D*, Brussels sprouts; *E*, pointed-head cabbage; *F*, round-head cabbage; *G*, cauliflower. (From Transeau, Sampson, and Tiffany, *Textbook of Botany*; copyright, Harper.)

Bantam are all probably derived from one species, the jungle fowl of India. There are hundreds of varieties of apples with the widest variation in color, size, flavor, and time of ripening; but the source of them all is probably the wild apple of Europe. In his *Origin of Species*, Darwin made an important point of the development of new breeds and varieties by artificial selection. According to him, natural selection is analogous to artificial selection, but with *nature* (i.e., natural conditions), rather than man, playing the part of selector.

Selection and Hereditary Factors. Selection of hereditary characters must involve selection of the factors associated with them. Consequently, varieties and species should come to differ from their ancestors and each other with respect to many of the genes they have. Studies of domestic animals and cultivated plants have shown something of the nature of their genetic differences. Occasionally single genes are responsible for outstanding differences. For example, the whiteness (albinism) of various breeds of rabbits is due to a single recessive gene. On the other hand, outstanding varietal differences probably depend more often on a number of factors. It is likely that interspecific differences invariably depend on numerous genes.

Recessiveness of Mutant Genes. It was pointed out in the preceding chapter that because of recessiveness selection sometimes runs into difficulties, with unexpected harmful characters appearing occasionally and deleterious traits being eliminated only gradually. Studies of mutant genes have shown that they are often recessive to their normal alleles. Consequently, natural selection may also be expected to be complicated by recessiveness. Disadvantageous mutant genes, instead of being eliminated immediately after they originate, may be carried through many generations, though they may be expected to be discarded in the long run. It has been suggested that the recessiveness of mutant genes (and the diploid condition, which makes it possible) is of importance in evolution because it permits genes to be carried for many generations before being eliminated. Environments change, and a gene that is un-

FIG. 410. Scotch collie. Dogs probably have been domesticated longer than any other animal. The extremely varied domesticated types have descended, it is believed, from several different wild species similar to the wolf and jackal.

desirable in one environment may be beneficial in another one; hence retaining a gene for some time after it originates may enable the organism eventually to find a use for it. For example, a gene that causes reduction or elimination of the wings of an insect may ordinarily be disadvantageous; but in an environment with much wind (as on an oceanic island), winglessness may be desirable, because winged insects are in danger of being blown away.

Sex. The widespread phenomenon of sexual reproduction may be explained in terms of natural selection on the basis of what is known about the distribution of genes and characters accompanying this mode of reproduction. As was shown in the preceding chapter, the mating of two genetically different types brings their different genes together, and sexual reproduction of their offspring is accompanied by the formation of various possible combinations of these genes in their gametes and in the individuals of the next generation. Thus, an F_2 generation may be highly variable in both genotype and phenotype. In situations in which the environment is changing, the rapid production of many different gene and character combinations by an organism may be important for its survival, because some of these combinations may be able to take advantage of the new environment. It was pointed out in Chapter XXII (page 393) how the black stem rust of wheat must give rise by sexual reproduction to new strains capable of attacking otherwise resistant wheat. Thus sexual reproduction itself may be considered a characteristic advantageous to the organism because of its contribution to variability, and hence one which natural selection has caused to prevail. However, since environments are sometimes rather stable, the ability to change rapidly may not always be important; therefore asexual reproduction may not always be disadvantageous and may even be advantageous because of the stability of type which it affords. Thus, although sexual reproduction has come to be very widespread, asexual reproduction has not been completely replaced.

Establishment of Hereditary Variation in Other Ways. It has been pointed out that mutation itself may sometimes be responsible for the establishment of a kind of gene in a population of organisms. If a gene comes into existence repeatedly by mutation, it may eventually become widespread, even though *reverse mutation* (reverse transformations of genes are known in experimental organisms) and adverse selection (the mutant gene is likely to be deleterious) tend to eliminate it. This tendency of a mutant gene to increase through repetition of the same mutation has been called *mutation pressure*. Still another factor that influences the increase (or decrease) of a gene in a population is *chance*. We saw in the preceding chapter that the ratios of genetics depend on chance events—the fertilizations that give rise to the individuals of a generation. When the number of individuals is large, the observed ratio is usually close to the expected one; but when there are few offspring, chance may cause the actual ratio to be very far from the expected one (certain classes of individuals may even be missing). In small populations of plants or animals (where chance must also govern the combinations of individuals in matings), it has been suggested that there should be considerable fluctuations in the frequencies of genes and the characters they produce. Because of chance, a gene may come to prevail (or be reduced in frequency or even eliminated), regardless of whether it is beneficial, neutral, or harmful.

Reproductive Isolation. The early naturalists realized that the mating of different varieties and species resulted in a mingling of their characteristics; it was also suspected that if such mating took place freely the distinctness of these groups of organisms would eventually be lost. It may be observed that in nature there are various mechanisms which prevent the free interbreeding of different species. Two species may be separated geographically, and hence have no opportunity to mate; even if they inhabit the same region, they may encounter each other rarely because of their different way of life (e.g., animals may frequent different food plants or have different breeding seasons). Moreover, even if two species are not prevented from mating by external factors, they may show no inclination to mate when given the opportunity; or, if they attempt crossing, their mating may yield no offspring. Furthermore, when hybrids between species are produced, though they are often vigorous they are frequently sterile, and thus incapable of continuing the process of mixing the hereditary characteristics of the parent forms. The mule (Fig. 411) is a common example of a species hybrid, being the product of a cross between the female of the horse (*Equus caballus*) and the male of the ass (*Equus asinus*). Although mules have in rare cases been reported to produce offspring, they are generally sterile. Investigations of hybrid sterility have shown that it sometimes results from a failure of the chromosomes of the parent species to form regular pairs and separate properly at meiosis, so that gametes with various abnormal chromosome numbers are produced. However, still other factors (e.g., interactions of the genes of the two species) must also frequently be involved.

An important factor in the origin of species would be expected to be the development of isolating mechanisms. Geographical isolation might serve as a starting point in species formation. Following this, because of the establishment of different mutant genes in the separated groups, different characteristics, including those responsible for other isolating mechanisms, may come into existence. For example, it has been reported that a new species of rabbit has arisen in the Madeira Islands in this manner. About five centuries ago a litter of European rabbits was taken by navigators to these islands and liberated there. The descendants of these rabbits are considerably smaller, darker in color, and more timid than the present European type, with which they refuse to mate. They have been given a different species name. Of the several changes that have taken place, it is not certain which are adaptive, i.e., fitting the rabbits for their island environment, and which are due to the establishment of hereditary characters for other reasons.

Hybridization and Evolution. Though groups of organisms recognized as separate species frequently either fail to mate or produce sterile hybrids, cases are known in which interspecific hybrids have been capable of reproducing. Thus, it may be expected that when different species have the opportunity to mate, the mingling of their hereditary characters and the factors responsible for them will sometimes occur. Such hybridization may be expected to be of importance in the origin of new types, inasmuch as recombinations of the genes of the two groups may give rise to ad-

Fig. 411. Upper left, a type of mare (*Equus caballus*) used to produce draft mules. Upper right, a jack (*Equus asinus*) used to breed mules. Below, a pair of draft mules. (Courtesy of the Bureau of Animal Industry of the U.S. Department of Agriculture.)

vantageous characteristics. Among the vascular plants there is considerable evidence for a process whereby even rather sterile hybrids may contribute to the formation of new species. There is experimental evidence that interspecific crosses in these organisms followed by doubling of the chromosome number (*allopolyploidy*) result in vigorous, fertile individuals. Although polyploids within species are usually rather sterile, each kind of chromosome being represented more than twice so that meiosis is difficult, these allopolyploids are fertile, presumably because the chromosomes of *each species* are present in the diploid number and the chromosomes of the different species are sufficiently unlike so that they do not interfere with each other. For example, the Russian investigator Karpechenko observed that, although crosses between radishes and cabbages yielded almost completely sterile hybrids, doubling of the chromosome number of the hybrids (found in the rare offspring of the hybrids themselves) resulted in plants which were larger and entirely fertile (Fig. 412). Although this

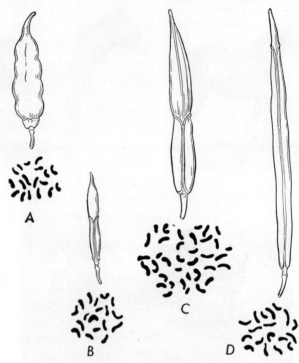

Fig. 412. *Raphanobrassica* (radish cabbage), a new kind of plant derived from chromosome doubling in the nearly sterile hybrid of radish and cabbage. *A*, Pod and chromosomes of the radish. *B*, Pod and chromosomes of the nearly sterile hybrid. *C*, Pod and chromosomes of *Raphanobrassica*. *D*, Pod and chromosomes of cabbage. (From Young and Stebbins, *The Human Organism and the World of Life*, rev. ed., copyright, 1951, Harper & Brothers; after Karpechenko.)

took place under cultivation (though spontaneously), there is abundant evidence that a comparable process sometimes occurs in nature. For instance, in the salt marshes of western Europe grows a kind of grass, Townsend's marsh grass (*Spartina townsendii*), which was first observed in the latter part of the 19th century and which is believed to have come into existence through the hybridization of a marsh grass introduced from

America and a native European grass, followed by the doubling of the chromosome number in the hybrid.

THE ORIGIN OF LIFE

Though there is much evidence for the reality of evolution, and understandable mechanisms for the process have been proposed, the beginning of evolution on the earth—i.e., the origin of life—remains obscure, hidden in the far distant past. However, certain speculations on the origin of living things on the earth may be offered on the basis of available evidence.

Most theories about the beginning of life on the earth have implied that life originated through the transformation of nonliving material into substance having the properties of life. It was noted in Chapter XX that the spontaneous origin of living things, even microorganisms, does not take place under any conditions known to man. But the possibility remains that under certain special conditions (perhaps those existing during the early history of the earth) spontaneous generation may take place. It seems reasonable to suppose that the first organisms were very simple, perhaps comparable to the simplest of the existing forms of life, the *viruses* (page 345). Not only are viruses exceedingly small (in the neighborhood of some of the protein molecules in size), but some of them have been obtained in crystalline form, which suggests that they are on the very border line between nonliving and living matter. Viruses have a number of characteristics in common with genes: (1) they are of similar size (though the sizes of genes are not definitely known); (2) they are similar in chemical nature (both consist of *nucleoprotein*); (3) they have the power of self-reproduction; and (4) they are capable of change, or mutation. It has even been suggested that viruses are free genes (or plasmagenes). However, studies of certain viruses have revealed that they are more complex than was formerly believed, that they consist of subunits that serve as hereditary factors and are comparable to genes. Perhaps the first living things were like genes. The ability of self-reproduction and the fact of occasional variation (mutation) seem to provide the necessary conditions for evolution by natural selection. When the struggle for existence began, certain variants should have survived more readily than others, but many of them perished. Advantageous for survival might be expected to be such mechanisms as association of genes in chromosomes, formation of cells and many-celled organisms, sexual reproduction. Thus these phenomena of life, having come into existence, must have become established. More progressive evolution then became possible and eventually occurred.

EVOLUTION AND HUMAN THOUGHT

Evolution is not only one of the greatest of biological generalizations; it is an idea that has done much toward molding thought and attitudes in other fields of human interest. Like the law of gravitation, evolution presents a far-reaching picture of the orderliness of the universe. As with gravitation, evolution need not be considered as degrading to man or subversive to the idea of a creative plan for the universe. Although, according to evolution, man is an animal and has been derived by descent from other organisms, the fact remains that man has many characteristics that make him very different from other living things—outstandingly, a high intelligence, which makes possible the formulation of ideas, the communication of knowledge, and considerable control over his environment. Man may indeed be considered a high achievement of the evolutionary process.

EXERCISES

1. May structures found in different organisms be both homologous and analogous? Explain.
2. How might we interpret the fact that chimpanzees have been found to belong to blood groups A and O; orangs to A, B, and AB; and gibbons to A? That the Rh factor was first discovered in rhesus monkeys?
3. Name examples of groups of organisms which were prominent during ancient geological times but have disappeared entirely. Name examples of contemporary organisms belonging to groups that have remained practically unchanged since ancient times.
4. What is amber? What kinds of fossils have been found in it?
5. How has radioactive carbon-14 been used to determine the age of ancient pieces of wood?
6. In what respects is man a highly specialized vertebrate? In what respects is he unspecialized?
7. Give examples of adaptations that suggest the inheritance of acquired characters. How else might they be explained?
8. If chromosome aberrations and gene mutations are the "raw material of evolution," why is it undesirable for the human mutation rate to be increased (as through exposure to x-rays)?
9. On the basis of natural selection, explain the existence of such plants as dodder, which obtain their food from other plants.
10. Give some examples of cultivated plants that are believed to have arisen through hybridization followed by polyploidy.
11. Since all known viruses depend on other living things for survival and propagation, how might one explain the persistence of a virus-like "organism" in a world in which other living things had not yet evolved?

REFERENCES

Blum, H., *Time's Arrow and Evolution*, Princeton Univ. Press, 1951.

Clausen, J., *Stages in the Evolution of Plant Species*, Cornell Univ. Press, 1951

Darwin, Charles, *Origin of Species*, London, 1859.

Darwin, Charles, *The Descent of Man*, London, 1871.

de Vries, Hugo, *Species and Varieties: Their Origin by Mutation*, Open Court Publishing Company, 3rd ed., 1912.

Dobzhansky, T., *Genetics and the Origin of Species*, Columbia Univ. Press, 3rd ed., 1951.

Dodson, E. O., *Evolution*, W. B. Saunders Company, 1952.

Fisher, R. A., *The Genetical Theory of Natural Selection*, Oxford Univ. Press, 1930.

Gamow, G., *Biography of the Earth*, Pelican Mentor Books, 1948.

Gregory, W. K., *Evolution Emerging*, The Macmillan Company, Vols. I, II, 1951.

Haldane, J. B. S., *The Causes of Evolution*, Harper & Brothers, 1932.

Hooton, E. A., *Up from the Ape*, The Macmillan Company, rev. ed., 1946.

Lindsey, A. W., *Principles of Organic Evolution*, The C. V. Mosby Company, 1952.

Lull, R. S., *Organic Evolution*, The Macmillan Company, 3rd ed., 1947.

Mayr, E., *Systematics and the Origin of Species*, Columbia Univ. Press, 1942.

Morgan, T. H., *The Scientific Basis of Evolution*, W. W. Norton & Co., 2nd ed., 1935.

Newman, H. H., *Evolution, Genetics, and Eugenics*, Univ. of Chicago Press, 3rd ed., 1932.

Oparin, A. I., *The Origin of Life*, The Macmillan Company, 1938.

Pincher C., *"Reason Why" Series: Evolution*, Herbert Jenkins, 1952.

Romer, A. S., *Man and the Vertebrates*, Univ. of Chicago Press, 1941.

Shull, A. F., *Evolution*, McGraw-Hill Book Company, Inc., 2nd ed., 1951.

Simpson, G. G., *The Meaning of Evolution*, Yale Univ. Press, 1949.

Stebbins, G. L., *Variation and Evolution in Plants*, Columbia Univ. Press, 1950.

Wright, S., "Evolution in Mendelian Populations," *Genetics*, 16:97–159, 1931.

Chapter XXX

THE ORGANISM AND THE ENVIRONMENT

Ecology, the study of the relation of organisms to their environment, has already received considerable attention but may appropriately be emphasized at this point. The environment of any organism is made up of *physical* or inorganic and *biotic* or organic factors.

PHYSICAL FACTORS

Oxygen. The great majority of organisms are *aerobic;* that is, they require oxygen for the release of the energy they need for the performance of life functions. Some, such as the yeast plant, are *anaerobic;* they release energy by means of chemical reactions that do not involve the taking in of free oxygen. Terrestrial aerobic organisms draw directly upon the oxygen of the air; aquatic organisms for the most part use oxygen that is dissolved in water. Most plants require free oxygen for their roots as well as for the parts above ground. In waterlogged soils where little oxygen can reach the roots, plants become stunted, turn yellow, and eventually die by drowning. The larger water plants are usually provided with extensive air spaces or channels which permit the distribution of oxygen from the floating or emerged portions to the portions beneath the water. In spores and seeds of plants and in encysted or hibernating animals, activity is at a low ebb and little or no respiration goes on.

Temperature. Since water is the solvent of all substances used by the organism, active life can exist only at temperatures between the freezing and the boiling points of water. Actually the limits are considerably narrower, for activity usually ceases several degrees above the freezing point, and at a considerable distance below the boiling point the proteins of protoplasm become coagulated and life ceases. Some of the cold-blooded animals may be frozen stiff and still retain life if thawed out very slowly. Bacteria and fungus spores taken to an altitude of fourteen miles by a stratosphere balloon retained their vitality, although both temperature and pressure are exceedingly low at this great height. At the other extreme, spores of bacteria have been boiled in water for hours without being killed. But warm-blooded animals cannot survive a change of many degrees from their normal internal temperature.

Adjustment to Light Direction. The influence of light on the direction of growth of plant parts is known as phototropism (Gr. "light turning"). Stems above ground show a marked tendency to grow toward the light, hence are *positively phototropic*. Leaves usually grow at right angles to the average direction of incident light, although those of a few plants, known as *compass plants*, develop with their edges in a north-south direction. Many roots, such as the clinging roots of ivy, are *negatively phototropic*; i.e., they turn away from the light. The leaves of certain plants, such as the bean, respond to changes in light direction by changes in turgor in the cells of their *motor organs* (swollen portions of the stalks of the leaf and leaflets, also called *pulvini*). This results in the upper leaf surfaces being kept at right angles to light during the day, and in a drooping or folding of the leaves at night. Many of the lower plants which have the power of locomotion travel toward or away from the light. The same is true of many animals. This response is called *phototaxis*.

Photoperiodism. This is the behavior response of a plant to the relative duration of light and darkness. Many plants, such as *Coreopsis*, are long-day plants, producing their blossoms when subjected to long daylight periods alternating with short periods of darkness (Fig. 413); many others, such as Klondyke cosmos, are short-day plants, coming into blossom when the light periods are short and the dark ones long. This knowledge explains, to a large extent, why the various species have regular blossoming times, and it enables the plant grower to exercise a certain amount of control over the flowering of his plants.

It has also been found that light stimulates the sex hormones of certain animals. Illumination of poultry houses to increase egg production is now a common practice.

Luminescence. Certain plants, particularly among the bacteria and higher fungi, and certain animals representing many of the phyla from protozoans to chordates have the power of emitting light, which, like any other form of released energy, is based on a process of oxidation in the organism. It is thought that emitted light helps fishes and other organisms that inhabit the deep sea, where darkness is complete, to find their way about (Fig. 173). In the firefly the intermittent flashes of light are signals that brings the sexes together for mating; but in many of the luminous organisms the value of the light is uncertain.

Fig. 413. Effect of day length upon flowering. Above, *Coreopsis lanceolata,* var. *grandiflora,* a long-day plant. The one on the left received supplementary light in the greenhouse in winter and spring from sunset to midnight; that on the right received only daylight during this same period. Below, Klondyke cosmos (*Cosmos sulfureus*), a shortday plant. The one on the left received ten hours of light each day during the summer in Washington, D.C., and the one on the right received the normal period, about fifteen hours. (Photos, courtesy of W. W. Garner.)

Water. We have already noted the importance of water as the solvent of all that enters and all that leaves the cells, the carrier of all that circulates through the organism, a raw material for the manufacture of carbohydrates by plants, and, because of its part in rendering the cell turgid, an indispensable agent in cell growth. Many organisms live in water; those that do not must absorb (or drink) water as such, or must secure it from moist foods. Organisms that live where water is scarce often have facilities for water storage, such as the fleshy stems of cactus (Fig. 4), the fleshy leaves of the century plant, and the water-storing sacs in the stomach of the camel. Furthermore, the surfaces of these organisms are often sufficiently waterproofed to prevent much loss. Most plants are provided with cutinized outer epidermal walls, and the stomata are so constructed that they close at the times when carbon dioxide is not needed, and also when water is so scarce that their remaining open would endanger the life of the plant. In accordance with their water demands plants are classified as *hydrophytes*, *mesophytes*, and *xerophytes*. Hydrophytes (Gr. "water plants"), such as water lilies and cattails, live in water or in very wet places. Their stems and leaves are usually well provided with air passages and their roots and vascular systems are generally poorly developed. Mesophytes (Gr. "medium plants") include the vast number of plants that live under conditions of moderate supply; xerophytes (Gr. "dry plants") grow in arid regions. The leaves of the latter may be fleshy and waterproofed (Fig. 414), or they may be much reduced, the work of photosynthesis being left to the fleshy stems.

Fig. 414. Joshua tree (*Yucca brevifolia*), a tree with heavy waterproofed leaves that grows in the deserts of southern California. Note the panicle of flowers at the tip of the highest tree. (Photo by H. N. Goddard.)

Gravity. We have observed that crustaceans orient themselves with respect to gravity by response to the pressure of grains of sand or similar solid bodies on sensory hairs in the statocyst, and that vertebrates accomplish the same end by response to the pressure of the fluid in the semicircular canals of the ear on special nerve endings. Response to the stimulus of gravity is known as *geotropism* (Gr. "earth-turning"). Plants as well as animals exhibit geotropism; the taproot, which is positively geotropic, grows downward, and the shoot, which is negatively geotropic, grows upward. These responses are probably governed by growth hormones.

Pressure and Contact. Animals of the deep sea must be adapted to withstand tremendous pressures on their surfaces, and organisms of high mountain tops must be adjusted to air pressure decidedly less than they would be under at sea level. Tendrils of plants respond to contact with a solid object by curling about it and tightening their hold upon it (Fig. 350). This is known as *thigmotropism* (Gr. "touch-turning"). Another type of contact movement is the folding of the leaves of certain plants, such as the sensitive plant, when they are touched or jarred (Fig. 415). This movement gives greater protection against injury from storms or other mechanical agencies; it is brought about by changes in the turgor of motor organs at the bases of the leaflets, the leaf subdivisions, and the leaves themselves. A similar protective folding occurs each night.

Fig. 415. Sensitive plant (*Mimosa pudica*). The plant on the right has just been jarred and shows the leaves completely folded. The middle one is shown after five minutes' recovery. The left one shows complete recovery, after ten minutes.

Chemical Nature of Surrounding Medium. Most organisms are adapted to an atmosphere containing about 21 percent oxygen and 0.03 of one percent carbon dioxide, or to water containing these gases in solution. A marked change in the percentage of either may be detrimental. Poisonous gases may injure plants as well as animals; the sparseness of vegetation in the vicinity of smelters and other chemical manufacturing establishments is a matter of common observation. The various mineral salts occur in rather constant proportions in sea water; and the first living forms, which probably arose along the shores of a primitive sea less salty than the modern oceans, became adjusted to these salts. Of the two great lines of descent from these early organisms, that which remained in the sea became adapted to the gradually increasing salt content of the water, while that which invaded the fresh waters and the land came to consist of organisms provided with body fluids, such as lymph and blood, which contain the same salts that are found in sea water and in about the same proportions, although in much lower concentration. Certain fishes and other animals can adjust to a considerable variation in the salt content of the water they inhabit. Most species of plants will not thrive if the salt concentration of the soil water is greatly increased, because the change in osmotic relations makes water absorption difficult. In the species that grow in salt marshes and alkaline deserts the concentration of cell sap is slightly higher than that of the water that surrounds their roots. Furthermore, they often have reduced leaves, waterproofed surfaces, and other features that suggest xerophytes or desert plants. Such plants are called *halophytes* (Gr. "salt plants").

BIOTIC FACTORS

FOOD

Types of Nutrition. A food supply is the most essential factor in the life of an organism. All life must have energy available for carrying on life processes. Most plants are *independent*, or *autotrophic* (Gr. "self-nourishing"); they secure their stores of food by building simple inorganic substances into organic compounds. These include all *photosynthetic* (green) plants and the few kinds of bacteria that are *chemosynthetic* (page 344). *Dependent* plants (*parasites* and *saprophytes*) and all animals are *heterotrophic* (Gr. "nourished by another"). Animals may feed on plants or plant products, they may eat dead animals, they may be *predators* and kill living animals for food, or they may be *parasites* and feed upon a victim which continues to live.

Food Pyramids. Heterotrophic organisms have a profound effect upon, and are themselves greatly affected by, the abundance of the organisms on which they are accustomed to feed. A pond or lake, for example, contains a host of organisms, both plants and animals. Each species consumes more than its bulk in food, and it in turn becomes part of the food of another. As shown in the pyramid in Fig. 416, the pond contains a large quantity of independent plants (algae and aquatic seed plants). These are

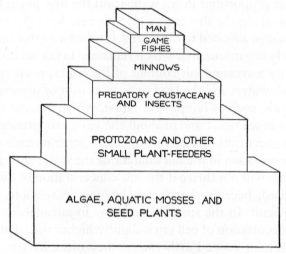

Fig. 416. Diagram illustrating the "food pyramid" as it may exist in a lake or fish pond.

fed upon by a smaller number of plant-eating animals, such as protozoans and aquatic insect larvae. These in turn are preyed upon by a still smaller number of small crustaceans, such as water fleas, and such predatory insects as dragon fly larvae. These small predators feed the minnows, which in turn are eaten by game fishes. The game fishes are a part of human food. Similar pyramids can be constructed for life in the various ocean, freshwater, and land habitats. Of course this is a great simplification of the actual picture, for there are many complex food relationships among the many forms in all habitats.

Parasitism. *Parasitism* is the intimate relation of two species in which one, the *parasite*, receives its food at the expense of the other (the host) without immediately killing the latter. Some animals, such as fresh-water clams (Fig. 101), are parasitic only in the larval stage; others, such as *Sacculina* (Fig. 124), only in adult life; still others, such as tapeworms (Fig. 82), spend almost their entire life parasitically. Parasites may live on the surface of the host (*ectoparasites*, Fig. 136) or within the body (*endoparasites*). A *heteroecious* (Gr. "different house") *parasite* is one that alternates between two host species. Examples that have been discussed in preceding chapters are the flukes (Fig. 81), which alternate between a snail and a mammal; the malaria protozoan (Fig. 49), which alternates between the *Anopheles* mosquito and man; and the wheat rust (Fig. 301), which alternates between the wheat plant and the common barberry. Sometimes the harm done by parasites is negligible, the host living as long and remaining in as good health as if they were not present; but usually parasites injure the host by destroying tissues, using digested or stored food, or causing waste of blood or other body fluids. Not infrequently a parasite causes more serious injury by making a wound which easily becomes infected with secondary parasites (disease germs), or by itself introducing such parasites.

Galls. An interesting result of parasitism, common on host plants, is the enlargement known as a gall (Fig. 417). Galls have characteristic forms, depending on the host plant and the parasite involved in their formation. Hundreds of types are found on the oaks alone. The abnormal growth of the plant is apparently induced by some chemical substance either injected with the egg or secreted by the organism or organisms that occupy the gall. Gall-forming organisms include gall wasps, gall flies, aphids, mites, bacteria, and true fungi.

Some Transmitters of Disease Parasites. Insects (as well as certain mites and ticks belonging to the arachnid group) are responsible for the transmission of numerous diseases of man and the other vertebrates. Some, such as the housefly, are merely mechanical carriers which pick up germs from body wastes or infected sores and transfer them to our foods or directly to our bodies. They carry the germs of typhoid, cholera, and dysentery, and are suspected of transmitting the virus of infantile paralysis. Others are biting insects that gorge themselves with germ-containing blood and regurgitate part of it into a later victim; an example is the flea, which is responsible for carrying the plague bacillus. Ordinarily the flea picks up this germ from a rat that is affected with or has died of plague and carries it to a person, but the germ may be carried from any infected to any susceptible mammal. Other transmitters are biting insects within which the disease organism undergoes a course of development before it is capable of infecting its vertebrate host. The sporozoan of malaria, which undergoes this secondary development in *Anopheles*, and the trypanosome of sleeping sickness, which passes through certain modifications in the tsetse fly, were considered in Chapter VII. Various parasitic flatworms and threadworms which pass part of their life cycle in intermediate hosts were discussed in Chapter X. Among diseases which are carried by insects are yellow fever, carried by the mosquito, *Aëdes;* typhus fever, carried by the body louse; tularemia, carried by the deer fly; kala-azar, carried by the sandfly; and Chagas' disease, carried by the kissing bug (*Triatoma megista*). Texas cattle fever and the human diseases, relapsing fever and Rocky Mountain spotted fever, are carried by ticks, members of the ARACHNOIDEA.

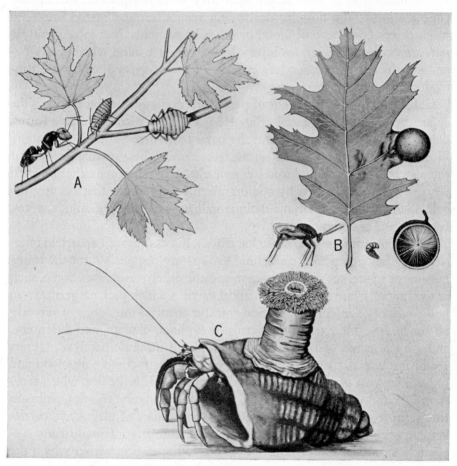

FIG. 417. Examples of symbiosis. *A*, Mutualism between two insect species, aphid and ant. Ants care for the aphids, and in turn feast upon honeydew secreted by the latter. *B*, Parasitism of an animal (a gall wasp) upon a plant (an oak). The enlargement of the leaf tissue is produced by some chemical introduced with the egg or secreted by the larva. The smaller figures below show the adult wasp, the larva, and a section of the gall showing the small central cavity occupied by the larva. *C*, Sea anemone on the mollusk shell occupied by a hermit crab. The anemone is transported by the crab, and may in turn render a service to the crab by stinging predators with its nematocysts. This is interpreted as commensalism, possibly bordering on mutualism. (From a chart of *General Biology Series*, edited by Goddard, Kenoyer, and Hinds, published by Denoyer-Geppert Co., Chicago; by courtesy of the publishers.)

Predatory Plants. A few seed plants, such as Venus's-flytrap, pitcher plant, sundew, and bladderwort, have a unique method of supplementing their food supply (Fig. 418). Their leaves are modified to facilitate the capture of insects and other small animals which supplement the nitroge-

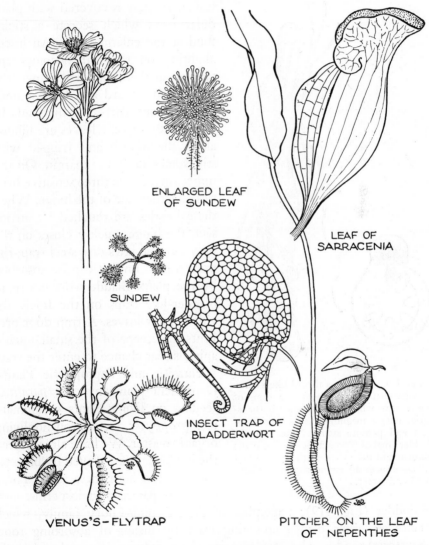

ENLARGED LEAF
OF SUNDEW

LEAF OF
SARRACENIA

SUNDEW

INSECT TRAP OF
BLADDERWORT

VENUS'S-FLYTRAP

PITCHER ON THE LEAF
OF NEPENTHES

FIG. 418. Insectivorous plants. Insects are caught between the hinged leaf halves in Venus's-flytrap, adhere to the sticky leaf glands of sundew, or are drowned in water retained in the pitchers of the pitcher plants (*Sarracenia* and *Nepenthes*). The trap door of the bladder of bladderwort retains small aquatic animals. The captured animals contribute to the nutrition of the plants.

nous food supply of the plant. The food trap usually secretes digestive enzymes which help to make this food available to the plant. In pitcher plants the trap is a pitcher, consisting of the whole leaf in *Sarracenia* and the tip of the leaf in the tropical *Nepenthes*. Insects drown in the water that is usually held in the pitcher. The leaf of sundew is covered with glandular hairs which secrete a sticky fluid at the enlarged end. An insect alighting on the leaf becomes entangled in this fluid, whereupon the hairs bend inward and hold it until its nutritious parts are digested. In Venus's-flytrap the leaves are hinged along the midrib and fringed with stiff spines along the margin. On the upper surface are three sensitive bristles on either side of the hinge. When these bristles are touched by an insect, the hinge quickly closes on the prey like the jaws of a steel trap; the prey is held until it can be absorbed by the plant. Bladderwort has small bladder-like traps on the finely divided water leaves. A trap door prevents the escape of the small aquatic animals that chance to enter the trap.

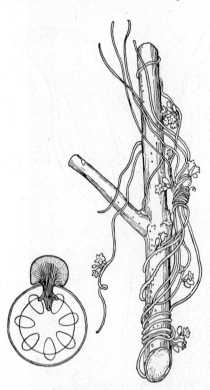

Fig. 419. Dodder, a thread-like yellow parasite that twines about the stem of the host, to which it is attached by haustoria; left, a magnified cross section of host and parasite stems. Note that the dodder makes contact with both the phloem and the xylem of the host, a fact which insures an ample supply of both food and water.

Parasitic and Saprophytic Plants. Dependent plants may be *parasites*, feeding on living plants or animals, or *saprophytes*, feeding on nonliving organic matter. We have already seen the important part played by bacteria and fungi in both these roles. There are a few parasitic angiosperms, such as dodder (Fig. 419), a member of the Morning-Glory family, which twines on other plants, attaching itself by means of absorbing roots (*haustoria*); and beechdrops, a brown plant often seen under beech trees, with whose small roots its haustoria make connection. Mistletoe is a partial parasite; it contains chlorophyll and hence depends on the host mainly for water. Indian pipe (Fig. 420) may be regarded as a parasite on a fungus, which in turn takes organic food from decaying vegetable matter.

Fig. 420. Indian pipe: *Monotropa uniflora* at left, *Monotropa hypopitys* at right. Fern fronds and a log of white birch are in the background. The Indian pipes have no chlorophyll, the former being pure white, and the latter yellowish. They obtain food from the decaying leaf mold by the aid of a fungus that occupies the cells of their underground portions. (From Swingle, *Plant Life;* copyright, Van Nostrand.)

AGGRESSION AND DEFENSE

Weapons. Most of the animal phyla afford excellent examples of organs used in capturing food and warding off enemies. Familiar weapons are the nettle cells of the coelenterates; the pincers of the crustaceans; the stings, piercing beaks, and biting jaws of many insects; the poison glands of spiders, centipedes, snakes, Gila monsters, and other animals; the claws and talons of birds of prey; and the claws, hoofs, and horns of many mammals. *Peripatus* ejects jets of slime to confuse the animals on which it feeds. One of the most remarkable offensive and defensive adaptations is the electric storage battery found in the electric ray and the electric eel, fishes that are able to administer a stunning electric shock to the aggressor or the victim. The ant lion larva constructs a conical pitfall in the sand for the capture of its prey (Fig. 421), and remains just underneath the sand at the base of the pit with its jaws in readiness to grasp its unwary victim. Any attempt of the ant to get away is rewarded by sand that the larva flips up to knock its victim back into the pit.

Armor. Defensive armor in the form of an exoskeleton is conspicuous in clams and snails, many echinoderms, crustaceans, many insects, turtles and other reptiles, and the armadillo (Fig. 422) and the pangolin (Fig. 209) among mammals. Formidable defensive spines are found on the sea urchin (Fig. 159), the spiny anteater (Fig. 197), the porcupine (Fig. 423), and others. These animals are for the most part sluggish in their movements and consequently, if not protected, would be in danger of extermination.

FIG. 421. The ant lion, an insect predatory in the larval stage. *a*, Larva (× 3); *b*, pitfall constructed by the larva for the capture of ants and other small insects, also an adult emerging from the cocoon; *c*, an adult. (*a* and *b* from Sanderson and Jackson, *Elementary Entomology*; copyright, Ginn; after Kellogg. *c* after Claus.)

Defensive Odors and Flavors. The skunk is notorious for its malodorous secretion, an extremely effective repellent to annoyers. Among insects, similar devices are found in the stinkbug and the lacewing fly. The bombardier beetle discharges with explosive violence a substance which has the odor of burning sulfur, the process resembling the firing of a small cannon. Many insects are reputed to be avoided by birds because of a disagreeable flavor, an example being the familiar monarch butterfly. Many plants species are avoided by grazing animals on account of spines, prickles, stings, or unpleasant odors or flavors.

Concealing Forms and Colors. Many animals have colors which resemble those of the environment in which they live, and therefore render them less readily visible. In some of them form enhances the effect, as in the Indian leaf butterfly, the walking stick, and certain caterpillars which

Fig. 422. Armadillo, an edentate mammal remarkable for its exoskeleton of bony plates covered by a horny substance. The skin between the rows of plates enables the animal to roll up when disturbed. (Photo, courtesy of Ernest P. Walker.)

resemble twigs (Fig. 424). Such concealing devices aid in securing protection against potential destroyers, as do, for example, the green color of many grasshoppers and insect larvae which feed on foliage, and the sand-like color of various desert animals; or they may help in aggression, as does the white color of the polar bear (Fig. 425), which enables the animal to slip up to its prey unobserved. A concealing color may be a single uniform pattern resembling the surroundings, or it may be a pattern of various colors and shades producing an effect similar to that of the camouflage employed in concealing battleships and gun emplacements (Fig. 426). It is a rather general rule that animals have

Fig. 423. Porcupine, a rodent, showing the sharp quills (greatly enlarged hairs) that serve for protection. (By permission of the Chicago Natural History Museum.)

darker colors above, concealing them from foes that look toward the dark backgrounds of vegetation or soil, and lighter ones below, which make them less conspicuous against the lighter background of the sky. In many species the female bird, which is on the nest much of the time and hence is in a less advantageous position than the male, is better concealed by her

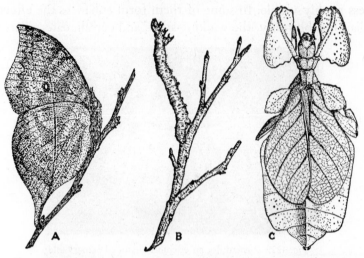

FIG. 424. Protective resemblance of insects. *A*, Leaf butterfly of India which when resting resembles a dead leaf; *B*, a moth larva which resembles a twig; *C*, a leaf insect of South America which in form and color resembles an assemblage of leaves. (From Wolcott, *Animal Biology*, McGraw-Hill Book Company, Inc.; *B* from Jordan, Kellogg, and Heath, *Animal Studies*, copyright, D. Appleton-Century.)

FIG. 425. Polar bear, illustrating concealing coloration serviceable in aggression. (By permission of the Chicago Natural History Museum.)

color than is the male. We have already mentioned the power of certain animals to change color when they move into a differently colored or shaded background. This is found in a striking degree in the flounder (Fig. 427), in certain amphibians such as the tree toad, and in certain reptiles such as the chameleon. It is generally accomplished by changes in the location or form of the pigment in the pigment cells. The periodic

FIG. 426. Woodcock and young (about two days old) near nest, Blackwater Migratory Bird Refuge, Maryland. The woodcock is an excellent example of protective coloration, for it is colored much like the sticks of the nesting site. The young are precocial. (Photo, courtesy of Fish and Wildlife Service, U.S. Dept. Int.)

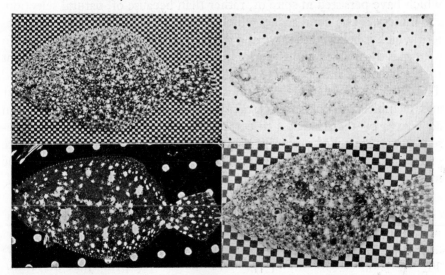

FIG. 427. The flounder on four different backgrounds, showing that it assumes a color pattern similar to that of the background. The change is accomplished by a visual stimulus transferred to the autonomic nervous system and stimulating the production of hormones which change the pigment cells. (Photographs, courtesy of S. O. Mast.)

molting of feathers in birds and of fur in mammals, together with the wearing away or breaking off of the ends of these structures, sometimes brings about varying protective color effects in the different seasons of the year. Thus the snowshoe rabbit, the arctic fox, the weasel, and certain birds such as the ptarmigan and snow bunting are white in winter but brown or gray in summer. An interesting concealing device is the ejection by the squid and cuttlefish of a dark fluid (sepia) from the ink sac, thus beclouding the water and making escape more easy.

Warning Marks and Signals. Organisms like the monarch butterfly, said to be disagreeable in flavor to birds and other predatory animals, and those endowed with a pronounced method of self-defense, such as the wasp, the skunk, the Gila monster (Fig. 185), and many of the poisonous snakes, are conspicuously colored or marked. Naturalists have considered such colors or marks as signals recognized by predatory animals and sparing the possessor the annoyance of being caught, even if not eaten, or of being compelled to use its weapons of defense. The rattle of the rattlesnake has been said to have a similar value. Some scientists, however, consider these explanations rather far-fetched. While the supposed useful character of such devices may account for their survival in the course of natural selection, it must be remembered that many organisms capable of vigorous self-defense are inconspicuous, whereas many that are relatively defenseless are brightly colored. In many cases, colors may be by-products which have persisted in spite of, rather than because of, natural selection.

Mimicry. The coral snake, which is poisonous, has a bright color pattern which is believed to serve as a warning signal. Closely resembling it in pattern is the nonvenomous scarlet king snake. The resemblance is thought to deceive other animals and to render the king snake less subject to attack. The edible viceroy butterfly bears a striking similarity to the slightly larger and inedible monarch, and certain nonstinging flies are said to gain an advantage by their likeness to certain stinging bees and wasps. Such resemblances are called *mimicry*. Many biologists think that the significance of mimicry has been overemphasized and that such resemblances may be mere coincidences.

OTHER RELATIONS BETWEEN SPECIES

Symbiosis. *Symbiosis* (Gr. "life together") in a broad sense signifies any close association of two species. Such association may be helpful to both (*mutualism*); indispensable to one from the standpoint of nutrition and harmful to the other (*parasitism*); or helpful to one and indifferent to the other (*commensalism*).

Mutualism. *Mutualism* is the type of symbiosis in which both the associated species are aided. Some authors limit the term symbiosis to such cases. Attention has already been called to the following examples: (1) relation of leguminous plants to root nodule bacteria, in which each partner contributes a portion of the food; (2) relation of alga to fungus in a lichen, in which the former provides food, the latter shelter; (3) relation of green fresh-water sponges and green hydra to the photosynthetic algae that occupy some of their cells; (4) relation of termites to the cellulose-digesting protozoans in their alimentary tracts. Another interesting example from the insect world is the relation between ants and aphids. When stimulated by the antenna of the ant, the aphid exudes from its alimentary tract a sweet liquid known as honeydew; this is relished by the ant (Fig. 417). The ants are believed, in turn, to assist the aphids by carrying them from plant to plant, and sometimes by taking them or their eggs into their own nest for protection during the winter. There are many mutually helpful relations between plants and animals, such as pollination of flowers by bees, distribution of the seeds of fleshy fruits by birds, and distribution of nuts by squirrels. Various tropical species known as "ant plants" have hollow stems or hollow spines which are occupied by fighting ants; sometimes, also, they bear special nectaries which furnish food to these insects. These ants probably serve the plant by keeping away leaf-cutting ants and other plant-destroying insects.

Commensalism. *Commensalism* (Lat. "at table together") is the type of association in which one partner is aided and the other unharmed. The aid to the one is commonly of some other nature than the reception of food directly from the other. As the term implies, the associated organisms may use the same food. It is thought that in many instances commensalism has brought the organisms together in a step that, in later evolution, may lead to parasitism.

An example of commensalism is the relation of the shark sucker to the shark (Fig. 428). The dorsal fin of the former is modified into an oval adhesive disk by means of which the sucker attaches itself to sharks or other large fishes, thereby obtaining free transportation. It releases its hold to feed on scraps of the food caught by the sharks. Similarly, a sea anemone fastens itself upon the shell occupied by a hermit crab (Fig. 417). If, as some believe, the crab gains protection from the nettle cells of the sea anemone, this may be a mild form of mutualism. Other examples of commensalism are the attachment of barnacles to the skin of whales; the advantage of shelter gained by owls and rattlesnakes in the burrows of prairie dogs; the dwelling of insects of many species in the underground homes of ants and termites.

Fɪɢ. 428. Shark sucker (*Echeneis naucrates*), bony fish of tropical seas, illustrating commensalism. Just above the head is the disk, a modified dorsal fin, by means of which it attaches itself to sharks. (Photo, copyright, courtesy of John G. Shedd Aquarium, Chicago.)

Slavery. Bordering on commensalism is a phenomenon which may be called *slavery*. Ants of certain species have the curious custom of raiding the nests of other species, securing larvae and pupae, and keeping them, when they reach adulthood, as slaves which make themselves useful in the various tasks connected with the maintenance of the masters' colony. In some cases this slave-keeping is incidental, but in others it is essential to the life of the keepers. The slaves do not seem to object to this enforced servitude—on the contrary, they are often loyal defenders of the colony. Of a similar nature is the habit of the European cuckoo and the American cowbird of laying their eggs in the nests of other species and thus securing free incubation service and feeding for their young.

Epiphytism. A common habit of plants, somewhat like commensalism, is that of growing upon other plants which serve as a support but not as a source of food. The supported plants are *epiphytes* (Gr. "upon plants"). Algae (such as *Protococcus*), lichens, and mosses are familiar examples. On trees especially in the moist tropics grow many vascular plants, such as ferns, orchids (Fig. 429) and bromeliads (Spanish moss is a well-known example of the last group). They thus find room to grow in a locality where competition is intense, and to secure an advantageous light supply (Fig. 442). Although the host tree is ordinarily unharmed, an overabundance of epiphytes may diminish its light supply or break down its branches.

Formations and Associations. A *formation* of organisms is a group that occupies a particular climatic region. Some of the great plant formations of the world are the tropical rain forest, which is green during the entire year; the tropical monsoon forest, which is leafless during the dry season; the temperate deciduous forest, which is leafless during winter; the prairie, produced by drier climatic conditions; the narrow-leaved evergreen forest of more northerly latitudes; and the desert, in lands of extreme dryness. Each of these has its characteristic animal as well as plant types. An *association* is the group of species found in a certain portion of the formation which has uniform conditions as regards soil, light, water, and other factors. In the temperate deciduous forest formation may be found the beech-maple-hemlock association (Fig. 430), containing beech, hard maple, hemlock, such shrubs as red-berried elder and prickly ash, such herbs as Dutchman's breeches, dog-tooth violet, and enchanter's nightshade, and various characteristic insects and other animals. These particular shrubs and herbs are here because they flourish in the shady conditions and rich leaf mold of the forest floor; the animals are here because of a supply of suitable food and other appropriate conditions. Another association in the same formation is the oak-hickory forest. Here the soil is poorer and the shade ordinarily less dense. Not only the trees, but, to a large extent, also the shrubs, herbs, and animals are different. The swamp forest and several other association types occur in the same formation. Animal associations are largely determined by plant associations because plants furnish the setting for animal life.

Fig. 429. An epiphytic orchid showing aerial roots which are provided with several outer layers of empty cells capable of absorbing rain and dew. (From Ganong, *Textbook of Botany for Colleges*; copyright, Macmillan.)

Successions. Neither the plant nor the animal association is static, for as the inhabitants change the environment, there is progress, step by step, from one association type to another. There is evidence, for example, that in the eastern United States the oak-hickory forest, under natural conditions, is very gradually accumulating humus and shade and being replaced

Fig. 430. A climax beech-maple-hemlock forest in northern Michigan. The largest trees are about 370 years old and have a maximum trunk diameter of about 34 inches. The forest floor is densely shaded and is covered mainly with ferns and low herbs. (Photo, courtesy of F. C. Gates.)

Fig. 431. Zonation about a lake and its outlet in northern Michigan. In the water are yellow and white water lilies; toward the shores, and in a detached central mat, is sedge (*Carex lasiocarpa*); at the edge of the water are bog shrubs, such as alder, birch, and honeysuckle; on the land is a forest of spruce and tamarack. (Photo, courtesy of F. C. Gates.)

by the beech-maple forest. If we were to go back to the first plant society in such an area we might find that it consisted of lichens covering an exposed rock or sandy waste. A lake is often bordered by successive zones of vegetation, each zone having its own particular requirements as to water depth. Thus there may be floating plants, such as duckweeds, in the deeper water; water lilies and cattails where the water is not too deep to allow rooted plants to come to the surface; sedges in somewhat shallower water; marsh shrubs along the border; then trees characteristic of swamp forest; and in the outermost zone, trees that require somewhat drier conditions. As the lake gradually disappears, each zone tends to move toward the old lake center. Thus any given spot on the lake border may pass successively through one after another of these vegetation stages (Fig. 431).

RELATIONS WITHIN THE SPECIES

The individuals of many species of plants and animals live in groups, flocks, herds, colonies, or societies of some sort. While some of the grouping is more or less accidental, brought about by common movement toward a favorable environment, much of it involves mutual assistance of some sort. Overcrowding may lead to severe competition for food or shelter, and the consequent death of many of the members of the group. It has been learned, however, that for many species there is an optimum population density, below which they seem not to thrive so well. Antagonism and struggle constitute only one side of the picture in plant and animal evolution. Quite as important is the tendency to cooperate.

Colonial Forms. In certain kinds of protozoans, sponges, coelenterates, tapeworms, bryozoans, and some other groups, the individuals are joined together in colonies. In some of these colonies there is division of labor among individuals. Portuguese man-of-war, for example, is one of the hydrozoan coelenterates in which the colony consists of several types of individuals or polyps. One is a large gas-containing float with a sail-like crest; some are nutritive, some sensory; some, nematocyst-armed, are offensive and defensive, and others are purely reproductive. When division of labor is lacking, as in sponge and coral colonies, mere aggregation and bulk are thought to be advantageous to the species.

Gregarious Forms. In most of the animal groups, from protozoans to chordates, are species that live, travel, or seek food in groups variously known as swarms, schools, flocks, or herds. The banding together may be merely temporary, such as that of most migratory birds during flight, or it may continue through the breeding season, as in many aquatic birds (Fig. 432). It permits mutual aid in search of food, mutual defense from enemies, or mutual control over the environment. The beaver colony with its elaborate system of dams and houses affords all of these advantages (Fig. 203).

Fig. 432. Flock of snow geese concentrated on Sacramento National Wildlife Refuge, California, where efforts are being made to build up the diminishing numbers of some of our game bird species. (Photo by P. J. Van Huizen, courtesy of Fish and Wildlife Service, U.S. Dept. Int.)

Order of Dominance. Recent investigations have shown that in social groups in many species of birds and mammals a rather definite order of social dominance exists among the members. In a flock of hens, for example, fights between individuals establish A's right to peck B, B's right to peck C, and so on down the line. Not only physical vigor, but age, length of time with the flock, endocrine balance, and other factors are instrumental in establishing this order of dominance. When a new hen enters the flock, contests with the old members individually establish her social status.

Social Forms. True social life is thought to grow out of family life. The production and care of the young is the supreme altruistic act of the animal world. Social life has its beginnings in the continuance together of parents and offspring for a period after the arrival of the latter. It is found in many groups of animals, but, aside from the human race, it probably attains its culmination among insects. It is said by Wheeler to have arisen independently twenty-four times in the insect world, but it is most pronounced in the fairly primitive order, ISOPTERA, or termites, and in the advanced group of HYMENOPTERA, with the ants, wasps, and bees as representatives.

FIG. 433. A termite mound about ten feet high in the Republic of Panama. (Photograph, courtesy of H. E. Enders.)

Termites are small, blind, and individually quite helpless, but are able to build up extensive flourishing colonies (Figs. 135, 433). As in many of the social insects, there is definite morphological differentation accompanied by division of labor among the members of the colony. Besides the functional males and females there are workers that perform the ordinary duties of the colony, and soldiers that defend it from enemies. Each of the latter groups includes both males and females, and each may consist of several different types or castes. Some of the tropical termites practice a sort of agriculture, growing fungi on the cellulose that has passed through their digestive tracts.

Among ants there is a similarly complex organization. Since ants have great ability to defend themselves, they have become remarkably successful, and are perhaps the most numerous insects. The ant colony may include winged and wingless males and females, intermediates between females and workers, major workers, minor workers, and soldiers. In the case of the leaf-cutting ant of the tropics, the major workers go along an established trail from the underground nest to the tree, cut off portions of the leaves, and carry them to their subterranean caverns, where the much smaller minor workers reduce the leaf material to pulp on which is grown a species of fungus. The swollen tips of certain of the fungus hyphae constitute a favorite food for the ants. In one species of ant, some of the individuals are curiously modified into honey pots; swollen with honeydew, they remain hanging from the ceiling of the underground home until their stores are required by other members of the colony.

The various species of wasps exhibit all gradations between solitary and colonial life. Like ants, the colonial wasps commonly practice mutual feeding. When the workers bring food to the larvae they lick a secretion that exudes from the larvae. This habit may be a bond that strengthens the colonial tendencies of these insects.

Bees also range from solitary species, through those like the bumblebee that organize small colonies, to the honeybee with its elaborate colony (Fig. 146). This bee probably represents the high point of arthropod evolution.

EXERCISES

1. Name three parasitic fungi; three parasitic seed plants; three external parasites on animals; three internal parasites on animals.
2. Give examples of the simplifications of structure resulting from the parasitic habit.
3. Describe the strangling fig, and justify its designation as a hemiepiphyte.
4. Give examples of hydrophytes, of mesophytes, and of xerophytes other than those mentioned in the text.
5. Name three organisms that emit light, and state possible advantages of this characteristic.
6. What advantages has the communal honeybee over the solitary wild bee? What disadvantages?
7. State advantages of mutualism other than those mentioned.
8. Name the principal plant associations in the succession from stream or lake to forest (or prairie) in your area; those from dry rock surface or sand hill to forest (or prairie).

REFERENCES

Allee, W. C., *Animal Life and Social Growth*, Williams and Wilkins Company, 1932.

Allee, W. C., Emerson, A. E., Park, O., Park, T., and Schmidt, K. P., *Principles of Animal Ecology*, W. B. Saunders Company, 1949.

Braun, E. Lucy, *Deciduous Forests of Eastern North America*, P. Blakiston's Sons, 1950.

Cott, H. B., *Adaptive Coloration in Animals*, Oxford Univ. Press, 1940.

Daubenmire, R. F., *Plants and Environment*, John Wiley & Sons, 1947.

Oosting, H. J., *The Study of Plant Communities*, W. H. Freeman & Company, 1948.

Pearse, W. S., *Animal Ecology*, McGraw-Hill Book Company, Inc., 1939.

Rothschild, M. and Clay, T., *Fleas, Flukes, and Cuckoos*, Philosophical Library, 1952.

Weaver, J. E., and Clements, F. E., *Plant Ecology*, McGraw-Hill Book Company, Inc., 2nd ed., 1938.

Welch, P. S., *Limnology*, McGraw-Hill Book Company, Inc., 2nd ed., 1952.

Chapter XXXI

CONSERVATION

Definition. Conservation is the intelligent use of our available resources —mineral, plant, and animal—keeping in mind the future needs of ourselves and our posterity. It does not mean hoarding for no useful purpose. It is a movement to counteract the waste which has been all too prevalent in the past. As one writer has said, "Conservation is a sustained effort to make good the mistakes of our pioneer forefathers, who were content to take all they could get out of their immediate environment and move on to fresh exploitation." "Consideration for others," says another, "is the cardinal principle of a sound conservation policy." These statements emphasize wise use, thought for others and for the future, and the guarding against exploitation and waste as the essentials of conservation.

Irreplaceable and Replaceable Resources. Our resources may be roughly classified as follows:

I. Irreplaceable:
- A. Metals. Metals are indispensable to civilization for both peacetime industries and military preparedness. Some are very restricted in their distribution, and the supply of a considerable number is becoming depleted.
- B. Nonmetallic minerals, including mineral fuels. Coal, oil, and gas furnish the energy for our culture. They are being used up at an alarming rate. Development of atomic sources of energy now holds out some hope for the future.
- C. Plant and animal species, many of which have become or are becoming extinct.

II. Slowly replaceable:
- A. Soil. This is indispensable for the production of food, clothing, and other important commodities. Its fertility may in part be restored; but when the soil is carried away by erosion, its replacement may require centuries.

III. More rapidly replaceable, with proper management:
- A. Forests and grasslands.

B. Fur and game mammals.
C. Birds.
D. Fish.
E. Water, which moves in cycles and is rather quickly replaced.

Depletion. The history of our country has involved far too rapid depletion of resources. The early settlers considered them to be limitless. Vast forests of magnificent trees covered much of the land, and the westerly areas were clothed with tall lush grasses. About 85 percent of our fine timber has been cut, much of it wastefully, and forest fires have been allowed to sweep the cutover areas after the lumbermen were through; prairies have been put to the plow, exposing their soil to disastrous wind erosion; the soil has been exploited without much attention to the use of fertilizers; numerous plant and animal species have become extinct; and our mineral wealth has been wastefully handled.

Awakening Interest in Conservation. Early in our national life, Washington and Jefferson expressed the importance of soil conservation. In the 1870's Congress established a Fish Commission to take steps toward preventing the depletion of the yield of fish; Arbor Day was established for the planting of trees; and Yellowstone, the first of the national parks, was established. The setting aside of national forests began in 1891. Theodore Roosevelt with the enthusiastic aid of Gifford Pinchot, gave marked impetus to the conservation movement, establishing several important governmental organizations directed to this end. The 1930's witnessed the establishment of the Civilian Conservation Corps, which did outstanding work during the depression years; of the Tennessee Valley Authority, a striking example of what may be accomplished in regional conservation; and of the Soil Conservation Service, which is doing splendid work all over the country in instituting practices to prevent soil depletion and erosion.

SOIL CONSERVATION

Soil. Man's existence depends upon the soil. It is the result of centuries of slow natural processes. Some of these are the fragmentation of rocks by temperature changes, by freezing and thawing, and by the prying action of plant roots; the dissolving of minerals by the chemical action of root secretions; the addition of organic matter by the action of microorganisms on accumulating plant and animal remains and the mixing in of this matter by the burrowing of earthworms and other animals. What requires centuries for building may be broken down or carried away in a very few years. Before intensive cropping and lumbering the natural cover of vegetation effectively preserved soils except where grades were very steep. The removal of this cover, together with overgrazing, fires, and unwise methods of cultivation, has permitted its rapid depletion.

Conserving Soil Fertility. Since crops take much out of the soil in the way of mineral ingredients such as nitrogen, phosphorus, and potassium, wise farming practices should aim to return or replace as much of these materials as possible. This may be accomplished by:

1. Saving *barnyard manure*, the most valuable fertilizer resource of the farm, and returning it to the soil. It should meanwhile be guarded against leaching by rain and against other losses.
2. Using *green manures*, or crops plowed under for the benefit of the soil. Leguminous crops are especially useful from this standpoint, because they harbor nitrogen-fixing bacteria in their root nodules (Fig. 276) and hence build up the nitrogen content of the soil.
3. *Rotating crops.* Wise farmers have long employed crop rotation. It has perhaps been most neglected in the one-crop cotton culture of the South. This neglect has shown itself strikingly in the worn-out lands of that region. The most desirable rotation varies with locality, character and use of crops, and convenience of management. Four- and five-year rotations are common. Legumes should ordinarily be included in crop rotations.
4. *Plowing and cultivating thoroughly* to keep down weeds, to reduce evaporation of water, and especially to allow the entrance of oxygen, which favors the growth of nitrite and nitrate bacteria.
5. Using *commercial fertilizers*. These may be so chosen that they will provide the minerals in which the soil is deficient.

Importance of Erosion. Erosion has carried away far more of the valuable soil ingredients than the crops have used (Fig. 434). It may be defined as the mechanical movement of soil through the agencies of running water and wind. The loss from this cause each year has been estimated at $400,-000,000, not including the damage to highways and railways and the costly silting of reservoirs, streams, and ditches. The amount of soil washed away annually is said to be three billion tons. The Soil Conservation Service has recently reported: "Erosion has ruined for cultivation approximately 50 million acres of our fertile land in this country. Another 50 million acres are in a condition almost as serious. About 100 million acres still in cultivation have been seriously impoverished by loss of soil, and about 100 million more are being depleted of productive soil at an alarming rate."

The minerals that have been used by plants can be restored, but there is no practicable way in which soil carried away by erosion can be replaced. To form new soil of equal value by natural processes would require hundreds of years. The problem of soil erosion does not involve simply the loss to owners; it is a national problem that affects the prosperity of the entire country and of every citizen.

Fig. 434. A mountain slope in North Carolina, showing the extensive erosion that has occurred because of the removal of the forest. (From Weaver and Clements, *Plant Ecology;* copyright, McGraw-Hill; photo, courtesy of U.S. Forest Service.)

Water Erosion. Water falling on any land surface may soak into the ground, evaporate, or be carried off by gravity. The splash of falling raindrops, if their momentum is not broken by grass or standing crops, loosens soil particles which are carried away by the runoff. The running water loosens and moves other particles. The size of the particles moved depends on the speed; this, in turn, depends on the steepness of the slope. Any inequalities in the surface lead to the formation of small grooves and ridges. The grooves become small gullies; these widen and deepen and the side wash starts to form tributaries. The particles carried by the water are tools by which the cutting power of the water is greatly increased. Gullies not only indicate a loss of useful soil, but if unchecked they soon make cultivation impossible.

Deposition of Eroded Material. As the water reaches less inclined portions of the stream bed its speed is decreased and the eroded materials begin to be deposited. The coarsest particles are deposited first, then others in the order of their size. Much of the finest material, which is the most valuable soil, is carried on to the rivers and ultimately to the sea. It is estimated that the Mississippi River annually deposits at its delta in the Gulf of Mexico the equivalent of six inches of soil spread over a million acres. Although river deposits may be useful in some places, they cause great damage by covering fertile soil with less fertile debris and by filling up reservoirs; the greater portion of them is spread over the sea bottom where it can be of no use.

Fig. 435. An approaching dust storm, about ten minutes distant in Baca, Colorado. (Photo 39-2-A, courtesy of Soil Conservation Service.)

Wind Erosion. Sand or silt if dry enough may be blown like snow, filling the air and forming drifts around buildings and other obstructions. The demand for food during the First World War stimulated the plowing and cultivation on the western plains of lands that had formerly been used only for grazing. A series of dry seasons followed, the loosened soil became dust, and during the 1930's this region experienced the most violent dust storms that the country has ever known (Figs. 435, 436). Dense clouds of dust filled the skies, huge drifts piled up about buildings, and large quantities of soil were carried away, leaving desolation over wide areas. The Chief of the Soil Conservation Service states that 300 million tons of soil were carried away by a single storm in 1934 and that the dust was seen from ships 200 miles from the Atlantic seaboard. Much land that had been good for grazing was thus ruined for any purpose.

FIG. 436. Dust erosion in Oklahoma. The drifted dust in the foreground has blown from the cotton field beyond the fence. Notice the tumbleweeds, which take advantage of the wind in the dispersal of their seeds. (Photo, Okla. 5025, courtesy of Soil Conservation Service.)

Control of Erosion. Some of the methods used in checking erosion are: (1) contour plowing, (2) strip cropping, (3) terracing, (4) the planting of trees or grasses, (5) the building of check dams, (6) conservation of humus, and (7) maintenance of forests and grasslands. Anything that decreases the slope of the land surface decreases the speed of flowing water and therefore the amount of erosion; hence the value of terracing and contour plowing. Plants, especially those with compact roots, such as grasses, small grains, legumes, and other cover crops, are especially effective. Deep-rooted plants, such as trees and shrubs, both bind together the surface soil and enter and hold the subsoil beneath; they also hold back the water and encourage the deposition of silt (Fig. 437). The humus formed on the forest floor by decayed leaves has great water-retaining power, breaks the force of the rain, and helps in preventing erosion and floods.

Fig. 437. Gully in a deciduous forest in Ohio, showing how the cover of shrubbery holds the steep banks against erosion. (Photo, Ohio 14–471, courtesy of Soil Conservation Service.)

In strip cropping, strips of cultivated crops are alternated with strips of grass, legumes, or other cover crops (Fig. 438). The strips of grass should be wide and approachable enough to allow convenience in harvesting the hay. Some areas are so sloping or have such poor land that they should never be used for cultivated crops but should be kept permanently in pasture. Along slopes or drainage lines where banks are steep, trees or shrubs are often planted. To check large gullies, check dams consisting of brush, logs, and other debris are used. This results in the deposit of soil back of the dam, and on this deposit grass may be established. To a large extent, the checking of erosion is a public problem, for the soil loss experienced by the individual landholder may be largely due to conditions on surrounding lands. It is therefore an encouraging sign that the government, through its Soil Conservation Service, is cooperating with states and communities in making a nation-wide attack on this important problem.

Fig. 438. Strip crop farming combined with contour plowing in South Carolina, showing strips of cotton (white) alternating with small grain. The strips follow the contour lines, preventing gullying. In the background just in front of the timber, terracing is used for the same purpose. (Courtesy of the U.S. Soil Conservation, S.C. 1065.)

FORESTS

Waste in Lumbering. Magnificent forests once covered nearly half of our area, or about 829 million acres. Of this, not more than half is now potentially valuable as forest and not more than one-eighth is mature timber. Much of the timber was discarded in the effort to get out the best, high stumps were left in cutting the trees, young trees were destroyed in logging operations, the brush was left to become a fire hazard, and wasteful methods of operating sawmills resulted in the loss of about 60 percent of the wood from each tree cut. Much timber was necessarily removed to provide agricultural land, but forest clearing was carried to such an extreme that large tracts of land valuable only for forests were cleared and farmed, only to be abandoned later as agriculturally unprofitable. Forests which should have been farmed as a crop and harvested with regard to the maintenance of future productivity were too largely exploited by the greed of the early lumber companies.

Forest Fires. After being cut over by the lumberman, the slash-filled area was frequently ravaged by fires (Figs. 439, 440). This meant not only death to the young trees but destruction of the leaf mold and humus and exposure of the soil to erosion, thus unfitting it to support anything but inferior types of trees. Standing timber, particularly in the coniferous forests, is constantly menaced by fire. It is estimated that 90 percent of our forest fires are man-made. Smokers who carelessly drop unextinguished matches or burning stubs are the greatest danger; other contributors are campers, brush burners, railways, and lumber companies. There are said to be 150,000 separate forest fires annually in the United States, and the an-

Fig. 439. An active forest fire in the Black Hills National Forest, South Dakota, 1936. (Photo by C. C. Averill, courtesy of U.S. Forest Service.)

nual loss from them is estimated at 50 to 100 million dollars. These losses include waste of valuable timber, destruction of young trees and plants, retardation of the growth of young trees, the killing of wildlife, loss of shelter for game, destruction of water-holding humus, increased soil erosion, increased severity of floods, the sapping of soil fertility, the marring of the beauty of the landscape, reduction of recreation grounds, and danger to human life.

Steps Toward Adequate Protection. The U.S. Forest Service in cooperation with state departments of forestry and private lumber companies has done much in recent years toward overcoming forest fire loss. Lookout fire towers are now familiar objects in the forest areas, scouting by airplanes has become established, efficient fire-fighting methods have been developed, ranger service extended, millions of seedlings planted, extensive experimentation carried on, and other steps taken to give a brighter picture for forestry. But in spite of present efforts, it is claimed that at least one million acres of forest are still unprotected. Although public agencies are doing a great deal, the problem of better conservation lies largely in the hands of the private citizen—the hunter, the tourist, the picnicker, and all who use or enjoy the forest areas. The following precautions should be

Fig. 440. A fire-devastated area in coniferous forest country in Oregon, 1934. (Photo by L. F. Ryan, courtesy of U.S. Forest Service.)

carefully observed: Always be careful of fire; be sure that no match or tobacco is thrown away while still burning; choose a safe place for a camp fire and make a small fire when cooking in the woods; put out camp fires with water and cover the spot with earth; never start a fire on a windy day; do not burn large brush piles; help create a sentiment for fire protection.

Conservation of Rainfall. As was noted in considering erosion, forests play an important part in conserving the water of any region. When rain falls on the land it may disappear in a number of ways. It may run off the surface from higher to lower levels, eroding hill slopes and filling the streams often to flood levels. This is *runoff water*. Another part may soak into the ground and either be carried downward between the soil particles to be stored as *underground water* or be held by capillary attraction between the soil particles as *capillary water*. The latter is most directly available to plants, though the underground water is also important as a reservoir from which the capillary water may be maintained. The amount of capillary water in any soil depends on the composition of the soil, on the soil texture—that is, the fineness or compactness of the particles—and on the presence of decaying organic matter, or humus, which readily absorbs water like a sponge. The best soil and one with maximum water-holding capacity is a mixture of sand and clay with an abundance of humus. Conditions in a forest are very favorable for developing such soil. The roots of trees and other plants promote rock weathering, and the falling leaves and other decaying parts of plants produce an abundant supply of humus.

When rain falls over a forest the force of the water is greatly diminished and the drops are broken up by the leaves and branches. The forest floor with its abundant humus absorbs and holds large amounts of water, thus reducing the amount of runoff and increasing the supply stored as underground water. The forest is therefore an important agency in conserving rainfall and preventing soil erosion and disastrous floods.

GRASSLANDS

The tall grasses of the western prairies and plains greatly impressed the early explorers. A writer in 1868 speculated that all the flocks and herds in the world could find pasturage in these unoccupied plains and on the mountain slopes beyond. In the 1870's a great cattle rush into this section resulted in serious overpasturing. Areas that would have been fully stocked with one cow to every forty acres were loaded until they were carrying one to every ten acres. Consequently, the better grasses were eaten to the roots and trampled out. Inferior grasses and weeds sprang up over the area. Man otherwise upset natural balances by killing the predatory animals and thereby allowing such rodents as prairie dogs to multiply; these had an added detrimental effect upon the grassland. Sheep were introduced in many parts of the West, and they were even more damaging than the cattle. This denuding of the land aided erosion by both wind and water. Then, as we have observed, there followed the plowing of vast sections for wheat cultivation, the subsequent disastrous dust storms, and the migration of many disappointed residents. Concerted efforts are now being made to correct these abuses, to limit grain farming to the more suitable areas, and to apply the methods already mentioned for checking erosion.

WILDLIFE

Man the Disturber. Every species of the plant and animal kingdoms is subject to certain balances. Its numbers are kept in check by other forms that feed upon or otherwise interfere with it, and these in turn are kept in balance by the food supply and by interrelation with still other species. Man has been the greatest disturber of this balance. In many cases his influence has been wholly selfish. Often the motive has been worthy, but harm has resulted through ignorance or thoughtlessness about the future. Conservation seeks to avoid these harmful disturbances in the interest of the general welfare in the future as well as in the present. Under natural conditions undisturbed by man, the law of balance operates to maintain fairly constant conditions with reference to wildlife in any particular locality. Whenever either plants or animals are transferred from one region to another widely separated region, there is always danger of upsetting or greatly modifying this balance. Many instances of this have occurred in the past, particularly in connection with the importation of foreign plants and animals into the United States. Over 400 very destructive insect pests have been brought into the country, largely with nursery stock. Examples are the European corn borer, the Mediterranean fruit fly, the Japanese beetle, the Mexican bean beetle, and the cotton boll weevil. The annual loss from these and other insect pests has risen steadily in recent years and is now estimated at over a billion dollars. Introduced into America about 1850, the English sparrow has now spread over the entire North American continent and has multiplied to such an extent that it has come to be regarded as a general nuisance because it eats enormous quantities of grain and interferes with the more useful and more attractive birds about the home.

Maintenance of Optimum Numbers. If any species is allowed to reproduce unhindered, it multiplies by geometrical progression, leading to potentially enormous numbers. Under actual conditions, however, a time arrives at which the rate of increase is highest. This is followed by a gradual slowing down until the population is practically stationary. This slowing down is due to competition among the members of the species for food and living room, greater prevalence of disease under crowded conditions which promote infection, greater pressure by other species, and other environmental factors. When there is too drastic restriction of deer hunting, for example, many deer die from starvation. The aim of conservation agencies is therefore to keep the population numbers of our native animals and plants somewhere near the point of most rapid increase. Trees for commercial lumbering should be cut before they reach the age at which there is too much slowing down of the growth rate. Research is being carried on by conservation departments and university research workers to determine the extent to which we can utilize our resources to the maximum advantage.

Maintenance of Varied Habitats. The conservationist does not want a state or national forest area completely stocked with mature and aging trees. Under such conditions there are little underbrush, a limited number of plant and bird species, and little cover and food for many of the fur-bearing and game animals. Hence he recommends careful harvesting of areas distributed through such forests, to permit development of under-brush and young timber and help maintain a varied flora and fauna. Like-wise a policy of limited control rather than complete extermination of predatory animals is encouraged because it prevents the animals preyed upon from increasing beyond reasonable bounds and helps maintain a bet-ter balance of life forms.

Conservation of Birds. The values of birds to man have been considered earlier. Notwithstanding their great usefulness, like most wild creatures, they have been subject to many enemies. Man himself has been one of the worst of these. In the past, sportsmen and hunters killed birds with little regard for the harm done in removing one of the best safeguards against the insects that destroy our crops. A century ago, immense flocks of passenger pigeons flew over our forests, but this bird is gone forever. A standing offer of $1000 for evidence of a pair of nesting pigeons has gone unclaimed since 1910. The heath hen (Fig. 441), the great auk, and the Labrador duck have vanished, the first of these in spite of heroic but somewhat belated efforts to preserve it. Few if any turkeys remain, and the trumpeter swan is extremely rare, existing for the most part only in a few bird sanctuaries. Hunters have reduced the ducks and geese to such a degree that restrictive measures have been necessary to prevent the practical extermination of many of the species. The eastern quail, one of the most useful birds in destroying harmful insects and weed seeds, has for a long time been on the verge of extinction in many states; it was saved only recently by laws establishing long closed seasons. Other insectivorous birds have been seri-ously reduced in numbers. Until a few years ago, market hunters in the southern states destroyed thousands of our migratory songbirds during their winter stay in the South. These were sold on the market for food, al-though each provided scarcely more than a mouthful. This slaughter, of course, greatly reduced the number of birds left to return north in the spring migration.

The plume hunters, up to a generation ago, were among the most ruthless of the bird destroyers. The egret or white heron was most sought after. The birds were killed wholesale during the breeding season for the delicate and beautiful feathers on the back, which appear only in this season (Fig. 442). This left the young to starve and the eggs to be destroyed. The birds were almost exterminated; they are still rare, although they have increased to some extent since they began to be protected.

Fig. 441. The heath hen, the last survivor of its species. Heath hens were once abundant on Martha's Vineyard. After 1916 the number dwindled rapidly; only this male was left in 1928. This photograph was taken in 1930; during 1932 the bird disappeared; hence the species is now listed with the dodo, the passenger pigeon, and the many others which have been unable to cope with a changing environment. (Photo, courtesy of A. O. Gross.)

Bird Protection Legislation. Fortunately, federal and state legislation has done much toward adequate protection for useful birds. The Lacey Act of 1900 prohibited the transportation of birds or their plumage from one state to any other state in which it was illegal to kill them. This has largely broken up the destructive millinery trade. An amendment to this law a short time later provided for bird protection in all federal bird sanctuaries. The law that has probably been most effective is the Federal Migratory Bird Conservation Act, passed in 1929. This law led to the determination of species to be protected, the establishment of closed seasons, and other important regulations. To make this legislation more effective, the United States has made bird treaties with Great Britain and a number of the countries of North and South America looking toward adequate and uniform protection, especially of migratory birds.

Fig. 442. White heron or egret in a cypress swamp in the southern United States. On the edge of the nest with the young is an adult. The delicate plumes on the back are carried only during the breeding season. Killing the parents means starvation for the young. The trees are festooned with Spanish moss (*Tillandsia*), an epiphytic seed plant. (Photo by American Museum of Natural History, New York.)

Fur-Bearing Mammals. During pioneer days in America, trading in furs was one of the most profitable occupations. Indians were skillful in trapping fur-bearing animals and were induced to sell them to the traders, often for a few trinkets or a little whisky, or at most for a paltry fraction of their cash value. Many fortunes were accumulated in this trade. Now the wild fur-bearing mammals are largely gone, and those that remain have been preserved only by strict control of trapping. Meanwhile fur farming has become a rather important industry.

American Big Game. The greatest tragedy among American mammals is that of the American bison (buffalo). At least fifty million of these immense animals once roamed the western plains. They sometimes reached a height of six feet at the shoulders and weighed as much as 2400 pounds. They were much valued for their meat; their hides furnished the buffalo robes of pioneer days, and their bones were extensively used as a fertilizer. They roamed over the grass-covered plains in immense herds, one of which was described as being 25 miles wide and as long as the eye could reach. Traffic on the Missouri River was sometimes delayed for days at a time by a herd that was swimming across it.

These vast herds were killed off in one of the most ruthless and wanton destructions ever known. Not only were they killed for their meat and

Fig. 443. American bison (buffalo). Herd under protection in Kaibab National Forest, Arizona. (Photo, courtesy of U.S. Forest Service.)

skins, but great numbers were killed to secure their tongues, which were considered a luxury. After the tongues were removed the carcasses were left for the wolves and coyotes, and the bones lay bleaching on the plains. After the transcontinental railways were built, many so-called sportsmen shot hundreds of these animals from the trains for the mere sport of killing them. Today this magnificent creature is practically extinct as a wild animal; scarcely more than 5000 are left, and nearly all of them live in protected parks or refuges (Fig. 443). Fortunately enough remain to give us an opportunity at least to see what the living animal was like. This tragedy should serve as a useful lesson for the future in planning for the wise conservation of the natural wildlife resources which still remain. While it might perhaps be argued that the passing of this great herd was to a large degree inevitable as the settlement of the country progressed, no intelligent person can condone the ruthless way in which it took place.

America still has a large group of superb mammals ordinarily thought of as big game. These include deer, elk, moose, Rocky Mountain sheep and goats, antelope, bear, and others. In view of the fact that these animals are capable of affording a valuable meat supply as well as reasonable recreation to the sportsman, the problem of conservation here is to provide adequate protection so that their numbers will remain as nearly constant as possible. It is estimated that each year over seven million hunters go out with guns. Without adequate restrictions concerning open seasons, number killed, areas of hunting, and possession limits, undoubtedly most of the forms would soon be reduced to the vanishing point. These restrictions are determined by federal and state authorities on the basis of an annual game census covering the entire country. It is encouraging to note that between 1921 and 1939 there was an increase of approximately 300 percent in the population of big game animals.

Fish Conservation.   The commercial fishing industry in the United States has been valued at about $240,000,000 annually. The supply of many species of valuable fishes has been so depleted by overfishing and pollution of waters as seriously to threaten the industry. In some localities along the Atlantic seaboard panic and poverty have resulted from the lack of wise conservation.

Pleasure fishing is probably the most popular American sport. About twelve million people annually engage in this activity, which, in addition to recreation, also provides a considerable portion of the nation's food supply. But our waters have been greatly depleted, and some of the species would long since have approached extinction had it not been for federal and state measures regulating the catch and replenishing the supply. With the latter end in view, fish hatcheries have been extensively developed by both federal and state agencies, nearly five hundred of them now being in operation. Their chief work is the propagation of young fish to be planted in streams and lakes. Eggs and sperms are secured from breeding fish by a process called stripping. When these are mixed, fertilization takes place; the fertilized eggs are then distributed for planting in favorable locations or are developed in the hatcheries under scientifically controlled conditions. The young fish may be distributed in the fry stage (just hatched), the fingerling stage (as long as the finger), or at a larger stage. The Fish and Wildlife Service has well-equipped working laboratories and cooperates with the states in the scientific study of fish habits and favorable habitats.

Flower Conservation.   In the economic development of our country it was inevitable that many of our beautiful wild flowers should be reduced almost to the point of extinction. This destruction has been hastened by the wanton gathering of great quantities by both children and adults, with little thought of the danger of reducing the numbers or the fact that other people were thus deprived of the pleasure of seeing them in their natural setting. Gathering flowers for market and digging plants for transplanting have added to the depletion. The need for wise protection of this element in the beauty of our landscapes is now recognized to a great extent. Laws prohibiting or restricting the gathering of certain flowers are in effect in many states and in most national and state parks. Complete protection may be given relatively rare flowers; in some cases flowers may be picked only by official permit or by permission of the owner of the property on which they grow. Among the types usually protected in the eastern and central states are lady's-slippers and other orchids, trailing arbutus, fringed and closed gentians, bluebells, columbine, mountain laurel, rhododendron, dogwood, trillium, pitcher plant, and Indian pipe (Fig. 420).

OTHER ASPECTS

Recreation. Probably the most worthy object for conservation is human health and happiness. Health, recreation, and education are promoted by the conservation of natural resources. Parks and sanctuaries not only preserve segments of our natural plant and animal life but give us an opportunity to see, enjoy, and appreciate this life. The automobile has permitted us to avail ourselves of these means of recreation on a scale hitherto impossible; hence, catering to tourists has become an industry of prime importance in some of our states.

National Parks. The policy of establishing national parks was initiated in 1872, when Congress set aside Yellowstone National Park with an area of over two million acres. Twenty-eight parks in all, with a combined area of over eleven million acres, have now been established and are controlled by the National Park Service, an agency under the Department of the Interior.

National Monuments. National monuments have been created by various Presidents by special proclamation. Their primary purpose has been the preservation of a historic structure, a landmark, or an area of special scientific interest. Some of them include a tract of land of considerable extent, such as Muir Woods in California. Others embody a single structure, like the Statue of Liberty in New York Harbor and the birthplace of George Washington. The first to be established was Devil's Tower in Wyoming. These parks and monuments, as well as 200 other wildlife refuges, give full protection to birds, mammals, and other wild animals.

National Forests. The first national forests were set aside from the public domain of the West. Because other sections needed help in forest management, the government was given authority by Congress in 1911 to purchase forest land. Now there are 152 national forests in at least 40 of the states; their combined area amounts to six times that of Pennsylvania. They produce much lumber on a sustained-yield basis, support a million people, provide recreation for 30 million annually, pasture six million livestock, contain thousands of miles of good fishing streams, and form a haven for large herds of big game animals.

State Protective Agencies. All the states have conservation departments or similar agencies. They promote and administer state legislation regarding open and closed seasons, bag limits, methods and times of shooting, and other matters of importance to conservation. They also foster and promote educational programs and expositions in the interests of conservation. They have been instrumental in establishing many state parks in which both animals and plants are protected and which are visited by large numbers of tourists each year.

Conservation Education. The most hopeful aspect of conservation at present is the widespread interest in its problems and the general consciousness of its importance. True, a great number of people still have the "grab all you can" spirit; they give little thought to the future or to the interests of other individuals. There are laws to prevent such people from wasting our resources or taking more than their share, but complete enforcement of such laws is of course extremely difficult. The greatest hope, in the long run, lies in wise education, especially of the younger generation. Both interest and activities in this direction are spreading rapidly. State conservation departments are doing effective work by publishing and distributing bulletins on the subject and by giving illustrated lectures to the public and the schools. Definitely organized technical curricula are now offered by certain colleges and universities. The great need at present is further organization of instructional materials, and adequate training of teachers and investigators who are alive to the need and are filled with enthusiasm for developing both the true spirit of conservation throughout the nation and an intelligent comprehension of the problem.

EXERCISES

1. State three reasons why you think conservation may be considered one of the most important problems in American life today.
2. Describe any instances of an unsound attitude toward conservation which you have observed.
3. What carelessness with regard to fire have you noticed in the woods or elsewhere? What precautions would you take?

4. What valuable truths about conservation have you learned from the Boy or Girl Scouts, or from some similar organization?
5. What agency or agencies regulate the conditions under which fishing or hunting may be carried on in any state? Where would you find the agency in your locality?
6. Suppose your home is in Michigan; whom would you have to consult in order to fish during a visit in Wisconsin?
7. What national or state parks or national forests have you visited? What conservation restrictions did you notice during these visits? What authority establishes these restrictions?
8. Find out what you can about Gifford Pinchot and Theodore Roosevelt as promoters of the conservation idea.
9. What was the CCC and what part did it take in conservation?
10. What is the Izaak Walton League and what is its main purpose? How did it get its name?
11. Describe the process of erosion and explain why it is a fundamental problem in conservation. Give some figures about the damage from it in the United States.
12. How do forests and prairies tend to check erosion?

REFERENCES

Bennett, H. H., and Pryor, W. C., *This Land We Defend*, Longmans, Green and Company, 1942.

Bristow, W. H., and Cook, K. M., *Conservation in the Education Program*, U.S. Office of Education, 1937.

Du Puy, W. A., *The Nation's Forests*, The Macmillan Company, 1938.

Elliott, C. N., *Conservation of American Resources*, Turner E. Smith & Company, 1940.

Gabrielson, I. N., *Wildlife Conservation*, The Macmillan Company, 1941.

Glover, K., *America Begins Again*, McGraw-Hill Book Company, Inc., 1939.

Gustafson, A. F., *Conservation of the Soil*, McGraw-Hill Book Company, Inc., 1937.

Gustafson, A. F., and others, *Conservation in the U.S.*, Comstock Pub. Co., Inc., 3d ed., 1949.

Leopold, A., *Game Management*, Charles Scribner's Sons, 1942.

Lieber, R., *America's Natural Wealth*, Harper & Brothers, 1942.

Lord, R., *To Hold this Soil*, Soil Conservation Service, U.S. Dept. Agric., 1938.

Osborn, F., *Our Plundered Planet*, Little, Brown Co., 1948.

Parkins, A. E., and Whitaker, J. R., *Our National Resources and Their Conservation*, John Wiley & Sons, Inc., 1939.

Renner, G. T., *Conservation of Natural Resources*, John Wiley & Sons, Inc., 1942.

Robbins, R. M., *Our Landed Heritage*, Princeton Univ. Press, 1942.

Sears, P. B., *Deserts on the March*, Univ. of Oklahoma Press, 1935.

Sears, P. B., *This Is Our World*, Univ. of Oklahoma Press, 1937.

Smith, G. H., *Conservation of Natural Resources*, John Wiley & Sons, Inc., 1950.

Van Hise, C., and Havemeyer, L., *Conservation of Our Natural Resources*, The Macmillan Company, rev. ed., 1930.

Weaver, J. E., and Fitzpatrick, T. J., *The Prairie*, Ecological Monographs, 4:109–295, 1934.

Webb, W. P., *The Great Plains*, Ginn and Company, 1931.

Williams, J., *Fall of the Sparrow*, Oxford Univ. Press, 1951.

Federal bulletins. Write the Superintendent of Documents, Washington, D.C., for lists and terms.

1. Department of Agriculture: Agricultural Adjustment Agency, Extension Service, Forest Service, Soil Conservation Service.
2. Department of the Interior: Bureau of Reclamation, Fish and Wildlife Service, National Park Service.
3. Independent federal agencies: Emergency Conservation Work, U.S. Office of Education.

State bulletins: State conservation departments, state departments of education, state agricultural experiment stations.

Appendix

CLASSIFICATION OF ORGANISMS

ANIMAL KINGDOM

Subkingdom PROTOZOA (Gr. "first animals")

1. Phylum PROTOZOA. One-celled animals.
    A. Class RHIZOPODA (Gr. "root-footed"). With pseudopods for loco-motion. *Amoeba.*
    B. Class FLAGELLATA (from Lat. "whip"). With one or a few flagella (whips) for locomotion. Some have plant characters. *Euglena, Volvox.*
    C. Class SPOROZOA (Gr. "spore animals"). Parasitic; usually with no special means of locomotion. *Plasmodium.*
    D. Class CILIATA (from Lat. "eyelid"). With cilia for locomotion. *Paramecium.*

Subkingdom METAZOA (Gr. "later animals")

2. Phylum PORIFERA (Lat. "pore-bearers"). With loosely coordinated cells and no nervous system. Food ingested by collar cells. Sponges.
3. Phylum COELENTERATA (Gr. "hollow intestine"). Diploblastic, with gas-trovascular cavity and nettle cells. Coelenterates.
    A. Class HYDROZOA (Gr. "hydra-like animals"). *Hydra,* hydroids.
    B. Class SCYPHOZOA (Gr. "cup animals"). Jellyfishes.
    C. Class ANTHOZOA (Gr. "flower animals"). Sea anemones, corals.
4. Phylum CTENOPHORA (Gr. "comb bearers"). With biradial symmetry. Comb jellies.
5. Phylum PLATYHELMINTHES (Gr. "flatworms"). Symmetry bilateral; with gastrovascular cavity but no coelom. Flatworms.
    A. Class TURBELLARIA (Lat. "disturbance," from currents produced by the cilia). *Planaria.*
    B. Class TREMATODA (Gr. "having holes"). Parasitic forms. Flukes.

C. Class CESTODA (Gr. "girdle"). Parasitic, in ribbon-like colonies. Tapeworms.

6. Phylum NEMERTEA (Gr. "unerring"). With alimentary canal and circulatory system. Proboscis worms.

7. Phylum NEMATHELMINTHES (Gr. "threadworms"). With alimentary canal and simple body cavity. Roundworms, such as *Ascaris, Trichinella*.

8. Phylum ACANTHOCEPHALA (Gr. "spiny-headed"). Parasitic. Spiny-headed worms.

9. Phylum ROTIFERA (Lat. "wheel-bearers"). Microscopic; with cilia surrounding mouth. Rotifers.

10. Phylum GASTROTRICHA (Gr. "belly hair"). Microscopic, with hairs distributed over body. Gastrotrichs.

11. Phylum CHAETOGNATHA (Gr. "bristle-jawed"). Marine worms with alimentary canal and coelom. Arrow worms.

12. Phylum BRACHIOPODA (Gr. "arm-footed"). Marine forms with dorsal and ventral shells. Brachiopods, or lampshells.

13. Phylum BRYOZOA (Gr. "moss animals"). Aquatic organisms forming branching colonies.

14. Phylum ANNELIDA (Lat. "little ring"). Segmented worms.

    A. Class ARCHIANNELIDA (Lat. "primitive annelids"). Marine worms without setae or appendages.

    B. Class POLYCHAETA (Gr. "many bristles"). Mostly marine, with well-developed appendages. *Nereis*.

    C. Class OLIGOCHAETA (Gr. "few bristles"). With setae. Earthworms.

    D. Class HIRUDINEA (Lat. "leech"). With suckers, but no appendages or setae. Leeches.

15. Phylum MOLLUSCA (from Lat. "soft"). Provided with a mantle, which usually secretes an external shell. Mollusks.

    A. Class AMPHINEURA (Gr. "nerves on both sides"). Shell usually of eight transverse plates. Chitons.

    B. Class GASTROPODA (Gr. "belly-foot"). Asymmetrical, usually with spirally twisted shell. Snails.

    C. Class SCAPHOPODA (Gr. "boat-foot"). Shell tubular, with both ends open. Toothshells.

    D. Class PELECYPODA (Gr. "hatchet-foot"). Shell two-valved; foot hatchet-like. Clams.

    E. Class CEPHALOPODA (Gr. "head-foot"). Foot consisting of a circle of tentacles surrounding mouth. Squid, *Nautilus, Octopus*.

16. Phylum ARTHROPODA (Gr. "jointed feet"). With segmented appendages. Arthropods.

    A. Class CRUSTACEA (Lat. "with crust or shell"). Gill breathers. Crayfishes, crabs, barnacles.

B. Class ONYCHOPHORA (Gr. "claw-bearer"). Primitive arthropods with annelid characteristics. *Peripatus*.

C. Class CHILOPODA (Gr. "lip-footed"). Segments many, single, one pair poison claws, many pairs walking legs. Centipedes.

D. Class DIPLOPODA (Gr. "double-footed). Abdominal segments double, each with two pairs walking legs. Millipedes.

✓ E. Class INSECTA (Lat. "cut into"). Three body regions; six legs. Insects.

    (1) Order THYSANURA (Gr. "fringe-tail"). Wingless. Fish moths.

    (2) Order COLLEMBOLA (Gr. "glue-peg"). Springtails.

    (3) Order ORTHOPTERA (Gr. "straight-winged"). Grasshoppers, crickets.

    (4) Order ISOPTERA (Gr. "equal-winged"). Termites.

    (5) Order NEUROPTERA (Gr. "nerve-winged"). Ant lions, Dobson flies.

    (6) Order EPHEMERIDA (Gr. "lasting but a day"). May flies.

    (7) Order ODONATA (Gr. "toothed"). Dragonflies, damsel flies.

    (8) Order PLECOPTERA (Gr. "twisted-winged"). Stone flies.

    (9) Order CORRODENTIA (Lat. "gnawing"). Book lice.

    (10) Order TRICHOPTERA (Gr. "hair-winged"). Caddice flies.

    (11) Order MECOPTERA (Gr. "long-winged"). Scorpion flies.

    (12) Order MALLOPHAGA (Gr. "wool-eating"). Biting (bird) lice.

    (13) Order ANOPLURA (Gr. "unarmed-tail"). Sucking lice.

    (14) Order THYSANOPTERA (Gr. "fringe-winged"). Thrips.

    (15) Order HEMIPTERA (Gr. "half-winged"). Stinkbugs, water bugs, squash bug.

    (16) Order HOMOPTERA (Gr. "similar-winged"). Cicadas, aphids.

    (17) Order DERMAPTERA (Gr. "skin-winged"). Earwigs.

    (18) Order COLEOPTERA (Gr. "sheath-winged"). Beetles.

    (19) Order LEPIDOPTERA (Gr. "scale-winged"). Butterflies, moths.

    (20) Order DIPTERA (Gr. "two-winged"). Flies, mosquitoes.

    (21) Order SIPHONAPTERA (Gr. "with tube, wingless"). Fleas.

(22) Order HYMENOPTERA (Gr. "membrane-winged"). Bees, wasps, ants.

F. Class ARACHNOIDEA (Gr. "spider-like"). Two body regions; eight legs.

    (1) Order XIPHOSURA (Gr. "sword tail"). King crabs.

    (2) Order SCORPIONIDA (Gr. "scorpions"). Scorpions.

    (3) Order ARANEIDA (from Lat. "spider"). Spiders.

    (4) Order PHALANGIDA (from Lat. name of organism). Harvestmen, or daddy longlegs.

    (5) Order ACARINA (from Gr. "mite"). Mites, ticks.

17. Phylum ECHINODERMATA (Gr. "spiny-skinned"). Secondary radial symmetry, water vascular system. Echinoderms.

    A. Class ASTEROIDEA (Gr. "star-like"). Starfishes.

    B. Class OPHIUROIDEA (Gr. "like a serpent's tail"). Brittle stars.

    C. Class ECHINOIDEA (Gr. "hedgehog-like"). Sea urchins, sand dollars.

    D. Class HOLOTHUROIDEA (Gr. "like a water polyp"). Sea cucumbers.

    E. Class CRINOIDEA (Gr. "lily-like"). Sea lilies.

18. Phylum CHORDATA (Gr. "with cord"). Chordates.

    I. Subphylum HEMICHORDATA (Gr. "half cord"). Worm-like marine forms with poorly developed notochord. *Balanoglossus*.

    II. Subphylum UROCHORDATA (Gr. "tail cord"). Notochord in larva only, discarded by adult. Sea squirts.

    III. Subphylum CEPHALOCHORDATA (Gr. "head cord"). Notochord persistent, extending from head to tail. Skull absent. Lancelets.

    IV. Subphylum VERTEBRATA (Lat. "jointed"). Notochord giving way to a backbone which is composed of vertebrae. Vertebrates.

        A. Class CYCLOSTOMATA (Gr. "round-mouthed"). Without jaws or limbs. Lampreys.

        B. Class PISCES (Lat. "fishes"). With jaws and limbs. Fishes.

            (I) Subclass CHONDRICHTHYES (Gr. "cartilaginous fishes"). Skeleton cartilaginous; mouth beneath. Sharks.

            (II) Subclass OSTEICHTHYES (Gr. "bony fishes"). Skeleton bony; mouth usually terminal.

                (1) Superorder DIPNOI (Gr. "with two breathing apertures"). Lung fishes of Africa, Australia, South America.

                (2) Superorder CROSSOPTERIGII. Lobe-finned fishes.

                (3) Superorder ACTINOPTERYGII. Ray-finned fishes, including the vast majority of bony fishes.

        C. Class AMPHIBIA (Gr. "both life"). With gills and lungs.

            (1) Order APODA (Gr. "without feet"). Worm-like amphibians without legs. Caecilians.

(2) Order URODELA (Gr. "evident tail"). Tail present. Salamanders.

(3) Order ANURA (Gr. "without tail"). Tail absent. Frogs, toads.

D. Class REPTILIA (Lat. "creeping"). Reptiles.

(1) Order RHYNCHOCEPHALIA (Gr. "snout head"). A primitive group with but one living representative—Tuatara of New Zealand.

(2) Order CROCODILIA (Gr. "crocodile"). Crocodiles, alligators, gavials, caimans.

(3) Order TESTUDINATA (Lat. "like a tortoise"). Turtles.

(4) Order SQUAMATA (Lat. "scaly").

(a) Suborder SAURIA (Gr. "lizards"). Lizards.

(b) Suborder SERPENTES (Lat. "creeping"). Snakes.

E. Class AVES (Lat. "birds"). Birds.

(I) Division RATITAE (from Lat. "raft"). Running birds.

(1) Order STRUTHIONIFORMES. Ostriches.

(2) Order RHEIFORMES. Rheas.

(3) Order CASUARIIFORMES. Cassowaries, emus.

(4) Order CRYPTURIFORMES. Tinamous.

(5) Order APTERYGIFORMES. Kiwis.

(II) Division CARINATAE (Lat. "keeled"). With keeled breastbone.

(1) Order SPHENISCIFORMES. Penguins.

(2) Order GAVIIFORMES. Loons.

(3) Order COLYMBIFORMES. Grebes.

(4) Order PROCELLARIIFORMES. Albatrosses, petrels.

(5) Order PELECANIFORMES. Pelicans, cormorants.

(6) Order CICONIIFORMES. Storks, herons, ibises, flamingos.

(7) Order ANSERIFORMES. Ducks, geese, swans.

(8) Order FALCONIFORMES. Vultures, hawks, eagles.

(9) Order GALLIFORMES. Grouse, quail, turkeys.

(10) Order GRUIFORMES. Cranes and rails.

(11) Order CHARADRIIFORMES. Gulls, sandpipers, plovers.

(12) Order COLUMBIFORMES. Pigeons.

(13) Order PSITTACIFORMES. Parrots.

(14) Order CUCULIFORMES. Cuckoos, anis.

(15) Order STRIGIFORMES. Owls.

(16) Order CAPRIMULGIFORMES. Goatsuckers, nighthawks.

(17) Order MICROPODIFORMES. Swifts, hummingbirds.

(18) Order CORACIIFORMES. Kingfishers, hornbills.

(19) Order PICIFORMES. Woodpeckers.

(20) Order PASSERIFORMES. Perching birds, songbirds.

F. Class MAMMALIA (Lat. "breast"). Mammals.

    (I) Subclass PROTOTHERIA (Gr. "first mammals"). Egg-laying mammals.

        (1) Order MONOTREMATA (Gr. "single hole"). Duckbill, spiny anteater.

    (II) Subclass METATHERIA (Gr. "later mammals"). Viviparous, but without placenta.

        (1) Order MARSUPIALIA (Gr. "pouch"). Marsupials. Opossums, kangaroos, wombats.

    (III) Subclass EUTHERIA (Gr. "true mammals"). Fetus nourished through a placenta. The great majority of mammals.

        (1) Order INSECTIVORA (Lat. "insect-eating"). Shrews, moles, hedgehogs.

        (2) Order DERMOPTERA (Lat. "skin-winged"). Flying lemurs.

        (3) Order CHIROPTERA (Gr. "hand-winged"). Bats, flying foxes.

        (4) Order CARNIVORA (Lat. "flesh-eating"). Bears, wolves, foxes, dogs, raccoons, weasels, minks, skunks, hyenas, cats, seals, walruses.

        (5) Order RODENTIA (Lat. "gnawing"). Squirrels, beavers, muskrats, porcupines, mice, rats, guinea-pigs.

        (6) Order LAGOMORPHA (Gr. "hare form"). Hares, rabbits, pikas.

        (7) Order ARTIODACTYLA (Gr. "even-toed"). Even-toed ungulates: Hippopotamuses, pigs, peccaries, camels, giraffes, antelopes, bison, cattle, sheep, moose, deer.

        (8) Order PERISSODACTYLA (Gr. "odd-toed"). Odd-toed ungulates: Tapirs, rhinoceroses, horses, zebras.

        (9) Order PROBOSCIDEA (Gr. "feeding before"). Elephants.

        (10) Order HYRACOIDEA (Gr. "shrew-like"). Conies.

        (11) Order EDENTATA (Lat. "without teeth," a misnomer, as only the anteater is entirely without teeth). Anteaters, sloths, armadillos.

        (12) Order PHOLIDOTA (Gr. "scaly"). Pangolins.

        (13) Order TUBULIDENTATA (Gr. "tubular-toothed"). Aardvarks.

        (14) Order SIRENIA (Lat. "sea nymph"). Sea cows, dugongs.

        (15) Order CETACEA (Lat. "whales"). Toothed whales, whalebone whales.

        (16) Order PRIMATES (Lat. "chief"). Lemurs, tarsiers, monkeys, apes, man.

PLANT KINGDOM

1. Phylum THALLOPHYTA (Gr. "thallus plants"). Plant body not at all or only slightly differentiated, usually living in water or moist organic substance.

    I. Subphylum SCHIZOPHYTA (Gr. "fission plants"). Cells without specialized nucleus, cytoplasm, and plastids. Reproduction asexual, by fission.

        A. Class SCHIZOPHYCEAE (Gr. "fission algae"). With photosynthetic pigments. Blue-green algae, as *Oscillatoria, Nostoc.*

        B. Class SCHIZOMYCETES (Gr. "fission fungi"). Generally without photosynthetic pigments. Bacteria.

    II. Subphylum ALGAE (Lat.). Cells with specialized nucleus, cytoplasm, and plastids. Photosynthetic pigments present. Generally aquatic. Usually with asexual spore formation, or sexual reproduction, or both. True algae.

        A. Class CHLOROPHYCEAE (Gr. "green algae"). Plastids green. *Protococcus, Spirogyra, Oedogonium, Vaucheria.*

        B. Class BACILLARIOPHYCEAE (Gr. "rod-like algae"). Unicellular, with siliceous wall; plastids brown. Diatoms.

        C. Class PHAEOPHYCEAE (Gr. "brown algae"). Multicellular; plastids brown. Brown algae, as *Fucus, Laminaria.*

        D. Class RHODOPHYCEAE (Gr. "red algae"). Plastids usually red; life histories complex. Red algae, as *Chondrus.*

    III. Subphylum FUNGI (Lat. "mushroom"). Cells specialized. Photosynthetic pigments lacking; living on other organisms or on organic matter.

        A. Class MYXOMYCETES (Gr. "slime fungi"). Nutritive stage ameboid. Slime molds.

        B. Class PHYCOMYCETES (Gr. "alga-like fungi"). Nutritive stage of coenocytic filaments; spores in sporangia. *Rhizopus.*

        C. Class ASCOMYCETES (Gr. "sac fungi"). Nutritive stage of partitioned filaments. Spores in 8-spored sacs (asci). *Peziza, Penicillium.*

        D. Class BASIDIOMYCETES (Gr. "basidia" or "little base" fungi). Nutritive stage of partitioned filaments. Spores 4, projecting from a club-like basidium. *Agaricus, Puccinia.*

        Fungi in which none of these characteristic modes of spore-bearing have been discovered are placed provisionally in the FUNGI IMPERFECTI.

2. Phylum BRYOPHYTA (Gr. "moss plants"). Generally terrestrial and somewhat differentiated. Conducting vessels absent. With alternation of generations, the sexual generation being the more conspicuous.

A. Class HEPATICAE (from Gr. "liver"). Sexual plant prostrate, often leafless. Liverworts, as *Marchantia*.

B. Class MUSCI (Lat. "mosses"). Sexual plant prostrate or erect, leafy. Mosses, as *Sphagnum, Polytrichum*.

3. Phylum TRACHEOPHYTA (Gr. "plants with water vessels"). Asexual generation the more conspicuous; provided with elongated cells or continuous tubes serving for the conduction of water and foods. Vascular plants.

    I. Subphylum LYCOPSIDA (like *Lycopodium*, which is literally "wolf foot"). Leaves small, scale-like, some of them having a sporangium in the axil. Clubmosses, as *Lycopodium, Selaginella*, and fossil tree-like forms.

    II. Subphylum SPHENOPSIDA (Gr. "wedge leaf," because some of the early groups had wedge-shaped leaves). Stems hollow; leaves reduced to circles of scales; spores in cones. *Equisetum*.

    III. Subphylum PTEROPSIDA (Gr. "feather-like," from the leaf form of many of the ferns). Leaves commonly larger than in preceding groups.

        A. Class FILICINAE (Lat. "ferns"). Sporangia on lower leaf surface; no seeds.

            (1) Order FILICALES. True ferns, as *Polypodium*.

            (2) Order HYDROPTERIDALES. Water ferns, as *Marsilea*.

            (3) Order OPHIOGLOSSALES. Adder's tongues, as *Botrychium*.

        B. Class GYMNOSPERMAE (Gr. "naked seeds"). Ovules and seeds exposed on a modified leaf. Gymnosperms.

            (1) Order CYCADALES. Palm-like, with pinnate leaves. Cycads, as *Dioon*.

            (2) Order GINKGOALES. Deciduous tree with fan-like leaves. *Ginkgo*.

            (3) Order CONIFERALES. Usually evergreen cone-bearing trees. Conifers, as *Pinus, Juniperus*.

            (4) Order GNETALES. Approaching angiosperms in certain respects. *Ephedra, Welwitchia*.

        C. Class ANGIOSPERMAE (Gr. "seeds in vessel"). Ovules enclosed in an ovary, which develops a fruit, surrounding the seeds. Angiosperms. A few of the many orders and families will be mentioned, the latter by their common names.

          (I) Subclass MONOCOTYLEDONEAE. Seed with one seed leaf; leaves usually parallel-veined; stems without cambium; flower parts usually in 3's. Monocots.

            (1) Order NAIADALES. Pondweeds and water plantains.

            (2) Order GRAMINALES. Grasses and sedges.

            (3) Order ARALES. Aroids and duckweeds.

(4) Order PALMALES. Palms.

(5) Order LILIALES. Lilies and irises.

(6) Order ORCHIDALES. Orchids.

(II) Subclass DICOTYLEDONEAE. Seeds with two seed leaves; leaves mostly netted-veined; stems with cambium; parts of the flower usually in 4's and 5's.

(1) Order FAGALES. Birches and oaks.

(2) Order CHENOPODIALES. Goosefoots and amaranths.

(3) Order CARYOPHYLLALES. Pinks and purslanes.

(4) Order RANUNCULALES. Buttercups and magnolias.

(5) Order PAPAVERALES. Poppies and mustards.

(6) Order ROSALES. Roses and legumes.

(7) Order GERANIALES. Geraniums and spurges.

(8) Order SAPINDALES. Sumacs and maples.

(9) Order MALVALES. Mallows and basswoods.

(10) Order OPUNTIALES. Cacti.

(11) Order UMBELLALES. Parsleys and dogwoods.

(12) Order ERICALES. Heaths.

(13) Order GENTIANALES. Gentians and milkweeds.

(14) Order POLEMONIALES. Phloxes, mints, figworts.

(15) Order RUBIALES. Madders and honeysuckles.

(16) Order CAMPANULALES. Bellflowers and composites.

GLOSSARY

Abdo'men. The part of an animal body posterior to the thorax.

Absorp'tion. The process of taking liquids or dissolved substances through cell membranes into the cells of the body.

Ac'id. A chemical compound containing one or more hydrogen atoms that ionize in solution.

Acquired character. Any change brought about by the influence of the environment upon an individual organism.

Adapta'tion. Modification of an organism fitting it to its environment.

Adjus'tor. A nerve cell connecting receptor and effector.

Adre'nal gland. An endocrine gland located on or near the kidney.

Adren'alin. See **epinephrine.**

Adventi'tious. Arising (as a bud or root) in some unusual place.

Ae'ciospore, aecid'iospore. One of the spores in chain-like rows within an aecium.

Ae'cium. The cup-like aeciospore-producing structure of a rust fungus; the cluster cup.

A'erobe. An organism which lives only in the presence of oxygen.

Af'ferent (nerve). Carrying impulses toward a center (the brain or cord).

Agglutina'tion. The clumping together of bacteria or of blood cells by the action of an agglutinin.

Agglu'tinin. An antibody capable of effecting agglutination.

Aggres'sive resemblance. Such resemblance to environment as would help an animal to reach its prey without being seen.

Air bladder. A gas-filled sac in the bony fishes which serves to adjust the specific gravity; a similar structure in brown algae.

Al'binism. A lack of pigment in skin, hair, or feathers, and eyes.

Albu'men. A protein found in the white of an egg in reptiles and birds.

Al'kali. A base in which hydroxyl is combined with an alkali metal (K or Na) or with the ammonium radical (NH_4).

Allan'tois. An embryonic membrane in birds, reptiles, and mammals, functioning chiefly in respiration.

Allele′. One of a pair, or series, of genes occupying the same locus; also **alle′-lomorph.**

Al′lopolyploidy. Polyploidy involving the chromosomes of more than one species.

Al′ternate (of leaves or branches). One at a node.

Alterna′tion of generations. Reproduction in rotation of sexual and asexual generations.

Altri′cial. Having the young hatched or born in a helpless condition.

Alve′olus. A small cavity or sac, as in the lungs.

Ami′no acid. An organic acid containing the amino radical, —NH_2; a constituent of a protein.

Amito′sis. Direct cell division which does not involve appearance of chromosomes.

Am′nion. The innermost membrane that encloses the embryos of reptiles, birds, and mammals; it contains the amniotic fluid.

Am′ylase. A starch-digesting enzyme.

Anab′olism. Constructive metabolism; the building up of simple substances to greater complexity.

Ana′erobe. An organism that respires without free oxygen.

Anal′ogous. Similar in function but not necessarily in structure.

An′aphase. The stage in mitosis at which the chromosomes are drawn toward the poles.

Anat′omy. The science of the gross structure of organisms.

An′giosperm. A plant that bears seeds in a closed ovary.

Animal pole. The pole near which the protoplasm is accumulated in a telolecithal egg.

An′nual ring. A layer which represents a year's growth of wood in the trunk or branch of a dicotyledonous or gymnospermous tree or shrub.

An′nulus. A ring around the stipe of certain gill fungi; a ring of thick-walled cells completely or partly surrounding the sporangium of a fern.

Anten′na. A segmented sensory appendage at the front end of the head of most arthropods.

Anten′nule. The smaller of the two pairs of antennae of a crustacean.

Ante′rior. Pertaining to the front end.

An′ther. The pollen-containing part of the microsporophyll or stamen in an angiosperm.

Antherid′ium. A reproductive structure that produces sperms; used in plants.

Antibiot′ic. A chemical produced by an organism and destructive to an organism of another kind. Generally applied to such a substance made by a microorganism.

An′tibody. A substance contained in the tissues or fluids that opposes the action of another substance.

An'tigen. A substance which, when introduced into the body, gives rise to an antibody, or reacts with an antibody already there.

Antip'odal (cells). The cells at the opposite end from the egg in the female gametophyte of an angiosperm.

Antisep'tic. A substance that prevents bacterial growth.

Antitox'in. A substance developed by the cells of an organism to neutralize or counteract a toxin or poison.

Antiven'in. An antitoxin which acts against snake venom.

A'nus. The posterior opening of the alimentary canal.

Aor'ta. The large artery which carries blood from the heart to the tissues of the body.

Appen'dage. One of the paired extensions from the body in annelids, arthropods, and chordates.

Appendic'ular skeleton. The part of a vertebrate skeleton which belongs to the limbs and their attachments.

Appen'dix (vermiform). A small tube or sac opening into the caecum of the vertebrate intestine.

A'queous humor. The liquid between the crystalline lens and the cornea of the vertebrate eye.

Archego'nium. A structure that contains the egg cell in the sexual generation of bryophytes and vascular plants.

Archen'teron. The primitive digestive cavity in the gastrula stage of the embryo.

Ar'tery. A blood vessel carrying blood away from the heart.

Artifi'cial selection. Improvement by man of domesticated plants and animals, by the selection of superior individuals for breeding.

As'cocarp. A fruiting body composed of or containing asci.

Ascor'bic acid. Vitamin C, which is useful as a preventive of scurvy.

As'cospore. A spore produced in an ascus.

As'cus. A club-shaped spore sac of an ascomycete, containing usually eight ascospores.

Asex'ual. Without sex; producing young by division from a single parent.

Assimila'tion. The process of converting digested food into the substances of the organism.

Asymmet'rical. Not capable of being cut into similar halves.

At'om. The very small structural unit of a chemical element, which unites with other units of the same or different elements to form molecules.

Au'ditory nerve. The eighth cranial nerve of a vertebrate, which carries impulses from ear to brain.

Au'ricle. The chamber, or one of the two chambers, at the anterior end of the heart of vertebrates.

Autonom'ic. Self-acting; applied to the portion of the nervous system which controls the vital processes without the conscious effort of the individual.

Autot′omy. The power of breaking off body parts to escape an enemy or to discard injured tissue.

Autotroph′ic. Self-nourishing, as a green plant.

Ax′ial skeleton. The main skeletal axis of a vertebrate, including the spinal column and the skull.

Ax′il. The angle formed by the petiole of a leaf and the stem above its attachment.

Ax′illary. Appearing in the axil.

Ax′on. The chief process of a nerve cell, in which impulses are conducted away from the cell body.

Bacteriol′ogy. The science of bacteria.

Bacte′riophage. An ultramicroscopic virus that destroys bacteria.

Bark. The portion of a stem outside the cambium.

Basal (leaf). Growing from a much shortened stem just above ground.

Base. A chemical compound containing one or more hydroxyl groups which ionize in solution.

Basid′iospore. A spore borne on a basidium.

Basid′ium. The club-shaped cell of a basidiomycete, bearing at its summit four basidiospores.

Bien′nial. A plant that develops seed at the end of its second year of growth and then dies, e.g., a beet.

Bilat′eral symmetry. A plan of arrangement in animals in which the body parts are arranged similarly on either side of a central longitudinal plane.

Bile. A secretion of the liver, containing decomposition products of the blood pigment and helping to emulsify fats.

Bino′mial no′menclature. The recognized system of naming an organism by designating its genus name followed by its species name.

Biogen′esis. The conception that, since the beginning of life, all life has arisen from previous life; opposed to spontaneous generation.

Biol′ogy. The science of life.

Bisex′ual. Having both male and female reproductive organs in the same organism.

Blad′der. A membranous sac, particularly that in which urine accumulates until its discharge.

Blade. The flat part of a leaf.

Blas′tocoel. The cavity of a blastula, also called the cleavage or segmentation cavity.

Blas′topore. The opening into the primitive intestine of a gastrula.

Blas′tula. An early stage in embryonic development, typically a hollow sphere.

Blood vessel. A tube that carries blood.

Body cavity. Space between body wall and alimentary canal.

Bot′any. The science of plants.

Bot′ulism. Poisoning from an anaerobic bacillus sometimes found in canned foods.

Bra′chial. Pertaining to the arm.

Bract. A reduced leaf associated with a flower.

Brain. The highly developed center of the nervous system, located at the anterior end of the body in animals.

Bran′chial. Pertaining to the gills.

Bron′chiole. A small branch of a bronchus.

Bron′chus. One of the tubes which lead from the trachea into the lung.

Buc′cal. Pertaining to the mouth.

Bud. An undeveloped shoot.

Budding. Reproduction by development of the new individual from a small process from the old, as in yeast; a method of grafting whereby a single bud is attached to the stock.

Bulb. An underground storage organ of plants, the major part of which is composed of fleshy leaf bases.

Bul′bil. A small reproductive bud.

Cae′cum. A "blind" or closed pouch, especially that at the anterior end of the large intestine of mammals.

Calcif′erol. Vitamin D.

Calcif′erous. Lime-containing.

Cal′orie (large). See **Kilocalorie.**

Ca′lyx. The sepals, considered collectively.

Cam′bium. The layer which, by growth and division, adds to the thickness of the stem (dicotyledons and gymnosperms).

Cap′illary. One of the minute blood vessels which form a network between arteries and veins.

Cap′sule. In higher animals, the enlarged inner end of a uriniferous tubule; in mosses, the spore-containing body; in certain angiosperms, a dry dehiscent seed pod.

Car′apace. The dorsal portion of the exoskeleton of a crustacean or turtle.

Carbohy′drate. One of a class of foods containing carbon, hydrogen, and oxygen, the two latter usually in the ratio of two to one.

Car′diac. Relating to the heart.

Carniv′orous. Flesh-eating.

Car′otene. A yellow pigment associated with chlorophyll in leaves.

Carot′id. Pertaining to the arteries which supply the head.

Car′pal. One of the wrist bones.

Car′pel. The megasporophyll of a seed plant.

Ca′sein. The protein found in milk.

Catab′olism. Destructive metabolism.

Cat′alyst. A substance which promotes chemical action in other substances without itself being consumed in the reaction.

Cau′dal. Pertaining to the tail.

Cell. A mass of protoplasm containing a nucleus; the structural and physiological unit of living things.

Cell sap. The solution contained in the vacuoles of living cells.

Cell theory. The theory that all living things are composed of cells.

Cell wall. The nonliving covering of the cell secreted by the protoplast.

Cel′lulose. A carbohydrate which is generally abundant in the cell walls of plants.

Central nervous system. The part of the nervous system which receives afferent and sends out efferent impulses; it usually includes the brain and spinal cord.

Cen′triole. Small, deep-staining particle released by centrosome during mitosis.

Centrolec′ithal. Relating to an egg in which the main part of the yolk is gathered at the center, as in that of insects.

Cen′trosome. A small, cytoplasmic body in animal cells and a few plant cells; this liberates the centrioles during mitosis.

Cen′trum. The main body of a vertebra.

Cephaliza′tion. The localization of the brain and principal sense organs at the head end of the animal.

Cephalotho′rax. The fused head and thorax of certain arthropods.

Cercar′ia. The tailed larva of a fluke.

Cerebel′lum. The "little brain"; the front lobe of the hind brain.

Cer′ebrum. The main portion of the forebrain.

Cer′vical. Pertaining to the neck.

Chala′za. The stringy, whitish strands of albumen at each end of a bird's egg which holds the yolk in place near the center.

Chel′iped. A large thoracic appendage of a crustacean; the pincer.

Chem′ical compound. A substance composed of similar molecules which are made up of two or more kinds of atoms.

Chem′istry. The science of chemical changes, or changes in substance.

Chemosyn′thesis. Process of manufacturing food by energy liberated by oxidation of some substance in the organism.

Chi′tin. A nitrogenous compound contained in the exoskeleton of the arthropods.

Chlo′ragen or **chlo′ragogen cells.** The greenish cells which form the outer layer of the intestinal wall in the earthworm and allied forms.

Chloren′chyma. Tissue containing chlorophyll.

Chlo′rophyll. The green coloring matter of plants.

Chlo′roplast. A plastid containing chlorophyll.

Chon′driosome. A kind of cytoplasmic inclusion found in many cells.

Cho′rion. A membrane outside of the amnion in the embryo of mammals; it is attached by villi to the wall of the uterus.

Cho'roid. A pigmented coat which lies between the retina and the sclerotic coat in the vertebrate eye.

Chro'matin. The nuclear material of which the chromosomes are made.

Chromat'ophore. A colored plastid in plants; a pigment cell in animals.

Chro'moplast. A plastid of another color than white or green.

Chro'mosome. One of the highly staining bodies of the nucleus which split lengthwise in cell division, effecting the equal distribution of the genes to the daughter cells.

Chromosome aberra'tion. Microscopically visible alteration of the chromosomes as to number or form.

Cil'ium. A motile, hair-like projection from a cell.

Circula'tion. The movement, through the body, of a liquid which distributes food and oxygen to the cells, and collects wastes.

Clad'ophyll. A stem having the appearance and function of a leaf, as in asparagus.

Class. The classification group between phylum and order.

Cleav'age. The cell divisions which occur in the early stages of the development of an embryo.

Clitel'lum. A glandular thickening in the body of the earthworm; it secretes a cocoon to receive the eggs and sperms.

Cloa'ca. A common passageway to the outside of the body for digestive, excretory, and reproductive systems in certain vertebrates.

Cni'doblast. A special ectodermal cell of a coelenterate, containing a nematocyst or stinging structure.

Cni'docil. A spine-like "trigger" projecting from the cnidoblast.

Coc'cyx. The bones which constitute the rudiment of a tail in man.

Cocoon'. A protective covering, as that of the pupa of certain moths.

Coe'lom. A body cavity found in most of the multicellular animals, formed by the splitting of the mesoderm.

Coe'nocyte. A structure containing several or many nuclei in a continuous cytoplasm, as the filament of *Vaucheria* or a voluntary muscle fiber.

Col'chicine. A substance which interferes with mitosis, resulting in doubling of the chromosome number.

Cold-blooded. Said of organisms which change in temperature as the surrounding medium changes.

Collen'chyma. A strengthening tissue, in younger plant parts, of cells with walls thickened at the angles.

Col'loid. A substance of glue-like or jelly-like consistency which forms a suspension in water and does not pass through a differentially permeable membrane.

Col'ony. An association of individuals descended from a common ancestor and remaining organically or functionally connected.

Columel'la. A little column, as in the sporangium of *Rhizopus* or of a moss.

Commen'salism. The living of one organism of a species with, on, or in one of another species for some advantage other than parasitism.

Commu'nalism. Social organization in which the colony is made up of differentiated individuals, as among termites.

Compan'ion cell. A cell of which there is often a row beside a sieve tube in vascular plants.

Com'pass plant. A plant in which the leaves tend to arrange themselves with the edges north and south.

Com'pound. A substance formed of two or more elements uniting in definite proportion.

Com'pound eye. An eye made up of many parts (ommatidia), as in insects.

Conchi'olin. The nitrogenous substance in the shells of mollusks.

Conductiv'ity. The property of protoplasm by which impulses arising from outside stimuli are transferred from one part of the organism to another.

Cone. A kind of light-sensitive element of the vertebrate retina; a strobilus.

Conid'iophore. A stalk that bears conidia.

Conid'ium. A spore formed by constriction from the tip of a conidiophore.

Conjuga'tion. Sexual reproduction by union of like cells; temporary union for exchange of nuclei, as in *Paramecium*.

Connec'tive tissue. Tissue binding together the parts of the animal body.

Contrac'tile vacuole. See **pulsating vacuole.**

Contractil'ity. The power, shown by protoplasm, of drawing into a more compact form.

Coordina'tion. The bringing about of unified action among the various tissues of the body.

Copula'tion. Temporary union of animals to transfer sperms from one individual to another.

Cork. A tissue forming part of the bark in woody stems and serving for protection.

Corm. A short, erect underground stem, bulb-like but solid.

Cor'nea. The transparent front portion of the outer coat of the eye.

Corol'la. The petals considered together.

Cor'pus lu'teum. The mass of endocrine-secreting cells which replaces a discharged follicle of the ovary of a vertebrate.

Cor'tex. An outer layer, as of the brain or a stem.

Cor'tin. The endocrine secreted by the adrenal cortex.

Cort'isone. A component of cortin.

Cotyle'don. A seed leaf, or the first leaf of a seedling.

Cox'a. The first segment of the leg of an insect.

Cra'nium. The brain case in vertebrates.

Cre'tin. One who is defective because of lack of thyroxin during early development.

Cross-fertiliza'tion. Fertilization of the egg of one organism by the sperm of another.

Crossing over. The exchange of corresponding sections by homologous chromosomes.

Cross-pollina'tion. The transfer of pollen from the anther of one flower (or plant) to the stigma of another.

Crys'talline lens. A refracting structure of the vertebrate eye, just back of the pupil.

Cu'ticle. In unicellular animals, the pellicle; in higher animals, the epidermis; in plants, the hardened, outer part of the epidermal wall.

Cu'tin. A waxy substance which waterproofs the walls of epidermal cells of many plants.

Cut'ting. A vegetative portion removed from one plant and used in propagating a new one.

Cyst. A protective capsule.

Cytol'ogy. The science of cells.

Cy'toplasm. The protoplasm surrounding the nucleus.

Decid'uous. Falling periodically, as the leaves of certain trees.

Defic'iency. Lack of a portion of a chromosome.

Deliques'cent. In plants, the type of branching in which the main stem soon loses its identity.

Den'drite. The branching processes by way of which an impulse reaches the cell body of a neuron.

Deni'trifying bacteria. Soil bacteria that reduce nitrates to ammonia or free nitrogen.

Den'tal form'ula. Diagram showing the number of teeth of the four kinds (incisors, canines, premolars, molars) in either the right or left half of the mouth of a mammal.

Den'tine. Bony substance under the enamel of a tooth.

Deox'ygenated. Deprived of oxygen, as blood after passing through the body capillaries.

Der'mis. The inner layer of the skin of a vertebrate.

Dex'trose. See glucose.

Diabe'tes. A disease characterized by an excess of sugar in the blood and caused by a deficiency of insulin.

Di'aphragm. A muscular partition between the thoracic and abdominal cavities of a mammal.

Di'astase. An enzyme that changes starch to maltose.

Dichot'omous. Term applied to the type of branching in which the axis repeatedly forks.

Dicotyle'donous. Having two seed leaves.

Dienceph'alon. The region of the vertebrate brain to which are attached the pineal and pituitary bodies.

Differentia′tion. The process by which cells become structurally and functionally different.

Diffu′sion. The dispersal of molecules or other small particles of one substance among those of another substance.

Diges′tion. The process of changing food into a form capable of absorption.

Dig′itigrade. Placing only the digits against the ground in walking.

Dioe′cious. Having male and female reproductive organs (or, in the higher plants, megaspores and microspores) in separate individuals.

Diploblas′tic. Having but two germ layers, as the coelenterates.

Dip′loid. Having the double number of chromosomes, as in the stage following union of egg and sperm.

Disac′charid. A sugar, the molecule of which may be broken into two monosaccharid molecules.

Discoi′dal. Term applied to cleavage which is restricted to the area at one side of the yolk, as in birds.

Disinfec′tion. The destruction of microorganisms, as by chemicals.

Dom′inance. Property of a gene whereby it expresses itself to the exclusion of the effect of its allele; similarly applied to the characteristic due to such a gene.

Dor′sal. Pertaining to the back.

Duode′num. The portion of the small intestine just posterior to the stomach.

Ecol′ogy. The study of organisms in relation to their environment.

Ec′toderm. The outer germ layer of the young animal embryo.

Ectopar′asite. A parasite that feeds on the surface of the host.

Ec′toplasm. The outer part of the cytoplasm of a protozoan.

Effec′tor. The part of an organism that responds in a reflex act, as a muscle.

Ef′ferent. Leading away from a center, as a nerve.

Eges′tion. The elimination of indigestible waste.

Egg. The female gamete.

Elec′tron mic′roscope. A device using a beam of electrons to magnify very small bodies; suitable for revealing virus particles.

El′ement. A substance whose molecules are made up of atoms of the same kind.

Em′bryo. An animal during its development from the fertilized egg to hatching or birth; a plant while enclosed in the parent generation.

Embryol′ogy. The study of the early development of the individual organism.

Emul′sion. A mixture of two liquids, one of which is suspended in the other in the form of very fine globules, as oil in water.

Enam′el. The hard, outer layer of a tooth.

Encyst′ment. The secretion of a protective cyst.

En′docrine. See **hormone**.

En′doderm. The innermost germ layer, which forms the lining of the digestive tract.

Endoder'mis. The innermost layer of the cortex in vascular plants.

Endopar'asite. A parasite that lives within the host.

En'doplasm. The inner portion of the cytoplasm of a protozoan.

Endop'odite. The inner, distal branch of a typical appendage in the crayfish and allies.

Endoskel'eton. A skeleton within the body, as in vertebrates.

En'dosperm. The food storage tissue surrounding the embryo in a seed.

En'dospore. An asexual spore developed within a cell, as in some bacteria.

Endotox'in. A poison that remains within the organism that produces it.

En'ergy. Ability to do work.

Entomol'ogy. The study of insects.

En'zyme. An organic catalyst.

Ep'icotyl. The part of the embryo of a seed plant lying above the cotyledon or cotyledons.

Epider'mis. The outer or epithelial layer of the skin; the outer layer of cells in the plant.

Epigen'esis. The theory that the embryo arises from an undifferentiated germ cell; opposed to preformation.

Epiglot'tis. A covering for the glottis, found in mammals.

Epineph'rine. The endocrine produced by the medulla of the adrenal gland.

Ep'iphyte. A plant which grows on another plant but derives no nourishment from it.

Epip'odite. A flap-like extension from the base of certain appendages of the crayfish.

Epithe'liomus'cular. Combining functions of epithelium and muscle.

Epithe'lium. A tissue covering the surface of an organism or lining one of the cavities within the body.

Esoph'agus. The part of the digestive tract extending from the pharynx to the stomach.

Es'trogen. The hormone secreted by the follicle cells of the ovary.

Eusta'chian tube. A tube connecting the pharynx with the middle ear in the vertebrates.

Evolu'tion. The process of derivation of the various types of plants and animals from previously existing different kinds by descent with modification.

Excre'tion. A process by which organisms eliminate the wastes of metabolism; also applied to such a waste substance.

Exop'odite. The outer, distal branch of a typical appendage in crayfish and allies.

Exoskel'eton. A skeleton on the outer surface of the body.

Exotox'in. A poison that passes out of the organism which produces it.

Expira'tion. The process of expelling air in breathing.

Exten'sor. A muscle which straightens a joint.

Extracel'lular. Outside of cells.

Eyespot. A pigment granule which is sensitive to light.

Fac'et. A division of the cornea in the compound eye of an insect or crustacean.

Fac'ultative. Relating to the capacity of some organisms to exist under widely varying conditions, as bacteria that can be either aerobic or anaerobic.

Fam'ily. Parents and offspring; also a taxonomic division ranking between the order and the genus.

Fas'cicled. Arranged in a bundle; applied to flowers, roots, stems, leaves.

Fat. An organic compound composed of carbon, hydrogen, and oxygen, with the oxygen relatively small in quantity; it is a union of a fatty acid and glycerin.

Fatty acid. An organic acid which combines with an alkali to form a soap, or with glycerin to form a fat.

Fau'na. The animal life of a region.

Fe'ces. Waste matter discharged from the intestine.

Feh'ling's solu'tion. A solution of copper sulfate, sodium potassium tartrate, and potassium hydroxide, capable of producing a red precipitate when boiled with a reducing sugar, such as glucose.

Fe'mur. The bone in vertebrates that extends from the hip joint to the knee and forms the upper part of the hind limb.

Fermenta'tion. Chemical change usually associated with gas formation, such as that produced by yeasts and certain bacteria.

Fer'tile. Having the power of producing offspring.

Fertiliza'tion. The process by which the sperm and the egg unite to form a zygote or fertilized egg.

Fe'tus. A mammalian embryo in the uterus after the form of the organism becomes clearly defined—about the second month in man.

Fi'bril. A small fiber; the term is applied to one of the parts of a striated muscle fiber.

Fi'brous root system. A system with a cluster of thread-like secondary roots equaling the main root in importance.

Fibrovas'cular bundle. A bundle of conducting and strengthening tissue, found in the organs of the vascular plants.

Fil'ament. A slender, thread-like structure; the term is applied to the plant body of certain algae and to the stalk which bears an anther in a flower.

Fis'sion. Asexual reproduction, especially in microorganisms, in which the parent divides into two equal daughter organisms.

Flagel'lum. A long, whip-like protoplasmic process used for movement by some protozoans.

Flex'or. A muscle which produces bending at a joint.

Flo'ra. The plant life of a region.

Flow′er. A branch modified for seed production in angiosperms.

Fluctua′tion. Any variation of an organism due to differences in environment rather than to altered germ plasm.

Food. Any substance that provides building materials and energy for metabolism.

Food vac′uole. A vacuole containing ingested food.

Foot (in bryophytes and lower tracheophytes). The organ by which the sporophyte absorbs food and water from the parent gametophyte.

Forebrain. The anterior of three main divisions of the embryonic vertebrate brain.

Forma′tion. A major ecological group of organisms, based upon the climate.

For′mula. A combination of symbols representing the composition of a chemical compound.

Fos′sil. Any portion, imprint, or replaced tissue of an ancient organism.

Frater′nal twins. Twins produced from two eggs; nonidentical twins.

Fruc′tose. A monosaccharid sugar found in fruits; levulose.

Fruit. A ripened ovary, often with accessory parts.

Funic′ulus. The short stalk which joins an ovule to the ovary wall.

Ga′lea. The middle division of the maxilla of an insect.

Gall. An abnormal enlargement in plants, produced by insects or other parasites.

Gall blad′der. A sac connected with the liver and storing bile.

Gam′ete. One of the germ cells that unite to form a zygote.

Game′tocyte. A cell which divides to produce one or more gametes.

Gametogen′esis. The process by which the germ cells are developed.

Game′tophyte. The sexual generation in plants which show alternation of generations.

Gan′glion. A group or aggregation of nerve cells.

Gas′tric cae′cum. A finger-like outpushing of the stomach in certain animals, as in some fishes and insects.

Gas′tric juice. A digestive fluid secreted by gastric glands located in the lining of the stomach.

Gas′tric mill. A set of three chitinous teeth in the cardiac stomach of the crayfish and allies.

Gas′trodermis. The cell layer lining a gastrovascular cavity.

Gastrovas′cular cav′ity. A central cavity which serves for both digestion and circulation in coelenterates and flatworms.

Gas′trula. The two-layered stage in the early embryology of animals.

Gastrula′tion. The development of a gastrula from a blastula.

Gel. The rigid or jelly-like state of a colloid.

Gene. A unit of heredity carried by a chromosome.

Gene muta′tion. The transformation of a gene from one allele to another.

Gen′erative cell. A cell in the pollen grain from which two sperms are developed.

Genet′ics. The science of heredity.

Gen′otype. The genetic constitution of an organism.

Ge′nus (*pl.*, **gen′era**). A group of closely related species.

Geot′ropism. Influence of gravity upon the direction of growth or movement.

Germ cell. A reproductive cell.

Germ layers. The primary cell layers from which the tissues are developed in the embryology of an organism.

Germina′tion. The process of starting growth, as in a seed or spore.

Gesta′tion. In mammals, the condition of the female when carrying unborn young.

Giant fibers. Large nerve fibers which are located dorsally in the nerve cord of an annelid and extend along its entire length.

Gill. An organ for respiration in many aquatic animals; also a spore-bearing membrane in mushrooms.

Gill slit. A cleft at the side of the neck in chordates, usually extending from the pharynx to the exterior and separating the gill arches.

Giz′zard. A muscular part of the alimentary canal which contains abrasives used for grinding the food.

Gland. An organ of secretion.

Glochid′ium. The larva of a clam.

Glomer′ulus. A mass of blood capillaries enclosed by the capsule of a uriniferous tubule in the kidney of vertebrates.

Glot′tis. The opening from the pharynx into the larynx in air-breathing vertebrates.

Glu′cose. One of the monosaccharid sugars; dextrose.

Glyc′erin or **glyc′erol.** An alcohol which combines with a fatty acid to form a fat.

Gly′cogen. A polysaccharid formed from absorbed monosaccharids and stored in the liver of a vertebrate; found also in mollusks, fungi, and blue-green algae.

Goi′ter. An abnormal enlargement of the thyroid gland.

Gol′gi apparat′us. System of cytoplasmic granules and threads found in many animal cells.

Gon′ad. An organ which produces eggs or sperms.

Grape sugar. Same as glucose.

Graph′ic formula. A formula which shows the arrangement of atoms in a molecule.

Gray matter. The part of the vertebrate brain or spinal cord which consists mainly of cell bodies, as opposed to the white part, which contains the fibers; in the mammalian brain the gray matter constitutes the outside layer, but in the cord it is the inside part.

Green glands. Kidneys of a crustacean.

Gregar'iousness. Social grouping of organisms of a species, without structural differentiation between individuals.

Growth hormone. A hormone secreted by the vertebrate pituitary gland and conducive to bone growth; a hormone conducive to growth in plants.

Guard cells. Cells surrounding the slit-like opening (stoma) of a leaf or stem.

Gym'nosperm. A plant with naked seeds.

Hab'itat. The particular area in which any organism or species normally lives.

Hair. A rod-like structure of hardened epithelial cells in mammals; a structure of similar appearance in various other organisms.

Hal'ophyte. A plant that lives in a place of high salt concentration.

Halte'res. The rudimentary posterior wings of insects of the order DIPTERA; balancers.

Hap'loid. The reduced number of chromosomes after reduction division in gametogenesis; generally one-half the diploid number.

Hausto'rium. A sucker-like rootlet that a parasitic plant sends into the tissue of the host, as in dodder and the fungi.

Head. The anterior part of the animal body; a flower cluster in which sessile flowers are attached to a common receptacle.

Heart. The pumping organ in the circulatory system of animals.

Hemat'ochrome. A pigment present in the eyespot of certain protozoans, as *Euglena*.

Hemicel'lulose. One of the polysaccharids closely related to cellulose; found in date seeds.

He'mocoel. A body cavity, as in arthropods, used for the circulation of the blood.

Hemocy'anin. A nearly colorless, oxygen-carrying copper compound found in the blood of certain animals such as the crayfish.

Hemoglo'bin. The respiratory pigment in the red corpuscles of vertebrates; also in solution in the earthworm.

Hepat'ic. Relating to the liver.

Herb. A plant which lacks a persistent stem above ground.

Hered'ity. Transmission of characteristics from generation to generation; factors responsible for such transmission.

Hermaph'rodite. A monoecious animal.

Het'erocyst. An enlarged cell in some of the blue-green algae, usually constituting the natural breaking point of the filaments.

Heterog'amy. The production of differentiated gametes, such as the sperm and the egg.

Het'eroploidy. Chromosome aberration in which one or more chromosomes of an organism (but not a whole set) are added or subtracted.

Heteros'pory. A condition in the higher vascular plants in which two kinds of spores are produced by the sporophyte plant.

Heterotroph'ic. Deriving nourishment from without; opposed to autotrophic.

Heterozy'gous. Having a pair of unlike genes.

Hi'bernate. To pass the winter in a dormant state.

Hi'lum. A scar which represents the place of attachment of a seed to its stalk.

Hindbrain. The posterior of three main lobes of the embryonic vertebrate brain.

Histol'ogy. A study of the structure of tissues; microscopic anatomy.

Hold'fast. The organ of attachment of an alga.

Homolec'ithal. Relating to an egg in which the yolk is uniformly distributed throughout the cytoplasm.

Homol'ogy. Structural similarity due to common origin.

Homozy'gous. Having paired genes alike; of pure breed.

Hon'ey sac. A sac in the worker bee for the temporary storage of nectar.

Hor'mone. A chemical substance secreted by a ductless gland directly into the blood stream or body fluid and having a marked influence on metabolism; an endocrine.

Host. An organism that supports a parasite.

Hu'merus. The bone that articulates with the shoulder in the fore limb of a vertebrate.

Hy'brid. The offspring of a mating between genetically very different parents, even members of different species.

Hy'drolyzing. Splitting chemically by the addition of water.

Hy'drophyte. A plant adapted to life in water.

Hydrot'ropism. The influence of water upon the direction of growth or movement of an organism.

Hydrox'yl. The univalent radicle (-OH) as found in bases.

Hyme'nium. A thin fruiting surface which produces spores, as in the mushrooms.

Hy'pha. A single filament of a fungus.

Hypocot'yl. The axis or stem of a plant embryo below the attachment of the cotyledons.

Hypophar'ynx. A tongue-like mouth part in certain insects, such as the grasshopper.

Hy'postome. An anterior conical projection in coelenterates, at the tip of which is the mouth.

Iden'tical twins. Twins developed from the same egg cell.

Il'eum. The last and longest division of the small intestine in the vertebrates.

Il'iac. The artery that branches from the dorsal aorta and enters the leg.

Immu'nity. The power of resisting infectious disease.

Imper'meable. Applied to membranes that do not allow water or solutes to pass through them.

Im'pulse. A change transmitted through neurons and resulting in some physiological activity.

In'breeding. Breeding among forms closely related genetically.

Inci'sor. One of the front biting teeth of mammals.

Induced' muta'tion. A mutation brought about by an experimental change of environment, as by the application of X-rays.

Indu'sium. The membrane which covers the sporangia in the sorus of a fern.

Infec'tious disease. A disease which may be conveyed from one person to another.

Inges'tion. The taking of food into the digestive tract.

Inorgan'ic. Composed of matter not produced by living things.

Insectiv'orous. Insect-eating.

Inspira'tion. The process of taking air into lungs or tracheae.

In'stinct. A mode of action determined by an inherited pattern.

In'sulin. A hormone secreted by the island cells in the pancreas; it regulates the storage and oxidation of sugar.

Integ'ument. One of the coats of an ovule or seed.

Intercel'lular. Between or among cells.

In'ternode. A portion of a stem between two nodes or joints.

In'terphase. The period between two successive cell divisions.

Intersti'tial cells. In coelenterates, certain undifferentiated cells near the base of one of the body layers; in vertebrates, endocrine-secreting cells of the testis.

Intes'tine. The posterior part of the alimentary canal in which part of digestion and most of absorption take place; in the vertebrates it is divided into small and large portions.

Intracel'lular. Within the cell.

Invagina'tion. An infolding.

Inver'sion. The turning about of a portion of a chromosome.

Invert'ase. An enzyme that changes sucrose to glucose and fructose.

Inver'tebrate. An animal that lacks a backbone.

In'volucre. A whorl of bracts beneath a flower or a flower cluster.

I'on. One of the electrified particles into which certain molecules divide when dissolved.

I'ris. The circular pigmented structure surrounding the pupil in the vertebrate eye.

Island of Lang'erhans. A group of insulin-secreting cells in the pancreas.

Isog'amy. Reproduction in which similar gametes unite to form a zygote.

Kid'ney. An excretory organ for the elimination of nitrogenous wastes from the animal body.

Kil'ocalorie. The energy required to raise the temperature of a kilogram of water one degree centigrade.

La'bium. A lip-like portion of the insect exoskeleton which forms the posterior boundary of the mouth.

La'brum. A lip-like part of the insect exoskeleton which forms the anterior boundary of the mouth.

Lach'rymal gland. The gland which secretes the fluid that moistens the eye.

Lacin'ia. The inner division of the maxilla of an insect.

Lac'teals. Fine divisions of the lymphatic system which collect digested foods, especially fats, from the small intestine and carry them to the thoracic duct, through which they enter the blood stream.

Lac'tose. The sugar of milk; a disaccharid consisting of the combination of a galactose and a glucose molecule.

Lar'va. An immature stage in those animals which undergo metamorphosis after hatching from the egg.

Lar'ynx. In vertebrates, a cartilaginous box which contains the vocal cords and forms an air passage leading usually through the trachea to the lungs.

Leaf. The carbohydrate-manufacturing organ of a higher plant.

Leaf scar. The scar left by the falling of a leaf.

Legume'. A plant of the Pea family; also the fruit of such plant.

Lens. A transparent body in the eye of higher animals which focuses the entering rays of light.

Len'ticel. An area of loose tissue through which air enters the plant stem.

Le'thal factor. A genetic factor which causes the early death of the organism.

Leu'cocyte. An ameboid cell found in the blood or lymph; a kind of white blood cell.

Leu'coplast. A white plastid which acts as a center for the accumulation of starch in storage tissue of plants.

Lev'ulose. See **fructose.**

Lian'a. A climbing plant.

Li'chen. A symbiotic association of an alga with a fungus.

Lig'ament. Fibrous connective tissue that binds the bones together at the joints.

Lig'nin. Wood; a stiffening substance composing the walls of certain plant cells.

Link'age. Tendency of genes on the same chromosome (and their characters) to be passed on together to the offspring.

Lip cell. One of two large thin-walled cells opposite the annulus in a fern sporangium, forming an easy point of rupture to discharge the spores.

Li'pase. An enzyme that changes fats to glycerin and fatty acids.

Liv'er. A large gland that secretes bile and stores glycogen.

Loc'ule. One of the cavities, or compartments, in the ovary of a plant.

Lung. An organ of respiration in most air-breathing animals.

Lymph. A nutritive fluid in the lymphatic system, consisting of blood without the red corpuscles.

Lymphat'ic. One of the vessels of the system which collects tissue fluid and conveys it as lymph to the veins.

Ly'sin. An antibody which dissolves bacteria in the blood.

Macronu'cleus. The larger of two nuclei in a cell of most ciliates.

Malar'ia. A disease caused by the protozoan, *Plasmodium.*

Malpigh'ian tubule. One of the small tubes connected with the intestine of an insect and serving as excretory organs.

Mal'tase. An enzyme that changes maltose to glucose.

Mal'tose, malt sugar. A dissacharid found in germinated grains (malt); a combination of two glucose molecules.

Mam'mary gland. A milk-secreting gland of a female mammal.

Man'dible. In arthropods, a mouth part for chewing; modified for sucking in many forms; skeleton of the lower jaw in mammals.

Man'tle. A sheet-like fold of the body wall which partially envelops the body in mollusks and (in most of them) secretes the shell.

Marsu'pial. A mammal with a ventral pouch (marsupium) for carrying and suckling the young.

Matura'tion. The late stages of gametogenesis, in which the reduction division takes place.

Maxil'la. A mouth part, of which there are two pairs in crustaceans, one in insects; the skeleton of the upper jaw in mammals.

Maxil'liped. One of the three anterior thoracic appendages, back of the maxillae, in crustaceans.

Medul'la. The central portion of an organ; the posterior portion of the vertebrate brain, connecting with the spinal cord.

Med'ullary ray. A radially arranged strip of cells connecting the cortex with the pith and acting as conducting tissue in dicotyledonous stems.

Medu'sa. The sexual generation of hydroid coelenterates.

Megasporan'gium. A sporangium that produces megaspores.

Meg'aspore. The larger of two kinds of spores produced by the higher tracheophytes; it produces a female gametophyte.

Megaspor'ophyll. A modified leaf that bears megaspores, as the scale of a cone or the carpel of a pistil.

Meio'sis. The reduction of the chromosome number from diploid to haploid.

Menstrua'tion. The monthly shedding of epithelial tissue from the human uterus.

Mer'istem. Plant tissue that is undergoing active division.

Merozo'ite. An asexual spore formed by the malarial parasite within the red corpuscle, or the cell of some internal organ.

Mes'entery. A fold of the peritoneum which attaches the alimentary canal of vertebrates to the body wall; an infolding of the body wall in ANTHOZOA.

Mes'oderm. The middle primary germ layer in the development of animals above the coelenterates.

Mesogle'a. The noncellular layer between epidermis and gastrodermis in coelenterates.

Mes'ophyll. The tissue between the upper and lower epidermis of a leaf.

Mes'ophyte. A plant adapted to a medium water supply.

Mesotho'rax. The middle division in the thorax of insects.

Metab'olism. The sum total of the constructive and destructive processes in a living organism.

Metacar'pal. One of the bones of the palm of the human hand or in a corresponding position in the fore limb of other vertebrates.

Metagen'esis. In animals, the alternation of sexually and asexually reproducing generations, as in certain coelenterates.

Met'amere. See somite.

Metamor'phosis. A pronounced change in the form of an animal, occurring after birth or hatching.

Met'aphase. The stage of mitosis at which the chromosomes are arranged at the equatorial plate of the spindle.

Met'aplasm. Nonliving cytoplasmic material.

Metatar'sal. One of the bones of the foot of a vertebrate, extending between the ankle and the toes.

Metatho'rax. The posterior of the three divisions of the thorax of insects.

Metazo'a. Many-celled animals.

Mi'crobe, microor'ganism. Any very small organism; the term is usually applied to yeasts, filamentous fungi, bacteria, and protozoa.

Micronu'cleus. The smaller of the two nuclei which occur in ciliates.

Mi'cropyle. A small opening in the coat of the ovule of a seed plant for the entrance of the pollen tube, sometimes appearing as a slight depression at one end of the hilum in the seed; a pore in certain animal eggs, permitting entrance of the sperm.

Microsporan'gium. The spore case in which microspores are developed.

Mi'crospore. One of the smaller spores of a heterosporous organism.

Microspor'ophyll. A modified leaf which bears microsporangia.

Midbrain. The middle of three main divisions of the brain of a vertebrate embryo; from it the optic lobes develop.

Migra'tion. The periodic movement of certain species of animals from one area to another, influenced by changing food conditions, climate, or breeding habits.

Mim'icry. A resemblance of one organism to another of widely different classification, presumably for some advantage to the mimicking organism.

Miracid'ium. The earliest larval stage of a fluke.

Mito'sis. The nuclear process accompanying cell division, in which the chromosomes split lengthwise and their halves are equally distributed to the daughter cells.

Mo'lar. A grinding or crushing tooth of a mammal.

Molec'ular for'mula. A formula which shows the atomic content, but not the structure, of a molecule.

Mol'ecule. An electrically neutral particle consisting of closely united atoms of the same or different kinds.

Monocotyle'donous. Having one seed leaf.

Monoe'cious. Having both male and female reproductive organs (or, in the higher plants, megaspores and microspores) in the same individual.

Monosac'charid. A sugar which cannot be decomposed by hydrolysis into simpler sugars.

Morphol'ogy. The science that treats of the forms and structures of organisms.

Mosa'ic (leaf). A distinct pattern assumed by a group of leaves in adjusting the maximum surface to light.

Mosa'ic vision. Vision by means of a compound eye; the fitting together of the partial images produced by the ommatidia.

Mo'tor neu'ron. A nerve cell that transmits impulses from a ganglion to the organ of response.

Mul'tiple fac'tors. Numerous similar nonallelic genetic factors which influence the same characteristic.

Muta'tion. Change of the amount, arrangement, or nature of hereditary material. See **Chromosome aberration, Gene mutation.**

Mu'tualism. An association of two species in which there is advantage to both participants.

Myce'lium. A mass of hyphae or filaments which make up the plant body of a fungus.

Mycol'ogy. The science or study of fungi.

My'otome. One of the V-shaped muscle bands which develop along the backbone in the embryos of vertebrates and persist in the adults of simple forms.

Nai'ad. The water-dwelling young of an insect, such as a dragonfly, that undergoes incomplete metamorphosis; a kind of nymph.

Na'res. Respiratory passageways leading from the exterior to the mouth or pharynx in the vertebrates.

Na'sal. Pertaining to the nose.

Nat'ural selec'tion. The process by which the best-fitted types of organisms survive and produce offspring more readily than the others and thereby become established in nature.

Neck canal cell. One of the cells occupying the center of the neck of an archegonium.

Nec'tar. The sugary solution secreted in flowers by the glandular nectaries.

Nec'tary. A nectar-secreting organ.

Neg'ative response. A response in a direction away from the source of a stimulus.

Nemat'ocyst. The fluid-filled capsule and thread in the cnidoblast of a coelenterate.

Nephrid'iopore. The external opening of a nephridium.

Nephrid'ium. A primitive kidney for the elimination of nitrogenous waste, found in annelids and some other forms.

Neph'rostome. A ciliated funnel-like structure which constitutes the internal opening of a nephridium.

Nerve. A collection of nerve fibers enclosed in a sheath.

Net'ted. Forming a network, as the veins of a leaf.

Neu'ral arch. The arch of a vertebra surrounding the spinal cord.

Neu'ral groove. A dorsal infolding of the ectoderm of an embryo to form the beginning of the nervous system.

Neu'ral spine. A dorsal process on the neural arch of a vertebra.

Neu'ron. A nerve cell, including a cell body and all its branches or fibers.

Neur'ula. An embryo in which the neural groove is apparent, as in the frog.

Neutraliza'tion. The chemical reaction in which an acid acts on a base; in general, any chemical action in which one substance destroys the properties of another, as antitoxin and toxin.

Ni'acin. A vitamin that prevents pellagra.

Nic'titating membrane. A third eyelid well developed in most vertebrates but rudimentary in man.

Ni'trate bacteria. Bacteria that change nitrites to nitrates.

Ni'trite bacteria. Bacteria that change ammonia to nitrites.

Ni'trogen-fixing bacteria. Bacteria which use atmospheric nitrogen in forming nitrogen compounds.

Node. A point on the stem at which leaves normally occur.

No'tochord. A skeletal rod of turgid cells lying in a median line below the nerve cord in the embryos of the chordates; it persists in lower forms, but disappears in adults of higher forms.

Nucel'lus. A tissue which encloses the megaspore in the ovule of the spermatophytes.

Nu'clear mem'brane. The membrane surrounding the nucleus of the cell.

Nucle'olus. A sharply defined body in the nucleus, the function of which is uncertain.

Nu'cleoprotein. A substance made of protein and nucleic acid; found in chromosomes and viruses.

Nu'cleus. A highly organized portion of the protoplasm of a cell which forms a distinct body, contains the chromatin, and governs the constructive activities of the cell.

Nutri'tion. A name applied to the whole process of taking in, digesting, and assimilating food for growth and repair.

Nymph. The wingless stage of insects that undergo simple metamorphosis.

Occip'ital. A bone which forms the posterior part of the skull in the vertebrates.

Ocel'lus. A simple eye, as in an insect.

Olfac'tory lobes. Anterior lobes in the vertebrate brain which give rise to the nerves of smell.

Olfac'tory sac. A chamber lying between the external and internal nares in certain of the simpler vertebrates and containing the nerve ends of smell.

Ommatid'ium. A single element of the compound eye in the arthropods.

Ontog'eny. The development of an individual organism from the egg cell to the adult condition.

O'ocyte. A cell which forms an egg and polar bodies in oogenesis.

Oogen'esis. The process of egg production from primordial germ cells.

Oogo'nium. A one-celled egg-producing organ found in certain thallophytes; any of the small cells of an animal ovary that give rise to the primary oocytes.

Oper'culum. Any lid-like covering of a cavity or opening. In bony fishes, a plate-like covering of the gill chamber; in amphibian larvae, a fold of skin which grows back and covers the gills; in snails, a horny or calcareous plate covering the opening of the shell; in mosses, a cap-like lid covering the capsule.

Op'sonin. An antibody which renders bacteria more easily digestible by the white corpuscles.

Op'tic. Relating to the eyes.

Or'al. Relating to the mouth.

Or'der. A taxonomic division between class and family.

Or'gan. A group of tissues organized into a more or less definite form for the performance of some special physiological function.

Organ'ic. Pertaining to living things.

Or'ganism. A living individual, because it is made up of separate but mutually interdependent organs.

Or'ganizer. Part of an embryo that stimulates other embryonic tissue to develop according to a certain pattern.

Ornithol'ogy. The science of birds.

Os'culum. The exit opening in the water system of a sponge.

Osmo'sis. Diffusion taking place between the molecules or ions of two liquids or solutions separated by a differentially permeable membrane; applied more particularly to the movement of the solvent toward the more concentrated solution.

Osmot'ic pressure. An unbalanced pressure due to differences in concentration in solutions on opposite sides of a differentially permeable membrane.

Os'tium. An opening or entrance; applied to openings into the hearts of certain invertebrates such as mollusks and crustaceans, and to the inner openings of oviducts.

O'vary. A female reproductive organ in which egg cells develop; in angiosperms, the organ which contains ovules.

O'viduct. A duct which carries egg cells from the ovary to the exterior or in mammals to the uterus.

Ovip'arous. Producing eggs which develop outside the body of the parent.

Ovipos'itor. A structure in insects for placing the eggs in positions of protection for development.

Ovovivip'arous. Producing eggs which hatch within the mother but have no placental connection.

O'vule. The seed-forming structure of a spermatophyte.

O'vum. An egg cell.

Oxida'tion. A chemical process in which oxygen combines with other substances, liberating heat and energy and forming certain new products; respiration in organisms.

Ox'idizing enzyme. An enzyme that promotes oxidation; often called oxidase.

Ox'ygenated. Supplied with oxygen; applied to the water of an aquarium, or the blood after passing through the lungs or gills.

Oxyhemoglo'bin. A chemical compound formed by the temporary union of the blood protein, hemoglobin, with oxygen.

Paedogen'esis. The production of offspring by immature organisms, as in a liver fluke.

Paleontol'ogy. The science of ancient organisms as revealed by the study of fossils.

Palisade' cells. Cylindrical cells lying just beneath the upper epidermis of the leaves of flowering plants.

Pal'mate. Having the shape of a hand; used with reference to the leaflets of certain compound leaves or the veins of certain leaves.

Palp, pal'pus. A jointed branch of a mouth part in the arthropods, bearing nerve ends for touch and taste.

Pan'creas. A gland opening into the vertebrate small intestine, which secretes digestive enzymes and also (by means of cells forming the islands of Langerhans) a hormone, insulin.

Param'ylum. A starch-like carbohydrate manufactured and stored in the bodies of certain chlorophyll-containing protozoans, such as *Euglena.*

Paraph'ysis. A sterile filament beside the antheridia or archegonia of mosses, also beside asci and basidia in certain fungi.

Par'asite. An organism that lives in or upon another organism, deriving its support therefrom, often to the injury of the latter. The phenomenon is called parasitism.

Parathor'mone. The hormone of the parathyroid glands.

Parathy'roid. One of four small endocrine glands dorsal to the thyroid gland.

Paren'chyma. Thin-walled, nonelongated plant cells often used for storage, sometimes for food manufacture.

Parthenogen'esis. The development of an organism from an unfertilized egg.

Pasteuriza′tion. Prevention or checking of fermentation in milk or other fluid by heating for a time to about 140° F.

Pathogen′ic. Disease-producing.

Pathol′ogy. The study of disease.

Pec′toral. Relating to the breast.

Ped′icel. The stalk of an individual flower in a flower cluster.

Ped′ipalp. One of the second pair of appendages in Arachnoidea.

Pedun′cle. The stalk of a solitary flower or the common stem of a flower cluster.

Pella′gra. A disease caused by deficiency of niacin.

Pel′licle. A nonliving outer sheath or "wall" in many animal cells.

Pel′vic. Pertaining to the girdle of bones which serves as the attachment for the hind limbs.

Penicil′lin. A substance obtained from *Penicillium* and used in the treatment of certain bacterial infections.

Pe′nis. The male copulatory organ, found in animals of various groups.

Pep′sin. An enzyme, formed in the vertebrate stomach, that changes proteins to peptones.

Peren′nial. Persisting for more than one year.

Per′ianth. The calyx and corolla together.

Pericar′dium. In many invertebrates, the cavity which contains the heart; in vertebrates, the membranous sac which contains the heart.

Per′icarp. The matured wall of the ovary which forms an enclosure for the seed or seeds.

Per′icycle. A layer of cells which marks the outer part of the vascular cylinder in the vascular plants.

Peristal′tic. Relating to wave-like movements in intestine and similar structures, caused by a progressive contraction of circular muscles from one end of the structure toward the other.

Per′istome. A fringe of teeth surrounding the opening of a moss capsule.

Peritone′um. An epithelial lining of the coelomic cavity.

Per′meable. Capable of being penetrated by ions or molecules of liquids or dissolved substances.

Pet′al. One of the modified leaves which form the corolla in a flower.

Pet′iole. The stem of a leaf.

Petrifac′tion. The replacement of organic material by stone, as in the making of a fossil.

Phag′ocyte. A white corpuscle that has the power of engulfing and destroying other cells or foreign bodies.

Phalan′ges. Bones of the digits (fingers and toes).

Phar′ynx. A portion of the alimentary canal that connects the mouth cavity with the esophagus.

Phase contrast microscope. A microscope in which bodies differing in density or thickness are made to appear in sharp contrast; suitable for showing structures of living unstained cells.

Phe′notype. The appearance of an organism, irrespective of its genetic constitution.

Phlo′em. The part of a vascular bundle which transports manufactured food by means of sieve tubes.

Photosyn′thesis. A process in plants whereby carbohydrates are manufactured from carbon dioxide and water with the aid of chlorophyll and the energy of sunlight.

Photot′ropism. The response of a plant to light by the adjustment of its organs.

Phycocy′anin. A blue-green pigment often associated with chlorophyll, especially in the blue-green algae.

Phycoer′ythrin. A red pigment abundant in certain red algae and some others.

Phylogenet′ic tree. A diagram showing the course of evolution in a group of organisms.

Phylog′eny. The racial or evolutionary history of an organism.

Phy′lum. One of the major divisions of the animal or plant kingdom.

Physical mixture. A mixture of substances not involving chemical union.

Phys′ics. Science of physical change, or change other than in substance.

Physiol′ogy. A study of the functions and manner of operation of the parts of the living body.

Pi′leus. The cap of the fruiting body of a mushroom.

Pin′eal body. A dorsal outgrowth of the diencephalon of the vertebrate brain, probably a third eye in primitive vertebrates and now vestigial.

Pin′nate. Having the form of a feather; applied to compound leaves and leaf veining.

Pis′til. A single carpel, or a fusion of several or many carpels, in the angiosperm flower.

Pith. A tissue made up of large thin-walled storage cells, found in the center of dicotyledonous stems.

Pitu′itary gland. A ventral outgrowth of the diencephalon of the vertebrate brain, functioning as an endocrine gland.

Pitu′itrin. An endocrine secreted by the posterior lobe of the pituitary.

Placen′ta. A structure by which the embryo of a mammal is attached to the wall of the uterus and through which it receives food and gives off waste; it consists of a maternal and a fetal portion.

Plan′tigrade. A type of vertebrate foot in which the foot bends at the ankle and the animal steps on the entire sole.

Plas′ma. The liquid part of the blood or lymph, as distinguished from the corpuscles.

Plas′ma mem′brane. A living membrane which forms the outer boundary of the cytoplasm of a cell.

Plas'magene. Self-propagating hereditary factor of the cytoplasm. Distribution is less regular than that of nuclear (chromosomal) genes, and there seem to be various kinds of such cytoplasmic factors.

Plasmol'ysis. The contraction or shrinkage of the plasma membrane of a cell resulting from loss of water by osmosis when the cell is immersed in a solution of greater density than the cell sap.

Plas'tid. A body of specialized protoplasm in the cytoplasm of a cell; the term includes chloroplasts, chromoplasts, and leucoplasts.

Plas'tron. The ventral part of the shell of a turtle.

Plate'let. A small formed element of vertebrate blood, important in clotting.

Pleu'ron. A lateral extension from the tergum of a crustacean, well shown in the abdominal segments of the crayfish.

Plu'mule. See epicotyl.

Pod. Any dry fruit that regularly opens by valves or slits.

Po'lar body. One of two or three minute cells cut off from the egg during maturation.

Pol'ar nu'cleus. One of the two nuclei which contribute to endosperm formation in the female gametophyte of angiosperms.

Pol'len. The microspores of seed plants.

Pol'len chamber. The space just inside the micropyle in a gymnosperm.

Pol'len sac. A microsporangium or sac containing pollen in seed plants.

Pol'len tube. The male gametophyte of a seed plant, which conveys the sperm nucleus to the egg cell.

Pollina'tion. The process of transferring the pollen from the pollen sac of one flower to the stigma of the same or, more often, of another flower (in gymnosperms, to the pollen chamber).

Polymor'phism. The occurrence of more than one form of individual among the members of a species (aside from sex differences).

Pol'yp. *Hydra*, or any hydra-like individual among the coelenterates.

Pol'yploidy. The condition of having more than two complete sets of chromosomes.

Polysac'charid. A class of carbohydrates to which starch belongs; the molecule may be broken down into many monosaccharid molecules.

Por'tal. Pertaining to a portion of the circulation in which a vein breaks into capillaries which are reassembled to form another vein, as the hepatic and renal portal circulations of vertebrates.

Pos'itive response'. A response in which an organism turns or moves toward the source of a stimulus.

Postca'val. A vein in the vertebrates which collects blood from the posterior part of the body and carries it to the heart.

Poste'rior. Pertaining to the rear end, or remote from the head.

Preca'val. A vein in the vertebrates which collects blood from the anterior region of the body and pours it into the heart.

Precip'itate. A substance separated as a solid from a solution.

Precip'itin. An antibody which causes the precipitation of bacteria or their products, or of certain substances in the blood of animals.

Preco'cial. Having the young hatched or born with ability to run about.

Pred'atory. Relating to animals that prey on other animals.

Preforma'tion. A theory, now abandoned, that the parts of an organism were fully formed in the germ cell.

Premo'lar. One of the teeth found in the mammals, just in front of the molars.

Prena'tal. Before birth.

Prever'tebrate. A chordate having a notochord but no true backbone.

Proctode'um. An invagination of the surface of an embryo to form the posterior part of the alimentary canal with the anal opening.

Proem'bryo. An early stage in the development of an embryo; in seed plants it consists of a filament.

Proges'terone. A hormone produced by the corpus luteum of the ovary.

Proglot'tid. One of the individuals of a tapeworm colony.

Prolac'tin. A pituitary hormone that stimulates milk secretion.

Prono'tum. A dorsal often collar-like portion of the anterior thoracic segment in insects.

Prop root. A root that grows out from the stem above ground, as in corn.

Pro'phase. The first part of the process of mitosis, lasting until the chromosomes have become arranged at the equatorial plane of the spindle.

Prosen'chyma. Plant tissue made up of elongated cells.

Prosto'mium. A finger-like lobe or lip that extends forward dorsally from the first anterior segment of the earthworm.

Pro'tease. An enzyme, such as pepsin, trypsin, and erepsin, that acts on proteins.

Protec'tive resemblance. A resemblance to surroundings, serving for protection.

Pro'tein. One of a group of organic compounds containing carbon, hydrogen, oxygen, nitrogen, and often sulfur and phosphorus; it consists of united amino acids and forms an essential constituent of protoplasm.

Prothal'lus. A leaf-like plant which constitutes the gametophyte generation of ferns.

Protho'rax. The anterior thoracic segment in insects.

Protone'ma. A filamentous vegetative structure which develops from the spore of certain plants, such as the mosses.

Pro'toplasm. Living substance; the physical basis of life.

Pro'toplast. The entire living portion of a cell.

Protop'odite. The basal segment of a typical appendage in crustaceans.

Protrac'tor. A muscle which extends or draws forward an organ.

Pseu'dopod. A temporary protoplasmic projection which is used for motion in certain protozoa, as the ameba, and some metazoan cells.

Pty'alin. An amylase, or starch-digesting enzyme, in the saliva.

Pulmocuta'neous. Relating to the lungs and skin; applied to an artery in the frog.

Pul'monary. Relating to the lungs.

Pul'sating vac'uole. A vacuole whose contents are discharged periodically to the outside; occurs in protozoans.

Pulvil'lus. The pad between the claws on the foot of an insect.

Pulvi'nus. A fleshy thickening at the base of a leaf or of a leaflet, having the power of producing motion by changes in turgor in response to certain stimuli, such as light or contact.

Pu'pa. The stage during which insects having complete metamorphosis undergo a transformation from the larva to the adult.

Pu'pil. An opening in the center of the iris through which light reaches the retina.

Putrefac'tion. Decay, especially of proteins, producing unpleasant odors.

Pyc'nium. A structure occurring on the upper surface of a barberry leaf in the life history of rust and producing spermatia.

Pylor'us. An opening guarded by a circular muscle and located between the stomach and the small intestine; also called the pyloric valve.

Pyre'noid. A protein body found in the chloroplast of the cells of certain algae, such as *Spirogyra;* starch is often stored around it.

Ra'bies. A virus disease which is transmitted in the saliva of certain animals and attacks the nervous system.

Ra'dial sym'metry. The condition of having similar parts radiating from a central axis, as in the starfish.

Rad'icle. The root of a sprouting seed.

Ra'dius. The bone on the thumb side of the forearm of vertebrates.

Recapitula'tion theory. The theory that the individual in its embryological development retraces the history of its race; often stated, "Ontogeny recapitulates phylogeny."

Recep'tacle. The more or less expanded part of a flower axis which bears the floral leaves; the common base of a head of flowers.

Recep'tor. A sense structure, either a single cell or a definitely organized sense organ, whose function is to receive stimuli.

Reces'sive. Applied to a hereditary factor (gene) which does not manifest itself when its allele is present; similarly applied to the character due to such a factor.

Rec'tum. The terminal portion of the large intestine in animals.

Red cor'puscle. One of the hemoglobin-containing cells in the blood of a vertebrate.

Re'dia. A stage of the development of a fluke, produced from a sporocyst or another redia.

Re'flex action. Nervous reaction which takes place without any voluntary control.

Re'flex arc. A chain of neurons connecting a receptor (sensory cell or sense organ) with an effector (muscle or gland cell) and leading to reflex action.

Regenera'tion. The redevelopment of lost parts by an organism.

Re'nal. Pertaining to a kidney.

Re'nal por'tal vein. A vein that carries blood from the posterior part of the body to the kidneys in the lower vertebrates.

Res'in duct. A tube which transports a resinous liquid through the tissues of a conifer.

Respira'tion. The oxidation of food or protoplasm, accompanied by release of energy; the transport of oxygen to protoplasm and of carbon dioxide away from it is sometimes included in this term.

Response'. An action initiated by a stimulus.

Retic'ular. Having the form of a network.

Ret'ina. The membranous expansion of the optic nerve forming the inner coat of the vertebrate eye.

Retrac'tor. A muscle that withdraws a body part or pulls it backward.

Retrogres'sion. A backward evolutionary change in an organism by which it develops a condition characteristic of animals lower in the scale of life.

Rever'sion. The reappearance of an ancestral character after the lapse of several generations.

Rhi'zoid. A root-like structure, usually one-celled, occurring in lower forms of plant life.

Rhi'zome. An underground stem.

Ribofla'vin. A vitamin of the B group.

Root cap. A cap of older cells which forms a protection to young root tips.

Root hair. A hair-like outgrowth of an epidermal cell of a root.

Root nodule. A nodule-like thickening of the roots of certain plants, especially of the Pulse family, containing nitrogen-fixing bacteria.

Root'stock. See **rhizome.**

Ros'trum. An anterior beak-like projection of the cephalothorax in the crayfish and allies.

Rudimen'tary. So deficient in size or structure as to be incapable of performing its normal function.

Sa'crum. A group of vertebrae, located at the attachment of the pelvic girdle, which become fused in adults.

Sali'va. An enzyme-containing secretion poured into the mouth by the salivary glands.

Sanita'tion. Control of environment for protection from disease.

Sap'rophyte. A plant which absorbs food from dead organic matter.

Scap'ula. A flat, somewhat triangular bone which forms the dorsal part of the pectoral girdle; the shoulder blade.

Sci'ence. Knowledge based upon accurate observation, experimentation, and reasoning, and organized around related and generalized principles.

Scleren'chyma. A strengthening tissue in higher plants, characterized by cells with thick woody walls.

Scle'rite. One of the plates that make up the exoskeleton of the arthropods.

Sclerot'ic. Pertaining to the firm, fibrous outer coat of the vertebrate eye.

Sco'lex. The head of a tapeworm in either the larval or the adult stage.

Scur'vy. A disease caused by lack of vitamin C and characterized by general weakness, bleeding, especially of the gums, and loosening of the teeth.

Scute. One of the large transverse scales on the ventral surface of a snake.

Seba'ceous. Pertaining to oil glands usually connected with the hairs in mammals.

Sec'ondary sex character. A character other than the essential reproductive structures, in which males and females differ; their appearance is influenced by special sex endocrines.

Secre'tion. The process by which glands liberate substances needed by an organism; the term is also applied to the substance given off.

Seed. The ripened ovule of a gymnosperm or angiosperm.

Seg'ment. A natural division in the body of an organism; a somite.

Segmenta'tion. The process of breaking into segments, applied to early cleavage stages in the development of an embryo from a fertilized egg.

Segrega'tion. The separation of paired genes in the maturation of germ cells, whereby each gamete contains only one gene of the pair.

Self-fertiliza'tion. Applied to the uniting of germ cells when both sperms and eggs are produced by the same individual organism.

Self-pollina'tion. Transfer of pollen from stamens to stigma of the same flower.

Se'men. The fluid which contains sperms.

Semicir'cular canal. One of the three canals in the inner ear of vertebrates which function as organs of equilibrium.

Sem'inal groove. A longitudinal groove on the ventral surface of the earthworm for the transportation of sperms from the sperm-duct opening of one worm to the seminal receptacles of another during copulation.

Sem'inal recep'tacle. A sac-like structure which receives sperms during copulation and stores them until time for fertilization.

Sem'inal ves'icle. A sac-like structure which stores and sometimes helps mature the sperms before time for their transfer during copulation.

Sensa'tion. A consciousness arising in the brain, resulting from some external or internal stimulus.

Sense organ. An organ for the reception of stimuli, such as the eye or ear.

Se'pal. One of the modified leaves that form the calyx and usually surround the petals of a flower.

Sep'tum. A partition separating two cavities, as between the segments of an earthworm or between the nasal cavities in mammals.

Se′rum. The liquid which separates from the coagulated fibrin and corpuscles in the clotting of blood.

Ses′sile. Relating to a plant structure, such as a leaf or a flower, which is attached directly by its base without a stalk; also applied to an animal which is attached and incapable of locomotion, as an oyster.

Se′ta. A bristle such as that used by the earthworm in locomotion.

Setig′erous. Relating to muscles which move the setae.

Sex chro′mosome. A chromosome which is represented differently in the two sexes, e.g., X-chromosome, Y-chromosome.

Sex-linked char′acter. A character whose gene is located in a sex chromosome.

Sex′ual reproduc′tion. Reproduction initiated by the union of two cells.

Shoot. A stem with its leaves.

Shrub. A relatively small woody plant, usually with several trunks.

Sieve tube. A tube in the phloem, consisting of a row of cells with sieve-like end walls; it conducts manufactured foods.

Si′nus. A cavity enclosed by bone or other tissue; a blood space in certain invertebrates; space between two lobes of a leaf.

Si′nus veno′sus. A blood cavity formed in fishes and amphibia by an expansion of the large veins just before they reach the heart.

Skull. The bones of the head of a vertebrate.

Smooth mus′cle. Muscle without crossbands or striations.

Sol. The liquid state of any colloid, such as protoplasm.

Sol′ute. A substance dissolved in a liquid.

Sol′vent. The fluid or continuous medium in which a solute dissolves.

Somat′ic. Relating to the body cells of an organism as distinguished from the germ cells.

So′mite. A segment of the body of a segmented animal; a metamere.

So′rus. One of the structures on the under side of fern leaves containing a cluster of sporangia; also a cluster of spores in rusts and some other fungi.

Spe′cies (*pl.*, **species**). A group of similar organisms more or less reproductively isolated from other such groups.

Sperm. The fully developed male germ cell.

Sperm duct. A duct that conveys sperms from the spermary; the vas deferens.

Sper′mary. See **testis.**

Sper′matid. The cell which becomes differentiated to form the sperm.

Sperma′tium. One of the small spores produced in the pycnium of a rust fungus.

Sper′matocyte. The cell which, through a reduction process, divides into four sperms.

Spermatogen′esis. The development of sperms from primordial germ cells.

Spermatozo′on. The sperm of an animal.

Spic′ule. One of the calcareous or siliceous structures which constitute the skeleton in certain sponges.

Spi′nal canal. The canal in the spinal column which contains the nerve cord.

Spi'nal column. The bony column made up of vertebrae and containing the spinal cord.

Spi'nal cord. The nerve cord which with the brain constitutes the central nervous system.

Spin'dle. A dim, spindle-shaped figure which appears in mitosis and seems instrumental in distributing the chromosome halves from the equator to the two poles.

Spin'neret. A finger-like appendage on the under surface of the abdomen of a spider, used for spinning silk.

Spir'acle. A breathing opening leading into the tracheal system of insects, ONYCHOPHORA, centipedes, millipedes, and some spiders.

Spleen. A reddish organ in the abdominal cavitiy of the vertebrates, functioning in the destruction, and sometimes the formation, of red corpuscles.

Spon'gin. The horny substance which forms the supporting skeleton of the bath sponges.

Spon'gy cells. The loosely fitting cells below the palisade layer in a leaf.

Sponta'neous genera'tion. The development of life from nonliving material.

Sporan'giophore. A structure, usually stalk-like, on which a sporangium is borne.

Sporan'gium. A structure in which spores are produced; a spore case.

Spore. A reproductive body, typically unicellular and asexual, produced by plants and some protozoans.

Spor'ophore. A body that bears spores, as in the higher fungi.

Spor'ophyll. A modified leaf on which sporangia develop.

Spor'ophyte. The spore-bearing generation in the life history of plants that exhibit alternation of generations.

Sporozo'ite. A small, usually elongate spore produced by division of the zygote in SPOROZOA.

Squame. A sword-shaped structure which represents a modified exopodite in the antennae of crayfish and their allies.

Sta'men. A sporophyll which produces pollen grains in the seed-bearing plants.

Stam'inate. Relating to cones or flowers that produce stamens.

Staphylococ'cus. A coccus type of bacteria in which the individuals tend to arrange themselves in irregular clumps.

Starch. A polysaccharid found in many plants.

Stat'ocyst. An organ of equilibrium in many invertebrates.

Stat'olith. A stone or stone-like body in the statocyst.

Ste'le. The tissues inside the cortex in the root or stem of a vascular plant.

Stem. A leaf-bearing structure in a plant.

Sterig'ma (*pl.*, **-mata**). Short spore-bearing stalks at the outer end of the basidia in the BASIDIOMYCETES.

Ster'ile. Not capable of reproduction.

Steriliza′tion. Rendering an organism sterile by cutting the ducts which transport the germ cells, or by other means; killing of microorganisms in or upon any object.

Ster′num. The ventral part of a somite in arthropods; the breastbone of vertebrates.

Stig′ma. The pigmented eyespot in protozoans; the part of the pistil which receives pollen.

Stim′ulus. Some influence, either external or internal, which causes a response in a living organism.

Stipe. The stalk which bears the cap in the fruiting body of a mushroom.

Stip′ule. A leaf-like structure, two of which may occur at the base of the petiole of a true leaf.

Sto′ma (*pl.*, **-mata**). An opening in leaves surrounded by two guard cells and permitting exchange of gases.

Stom′ach. An enlarged part of the ailmentary canal in which food accumulates and is broken up and partly digested.

Stomode′um. The ectodermal invagination which forms the mouth cavity in the development of an embryo; opposite the proctodeum.

Streptococ′cus. A coccus type of bacteria in which individuals are arranged in chains.

Strob′ilus. A sporophyll-bearing branch found in some pteridophytes and in spermatophytes; a cone.

Style. The stalk between the ovary and the stigma.

Substra′tum. The substance or base on which a plant grows.

Su′crase. An enzyme that digests sucrose.

Su′crose. Cane sugar, a disaccharid, convertible into glucose and fructose.

Superfi′cial cleav′age. Cleavage of a centrolecithal egg, involving only the surface portion.

Suprascap′ula. A bone dorsal to the scapula in an amphibian.

Susceptibil′ity. Lack of immunity.

Suspen′sion. A mixture of a finely divided solid with a liquid.

Suspen′sor. A row of cells forming a stalk in the embryo of certain flowering plants and having the function, by its growth, of pushing the body of the embryo into the food supply of the endosperm.

Sweat gland. In many mammals, a skin gland which secretes and exudes perspiration.

Swim′meret. An abdominal appendage of the crayfish or its allies.

Symbio′sis. An association of two organisms of different species; sometimes limited to a necessary and mutually helpful association.

Sym′metry. Similarity of body parts on either side of a longitudinal plane or around a common center.

Synapse′. The point of contact between the processes of two different neurons.

Synap′sis. The pairing of homologous chromosomes (ordinarily restricted to meiosis).

Syner′gid. One of two nuclei associated with the egg at the micropylar end of the female gametophyte of an angiosperm.

Syr′inx. A vocal structure in birds located just above the junction of the bronchial tubes.

System′ic. Pertaining to the body generally; the systemic aorta, or arch, sends branches to the main parts of the body.

Tac′tile. Pertaining to touch.

Tad′pole. The frog or toad larva from the time of hatching to the disappearance of the tail.

Tap′root. A primary root which grows more rapidly than its branches and pushes vertically into the soil, providing for absorption of moisture from deep layers.

Tar′sus. The ankle bones in vertebrates; the distal segments of the leg in insects and spiders.

Taxon′omy. The systematic study of the names and classification of organisms.

Teg′men. The inner coat of a seed.

Te′liospore; teleu′tospore. A winter spore of the rusts occurring in black clusters on the surface of stem or leaves.

Telolec′ithal. Applied to an egg in which the yolk is abundant and massed at the vegetal pole, the protoplasm being accumulated at the opposite animal pole.

Tel′ophase. The final or end phase in mitosis, during which the chromosome material is incorporated into nuclei in the daughter cells.

Tel′son. A central, posterior abdominal extension in the crayfish and allies which acts with the uropods as a tail fin.

Ten′don. A cord of connective tissue uniting a muscle to the skeleton and transmitting the force exerted by the muscle.

Ten′dril. A modified leaf or stem which attaches a climbing plant to its support.

Ten′tacle. A feeler or grasping organ usually attached to the mouth or head of certain invertebrates.

Ter′gum. The dorsal portion of a typical segment of arthropods.

Tes′ta. The outer coat of a seed.

Tes′tis (*pl.*, -es). A reproductive structure that produces sperms and sometimes hormones which promote the development of secondary sex characters.

Testos′terone. The hormone secreted by the interstitial cells of the testis.

Tet′anus. A bacterial disease, often fatal, which causes spasmodic muscular contraction or rigidity; it is called lockjaw when it affects the muscles of the jaw.

Tet'rad. In plants, a group of four spores resulting from two nuclear divisions of a spore mother cell.

Thal'lus. A simple or undifferentiated plant body which may consist of masses of cells, filaments, or leaf-like forms.

Thi'amine. Vitamin B_1, important in growth and in the prevention of nervous diseases.

Tho'rax. The middle portion of the body of many animals, connecting the head and abdomen.

Thorn. A stem or leaf modified into a pointed, defensive organ.

Thy'mus. A body in the lower part of the neck or in the upper thoracic region in vertebrates, possibly functioning as an endocrine gland.

Thy'roid. An endocrine gland that is located in the neck region of vertebrates and secretes a hormone, thyroxin, which has an important effect on growth and mental development.

Tib'ia. The larger of two bones in the lower hind leg of most vertebrates; also the segment of an insect's leg just beyond the femur.

Tis'sue. A group of similar cells and their products which have a common function.

Tocoph'erol. Vitamin E, the antisterility vitamin.

Tox'in. A poison formed by pathogenic bacteria.

Tox'in-antitox'in. A mixture of toxin and antitoxin formerly used to develop immunity to diphtheria.

Tox'oid. A toxin, such as that of diphtheria, treated to destroy its toxicity while retaining its power to produce antibodies.

Tra'chea. An air passage present in most land vertebrates, leading from the larynx to the bronchial tubes; a respiratory tube of insects and related forms; a water-conducting tube (vessel) of a vascular plant.

Tra'cheid. A plant structure similar to a trachea in location and function, but smaller, with pointed ends, and originating from a single cell.

Transloca'tion. A chromosome aberration in which a part of one chromosome becomes separated and attached to a nonhomologous chromosome (usually involves exchange of material).

Transpira'tion. The giving off of water vapor by evaporation from plants.

Transverse' process. A lateral process on a vertebra for the attachment of muscles or of ribs.

Tree. A large woody-stemmed plant, usually with a single main stem.

Tri'ceps. The muscle having a triple origin (three heads), which straightens the arm or leg.

Trichino'sis. A disease caused by a parasitic round worm (*Trichinella spiralis*).

Trich'ocyst. A sac-like defensive (?) structure located in the outer layer of *Paramecium*.

Triploblas'tic. Possessing three germ layers: ectoderm, mesoderm, and endoderm.

Trochan'ter. The second segment in the leg of an insect.

Tro'pism. A direct response to some external stimulus.

Trun'cus arterio'sus. The main arterial trunk, particularly in AMPHIBIA.

Tryp'sin. An enzyme in the pancreatic secretion which changes proteins to amino acids.

Tu'ber. A much-thickened underground stem, like the potato.

Tur'gor. A plump and rigid condition of any plant tissue resulting from osmotic pressure within the cells.

Tympan'ic mem'brane. A membrane stretched across the outer opening of the vertebrate middle ear, vibration of which gives rise to the perception of sound.

Tym'panum. The cavity of the vertebrate middle ear; also sometimes applied to the tympanic membrane.

Typh'losole. A dorsal longitudinal infolding of the intestine of the earthworm.

Ul'na. The human forearm bone on the side of the little finger.

Umbil'ical cord. A cord which connects the mammalian fetus to the placenta.

Unequal cleavage. The type of embryonic development in which early cleavage results in cells unequal in size.

Un'guligrade. Walking on hoofs or the tips of the toes.

Unit char'acter. An attribute of an organism with variation depending on a single pair (or series) of alleles.

Ure'a. A nitrogenous compound which results from the destructive metabolism of proteins; it is eliminated through the kidneys in solution in a liquid known as urine.

Ure'dospore, uredin'iospore. A unicellular spore of a rust fungus, such as that formed in early summer on wheat.

Ure'ter. One of a pair of tubes which transport urine from the kidneys to the cloaca in lower vertebrates, or to the bladder in mammals.

Ure'thra. A duct which transports urine from the urinary bladder to the exterior.

Urinif'erous tubule. One of the convoluted tubules in the kidney which collect and carry the urine to the ureters.

Ur'opod. One of the posterior abdominal appendages in the crayfish and allies.

Ur'ostyle. A bone in the frog that forms an extension of the spinal column.

U'terus. An expanded portion of the oviduct which stores the eggs, or, in mammals, retains them during embryonic development.

Vac'cine. Originally the virus of cowpox; preparations of weakened or killed organisms used in fighting disease.

Vac'uole. A sap-containing cavity in the cytoplasm.

Vagi'na. A passageway in the female of many animals, leading from the uterus to the outside.

Va'lence. The combining capacity of an atom.

Varia'tion. A difference in structure or function among individuals.

Vas def'erens. The principal sperm duct.

Va'sa efferen'tia. Small sperm ducts in vertebrates, leading from the testis to the vas deferens.

Vas'cular bundle. A group of transporting tubes (with some other tissues) in a vascular plant.

Vas'cular system. A system in plants or animals for conducting fluids.

Veg'etal pole. The pole at which the yolk is accumulated in telolecithal eggs.

Vein. A vessel which collects blood from the capillaries and carries it to the heart.

Ven'ter. The enlarged basal part of an archegonium.

Ven'tral. Pertaining to the lower surface of an animal, i.e., away from the back; opposite of dorsal.

Ven'tral canal cell. A cell at the base of the neck in an archegonium, next to the egg.

Ven'tricle. A chamber or cavity in an organ; specifically a chamber of the heart from which blood is sent out, or a cavity in the brain.

Ver'tebra. One of the bones of the spinal column in vertebrates.

Ver'tebrate. An animal with a backbone.

Ves'icle. A small sac-like structure, especially one filled with fluid.

Vestig'ial. Rudimentary or undeveloped, but giving evidence of having changed from a more highly developed condition in ancestral forms.

Vil'lus. A finger-like vascular projection which functions as an organ of absorption, found in the lining of the small intestine and in the placenta of mammals.

Vi'rus. A filter-passing substance, possibly living, capable of developing only in connection with living organisms.

Vis'ceral. Pertaining to the soft organs in the coelomic cavity, often extended to the pharyngeal arches.

Vi'talism. The conception of a vital force, not subject to the laws of chemistry or physics, to which life phenomena must be referred.

Vi'tamins. A group of substances which have been found necessary in foods for normal metabolism.

Vit'reous. Glassy; applied to the transparent jelly-like fluid which fills the cavity back of the lens in the vertebrate eye.

Vivip'arous. Pertaining to animals that give birth to fully organized young after embryonic development in the uterus.

Vol'va. A cup-like structure that remains at the base of the stalk of certain mushrooms after the young fruiting body has burst the outer skin.

Vo'merine. Pertaining to a bone which separates the nasal cavities in vertebrates or to patches of teeth borne on this bone in the frog.

Wall. The nonliving covering of a cell.

Warm-blooded. Maintaining a uniform body temperature.

White cor'puscle. A white cell carried in the blood.

White matter. The portion of the brain and spinal cord which consists only of nerve fibers.

Whorled. Occurring in circles about the stem at the node.

X-chromosome. A kind of sex chromosome. In many animals the body cells of the female have two and those of the male only one; this is true of the human species.

Xan'thophyll. A yellow coloring matter in leaves, usually associated with chlorophyll.

Xerophthal'mia. A disease of the eyes caused by deficiency in vitamin A.

Xer'ophyte. A plant adapted to living in dry places.

Xy'lem. The part of a vascular bundle which consists mainly of woody-walled water tubes and wood fibers.

Y-chromosome. A sex chromosome found only in the male in many animals, including man.

Yolk. A complex food material stored in an egg cell.

Yolk gland. A more or less definite group of gland cells which secrete yolk.

Yolk plug. A disk-like portion of the yolk visible in the frog embryo at a late gastrula stage.

Yolk stalk. The connection of the yolk sac to the embryo in amniotic vertebrates.

Zool'ogy. The science of animals.

Zo'ospore. An asexual spore which is motile, like an animal.

Zy'gote. The cell formed by the fusion of gametes.

Zy'mase. The principal enzyme in yeast; it changes sugar to alcohol and carbon dioxide.

REFERENCES[1]

BIOLOGIES

Baitsell, G. A., *Human Biology*, McGraw-Hill Book Company, Inc., 2nd ed., 1950.

Etkin, W., *College Biology*, Thomas Y. Crowell Company, 1950.

Gardiner, M., *Principles of General Biology*, The Macmillan Company, 1952.

Hardin, G., *Biology: Its Human Implications*, W. H. Freeman and Company, 2nd ed., 1952.

Marsland, D., *Principles of Modern Biology*, Henry Holt & Company, Inc., rev. ed., 1951.

Martin, A. C., and others, *American Wildlife and Plants*, McGraw-Hill Book Company, Inc., 1951.

Mavor, J. W., *General Biology*, The Macmillan Company, 4th ed., 1952.

Milne, L. J. and M. J., *Man and the Biotic World*, Prentice-Hall, Inc., 1952.

Moment, G. B., *General Biology*, Appleton-Century-Crofts, 2nd ed., 1950.

Pauli, W. F., *The World of Life*, Houghton Mifflin Company, 1949.

Stauffer, A. (ed.), *Introductory Biology*, D. Van Nostrand Company, Inc., 1949.

Strausbaugh, P. D., and Weimer, B. R., *General Biology*, John Wiley & Sons, Inc., 3rd ed., 1952.

Thomson, J. A., and Geddes, P., *Life; Outlines of General Biology*, Harper & Brothers, 2 vols., 1931.

Villee, C. A., *Biology: The Human Approach*, W. B. Saunders Company, 1950.

Wells, H. G., Huxley, J. S., and Wells, G. P., *The Science of Life*, Doubleday & Co., Inc., 1931.

Winchester, A. M., *Biology and Its Relation to Mankind*, D. Van Nostrand Company, Inc., 1949.

Woodruff, L. L., and Baitsell, G. A., *Foundations of Biology*, The Macmillan Company, 7th ed., 1951.

Young, C. W., and Stebbins, G. L., *The Human Organism and the World of Life*, Harper & Brothers, rev. ed., 1951.

[1] See also the references at the end of the chapters.

BOTANIES

Emerson, F., *Basic Botany*, The Blakiston Company, 1947.

Fuller, H. J., *The Plant World*, Henry Holt & Company, Inc., 2nd ed., 1951.

Fuller, H. J., and Tippo, O., *College Botany*, Henry Holt & Company, Inc., 1949.

Gibbs, R. D., *Botany*, The Blakiston Company, 1950.

Hill, J. B., Overholts, L. O., and Popp, H. W., *Botany*, McGraw-Hill Book Company, Inc., 2nd ed., 1950.

Hylander, C. J., and Stanley, O. B., *College Botany*, The Macmillan Company, 1949.

Maugham, S., *Earth's Green Mantle*, The Macmillan Company, 1944.

Olmsted, C. E. (ed.), *The Story of Living Plants*, University of Knowledge, Inc., 1938.

Pool, R. J. *Basic Course in Botany*, Ginn & Company, 1940.

Sinnott, E. W., *Botany, Principles and Problems*, McGraw-Hill Book Company, Inc., 4th ed., 1946.

Smith, G. M., and others, *A Textbook of General Botany*, The Macmillan Company, 4th ed., 1942.

Swingle, D. B., *Plant Life*, D. Van Nostrand Company, Inc., 1943.

Transeau, E. N., Sampson, H. C., and Tiffany, L. H., *Textbook of Botany*, Harper & Brothers, rev. ed., 1953.

Wilson, C. L., *College Botany*, The Dryden Press, Inc., 1952.

ZOOLOGIES

Baitsell, G. A., *Human Biology*, McGraw-Hill Book Company, Inc., 1950.

Borradaile, L. A., and Potts, F. A., *The Invertebrata*, The Macmillan Company, 2nd ed., 1935.

Brown, F. A. (ed.), *Selected Invertebrate Types*, John Wiley & Sons, Inc., 1950.

Buchsbaum, R., *Animals Without Backbones*, University of Chicago Press, rev. ed., 1948.

Bullough, W. S., *Practical Invertebrate Anatomy*, Macmillan & Company, Ltd., 1950.

Curtis, W. C., and Guthrie, M. J., *Textbook of General Zoology*, John Wiley & Sons, Inc., 4th ed., 1947.

Elliott, A. M., *Zoology*, Appleton-Century-Crofts, 1952.

Guyer, M. F., *Animal Biology*, Harper & Brothers, 4th ed., 1948.

Hall, T. S., *A Source Book in Animal Biology*, McGraw-Hill Book Company, Inc., 1951.

Hegner, R. W., *Parade of the Animal Kingdom*, The Macmillan Company, 1935.

Hegner, R. W., and Stiles, K. A., *College Zoology*, The Macmillan Company, 6th ed., 1951.

Hunter, G. W., and Hunter, F. R., *College Zoology*, W. B. Saunders Company, 1949.

Hyman, L. H., *The Invertebrates: Vol. I, Protozoa Through Ctenophora*, McGraw-Hill Book Company, Inc., 1940.

Hyman, L. H., *The Invertebrates: Vol. II, Platyhelminthes and Rhynochocoela*, McGraw-Hill Book Company, Inc., 1950.

Hyman, L. H., *The Invertebrates: Vol. III, Acanthocephala, Aschelminthes, and Entoprocta*, McGraw-Hill Book Company, Inc., 1951.

Parker, T. J., and Haswell, W. A., *Textbook of Zoology*, The Macmillan Company, 6th ed., 1940.

Perry, James C., *The Science of Zoology*, Bruce Pub., 1952.

Potter, G. E., *Textbook of Zoology*, C. V. Mosby Company, 2nd ed., 1947.

Rand, H. W., *The Chordates*, The Blakiston Company, 1950.

Romer, A. S., *Man and the Vertebrates*, University of Chicago Press, 3rd ed., 1941.

Storer, T. I., *General Zoology*, McGraw-Hill Book Company, Inc., 2nd ed., 1951.

Ward, H. B., and Whipple, G. C., *Fresh-Water Biology*, John Wiley & Sons, Inc., 1918.

Weimer, B. R., *Man and the Animal World*, John Wiley & Sons, Inc., 1951.

Wolcott, R. H., *Animal Biology*, McGraw-Hill Book Company, Inc., 3rd ed., 1946.

Index

Boldface numbers refer to pages with or including illustrations.

Abalone, 160
Abdomen, 165, 182
Abdominal cavity, 224
A-B-O blood groups, 283, 502
Aboral pole, surface, 107, 213
Absorption, 61, 82
Acanthocephala, **134**
Acid, 41
Acorn worm, **220**
Acquired character, 529
Acromegaly, 307
Adaptation, 532
Addison's disease, 307
Adductor, **154**, 155
Adiantum, **415**
Adjustor, 145
Adrenal gland, **291, 304, 307**
Adrenotropic hormone, 305
Aeciospore, aecium, **392, 393**
Aedes, 549
Aeolosoma, **151**
Aerial root, **561**
Aerobic respiration, 542
Aeschna, **185**
Afferent nerve, 145
Afferent vessel, **171**
African sleeping sickness, 87
After-ripening, 471
Agar, 375
Agaricus, **388**
Agglutination, agglutinin, agglutinogen, 283, 359
Aggressive color, 555
Albinism, 499
Albugo, 381
Alcohol, 384
Aleurone, 53
Alga, 335, **367–377**
Alga-like fungus, **380–382**
Alimentary canal, 139
Allantois, **322–326**
Allele (allelomorph), 481
Alligator, 236, **237**
Alpine vegetation, **7**
Alsophila, **418**
Alternation of generations, **374, 397**, 398
Altricial bird, **247**; mammal, 327

Alveolus, **279–281**
Alytes, 235
Amanita, 387, **389**
Ambystoma, **232**, 233
Ameba, **80–85**
Amebic dysentery, 85
Amino acid, 38, 53
Amitosis, 30
Amnion, **322–326**
Amphibia, **230–235**
Amphineura, 153, **154**
Amphioxus, 221, **222**
Ampulla, echinoderm, 214, **215**; vertebrate, 302, **303**
Amylase, 141
Amylopsin, 279
Anabaena, 340
Anabolism, 48
Anaerobic respiration, 64, 383, 542
Analogous organs, 512
Anaphase, 29
Anatomy, 12
Angiosperm, 337, 422, **434–476**
Animal, 4
Animal kingdom, **76–78**
Animal pole, 316
Annelida, 77, **136–151**
Annulus, **387–389**, 414
Anodonta, **154**
Anolis, 239
Anopheles, **88**, 200
Anoplura, **193**
Ant, 200, **550, 559, 560, 565**
Ant lion, **554**
Antagonistic muscles, **166**, 275
Anteater, **256, 263**
Antenna, **167**, 168, 186, **188**
Antennule, 167, 168
Anther, 457, **466**
Antheridium, alga, **368**; fern, **416, 417**; moss, **397, 398**
Anthocyan, 453
Anthozoa, 118, **120**, 121
Anthrax, **342, 343**
Antibiotic, 361
Antibody, antigen, 283, 359
Antipodal cell, 459, **460**

Antiseptic, 349; surgery, 358
Antitoxin, 359
Antivenin, 243
Anus, clam, **157**; crayfish, **169**; earthworm, 137; grasshopper, 188; *Paramecium*, 92; roundworm, 132, 137; vertebrate, **276**, **277**
Aorta, 286, **287**
Ape, 265, **266**
Aphid, **196–197**, **550**, 559
Apical cell, 417
Apis, **72**, 73, **201–204**
Apoda, 231
Appendage, **167**
Appendix, 513, **514**
Aqueous humor, **301**
Arachnoidea, 165, **207–210**
Araucarioxylon, **516**
Arcella, **81**
Archaeornis, 250, **252**
Archegonium, fern, **416**, **417**; moss, 397, 398; pine, 427
Archenteron, 315
Archeozoic era, 519
Archiannelida, 150
Aristotle, 69, **70**, 313, 348
Aristotle's lantern, 215
Armadillo, 264, 554, **555**
Armor, 554
Arterial arches, 286, **287**
Artery, 156, 286
Arthropoda, 77, 181–212
Artificial parthenogenesis, 217
Artificial selection, 532
Artiodactyla, 259, **261**
Ascaris, 132, **486**
Ascocarp, ascus, 385, **386**
Ascomycetes, **382–387**
Ascon type, 110, **111**
Ascophyllum, **373**
Ascorbic acid, 57
Asexual reproduction, 31
Aspergillus, 384, **385**
Aspidiotus, **196**
Ass, 536, **537**
Assimilation, 61, **83**
Association, ecological, 561
Association neuron, 145
Aster, 29, **30**
Asteroidea, 213
Asymmetry, 108
Atabrine, 91
Atom, atomic weight, 36
Atrium, 222
Auditory canal, nerve, 302, **303**
Aurelia, **119**
Australia, 528
Australopithecus, 525

Autonomic system, 299
Autotomy, 175, 217
Autotrophic plant, 344, 547
Auxin, 333
Aves, **243–253**
Axil, **435**
Axolotl, **232**, 233
Axon, 104, **105**, 145

Bacillus, **341–345**, 355
Back swimmer, 195
Backbone, 222
Backcross, 489
Bacteria, **341–364**
Bacteriology, 341
Bacteriophage, 346, **348**
Balanoglossid, 220
Bald cypress, **430**
Banting, 308
Barberry, 392
Bark, **441**
Barnacle, 177, **178**
Barton, 5
Basal disk, 114
Basal metabolism, 304
Base (chemistry), 41
Basidiomycetes, **387–394**
Basidium, basidiospore, 387, **388**, 392
Basket star, 213
Bast fiber, 442
Bat, 256, **258**, 511
Beak (bird), **250**
Bean, fruit, seed, **469**, 470
Bear, **556**
Beaver, **260**
Bedbug, **195**
Bee, **72**, 73, **201–204**, 566
Beebe, 5
Beebread, 201
Beetle, **197**, 198
Beriberi, 56
Biceps, 275
Bilateral symmetry, 107, **108**
Bile, 276, 279
Binomial nomenclature, 73
Biology, 3
Biotic factor, 547–566
Bird, **243–253**; conservation, 580–582; embryology, 322–324
Birth, 327
Bison, **583**
Black knot, 385
Black rot, 362
Black snake, 242
Bladder, gall, **276**; urinary: clam, **157**; crayfish, 171, **172**; earthworm, 143, **144**; vertebrate, **276**, 289–294
Bladder worm, 130, **131**

Bladderwort, **551,** 552
Blastocoel, 314
Blastopore, **315,** 322
Blastula, 99, **315, 317**
Blight, 363
Blindworm, 231
Blood, crayfish, 171; earthworm, 142; groups, 283, 284, 502–504; insect, 189; mollusk, 156; similarities, 516; transfusion, 283; vertebrate, **103, 281, 282**
Blue racer, 242
Blue-green algae, **339–341**
Body cavity, 130
Bog moss, 400, **401**
Boll weevil, 579
Bombardier beetle, 554
Bone, **102,** 103
Book lung, 208
Bordeaux mixture, 381
Botany, 3
Bowman's capsule, 289, **290**
Brachiopod, **163, 520**
Bracken, 411, **413**
Bracket fungus, 388, **390**
Braconid, **205**
Brain, 125, 189, 222, **512**
Branchio-cardiac sinus, **171**
Brassica, **533**
Bread mold, **380**
Bread making, 384
Breathing, 63
Brittle star, 215, **216**
Bronchial tube, bronchus, 279–281
Bronchiole, **280,** 281
Brontosaurus, **264**
Brown, Robert, 17, 42
Brown algae, **371–375**
Brown rot, 385
Brownian movement, 42, **43**
Bryophyta, 335, **396–403**
Bud, 440
Budding, 382, **384**
Buffalo, **261, 583**
Buffer, 41
Bug, **195**
Bulb, **454**
Bullfrog, **269**
Bumblebee, 566
Butterfly, 198
Byrd, 5

Cabbage, **533, 538**
Cabbage worm, 199
Cactus, **8, 456**
Caecum, **514**
Calciferol, 58
Calciferous gland, 140
Calorie, 66

Calorimeter, 65
Calvatia, **391**
Calyptra, 398, 399
Calyx, 457
Cambarus, **166**
Cambium, **405, 423, 424,** 442
Cambrian period, 520
Camel, 260
Camptosorus, **414**
Cancer, 362
Cane sugar, 50
Canine tooth, 254
Canna, **454**
Capillary, 281
Capsule, Bowman's, 289, **290;** fern, **414;** moss, 398, **399**
Carapace, 167, 237
Carbohydrate, 36, 50, 51
Carbon cycle, 351, **352**
Carboniferous forest, **521**
Cardiac chamber, 169
Cardinal, 250
Caretta, **238**
Carex, **460**
Carinatae, 251
Carnivora, **258**
Carotene, 331, 453
Carotid arch, 286, **287**
Carpal, 272–274, **511**
Carpel, 458
Carpet beetle, 198
Cartilage, **102,** 222
Cartilaginous fish, **225, 226**
Cassowary, 251
Cast, 517
Caste, **194**
Castor, **260**
Cat, **71, 258**
Catabolism, 48
Catalyst, 48
Caterpillar, 186, **198**
Cattle, 260
Caudal fin, **222, 225, 227**
Cecropia, 186
Cedar apple, 393
Cell, **14–25;** division, **26–30;** plate, 29; theory, 16; wall, **20, 23**
Cellular respiration, 64
Cellulose, 23, 52
Cement, **278;** gland, 175, **188,** 190
Cenozoic era, 519, 522
Centipede, 77, **78, 206**
Centipede plant, **456**
Centriole, **20,** 22, 29, **30**
Centrolecithal egg, **314**
Centrosome, 20, **22,** 29, **30**
Centrum, 222, **223**
Cephalization, 124, 144

Cephalochordata, 219, 221, **222**
Cephalopoda, 153, **161**, **162**
Cephalothorax, 167, **170**
Cercaria, **127**
Cercus, 188
Cerebellum, **295–297**, 320, **512**
Cerebrum, **295**, **296**, 320, **512**
Cervical groove, 167
Cetacea, **264**
Chaetognatha, 77, **134**, 135
Chagas' disease, 87
Chalaza, **323**
Chalk, 96
Chambered nautilus, 162
Chameleon, **239**
Character (characteristic), 477
Chelicera, 207
Cheliped, **167**, 168, **170**, **175**
Chemical resemblance, 515
Chemical sense, **300**
Chemistry, 3; of protoplasm, 35
Chemosynthesis, 59, 344, 547
Chestnut blight, 385
Chewing mouth, **187**, 192
Chewing-lapping mouth, **191**, 192
Chiasma, **484**, **491**
Chick embryo, **324**
Chickadee, 253
Chicken cholera, 357
Chigger, **209**
Chilopoda, 165, **206**
Chimpanzee, **266**, 525
Chinch bug, 195
Chipmunk, 259
Chiroptera, 256
Chitin, 165
Chiton, 153, **154**
Chlamydomonas, **100**
Chloragen (chlorogogue) cell, **138**, 139, 140, 144
Chlorenchyma, 406, **425**
Chlorophyceae, **365–370**
Chlorophyll, 21, 58, 331
Chloroplast, **20**, 21, 58, **86**, 331, 365
Chloroquin, 91
Cholera, **342**
Chondrichthyes, 226
Chondriosome, **20**, 21, 24
Chondrus, **372**, **376**
Chordata, 77, **78**, 219–268
Chorion, 310, 325, **326**
Choroid coat, **301**
Christmas fern, **419**
Chromatin, **20**, 22, 24
Chromatophore, 270, **271**
Chromoplast, 21
Chromosome, **26–33**, 400, 483; aberration, **491–494**, 531; map, 491, **493**

Chrysemys, **237**
Cicada, 196
Ciliary comb, 122
Ciliary muscle, **301**
Ciliata, 80, **91–95**
Cilium, **91**, 125
Cinchona, 90
Circulation, 61; ameba, 82–83; clam, 156; crayfish, 171, Plate I; earthworm, 142; insect, 183, 189; vertebrate, 284–288, Plate I
Circumesophageal connective, **172**, 188
Circumpharyngeal connective, 144
Civet, **71**
Cladophyll, **456**
Clam, 77, **154–160**
Clamworm, 77, **151**
Class, 75
Classification, 71–78
Clavicle, **272–274**
Cleavage, **314–317**; cavity, **317**
Cleistogamous flower, 461
Climax forest, **562**
Clitellum, **137**, 138, 146, **148**, 149
Cloaca, **157**, **276**, 277, **290–293**
Clonorchis, 128
Clotting, 282
Club moss, **406–408**, 520, **521**
Cnidoblast, cnidocil, **115**, 116
Coal, 518, 520
Coccus, 341, 355
Coccyx, **273**, 274, **513**
Cochineal, 181
Cochlea, 302, **303**
Cockroach, 183, 192, **521**
Cocoon, **198**
Codling moth, 198
Coelenterata, 76, **78**, 113–121, 520
Coelom, 135, 139, **140**, 163, 169, 214, **223**, 316
Coenocyte, **24**, **104**, 369, **370**
Colchicine, 493
Cold-blooded organism, 243
Coleoptera, **197–198**, 511
Collar cell, 110, **111**
Collarbone, 274
Collenchyma, **405**, 406, 442
Colloidal dispersion, 42, **43**
Colonial organism, 98, **99**, 563
Color, amphibian, 270; bird, 245; flower, 463; concealing, **554–557**; warning, 558
Color blindness, 502, **503**
Colorado potato beetle, 517
Coluber, **242**
Columella, **380**, 381
Comb jelly, 77, **108**, 121
Commensalism, 129, **550**, 559
Common name, 73–75

Companion cell, **445**, 446
Compass plant, 543
Complete double circulation, 285
Complete (complex) metamorphosis, 186, **199**, **200**
Composite family, 465–467
Compound, 35
Compound eye, 172, **173**, 183, **191**
Compound microscope, 14
Concealing devices, **554**
Conceptacle, 372, **373**
Conchiolin, 155
Concordance, 505, 506
Cone, of eye, 301, **302**; of plants, **407**, **408**, **425**–**427**
Conidiophore, conidium, 384, **385**
Conifer, 431
Conjugation, 93, **94**
Connective tissue, **101**–**103**
Conservation of resources, 568–588
Contact, reaction to, 546
Contact poison (insect), 204
Continuous variation, 497
Contour feather, 244
Contour plowing, 574–**575**
Control (experimental), 2
Convergent evolution, 162
Coordination, 104, 157, 189
Coot, **251**
Copperhead, 242
Coprinus, **389**
Copulation, 126, **149**, 174, 182, 293
Coracoid, 274
Coral, **6**, 76, 121; horn, **520**
Coral snake, 242, 243
Coreopsis, 543, **544**
Cork, **16**; cork cambium, 444
Corm, **454**
Cormorant, 251
Corn, flower, **462**; grain, 470, **471**, **492**; hybrid, **500**, 501; stem, **445**
Corn borer, 579
Cornea, **173**, 301
Corneum, **271**
Corolla, 457
Corpus allatum, 186
Corpus luteum, 305, 310
Cortex, adrenal, **307**; kidney, 289; plant, **437**–**439**, 442
Cortin, cortisone, 305, 307
Corydalis, **183**
Cosmos, **544**
Cotyledon, **428**, 429, **469**
Cougar, **74**
Cover slip, 19
Cowbird, 248, 560
Cowry, **160**
Coxa, 187

Crab, **175**, **176**, 179
Cranial nerve, **295**, 297
Cranium, 222, 274, 296
Craspedacusta, **118**, 119
Crayfish, 77, **165**–**175**
Cretaceous period, 522
Cretin, 305, **306**
Cricket, 183, 192, 252
Crinoidea, 213, **216**
Crocodilia, 235–**237**
Crocus, **454**
Cro-Magnon man, **525**–**527**
Crop, 140, **188**, 245
Crop rotation, 570
Cross-fertilization, 126, 149
Crossbill, **250**
Crossingover, 491, **492**
Cross-pollination, 461
Crow, **250**, 251, 253
Crown gall, 363
Crustacea, 77, **78**, **165**–**179**
Crystalline cone, **173**
Crystalline lens, **301**
Ctenophora, 77, **108**, 121–122
Cuckoo, 560
Culex, **200**
Cup fungus, 382
Cuticle, 137, **140**
Cutin, 442
Cutworm, 199
Cycad, cycadales, **252**, 429, **430**, 522
Cyclops, 134, **177**
Cyclostomata, 224, **225**
Cypris, 177
Cyst, **85**–**87**, 89, **127**, 132, **133**, **156**
Cysteine, 53
Cytological map, 494
Cytology, 12
Cytoplasm, 19, **20**–**22**, 24

Damsel fly, 193
Daphnia, **177**
Darwin, 70, 510, 531, **532**
Dasya, **376**
Decay, 349
Deep-sea life, **6**, 230, **231**, 546–547
Deer, 259
Defense, adaptations for, **554**
Deficiency (chromosome), **494**
Deliquescent stem, 441
Delphinium, **497**
Dendrite, 104, **105**, 145
Denitrifying bacteria, 352, **353**
Dental formula, 278
Dentine, 259, **278**
Dermal branchia, 214, **215**
Dermis, 270–**272**
Development, genetic basis of, 498

Devilfish, 162
Devil's darning needle, 193
Devonian period, 520
De Vries, 531
Dextrose, 52
D'Herelle, 346
Diabetes, 308, 505
Diaphragm, 224, 254, **277**
Diarrhea, 199, 362
Diastase, 279
Diatom, 370, **371**
Dicot, dicotyledon, 434
Dictyophora, 391
Didinium, **92,** 95
Diencephalon, **295,** 296, 320
Difflugia, **81**
Diffusion, 43, **44**
Digestion, 60, 61; ameba, 82; clam, 156; crayfish, 169; earthworm, 139; grasshopper, 188; hydra, 116; planaria, 123; sponge, 111; vertebrate, 275–279
Digestive enzyme, gland, 157, **169, 215, 277,** 279
Digitigrade mammal, **266,** 267
Dinosaur, 235, 521, **522**
Dioecious, animal, 126; flowering plant, 459
Dioon, **430**
Diphtheria, 355, 362
Diploblastic animal, 100, 316
Diploid number, 32
Diplopoda, 165, 206, **207**
Diptera, **199, 495,** 511
Disaccharid, 50, 52
Discoidal cleavage, **314,** 315, 332
Discordance, 505
Disease, 354–363; carriers, 549
Disk flower, **466,** 467
Dispersal, plant, 471, **472**
Dobson fly, **183**
Dodder, **552**
Dog, **71,** 258, **266, 534**
Dogfish, 225
Dominance, 479
Dormancy of seed, 470
Dorsal aorta, **227,** 287
Dorsal fin, 225, **227,** 231
Dorsal pore, 138
Dorsal spine, 223
Dorsal vessel, **138, 140, 141,** 142
Double fertilization, 467
Down feather, 244
Dragonfly, **185,** 193, **521**
Drone, **201**
Drosophila, **487–495**
Dryopithecus, 525
Dryopteris, **414, 415**
Duck, **250, 251**

Duckbill, **255**
Duodenum, 275, **304,** 308
Duplication (chromosome), **494**
Dutch elm disease, 385
Dysentery, **85**

Ear, 183, 228, 254, 270, 302, **303**
Earthworm, **78, 136–150**
Eberthella, **355**
Echeneis, **560**
Echinodermata, 77, **78, 213–218**
Echinoidea, 213, **216**
Ecology, 12, 542
Ectoderm, 99, **315, 326**
Ectoparasite, 548
Ectoplasm, 80
Edentata, **263,** 264
Edelweiss, 6
Effector, 145
Efferent nerve, 145
Efferent vessel, 170, **171**
Egestion, 67, 83, 104
Egg, alga, **368,** 369; angiosperm, 459, **460;** crayfish, **174;** dinosaur, **522;** earthworm, **147;** fern, 417; frog, **315;** grasshopper, **190;** hen, **323;** human, **31;** hydra, 117; mammal, **31, 32;** moss, 398; pine, 428; *Plasmodium*, **89**
Egg apparatus, 459
Egg capsule, **147, 149, 190**
Egg sac, 146, 148
Egg string, **147**
Egg tooth, 324
Egret, **582**
Ehrlich, 360
Ejaculatory duct, 190
Elastic ligament, 154, 155
Elater, 409
Electric eel, ray, 554
Electron microscope, 14, **347, 348**
Element, 35
Elephant, 260, **262, 264**
Elephantiasis, 134
Elodea, 17, **20,** 46
Embryo, animal, **313–329,** 514; plant, **428, 460, 462, 466,** 468
Embryo sac, 459
Embryological resemblance, 514
Embryology, 313; bird, **322–324;** experimental, **320;** frog, **316–321;** mammal, **325–327;** reptile, 322–324
Embryonic stages, 100, 325; shield, 325, **326**
Emu, 251
Emulsion, 42
Enamel, 259, **278**
Encystment, **85**
Endamoeba, **85**

Endocrine, 67, 303; system, **303–311**
Endoderm, 99, **315, 326**
Endodermis, 437, **439,** 442
Endoparasite, 548
Endoplasm, 80
Endopodite, **167,** 168, **169**
Endosperm, 459, **460,** 467
Endoskeleton, 222
Endotoxin, 360
Energy, 34
Energy value of foods, 65
Entomology, 3
Environment, 504
Enzyme, 48–50, 279
Eoanthropus, **525,** 526
Eocene epoch, **524**
Eohippus, **524**
Ephedra, 432
Epicotyl, 429, **469**
Epidermis, 14, **113–115, 270–271,** 442
Epigenesis, 313
Epiglottis, **277,** 281
Epilachna, **198**
Epinephrine, 307, 308
Epiphyte, 560
Epithelial tissues, **21,** 25, **101,** 115
Epithelio-muscular cell, **115**
Eptesicus, **258**
Equal cleavage, 314
Equatorial plate, **28, 30**
Equisetum, **408–410**
Equus, 262, **524**
Erepsin, 279
Ergot, 386
Erosion, **570–574**
Erythroblastosis, 284
Erythrocyte, **281**
Esophagus, crayfish, **169;** earthworm, 139; grasshopper, 188; vertebrate, **275–277**
Esox, **229**
Estrogen, 305, 309
Estrus, 309
Eubranchipus, 177
Eugenics, 506
Euglena, 80, **86, 96,** 98
European corn borer, 182
Eustachian tube, **276,** 302, **303**
Eutheria, 255, **256–266**
Evolution, 69, 329, **510–541;** man, **523–527;** plant, 337
Excretion, **67,** ameba, 83–84; clam, 157; crayfish, 171, 172; earthworm, 143; flatworm, 124; grasshopper, 189; vertebrate, 289–293
Excurrent siphon, **154–157**
Excurrent stem, 440
Exophthalmic goiter, 304
Exopodite, **167,** 168, **169**

Exoskeleton, 165, 182, **237**
Exotoxin, 360
Experiment, 1, 2
Expiration, 63
Extensor, **169,** 174, **275**
External nares, 270, 280
Extracellular digestion, 116, 124
Extraembryonic coelom, 322, **323, 326**
Eye, cephalopod, 161; crayfish, **173;** grasshopper, 186; *Nereis,* **151;** planarian, **124,** 125; vertebrate, **300–302**
Eyelash, 254, **301**
Eyelid, 241, 254, **301**
Eyepiece, 14
Eyespot, **86, 215, 222**

Fairy ring, 388, **389**
Fairy shrimp, 177
Family, 75
Fang, **243**
Far-sightedness, 301
Fasciola, 126, **127**
Fat, 35, 50, **52–53**
Fat body, **291**
Fatty acid, 50, 53
Feather, 224, 244, 271
Feet (birds'), **251**
Fehling's solution, 51
Felis, **74, 258**
Female animal, 105
Femur, **184,** 187, **272, 273,** 274
Fermentation, 345, 383
Fern, **411–421,** 517, 520, 521
Fertilization, 31, 293, 313, 325, 428, 467, 485, **486**
Fetus, 325, 327
Fiber tissue (plant), **405,** 406
Fibril, 92
Fibrous root, **437**
Fibula, 273
Fiddler crab, **175,** 176
Filament, 457, **466**
Filaria, 133, **199**
Filicineae, 337
Fin, **161, 225, 227**
Fire blight, 362
Fishes, **225–230;** conservation, 584
Fission, 87, **91,** 93, 125, 126; fission plant, 339
Fixation, fixative, 19
Flagellata, 80, **86, 87**
Flagellum, **86, 87,** 341
Flame cell, 124, **125**
Flatworm, **78, 123–130**
Flea, **195,** 199–200, 259
Flexor, **275**
Flicker, **250, 251**
Flight, 244

Flipper, 224
Flounder, 230, **557**
Flower, **457–467**; conservation, 584
Flowering plants, **434–476**
Fluke, 77, **126–129**
Fly, 181, 182, 186, **191**, 192, **199, 487**
Flycatcher, 251, 253
Flying fish, 230
Flying reptile, 521
Follicle, hair, **271**; ovarian, **147, 309**
Follicle mite, 209
Follicle-stimulating hormone, 305, 310
Fomes, 390
Food, 36, 50–54; accessory, 50, 51, 54–58; pyramid, 547, **548**; vacuole, **81**, 83
Foot, bird, **251**; mammal (posture), **266**; mollusk, 153, **154, 155, 157**
Foraminifera, **81**
Forebrain, 295, 320, **324**
Forelimb, **511**
Forest, **574–578**
Formation, 561
Formed elements, **281**
Formula, chemical, 37–39; dental, 278
Fossil, 70, **517**
Four-o'clock, **482**
Fox, 258
Fraternal twins, 505
Frog, 233, **269**; ontogeny, **316–322**
Frond, 411
Fructose, 51
Fruit, **466**, 469, 471
Fruit fly, 485, **487**
Fucoxanthin, 372
Fucus, 372, 373
Fungi, 335, **378–395**; Imperfecti, 394
Fur mammals, 582

Galactose, 279
Galapagos Islands, 528
Galea, 186, **187**
Gall, 548–550
Gall bladder, **276, 277**
Gall wasp, 200, **550**
Gamete, **31, 367, 380**
Gametocyte, **88, 89**
Gametogenesis, 104–105, **106, 484**
Gametophyte, alga, **374**; fern, **415–418**; lily, 459, **460**; moss, **397**; pine, **427, 428**
Ganglion, 125, **144, 157, 172, 188, 298**
Garter snake, 241
Gastric caecum, **188**, 189
Gastric juice, 277, 279
Gastric mill, **169**
Gastrodermis, **113, 114, 115**
Gastropoda, **78**, 153, **160, 161**
Gastrotrich, 77, **96, 97**
Gastrovascular cavity, **113, 114, 124**

Gastrula, **100**, 315, **317**
Gastrulation, **315**
Gavial, 235
Gel, 42
Gemma, **402**
Gene, 23, 478; location of, 491; mutation, 496
Generative cell, **457, 459**
Genetic map, **493**
Genetics, **477–507**
Genital chamber, **124**, 125
Genital pore, **124, 132, 188**
Genital seta, **137**
Genotype, **481**
Genus, 72
Geographical distribution, 528
Geographical isolation, 536
Geological time, 518, 519
Geology, 3
Geotropism, 546
Germ layer, 117
Germination of seed, **469–471**
Gestation period, 327
Giant fiber, **140, 144, 146**
Giant monitor lizard, **241**
Giant salamander, **232**
Giant water bug, 195
Gibbon, 266, **525**
Gila monster, 239, **240**
Gill, crustacean, **170**; fish, 227; mollusk, **157**; tadpole, 318
Gill arch, 227, 318
Gill bailer, 171
Gill chamber, 170
Gill cover, 167
Gill fungus, **387–389**
Gill slit, **219–222**; **225–227**, 318
Ginkgo, 431, 522
Giraffe, 260
Gizzard, **141**, 188, 245, **246**
Gland, **66**
Gleocapsa, **340**
Gleotrichia, **340**
Glochidium, **158**
Glomerulus, 289, **290**
Glottis, 246, **276**, 279, 280, 281
Glucose, 51
Glycerin, glycerol, 50, 53, 60
Glycine, 38
Glycogen, 22, 50, 52, 339
Glyptodon, **523**
Gnat, 199
Gnetales, **431**, 432
Goat, 260
Goiter, 54, 304, 305
Golden plover, 248, **249**
Golgi apparatus, 20, 22, 24
Gonad, 104

Gonadotropin, 305, 310
Gonium, 98, **99, 100**
Gonorrhea, **342**
Goose, 248
Goose barnacle, **178**
Gorilla, 266, 525
Grackle, 247
Gradual metamorphosis, 184, 190
Grafting, 149–150
Grape, **455**
Graphic (structural) formula, 38
Grasshopper, **184, 186–190**
Grassi, 90
Grassland conservation, 578
Gray matter, 297, **298**
Great anteater, **263**
Great Barrier Reef, **121**
Greater yellowlegs, **251**
Green algae, **365–370**
Green gland, **169,** 171, **172**
Gregarious organisms, 563
Grinnellia, **376**
Ground pine, 406, **407**
Ground sloth, 522, **523**
Grouse, 248
Growth hormone, 305, 306, 333
Growth stage, 27
Guard cell, **451, 452**
Guinea worm, 134
Gull, 252, 253
Gum (of jaw), **278**
Gymnosperm, 337, **422–433**

Haeckel, 100
Hagfish, 225
Hair, 254, **271,** 272
Halophyte, 547
Haltere, 199
Haploid number, 32, 33, 105
Haploidy (chromosome aberration), **493**
Hard shell clam, 159
Hare, 259
Harvestman, 207
Harvey, **284**
Haustorium, 379, 552
Hawk, **250, 251,** 253
Hawthorn, **455**
Head louse, 193
Health, 9
Hearing, 302, 303
Heart, crustacean, **171;** earthworm, **138;** insect, **188;** mollusk, **157, 161;** vertebrate, 285
Heart muscle, **104**
Heath hen, **581**
Hedgehog, 256
Heidelberg man, 526
Helianthus, **466**

Heloderma, **240**
Hellbender, 233
Hellgramite, **183**
Hemibasidiomycetes, **390–394**
Hemicellulose, 50, 52
Hemichordata, 219, **220**
Hemiptera, **195**
Hemocoel, 169, 188
Hemocyanin, 171
Hemoglobin, 64, 142, 280, 282
Hemophilia, **502**
Hemorrhage, 56
Hepatic portal vein, **288**
Hepaticae, 401, **402**
Herb, **439**
Heredity, 70, **477**
Hermaphrodite, 146
Hermit crab, **176, 550, 559**
Heron, **582**
Heterecious parasite, 548
Heterocyst, **340**
Heterogamy, **368,** 369
Heteroploidy, **493**
Heterosis, **500, 501**
Heterospory, **408,** 419
Heterotrophic organism, 547
Heterozygote, **482**
Hilum, **470**
Hindbrain, 295, 320, **324**
Hipparion, **524**
Hippopotamus, 260
Hirudinea, *Hirudo*, 150, **151**
Histology, 12
Hoatzin, 251
Hoof, 254, **261, 266**
Hog-nosed snake, 242
Holothuroidea, 213, **216**
Homo, **525**
Homolecithal egg, **314, 315,** 325
Homologous chromosomes, 485
Homologous organs, **511, 512**
Homoptera, 192, 195, **196,** 197
Homozygote, **482**
Honeybee, **72, 201–204**
Hooke, 15, **16**
Hookworm, 77, 133
Hormone, 67, 186, 303, 305; plant, 333, 334
Horned lizard ("toad"), 239, **240**
Horn, 254
Horn coral, **520**
Horntail, 200
Horse, 260, **403, 511, 522–524; 536, 537**
Horseshoe crab, **209**
Horsetail, **408–410,** 520, 521
Host, 85
Housefly, **108, 199**
Humerus, 246, **272–273, 511**

Hummingbird, 247, 250
Humoral theory of disease, 354
Huntington's chorea, 506
Hyacinth, **454**
Hybrid, 501; corn, **500**–501; sterility, 536; vigor, 501
Hydatina, **134**, 135
Hydra, **100**, **113**–118
Hydrolysis, 49, 60
Hydrophyte, 545
Hydrozoa, **118**, 119
Hyena, **71**
Hymenium, **382**
Hymenoptera, **200**–205
Hypha, 379
Hypocotyl, 429, **469**
Hypohippus, **524**
Hypopharynx, 186, **187**, **188**, 189
Hypostome, **113**, 114
Hypothesis, **3**

Ichneumon wasp, 201
Identical twins, **505**
Ileum, 276, 277
Ilium, **272**–**273**
Immunity, 357–360
Impression (fossil), 517
Impulse (nerve), 145
Inbreeding, inbred line, 499, **500**, 501
Incisor, 254, 278
Incomplete metamorphosis, **185**, 186
Incurrent pore, **111**
Incurrent siphon, **154**, 155, 158
Independent assortment, Law of, 480
Indian pipe, **553**
Indusium, 413, **414**
Infantile paralysis, 346
Infectious disease, 354, 356
Influenza, 346
Infundibulum, **280**, 281
Ingestion, 59, 82
Inheritance, 477
Ink sac, **161**
Innominate bone, **273**, 274
Insect, **78**, 165, **181**–205
Insect pollination, 463
Insectivora, 256, **257**, 525
Insectivorous plants, 60, **551**
Insertion, 274
Inspiration, 63
Instar, **184**
Instinct, 190
Insulin, 305, 308
Integumentary system, **270**–271
Intercellular digestion, 116
Intermediate neuron, 145
Internode, 440
Interphase, 27, **28**, 29, **30**

Interrupted fern, **419**
Interstitial cell, **308**, 309, **115**, 117
Intestinal juice, 277, 279
Intestine, 62; crayfish, **169**; earthworm, 140; grasshopper, 188; vertebrate, **275**–**277**
Intracellular digestion, 116
Inversion, **494**
Invertebrate, 219
Involuntary muscle, 103, **104**, 275
Iridescence, 137, 155
Iris (of eye), **301**
Irish moss, 375, **376**
Iron bacteria, 344
Ischium, **273**, 274
Island of Langerhans, **307**, 308
Isogamy, **367**
Isolation, reproductive, 535, 536
Isoptera, 193, **194**
Itch mite, **209**

Japanese beetle, 198
Java man, **525**, 526
Jay, 251
Jellyfish, 76, **119**, 120
Jenner, 357
Joshua tree, **545**
June bug, 196
Jurassic era, 522

Kala-azar, 550
Kangaroo, 256
Karpechenko, 538
Katydid, 192, **193**
Keel, 251
Kelp, 373, **374**
Kidney, clam, **157**; crayfish, 171, **172**; vertebrate, **67**, **289**–**293**
Killdeer, 247
Kilocalorie, 66
Kindred, 501
Kinetoplast, **87**
King-crab, 207, **209**
Kingfisher, 251
Kiwi, 251
Koala, 256, **529**
Koch, 354, 355

Labellum, **191**
Labial palp, **157**, **191**, 192
Labium, 186, **187**, **188**, **191**, 192
Labrum, 186, **187**, **188**, **191**
Labyrinth, 302
Lacewing fly, 204
Lachrymal gland, 301
Lacinia, 186, **187**
Lacrymaria, **95**
Lactase, 279

Lacteal, **62**, 289
Lactic acid, 64, 65
Lactose, 50, 52
Lady beetle, 204
Lagomorpha, 259, **261**, 516
Lamarck, 70, 530
Laminaria, 373, **374**
Lamprey, **225**
Lampshell, 77, 162, **163**, **520**
Lancelet, 100, 221, **222**
Lark, 253
Larva, 178, **179**, 186, **198**, **199**, **221**, 313
Larynx, 245, 254, 279, **280**, 281, 320
Lateral line, **227**, 228
Latimeria, 229
Law, scientific, 3
Leaf, 414, 446–454; arrangement, **447**; color, 453; division, **449**; fall, 453; fossil, **517**; parts, 447; scar, **440**; structure, **451**, **452**; trace, **440**; veining, **450**, 451
Leaf butterfly, 555, **556**
Leaf curl, 385
Leaven, 384
Leech, 77, 150, **151**
Leeuwenhoek, van, **15**, 345
Leishmania, **96**
Lemur, 265, 525
Lens, eye, 228, **301**; microscope, 15
Lenticel, **440**, **444**
Lepidoptera, **198**–199
Lepidosaphes, **196**
Lethal factor, 499, 531
Leucocyte, **281**
Leucoplast, **22**
Levulose, 52
Lichen, 5, 41, **386**, 387, 559
Life, 3
Ligament, 103, 274, 301
Light, 543
Lily, 460
Limbs, 223, 269
Limpet, **160**
Lindbergh, 6
Linkage, **489–492**
Linnaeus, **73**
Lip cell, 415
Lipase, 141, 279
Lister, 358
Litmus, 41
Liver, clam, **157**; crayfish, **169**; vertebrate, **276–279**, 282, 358
Liver fluke, **126–128**
Liverwort, 401, **402**
Lizard, **238–241**
Llama, 517
Lobe-finned fishes, 229
Lobster, 165, **175–176**
Loeb, 217

Loggerhead turtle, **238**
Longevity of seed, 470
Long-neck clam, 159
Louse, 192, 193, **195**, 517
Loxodonta, **264**
Lubber grasshopper, 184
Lumbricus, **136–150**
Luminescence, 230, **231**, 543
Lung, **63**, 279, **280**
Lung fluke, 128
Lungfish, **228**, 229
Luteinizing hormone, 305, 310
Lycoperdon, **391**
Lycopodium, 406, **407**
Lycopsida, 335, **406–408**
Lymph, 289; heart, 289; node, 289, 358; space, 270, 275
Lymphatic system, 289; vessel, 289
Lymphocyte, **281**
Lysin, 359

Macrocystis, 373
Macronucleus, **91**, 93
Macropus, **257**
Madreporite, 214, **215**
Magellania, **163**
Maggot, 182, 186, **199**
Maidenhair fern, **415**
Maidenhair tree, 431
Malaria, **87–91**, 199, 200
Male animal, 105
Malpighian layer, **271**
Malpighian tubule, **188**, 189
Maltase, 279
Maltose, 52
Mammal, mammalia, 78, **254–267**; embryology, **325–327**
Mammary gland, 254, 305
Man, classification, 262; evolution, **523–527**; inheritance, **501–507**
Mandible, **167**, 168, 186, **187**, **191**, 273
Mantis, 192
Mantle, **153–156**, 161, 162
Manure, 570
Marchantia, 401, **402**
Marsilia, 419
Marsupial, 256, **257**, 528, **529**
Matter, 34
Matrix, 28
Maxilla, **167**, 168, 186, **187**, **191**, 273
Maxillary palp, **191**
Maxillary teeth, 275, **276**
Maxilliped, **167**, 168
May beetle, 197
Measles, 346
Medulla, **246**, **295–297**, 320, **512**
Medullary ray, **424**
Medusa, **108**, **118**, 119

Megalobatrachus, 232
Megasporangium, 427, 457
Megaspore, 427, 457
Megasporophyll, 457
Megatherium, 523
Meiosis, 32, 106, 483, 484, 488
Melanin, 499
Melanoplus, 190
Membranous labyrinth, 302
Mendel, mendelian inheritance, 477–483
Menstruation, 310
Merismopedia, 340
Meristem, 405, 441
Merozoite, 88, 89
Merychippus, 524
Mesenchyme, 111
Mesentery, 120, 224, 276
Mesoderm, 100, 316, 326
Mesoglea, 113–115
Mesophyll, 451, 452
Mesophyte, 545
Mesothorax, 187
Mesozoic era, 519, 521
Metabolic gradient, 125
Metabolism, 48–68
Metacarpal, 272–274, 511
Metacercaria, 127
Metagenesis, 118, 119
Metamere, 109
Metamorphosis, 176, 184–186, 221, 231, 319
Metaphase, 28, 29, 30
Metaplasm, 20, 22, 23
Metatarsal, 272–274
Metatheria, 254–257, 528, 529
Metathorax, 187
Metazoa, 76, 98–109
Methyl alcohol, 38, 39
Mexican beaded lizard, 239
Mexican bean beetle, 197, 198, 579
Microbe, microbiology, 341
Micronucleus, 91, 93
Microorganism, 341
Micropyle, 426, 428, 459, 470
Microscope, 14–15
Microsphaera, 385, 386
Microsporangium, 425, 457
Microspore, 426, 457
Microsporophyll, 457
Microtome, 18, 19
Midbrain, 295, 296, 320, 324
Middle ear, 302, 303
Midge, 199
Migration, 248, 249
Mildew, downy, 381; powdery, 386
Milk, 254, 255
Milk snake, 242
Milk (temporary) teeth, 278

Millipede, 77, 165, 207
Milt, 228
Mimicry, 558
Mimosa, 546
Mink, 258
Miohippus, 524
Miracidium, 126, 127, 128
Mississippian period, 520
Mistletoe, 552
Mite, 207, 209
Mitosis, 26–33
Mixture, 41
Mohl, von, 17
Molar, 254, 258, 278
Mold, 380, 385
Mole, 256, 257
Molecule, 36
Mollusk, 78, 153–164
Molting, 166
Monarch butterfly, 554, 558
Monitor lizard, 241
Monkey, 265, 525
Monocot, monocotyledon, 434, 445
Monoecious, animal, 126; flowering plant, 459
Monosaccharid, 50
Monotreme, 255, 256
Monotropa, 553
Monuments, national, 585
Morchella, Morel, 382, 383
Morgan, 487, 489
Morphology, 12
Morula, 325
Mosaic vision, 173
Mosquito, 88–90, 199, 200
Mosquito hawk, 193
Moss, 396–401
Moss animal, 77, 163
Moth, 198, 199
Mother-of-pearl, 155, 156
Motor neuron, 104, 105, 146, 298
Mountain lion, 74
Mourning dove, 247
Mouse, 259
Mouth, clam, 157; crayfish, 169; earthworm, 137, 139; fish, 227; flatworm, 123, 124; frog, 275, 276; grasshopper, 188; hydra, 113, 114; mammal, 277; *Paramecium,* 91, 92; starfish, 213, 215; vinegar eel, 132
Mucous gland, 270
Mud puppy, 233
Muehlenbeckia, 456
Mulberry, 198
Mule, 536, 537
Muller, 496
Multiple alleles, 503
Multiple factors, 496
Musca, 199

Musci, 396–401
Muscle, 24, 103, **104; sense,** 303
Muscular system, crayfish, 174; earthworm, 139; insect, 184; vertebrate, 274–**275**
Mushroom, **388**
Musk turtle, 238
Muskrat, 259
Mutation, **497,** 531; pressure, 535
Mutualism, 183, 550, **558**
Mycelium, 379
Mycology, 3
Myotome, 318
Myrmecophaga, **263**
Myxomycetes, 378, **379**

Naiad, **185**
Nail, 254, 267
Nares, 270
Nasal cavity, **277, 300;** pit, 318
Nasturtium, **463**
National forests, monuments, parks, 585
Natural classification, 71
Natural selection, 529, 531–533
Nautilus, 162
Neanderthal man, **525, 526**
Near-sightedness, 301
Neck canal cells, 398, 418
Nectary, 463
Necturus, 233
Nemathelminthes, **78,** 130–**134**
Nematocyst, **113, 115,** 116
Nemertea, 77, **134**
Nepenthes, **551,** 552
Nephridiopore, **137,** 138, **140, 144**
Nephridium, 140, 143, **144**
Nephrostome, 143, **144**
Nereis, 150, **151**
Nerve, **172,** 297–299
Nerve cord, chordate, 219; crayfish, **172;** earthworm, 144; grasshopper, 189
Nerve impulse, 25, 145
Nerve net, **113,** 115
Nerve ring, **161,** 215
Nervous system, clam, 157; crayfish, 171, **172;** earthworm, 144; grasshopper, 189; hydra, 115; vertebrate, 295–300
Nervous tissue, 104, **105**
Nest-building, 246
Nettle cell, **115,** 116
Neural arch, 222, **223, 227,** 296
Neural cavity, **223, 224**
Neural folds, groove, **317,** 318, **321, 324**
Neural tube, 318, 320
Neuron, 104, **105,** 298
Neuroptera, **183**
Neurula, 318
Neutralization, 41
Newt, **320, 321**

Niacin, 56
Nictitating membrane, 302
Night blindness, 56
Nighthawk, 247
Nilsson-Ehle, 497, **498**
Nitrate bacteria, 344, 352, **353**
Nitrite bacteria, 344, 352, **353**
Nitrogen cycle, 351, **353**
Nitrogen-fixing bacteria, **353, 354**
Node, 440
Nodule, **353, 354,** 559
Nomenclature, 73
Northern yellowthroat, 253
Nostoc, 340–341
Nostril, **225,** 231, **246,** 270, **276**
Notochord, 77, 219, **221–223, 317,** 318
Nucellus, 427, 459
Nuclear membrane, **20,** 24; sap, **23,** 24
Nucleic acid, 36
Nucleolus, **20, 23,** 24
Nucleoprotein, 36, 539
Nucleus, 19, **20,** 22–24
Nuthatch, 251, 253
Nutrition, 82
Nuttall, 515
Nymph, **184, 185,** 186

Obelia, 119
Objective, 14
Obstetrical toad, 235
Ocellus, 183, **184,** 186, **188, 191**
Octopus, 153, **162**
Odonata, 193
Odors, defensive, 554
Oedogonium, 368
Offense, adaptations for, 553
Oil, 53
Oil gland, **246, 271,** 272
Oleic acid, olein, 53
Olfactory, capsule (sac), **226,** 228; cell, 300; chamber, 270; lobe, **295,** 296, **512;** nerve, 297
Oligochaeta, 150
Ommatidium, 172, **173**
One-egg twins, **505**
Onion, **20,** 27, 31
Onoclea, **419**
Ontogeny, 313–330
Onychophora, 165, 205, **206**
Oocyte, 105, **106,** 486, **488**
Oogenesis, 105, **106**
Oogonium, **368,** 369
Operculum, fish, 225–227, 319; moss, **399;** tadpole, 319
Ophiuroidea, 213, **216**
Opossum, 256
Opsonin, 359

Optic cup, 318; lobe, **295**–297, 320, **512**; nerve, **172**, 297, **301**
Opuntia, **456**
Oral groove, **91**; pole, 107; surface, 213
Orangutan, 266, 525
Orchid, 560, **561**
Order, 75
Order of dominance, 564
Ordovician period, 520
Organ, 25, 105
Organic chemistry, 35
Organism, 4
Organizer, 322
Origin, muscle, 274; of life, 539
Oriole, 247
Ornithology, 3
Ornithorynchus, **255**
Orthoptera, 192, **193**
Oscillatoria, **340**
Osculum, 110, **111**
Osmosis, 44, **45**
Osmunda, **419**
Osphradium, 158
Osteichthyes, 226
Ostium, invertebrate heart, **169**, 171, 189; vertebrate oviduct, 292
Ostrich, 251, **253**
Outer ear, 302, **303**
Ovary, clam, 158; crayfish, 174; earthworm, 146, **147**; flatworm, **124**, **131**; flower, 458, **466**; frog, 292, 293; grasshopper, 190; hydra, **113**, 117; mammal, 292, 293, **294**, **309**; roundworm, 132
Oviduct, crayfish, 174; earthworm, 146, **147**; flatworm, **124**; frog, **292**; grasshopper, 190; mammal, 291, **292**, 293, **294**, 326
Oviparous animal, 235, 295
Ovipositor, **188**
Ovoviviparous animal, 228, 235, 295
Ovulation, **310**
Ovule, 458, 459, **466**
Owl, 253
Ox-warble botfly, 199
Oxyhemocyanin, 171
Oxyhemoglobin, 64, 142, 282
Oyster, 153, **159**
Oyster shell scale, **196**

Paedogenesis, 126
Painted turtle, **237**
Paleontology, 70, 517
Paleozoic era, 520
Palisade, **451**, 452
Pallial line, **154**
Palp, **157**, 172, 186, **187**
Pancreas, 276–279, **307**, 308
Pandorina, 98, **99**, **100**

Pangolin, **263**, 264
Papilla, hair, **271**
Paramanis, 263
Paramecium, **91**–96
Paramylum, 86
Paraphysis, **382**
Parapod, 150, **151**
Parasite, 85, 178–**179**, 193, 200, 344, 379, 517, 547, 552
Parasitism, 129, 548
Parasympathetic system, 299
Parathormone, 305
Parathyroid, **304**–306
Parathyrotropic hormone, 305
Parenchyma, **405**, 406
Parrot fever, 346
Parthenogenesis, 177, **196**, 197
Partial cleavage, 314, **315**
Passenger pigeon, 580
Passeriformes, 245, 251
Pasteur, 91, **350**, 351, 357
Patella, **273**
Pathogenic microorganisms, 354
Pea, **455**, 477
Pearl, **156**, 159, 160
Peat, 401, 518
Pebrine, 91
Pectin, 339
Pectoral fin, **225**, 227, **230**
Pectoral girdle, 223, **272**, **273**
Pedal ganglion, **157**, 158
Pedicellaria, **215**
Pedigree, 501, **502**, **503**
Pedipalpus, 208
Pelecypoda, **78**, 153–160
Pellagra, 56
Pellicle, **20**, 23, **86**, **91**, 92
Pelvic fin, **225**, 227
Pelvic girdle, 223, **272**, **273**
Pen, **161**
Penetrant nematocyst, 116
Penguin, 251
Penicillin, 361
Penicillium, 361, 384, **385**
Penis, **124**, 190, 293, **294**
Pennsylvanian period, 520
Pepsin, 278, **279**
Peptide, 278, 279
Perch, **225**, 227, **512**
Pericardial cavity, **157**, 223
Pericardial sinus, 156, **171**
Pericarp, **468**
Pericycle, **442**
Periodic cicada, 196
Periostracum, 155, **156**
Peripatus, **206**, 554
Perissodactyla, 260, **262**
Peristaltic movement, 139, 279

Peristome, 399
Peritoneal cavity, 223, 224
Peritoneum, 139, 140, 223, 224, 316
Permanent teeth, 278
Permian period, 520
Petal, 457, 466
Petiole, 446, 447
Petrifaction, 516, 517
Petrochirus, 176
Petunia, 434, 435
Peziza, 382
Phaeophyceae, 371–375
Phagocyte, phagocytosis, 282, 358
Phalanges, 272–275, 511
Pharynx, earthworm, 139, 141; planarian, 123, 124; vertebrate, 227, 275, 276
Phascolarctus, 529
Phase contrast microscope, 18, 19, 21, 26, 495
Pheasant, 251
Phenotype, 481
Phenylthiocarbamide (PTC), 502
Phloem, 412, 413, 424, 442, 443
Pholidota, 263, 264
Photosynthesis, 21, 58, 331–333
Phototaxis, 543
Phototropism, 543
Phycocyanin, 339
Phycoerythrin, 375
Phycomycetes, 380–382
Phylogenetic series, 329
Phylogenetic tree, 70, 71, 524
Phylogeny, 100, 329, 514
Phylum, 75
Physalia, 119
Physical factor in environment, 542
Physical science, 3
Physics, 3, 34
Physiological resemblance, 514
Physiology, 12
Piercing-sucking mouth, 191, 192
Pig, 259
Pigeon, 246, 511, 512
Pigment cell, 173, 270, 271
Pigmy shrew, 256
Pika, 259
Pike, 229
Pileus, 387–389
Piltdown man, 525, 526
Pine, *Pinus*, 7, 10, 422–429
Pineal body, 236, 295, 297, 512
Pinna, 302
Pinnipedia, 258, 259
Pipa, 234
Pisces, 224–230
Pistil, 458
Pit viper, 242, 243
Pitcher plant, 551, 552

Pith, 441, 443
Pithecanthropus, 525
Pituitary gland, 304–307
Pituitrin, 305
Placenta, 255, 325, 326
Placoid scale, 226
Plague, 195, 341, 342, 549
Planaria, 123–126
Plant, 4
Plant kingdom, 335, 336, 337
Plant louse, 196
Plantigrade mammal, 266, 267
Plasma, 103, 281
Plasma membrane, 20, 21, 80
Plasmagene, 477, 539
Plasmochin, 91
Plasmodium, 87–91
Plasmodium (of slime mold), 378, 379
Plasmolysis, 45, 46
Plastid, 20, 21
Plastron, 237
Plate, 235, 238, 254, 271
Platelet, 281, 282
Platyhelminthes, 76, 78, 123–130
Platypus, 255
Pleistocene epoch, 523
Pleodorina, 98, 99
Plethodon, 233
Pleura, pleural cavity, 187, 224
Pleuron, 169
Plover, 248
Plumatella, 163
Plumule, 469
Pneumonia, 361, 362
Poison fang, 239, 242, 243
Poison gland (sac) 210, 270
Poisonous snake, 242
Polar bear, 555, 556
Polar body, 105, 106, 486
Polar nuclei, 459
Pollen basket, 202, 203
Pollen chamber, 427
Pollen grain, 426, 458
Pollen sac, 425
Pollen tube, 427, 428, 459, 466
Pollination, 461
Polychaeta, 150
Polymorphism, 120
Polyp, 118, 119
Polyploidy, 493
Polypodium, 412
Polyporus, 390
Polysaccharid, 50
Polystichum, 419
Polytrichum, 397
Porcupine, 259, 554, 555
Pore fungus, 389, 390
Porifera, 76, 78, 110–113

Pork tapeworm, 130
Porpoise, 264
Portal circulation, 288
Portuguese man-of-war, 119
Postcaval vein, 286, **288**
Potato, 454
Potato beetle, 197, 517
Potential energy, 34, 40, 62
Prawn, 176
Praying mantis, 192
Precaval vein, 286, **288**
Precious coral, 121
Precipitin, 359, 515
Precocial bird, 247
Precocial mammal, 327
Predatory animal, 547
Predatory plant, **551**
Preformation theory, 313
Pregnancy, 305, 310
Prehensile tail, **239**
Premolar, 254, 278
Prevertebrate, 219
Primary growth, 442
Primary lamella, **20**
Primary oocyte, 105, **106**
Primary spermatocyte, 105, **106, 308, 484**
Primates, **264–266,** 523, 525
Primitive streak, 322
Prionotus, **230**
Prismatic layer, 155, **156**
Proboscidea, 260, **262**
Proboscis, 123, **134, 191, 220**
Proboscis worm, 77, **134**
Proctodaeum, 319
Progamete, **380,** 381
Progesterone, 305, 310
Ploglottid, 129–**131**
Prolactin, 305
Pronotum, **184,** 187
Pronuba, 464, **465**
Prop root, **436**
Prophase, 27, **28, 30**
Prosenchyma, 406
Prostate gland, **294**
Prostomium, 136, **137**
Protective resemblance, **555–558**
Protein, 36, 51
Proterozoic era, 519
Prothallus, **415–417**
Prothoracic gland, 186
Prothorax, 187
Protoceratops, **522**
Protococcus, 365, **366**
Protonema, **397,** 399
Protoplasm, 17; chemical properties, 35; physical properties, 43
Protoplast, 17
Protopodite, **167,** 168, **169**

Protopterus, **228**
Prototheria, **254–256,** 528
Protozoa, 76, **78,** 80–**97;** colonial, 98, 520
Protractor, 139, **140, 154**
Pseudopod, 81, **85, 270**
Pteridium, 411, **413**
Pteridophyta, 334
Pteris, **415**
Pteropsida, 337, **411–476**
Ptyalin, 278, 279
Pubic louse, 193
Pubis, **273,** 274
Puccinia, **391–393**
Puffball, 389, **391**
Pulmocutaneous arch, 286, **287**
Pulmonary vein, 286, **288**
Pulp cavity, 278
Pulsating vacuole, **81, 83, 86, 91,** 92
Pulvillus, 187
Pulvinus, 543
Puma, **74**
Pupa, 186, **198, 199**
Pupil, **301**
Putrefaction, 345
Pycnium, 392
Pyloric caecum, 227
Pyloric chamber, 169
Pyloric stomach, **215**
Pylorus, 275, **276**
Pyrenoid, 366
Python, 241, **513**

Quadrate bone, 241
Quahog, 159
Quail, 248
Quantitative variation, 497
Quaternary period, 523
Queen bee, 181, **201**
Quill, 244
Quinine, 90

Rabbit, 259, **261,** 536
Rabies, 346, 357
Raccoon, **71,** 258
Radial canal, **91, 215**
Radial symmetry, 107, **108**
Radio-ulna, **272,** 274
Radish, **538**
Radius, **246, 273, 511**
Radula, 153
Rana, **269**
Raphanobrassica, **538**
Rasping-sucking mouth, 192
Rat, 2, **57,** 259
Rat flea, **195,** 259
Ratitae, 251
Rattlesnake, 242, **243**
Ray (cartilaginous fish), 226

Ray-finned fishes, 229
Ray flower, **466, 467**
Reaction, 39
Recapitulation, 100, 327–329, 514
Receptacle, **466**
Receptor, 145
Recessiveness, 479
Recombination, 489
Recreation, 585
Rectal caecum, **215**
Rectum, clam, 156; grasshopper, **188**; verte-
brate, **277**
Red algae, 375, **376**
Red corpuscle, **103, 281, 282**
Red marrow, 282
Red-back salamander, 233
Redi, 349, **350**
Redia, 126, **127**
Red-winged blackbird, 248
Reef, **121**
Reflex action, **298, 299**
Regeneration, 112, **117**, 125, 149, 175, 216,
217
Reindeer moss, 386
Renal corpuscle, 289, **290**
Renal portal vein, **288**
Rennin, 278, 279
Repellent, insect, 204
Reproduction, ameba, 85; clam, 158; cray-
fish, **174**; earthworm, 146; flatworm, 126;
frog, 316; grasshopper, **190**; hydra, 117;
Paramecium, **91**; vertebrate, **290–294**
Reproductive isolation, 535
Reproductive tissue, 105
Reptile, reptilia, **78, 235–243**
Reservoir, **86**
Resin duct, **423–425**
Resistance, disease, 358
Resources, 568
Respiration, **63**; ameba, 83, crayfish, **170**;
earthworm, 142; frog, man, **279–281**;
grasshopper, 189; hydra, 117
Respiratory enzyme, 64
Respiratory pigment, 63
Response, 84
Reticulitermes, **194**
Retina, **301, 302**
Retinal cell, **173**
Retractor, 139, **140, 154, 157**
Rh blood groups, 283, 284, 504
Rhinoceros, 260
Rhizoid, 397
Rhizome, 411, **454**
Rhizopoda, **80–86**
Rhizopus, **380**
Rhodophyceae, 375, **376**
Rhynchocephalia, 235, **236**
Rib, 272, **273**

Riboflavin, 56
Rickets, **57,** 58
Rickettsia, 356
Ring canal, 215
Ring of growth, 424, 443
Robin, 248, 250
Rock barnacle, **178**
Rockweed, **372, 373**
Rod (of eye), 301, **302**
Rodentia, 259, **260, 293,** 517
Romalea, **184**
Root, **435–439**
Root cap, 436, **438**
Root hair, 436–**438**
Rootstock, **454**
Rose, **455**
Rose-breasted grosbeak, 246
Ross, 90
Rostrum, 167, **170,** 222
Rotation, crop, 570
Rotifer, rotifera, **78, 96, 134,** 135
Roundworm, **78, 130–134**
Royal jelly, 201
Ruscus, **456**
Rust, 390

Saber-toothed tiger, 522
Sac fungus, **382–387**
Saccharomyces, **382–384**
Saccoglossus, 220
Sacculina, 178, **179**
Sacrum, **273, 274**
Sage, 463, **464**
Sagitta, **134**
Salamander, 231, **232, 233, 521**
Saliva, 189, 276, 279
Salivary gland, **161, 188, 277**; chromosome,
495
Salmon, 248
Salts, 41, 51, 54
Salvia, 463, **464**
San Jose scale, **196,** 197
Sand dollar, 215
Saprophyte, 344, 379, 552
Sargassum, **372, 373**
Sarracenia, **551, 552**
Sawfly, 200
Scale, 197, 271
Scale insect, **196,** 197
Scallop, 153
Scaly anteater, **263, 264**
Scaphopoda, 153
Scapula, **272, 273, 274**
Schizomycetes, 339, **341–363**
Schizophyceae, 339, 341
Schizophyta, 335, **339–363**
Schleiden, 17
Schwann, 17

Science, 1
Scientific law, 3
Scientific name, 72–75
Sclerenchyma, **405, 406**, 442
Sclerite, 186
Sclerotic coat, **301**
Scolex, 129, **131**
Scorpion, 207, **210**
Scrotum, 293, **294**
Scurvy, 56, 58
Scute, 239, 241
Scyphozoa, 118, **119**, 120
Sea anemone, **120, 550**
Sea cow, 264
Sea cucumber, 215, **216**
Sea fan, 121
Sea lily, **6, 216**
Sea lion, 258, **259**
Sea robin, **230**
Sea squirt, **221**
Sea star, 213
Sea turtle, 235, **238**
Sea urchin, 215, **216**
Sea walnut, **108**, 121
Seal, 248, 254, 258
Secondary growth, 442
Secondary oocyte, 105, **106**
Secondary radial symmetry, 213
Secondary sex character, 190, 245, 309
Secondary spermatocyte, 105, **106**, 308, 484
Secretin, 305, 308
Secretion, 66
Seed, **428, 429, 469**; dispersal, 471, **472**
Seed coat, 469
Seed fern, **521**
Seed plant, 422
Segmentation, 109, 165, 182, **324**
Segregation, of genes, 479; of chromosomes, 485
Selaginella, 407, **408**
Selection, artificial, 499, 532; natural, 531
Self-pollination, 461
Semen, seminal fluid, 105, 146, 190, 228, 293
Semicircular canal, 302, **303**
Seminal groove, **137**, 138, 148
Seminal receptacle, 146, **147, 148, 174, 188**, 190
Seminal vesicle, 146, **147**, 190, **294**
Senses, sense organs, clam, 158; crayfish, **172–174**; earthworm, 145; planarian, 125; vertebrate, **300–303**
Sensitive fern, **419**
Sensitive plant, **546**
Sensory neuron, 104, **146, 298**
Sepal, 457, **466**
Septum, 139, **144**
Sequoia, **10**

Serum, 282
Sessile leaf, **446**
Setae, **137**, 138, **140**, 150
Sex chromosomes, 485, **487, 488**
Sex (as evolution factor), 534
Sex hormone, 309
Sex linkage, **486–490**
Sexual reproduction, 31, 104, 367
Shaft, 244
Shark, **226**
Shark sucker, 230, 559, **560**
Sheep, 259
Shell, egg, 322; mollusk, 153, 155, **156**; turtle, **237**
Shellac, 181
Shepherd's purse, **468**
Shield fern, **415**
Shipworm, 160
Shoot, 434
Short shoot, 422
Shrew, 256
Shrike, 253
Shrimp, 174, **176**
Shrub, 439
Sieve plate, 214, **215, 217**
Sieve tube, 406, 442, **443**
Sight, 300–302
Silk gland, 208
Silkworm, **198**, 199
Silurian period, **520, 521**
Silverfish, 186
Simple eye, 183
Simple metamorphosis, 184
Simple microscope, 14
Sinanthropus, 526
Sinus, 156, 169, **171**, 189
Sinus venosus, 286, **288**
Siphon, **154**, 155, **157, 161**
Siphonaptera, **195**, 199–200
Siphoning mouth, **191**, 192
Sirenia, 264
Skate, 226
Skeletal muscle, 274, **275**
Skeleton, crayfish, 165, **166**; frog, **272**; man, **273**, 274
Skin, frog, **270**; man, **271**, 272
Skin-color inheritance (man), 502
Skin-gill, 214, **215**
Skipper, 198
Skull, **272**
Skunk, 258, 554
Slavery, 560
Sleeping sickness, 87
Slime mold, 378, **379**
Sloth, 264
Slug, **160**, 161
Smallpox, 357
Smell, 229, **300**

Smilax, **455**
Smooth muscle, 103, **104,** 275
Smut, 394
Snail, **108, 160,** 161
Snake, 241–243, **512, 513**
Snapping turtle, 238
Snipe, **250**
Snout beetle, 198
Snow goose, **564**
Social organism, 564
Soft-shell, clam, 159; turtle, 238
Soil conservation, 569–574; influence of earthworms, 150
Sol, 42
Solute, solvent, 42
Somatic layer, 316
Somite, 136
Songbird, 245
Sorus, **412–415**
Sow bug, **176**
Spanish moss, 396, 560
Sparrow, 253, 579
Spartina, 538
Species, 71–72
Spemann, 321–322
Sperm, **31,** 32, 105, 106, **147,** 291, **308,** 369, 459, **484**
Sperm duct, **124,** 146, **147, 169,** 174, 190, 291
Sperm funnel, **147**
Spermary, 104
Spermatid, 105, **106, 308, 484**
Spermatium, 392
Spermatocyte, 105, **106, 308, 484**
Spermatogenesis, 105, **106, 308, 484**
Spermatogonium, **308**
Spermatophyta, 334
Sphaerella, 98, **99**
Sphagnum, 400, **401**
Sphenodon, 236
Spherical symmetry, 107, **108**
Spicule, 110, **111**
Spider, **78,** 207–210
Spinal column, 222
Spinal cord, **223, 224,** 295, **298,** 320
Spinal nerve, 295, 296, **298,** 299
Spindle, **27–30;** attachment, 27
Spine, plant, **455,** 456; starfish, 214, **215**
Spinneret, 208
Spiny anteater, 255, **256**
Spiny-headed worm, **134**
Spiracle, insect, 183, **184,** 187, 189; tadpole, **319**
Spirillum, 341, 356
Spirobolus, **207**
Spirochaete, **356**
Spirogyra, 366, **367**
Spirostomum, **96**

Splanchnic layer, 316
Spleen, **227, 276,** 282, 358
Splint bone, 260, 513, 523
Sponge, **110–113,** 520
Spongin, 110, **111, 112**
Sponging mouth, **191,** 192
Spongy tissue, **451, 452**
Spontaneous generation, 349, 539
Sporangiophore, 380
Sporangium, 380, **407, 409, 412–415**
Spore, 87, **342,** 343
Spore mother cell, 400
Sporocyst, **88,** 126, **127**
Sporogenous tissue, 400
Sporophore, **387–391**
Sporophyll, 406, **407, 409**
Sporophyte, alga, 374; fern, 411; moss, 398, 399; pine, 422; sedge, **460**
Sporozoa, 87–91
Sporozoite, **88,** 89
Springtail, 186
Squamata, 236, **238–243**
Squame, 168, **172**
Squash, 455
Squash bug, 195
Squid, **161,** 162
Squirrel, 259
Stagbeetle, 191
Stamen, 457, **466**
Stanley, 348
Staphylococcus, 343
Starch, **22, 52, 54, 60,** 279
Starfish, **108, 213–215**
Statocyst, 158, 173, 174
Statolith, 173
Stele, 437, **439**
Stentor, **95, 96**
Sterigma, 387
Sterilization, 506
Sternal sinus, **171**
Sternum, **169, 174,** 187, 244, **273**
Stigma, *Euglena,* 86; flower, 458, **466**
Stimulus, 145
Sting, 202
Stink bug, 195
Stinkhorn, 390, **391**
Stipe, 387–389
Stipule, **446**
Stoma, **451, 452**
Stomach, crayfish, **169;** grasshopper, **188;** starfish, 214, **215;** vertebrate, 275–**277**
Stomach poison (insect), 204
Stomodaeum, 319
Stone canal, 215
Storage tissue, 400
Streptococcus, **342**
Streptomyces, Streptomycin, 361
Striated muscle, **104, 189**

Strip cropping, 574, **575**
Strobilus, **407**, **408**, 425–427
Structural (graphic) formula, 38
Struggle for existence, 531
Style, 458, **466**
Stylonychia, **95**
Subphylum, 76
Substance, 34
Substratum, 379
Succession, 361
Sucker, **151**, 318, **319**
Sucrase, 49, 279
Sucrose, 49, 52, 279
Suction disk, 225
Sugar, beet, cane, 35
Sugar, reducing, 51
Sulfonamides, sulfa drugs, 360
Sulfur bacteria, 344
Sulfur-bottom whale, 264
Sun animalcule, **108**
Sundew, **551**, 552
Sunflower, **466**, 467
Superficial cleavage, **314**, 315
Supporting tissue, 101–103
Suprabranchial chamber, 156–158
Suprascapula, **272**, 274
Surinam toad, 234
Survival of fittest, 532
Suspensor, **428**, **429**, **468**
Sweat gland, **271**, 272
Swimmeret, **167**, 168, **169**, **170**, **174**
Swimmer's itch, 128
Sycon type, 110, **111**
Sylvilagus, **261**
Symbiosis, **550**, 558
Symbol (chemical), 37
Symmetry, 107, **108**
Sympathetic system, **295**, 299
Synapse, 145, **146**, 298
Synapsis, **484**, 485
Syncerus, 261
Synergid, **459**, **460**
Syphilis, **342**, **356**
Syrinx, 245, **246**
System, 107
Systemic arch, 286, **287**
Systemic insecticide, 204

Tachyglossus, **256**
Tactile lobe, 123, **124**
Tadpole, 318, **319**
Taenia, 130, **131**
Tanager, 251
Tapetum, **457**
Tapeworm, 129, **131**
Tapir, 260
Taproot, **437**
Tarsals, 272–275

Tarso-metatarsals, **246**
Tarsier, Tarsius, **265**, 525; tarsioid, **525**
Tarsus, **184**, 187
Taste, 125, 229, 300; inheritance, **502**
Taste bud, **300**
Taxodium, **430**
Taxonomic series, 329
Taxonomy, 12, 71
Tegmen, 469
Teliospore, 391, **392**
Telolecithal egg, **314**, 322
Telophase, **28**, **29**, **30**
Telson, 169, **170**
Temperature, 542; regulation, 243
Temporary (milk) teeth, 278
Tendon, 103, 274, **275**
Tendril, 454, **455**
Tent caterpillar, 199
Tentacle, **113**, **151**, **161**, **222**
Teredo, 160
Tergum, **169**, 187
Termite, 183, 193, **194**, **565**
Terracing, 573, **575**
Territory (songbird), 246
Tertiary period, 522
Testa, 469
Testis, 104; crayfish, 174; earthworm, 146, **147**; flatworm, **124**, 126; grasshopper, 190; hydra, 113, 117; vertebrate, **291**, 294, **308**, 309
Testosterone, 309
Testudinata, 236, **237**, **238**
Tetanus, **342**, 343
Tetrad, 400
Tetraploidy, **493**
Texas fever, 550
Thallophyta, 335
Thallus, 339
Theory, 3
Thiamine, 56, **57**, 334
Thigmotropism, 546
Thoracic cavity, 254
Thorax, 165, 167, 182, **184**
Threadworm, 77, **78**, 130–134
Thrips, 192
Thrush, 250, 251
Thymus, 320
Thyroid, 54, 67, **304**, **307**
Thyrotropic hormone, 305
Thyroxin, 67, 304
Tibia, insect, **184**, 187; vertebrate, 273
Tibio-fibula, **272**, 274, **275**; tibio-tarsal, **246**
Tick, 207, 550
Tiger, 258
Tiger salamander, **232**, 233
Tillandsia, 396
Timber line, **7**
Tissue, 25; animal, **101–105**; plant, **405**, 406

Tissue culture, 18
Tissue fluid, 284, 289
Toad, 231, **234, 512**
Toadstool, 388
Tongue, 192, 254, 275, **276**
Tooth, 254, **278**
Toothed whale, 264
Tooth-shell, 153
Torpedo ray, 227
Tortoise, 236
Total cleavage, **314**
Touch, 302
Townsend's marsh grass, 538
Toxin, 344
Toxoid, 360
Trachea, insect, 183, **188, 189,** 208; plant, 406; vertebrate, **277, 280**
Tracheid, **405,** 406, 424
Tracheophyta, 335, **404–476**
Translocation (chromosome aberration), **494**
Transpiration, 453
Trap door spider, **207**
Tree, 439
Tree fern, **418,** 419
Tree toad (frog), **233,** 234
Trial and error, 9.
Triassic period, 522
Triceps, 275
Triceratops, **522**
Trichinella, Trichinosis, 131–133
Trichocyst, **92**
Trichodesmium, 341
Trilobite, 210, 520, **521**
Triploblastic animal, 100, 123
Triploidy, **493**
Trochanter, 187
Trochophore, 153, 163
Trophoblast, **325, 326**
Trophozoite, **89**
Tropical forest, 7, **9**
Tropism, 84
Truncus arteriosus, 286, **287**
Trypanosoma, **87**
Trypsin, 141, 279
Tsetse fly, 87
Tuatara, 235, **236**
Tube cell, **457,** 459
Tube foot, **214, 215**
Tuber, **454**
Tuberculosis, **362;** bacillus, **342, 343**
Tularemia, 550
Tunicate, 220, **221**
Turbatrix, 131, **132**
Turgor, **44, 46**
Turtle, 236, **237, 238**
Tusk, 259, 261
Twins, 322, **505**

Two-egg twins, 506
Tympanic membrane, grasshopper, **184,** 187; vertebrate, 302, **303**
Typhlosole, **140, 141**
Typhoid, 199, **342, 355**
Typhus, 193, **195,** 356, 549
Tyrannosaurus, **522**

Uca, **175,** 176
Ulna, **246, 274, 511**
Umbilical cord, 325, **326**
Umbo, **154**
Uncinate process, 244
Undulating membrane, 87
Ungulate, 259, 260, **261, 262**
Unguligrade mammal, **266,** 267
Unit character, 481
Urea, 67, 143, 290
Uredospore, **392,** 393
Ureter, **157,** 246, **289–294**
Urethra, 289, **294**
Uric acid, 290
Urinary tubule, 289, **290**
Urine, 67, 289
Urochordata, 219–221
Urodela, 231–233
Urogenital system, **291, 292**
Uropod, **167,** 168, **170**
Urostyle, **272**
Uterus, roundworm, **132;** vertebrate, 292–294

Vaccination, 357
Vacuole, **20, 21,** 23
Vagina, grasshopper, 190; vertebrate, 293, **294**
Valve, circulatory system, 142, 184, 284, 289; mollusk shell, 153, **154**
Vampire bat, 258
Vane (feather), 244
Varanus, **241**
Variation, 532
Vas deferens, 174, 291, **294**
Vas efferentia, **291**
Vascular bundle, **425**
Vascular cylinder, **425**
Vascular plant, 404–476, 520, 537
Vascular tissue, **405**
Vaucheria, 369, **370**
Vegetal pole, 314, **317**
Vegetative reproduction, **473**
Vein, blood vessel, 156, 286; insect wing, 182; leaf, **451**
Velum, 159, **222**
Ventral canal cell, 398, 418, 428
Ventral sucker, 318
Ventricle, **157,** 227, **285, 287, 288**
Venus's flytrap, **551, 552**

Vertebra, 222, **223, 272, 273**
Vertebrate, 219, 222, 312
Vessel, 406, 442, **443**
Vestibule, 302
Vestigial organ, **513, 514,** 530
Viceroy butterfly, 558
Villus, chorion, 325; intestine, 61, **62**
Vinegar eel, 131, **132**
Violet, **461**
Virus, 345–348, 539
Vitamin, 51, **55–59**
Vitreous humor, **301**
Viviparous animal, 132, 295
Vocal cord, 280, 281
Vocal sac, **276,** 280
Voluntary muscle, **104,** 274, **275**
Volva, 387–**389**
Volvocales, *Volvox,* 98, **99, 100,** 370
Vomerine teeth, 275, **276**
Vorticella, **95, 96**
Vulture, 253

Walking fern, **414**
Walking stick, 192, 555
Wallaby, **257**
Walrus, **71,** 258
Warbler, 249, 253
Warm-blooded animal, 243, 244
Warning marks, 558
Wart, 346
Wasp, 200
Water, 36, 54, 545
Water bug, **195**
Water fern, 419
Water flea, **177**
Water moccasin, 242
Water tube, 442, 443
Water vascular system, 213, **214**
Weapon, 553
Weasel, **71**
Welwitschia, **431**
Whale, 7, **264**
Wheat grain, 54; inheritance, 496, **498,** 499
Wheat rust, 390–394

Wheel animalcule, **78, 96, 134,** 135
Whelk, 153, **160**
White "ant," 193, **194**
White corpuscle, **103,** 142, 171, 281, 282
White fish, **27**
White grub, 197–198
White matter, **298**
Wiggler, 199
Wildlife, **579–584**
Wilt, 363
Wind erosion, **572, 573**
Wind pollination, 462
Wing, bat, 256, 511; bird, 244, 251, 511, 512; insect, **182–184,** 512
Wombat, 256
Wood, 441
Woodcock, **557**
Woodwardia, **415**
Worker bee, **201**
Worm, 123

Xanthophyll, 331, 453
X-chromosome, **486–490, 493, 503**
Xerophthalmia, 56
Xerophyte, 545
X-ray, 287, 492, 496, 507, 530
Xylem, 412, **413, 424, 437–439,** 442

Y-chromosome, **486–489**
Yeast, 382–**384**
Yellow fever, 199, 549
Yellowlegs, **251**
Yellowthroat, **251**
Yolk, **314,** 322, 323
Yolk gland, **124, 126, 131**
Yolk plug, **317**
Yolk sac stalk, 322–326
Yucca, 464, **465, 545**

Zebra, **262**
Zonation, **562**
Zooglea, 341
Zoology, 3
Zoospore, **368,** 369
Zygote, 31, 32, **106,** 367
Zymase, 383